Identification and Qualitative Chemical Analysis of Minerals

by

ORSINO C. SMITH, A.B., A.M.

Petroleum and Chemical Technologist

SECOND EDITION

D. VAN NOSTRAND COMPANY, Inc.

PRINCETON, NEW JERSEY

NEW YORK

TORONTO

LONDON

D. VAN NOSTRAND COMPANY, INC.
120 Alexander St., Princeton, New Jersey *(Principal office)*
24 West 40 Street, New York 18, New York

D. Van Nostrand Company, Ltd.
358, Kensington High Street, London, W.14, England

D. Van Nostrand Company (Canada), Ltd.
25 Hollinger Road, Toronto 16, Canada

01647b15

PRINTED IN THE UNITED STATES OF AMERICA
AMERICAN BOOK-STRATFORD PRESS, INC., NEW YORK

PREFACE

These mineral identification tables and this scheme of mineral analysis were first presented in the book Mineral Identification Simplified. Since its publication, much work and research have been done in improving and developing the analytical scheme into a simple, thorough system of qualitative analysis, given in such a way that it can be carried out not only by professionals, but also by those not technically trained, and without the necessity of elaborate facilities and expensive equipment.

The following references were used:

Outlines of Methods of Chemical Analysis; Lundell and Hoffman; John Wiley and Sons, 1938.

Analytical Chemistry; Treadwell and Hall; John Wiley and Sons, 1937 (ninth edition).

A System of Qualitative Analysis of the Rare Elements; Noyes and Bray; Macmillan Company, 1927.

Standard Methods of Chemical Analysis; Scott; D. Van Nostrand Company, 1938.

Qualitative Chemical Analysis; Noyes; Macmillan Company, 1928 (ninth edition).

Spot Tests; Fiegl; Nordmann Publishing Company, 1939 (second edition).

Handbook of Chemical Microscopy; Chamot and Mason; John Wiley and Sons, 1940 (second edition).

These mineral identification tables have been revised and brought up to date and include all minerals reported to January, 1945. Although it was not thought advisable to attempt to tabulate all sub-classes and varieties, a great many have been included. The following references were used in the compilation:

The American Mineralogist.

The Mineralogical Magazine.

Mineralogical Abstracts.

Dana's System of Mineralogy, Vol. 1, Seventh Edition; Palache, Berman and Frondel; John Wiley and Sons, 1944.

Mineral Identification Simplified; O. C. Smith; Wetzel Publishing Co., 1940.

The author wishes to express his deepest appreciation to Dr. F. H. Pough, Curator of Geology and Mineralogy, American Museum of Natural History,

New York; Dr. Thomas Clements, Professor of Geology, University of Southern California, Los Angeles, Calif.; Dr. G. E. F. Lundell, Chief, Division of Chemistry, National Bureau of Standards, Washington, D. C.; Mr. Roy L. Cornell, California Testing Laboratory, Los Angeles, Calif., and Mr. O. U. Bessette, for their help and suggestions in reviewing and criticizing the text; to Dr. Joseph Murdock, Associate Professor of Mineralogy, University of California at Los Angeles, for assisting in the selection of the mineral specimens for the plates; and to Mr. E. V. Rannells for his assistance with the photography.

O. C. SMITH.

Bell, Calif.,
October, 1945,

PREFACE TO SECOND EDITION

Since the first edition was published in 1946 a number of suggestions have been received by the author from teachers, professional mining men and amateurs. In view of these it is felt that a revision is in order.

A clarification and expansion of the procedures used in blowpiping in chemical analysis have been attempted. With the help of many new illustrations, it is felt that a fuller understanding of the processes involved has been achieved.

A condensed history of the blowpipe and blowpiping has been added. This was the first method of qualitative analysis and, although by today's standards it lacks much in many ways, it has in the past and still is finding an important use in the analytical field. Its history should be of especial interest to chemists and mining engineers.

A number of tests not found in the first edition or other books in print today have been included in the new edition.

No change in the Identification Tables has been made. Because of the new methods now in use in studying the structure and composition of minerals, it is being found that a number of substances which have been classified as distinct minerals are variations of other minerals, mixtures, etc., with the result that name changes and cancellations are in progress. This checking may take some time, and it is thought inadvisable to attempt to reclassify the minerals until this process is more complete.

O. C. SMITH.

Bell, Calif.
September, 1952.

CONTENTS

Chapter 1—Physical Properties

Chapter 2—History and Uses of Blowpiping

Chapter 3—Blowpipe Reactions

CONTENTS

List of Figures

LIST OF FIGURES

List of Plates (Color)

CHAPTER I

Introduction

By definition a mineral is a naturally occurring inorganic substance having a relatively constant chemical composition and fairly definite physical properties.

Chemical mineralogy is probably the most important branch of the science of mineralogy, because all of the properties of the minerals, the crystal forms assumed, and the final identification are dependent on the composition and molecular arrangement.

While minerals are considered to be of constant chemical composition, it must always be borne in mind that this does not mean they are chemically pure substances. Nature is not meticulously careful to prevent contamination, with the result that most minerals contain extraneous substances, and these often change the characteristics somewhat. Often it is these small amounts of extraneous substances which give the economic value to many mineral deposits, as for instance silver in galena, gold in pyrite, vanadium, chromium and titanium in iron minerals.

There are a number of elements that are quite easily interchangeable, with the result that one mineral may grade into another. Iron, aluminum and magnesium often partially replace each other, the iron in a mineral being partially replaced by aluminum or magnesium, or vice versa. Calcium and magnesium and sodium and potassium also act in the same way. Many of these types of substances may be considered as mixtures of two minerals, but in many cases the mineral is called by the name which represents the compound present in the greater amount; the other is considered an impurity. The distinction depends on the percentage of each, and the analyst must use his own judgment. If, for instance, a mineral was tested and found to be composed of a large amount of iron oxide, and a small quantity of titanium oxide was indicated, it would be regarded as an iron mineral with titanium as an impurity. If, however, the amount of iron and titanium were both large, it would probably be considered an iron-titanium mineral, such as ilmenite.

Identification of minerals by their physical properties only does not in any way indicate what elements are present. It does indicate that certain elements and compounds are in great preponderance. Magnetite, for instance, is not difficult to identify, but simple identification as such does not tell whether small amounts of vanadium, chromium, titanium, manganese, etc., are contained in it. Chemical analysis alone will determine this.

Chemical analysis of minerals therefore becomes very interesting and profitable and should be more widely used by both the professional and amateur chemist and mineralogist. It is firmly believed that many new mineral resources and deposits will be found by greater use of chemical methods.

The qualitative analysis of minerals is quite simple but has not been practiced to any great extent to date by non-professional or professional men on assigned jobs away from their place of business, because no practical system outlined in simple methods and language has been available. Those amateurs who do become interested are usually baffled the first time they open a text book on qualitative analysis, because of the technical expressions and phrases used, the references to normalities, ionizations, concentrations, etc., and the general idea of complexity in which they are engulfed. Chemical analysis is in reality a very simple mechanical sequence and, while it is admitted that certain conditions must be met and one must use some chemical terms, these can be kept to a minimum. If the procedure is understood by the operator these terms will soon become familiar to him, and without realizing it he will soon develop a fair chemical vocabulary and understanding. The carrying out of this idea has been attempted in the instructions given here.

The system of qualitative analysis set forth in this book is a combination of the blowpipe and wet systems. Each has its very decided advantages, and an effort has been made to adopt the good points of each, thus obtaining a system which by a routine procedure covers virtually all of the basic elements while retaining many excellent qualities of blowpiping. This is accomplished by group testing and separation by the wet method and blowpipe tests on the precipitates or residues.

Two new groups have been added to the ordinary scheme of wet analysis. These are the oxalic acid or rare earth group and the zirconium or titanium group. This has been done in order to simplify the iron group. The testing for and separation of these groups are as easy and complete as most of the other more common ones, and a great advantage is obtained. Elimination of possible elements is almost as important as confirmation in an analysis. These new groups assist greatly in the simplification of this procedure.

Iron is a very common element in minerals, with the result that a positive test for it is often obtained. Under the ordinary system of group separation, the iron group contains not only the commonly known elements, iron, manganese, cobalt and nickel, but also thorium, scandium, the rare earths, zirconium and titanium, with the result that a positive test for the iron group means that any one of these elements may be present, thus necessitating considerable work in separating and testing. By removing or showing the absence of the oxalic acid and zirconium groups as is done in this scheme, the iron group is converted from a complicated one of about 24 possible members to a very simple one of only 4 or 5 members.

INTRODUCTION

It may be argued that members of the oxalic acid and zirconium groups are not common elements. However, according to the best authorities, these elements appear in the earth's crust in greater amounts than the elements which we ordinarily look upon as common, and no simple system of analysis, either wet or dry, has been published which allows one to test for them in a routine procedure. In working with minerals, many of these elements are apt to be encountered and any analytical scheme should include them.

No attempt is made here to teach the principles of qualitative analysis. There are many excellent texts available on this subject. However, most all of them assume that complete laboratory facilities are at hand, with the result that the conditions required for separations are stated and described, but in virtually no case are specific instructions given as to how these may be obtained in a simple manner.

The endeavor here is to give these specific instructions, using the simplest possible means and methods to obtain the approximately correct conditions for the separations. In almost all cases this is accomplished by using the standard, concentrated reagents, which are of quite constant and uniform strength, drops from a dropping bottle, and specified volumes.

Considerable library research as well as tests on known and unknown minerals and mixtures have gone into the development of the procedure here recommended. Practical experience by amateurs and experts has reduced the tests to the simplest and most accurate routine.

The size of the sample is smaller than that ordinarily used in macro analysis but is large enough to give precipitates in quantity sufficient for identification, even when the element occurs in relatively small amounts. It can be handled by ordinary macro methods but is small enough to save much time in filtering and other operations.

The color reproductions of the blowpipe tests on charcoal and Plaster of Paris tablets, both per se and with the fluxes and the bead tests, greatly assist the analyst in the identification. Two new fluxes, not encountered in the literature, have been used, namely the bromide and chromate fluxes. In a number of cases these are not very specific and do not give pronounced films, but for some of the elements they give better results than are obtained by other means. Some of the charcoal slabs and plaster tablets show very little film, but it was thought best to include them so as to make the list as complete as possible, for here again a negative indication is about as important as a positive one in reaching a decision as to the composition and final results.

The chapter on ultra-violet light gives much information on its use in mining, mineralogy, and as a hobby. While very few minerals invariably give a specific reaction to "black light," many of them from certain localities, do fluoresce, because of the presence of some exciting substance. In these cases, the reaction to the light is specific for the mineral *of that locality*, and this fact should make the ultra-violet light quite useful. The fluorescent material itself may not be of commercial value, but may be associated with the valuable ore or mineral in such a way that it indicates where the values lie.

Good, efficient sources of ultra-violet radiations have been developed only in the last few years and much is yet to be learned about their possibilities. Since minerals from one district may fluoresce while those from another may not, all fluorescent material should be carefully examined chemically to determine its nature and to find if it contains commercial values, for there is undoubtedly a great deal to be discovered by the use of this light.

The Tables

There are two sets of tables. The tables of chemical reactions are based on the solubility of the minerals in the common acids and is for use with simple chemical tests as an aid in the identification. This set contains only the more common minerals and is an auxiliary to the identification tables, in which all of the known minerals are arranged in the order of their decreasing specific gravity and hardness, two of the most constant of the physical properties.

Specific gravity limits which divide the minerals into thirteen groups have been selected. All minerals whose gravity range lies within the bounds of a single group will be found only in that group. In cases where there is a considerable variation in the specific gravity, the mineral will be found in all of the groups which cover the specific gravity range. Garnet, for instance, has a specific gravity range of 4.3 to 3.15, and is therefore a member of all of the groups which are necessary to cover this range, namely, groups 5 to 8 inclusive.

In the various groups, the minerals are arranged in the order of their decreasing hardness so that *all minerals of similar specific gravity and hardness are grouped together*. Those which have specific gravity but no hardness reported are found at the end of the groups. In the last group are the ones on which no specific gravity has been reported. These usually are quite rare and unimportant. The tables contain all known minerals and many of the different varieties reported up to 1945. The more common minerals are in bold type.

Using the Tables. First determine the specific gravity. This throws the specimen into one of the groups. Next find the hardness. This shows that it can be one of only a possible few of that group. A study of the other physical properties (color, streak, etc.) will usually enable the mineral to be definitely identified. If still in doubt, the chemical tests in connection with the tables of chemical reactions are applied, which will give an idea of the chemical nature. Alternative and ultimate resort can be made to blowpipe tests and complete qualitative chemical analysis.

Many minerals can be identified from their physical properties and chemical characteristics, but there are some which differ from each other by only a slight variation of their percentage composition or optical properties. Where this is the case, complete equipment for quantitative analysis and the determination of the optical properties is necessary.

In using the table, it should be borne in mind that the physical properties listed are those of *pure minerals*, and the specimen should be carefully examined to be sure it is not a mixture or is not somewhat altered. Because of these possibilities it is always well to search the groups immediately before and after the one into which the mineral is thrown.

Finding the Properties of a Mineral

The **mineral index** lists alphabetically the names of all the minerals. To look up the properties of a mineral, locate its name in the mineral index at the back of the book. Following this will be found its location in the group and the group to which it belongs. For example, if one wishes to find the characteristics of tremolite, on looking in the mineral index under this name he will find on page 383 the designation Tremolite, 92–8, 48–9. This means that tremolite is item #92 (numerals at left side of page) in group #8 and is found on pages 286 and 287; also it is item #48 in group #9, which is found on pages 300 and 301.

Where the mineral appears in more than one group, it is because the range of the reported specific gravity falls within these groups. Minerals with a wide range of specific gravity may be members of several groups, as, for instance, gummite.

Specific Gravity

Its Determination. The specific gravity of a substance is its weight in air divided by the weight of a volume of water equal to the volume of the sample being tested. These weights need not be in any of the standard units, as it is not necessary to know the weight in grams or pounds. All that is required is that both weights be taken with the same units.

The specific gravity balance is one of the most useful simple instruments available to the mineralogist, prospector and mining engineer. It is easily constructed, gives quite accurate results and can be used for a number of purposes. It is only the lack of information as to the ease of specific gravity determinations and its many values that prevents it from being used a great deal more.

There are several types of apparatus by which the specific gravity may be determined. Among these are the **hydrometer, Jolly** and **beam** balances, the **pycnometer,** the **Berman** balance, the use of **heavy liquids,** and also any ordinary balance or scale.

The drawings show some of these pieces of apparatus in simple form. The construction and design have purposely been made simple and many refinements omitted in order to simplify the construction for those who wish to build their own equipment.

Probably the simplest method is the use of the **hydrometer**. Figure 1 shows a Baumé hydrometer for light oils, equipped to take the specific gravity of solids. A pan made of very light material is slipped over the top of the stem and another one is attached to the bottom of the hydrometer. This lower pan must be heavy enough to make the hydrometer sink to the 0 on the scale in

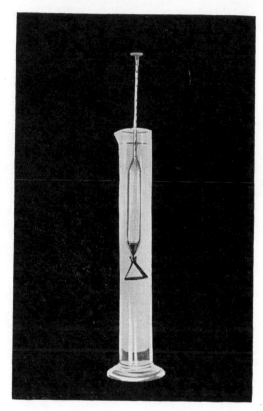

FIG. 1.   Hydrometer for Determination of Specific Gravity.

water at 39°F. This is the zero point. That is, with nothing in either pan the 0 on the scale in the stem must be exactly at the top of the water. A tall glass container, known as a hydrometer jar, is used to hold the water.

In taking the specific gravity with this piece of apparatus, a small sample of the mineral is placed in the top pan. This causes the hydrometer to sink part way. When it has come to rest and is floating freely in the water the reading at the top of the water is taken. We will presume this to be 10. The mineral sample is now taken from the upper pan and placed in the lower one, the hydrometer placed in the water, allowed to come to rest, and the reading at the top of the water again taken. This we will assume to be 8. From these two readings we can determine the specific gravity as follows: the first reading (10) less the second reading (8) leaves 2, which is the weight of the water equal to the volume of the sample in terms of the hydrometer units. This (2) divided into the first reading (10) gives 5, which is the specific gravity of the sample.

The hydrometer method is simple, quite accurate, and requires apparatus

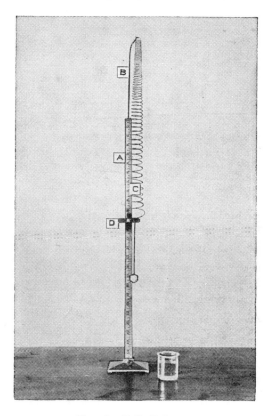

FIG. 2. Jolly Balance.

that is easily carried. It is limited to small pieces of not over 2 grams which, however, may be an advantage, as small pure specimens are usually easier to obtain than larger ones. It has the disadvantage that at the present time it is not on the market. Arrangements had been made for their manufacture, but during the war this was suspended.

A simply constructed **Jolly** balance is shown in Fig. 2. All of the parts necessary to build this instrument, with the exception of the spring, can be purchased from the 5 & 10 cent stores. The spring is the essential part of this piece of apparatus and must have the property of expanding equally throughout its entire range without permanent distortion; that is, it must not be permanently stretched or elongated by use. A satisfactory spring may be made on a lathe by winding a good grade of spring steel wire on a mandrel. The one shown in the cut is a spiral made of #6 piano wire and gives very satisfactory results.

Figure 3 is a drawing of a mandrel for making the coil spring. The mandrel is easily made on a lathe from a piece of cold rolled steel.

In making the spring, the end of a roll of #6 piano wire is passed through the small hole in the flange and is bent over so that it will hold during the winding. The small end of the mandrel is clamped in the lathe chuck and the other end is supported by the tail center. The wire is clamped between two pieces of hard

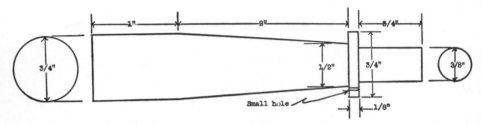

FIG. 3.   Mandrel for Making Coil Spring.

wood, bakelite or other similar substance, in the tool post tight enough to put a high strain on the wire as it is wound on the mandrel. Steel piano wire must be drawn very tight in order to get a good winding job. Run the lathe very slowly and wind about one and one-half inches on the mandrel. A longer or shorter spring may be made if desired. When sufficient wire has been wound, run the lathe backwards for a time to relieve the high tension the coil is under before cutting the wire. If this is not done, the operator may be cut by the wire as it unwinds. After removing the spring from the mandrel, the bottom and top ends are bent at right angles for supports.

The stand of the balance is a skirt marker, used by women to mark the length of dresses, with the measuring stick "A" turned upside down so that it reads from top down. This is in inches and eighths, which causes some inconvenience, as the readings must be converted to eighths. A measure divided into inches and tenths or a meter stick is much better.

Three screw-eyes are placed on the back of the upright about 4" apart, the middle one being out of line so that when wire "B" is passed through them it binds and will remain wherever placed. The top of this wire is bent to form a hook or eye for holding spring "C." Two metal broom holders, fastened together, are used for slide "D," one fitting around the upright "A," the other being flattened out and projecting in front, under the spring. A silk thread is suspended from the bottom of the spring.

The operation of the apparatus is as follows: slide "D" is placed at the top so as to read 0, then wire "B" is raised until the bottom of spring "C" barely touches the top of the slide. A piece of mineral is tied on with the silk thread and allowed to hang freely from the bottom of the spring. The slide is lowered until it is just at the bottom of the spring, and the reading is taken, say $10\frac{5}{8}''$. A glass of water is now held so that the mineral is covered completely with water but does not touch the glass. The specimen will rise to a fixed point.

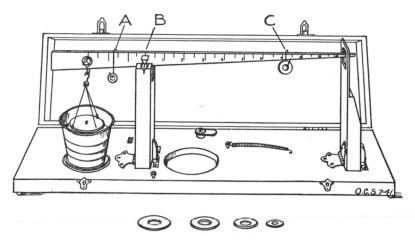

FIG. 4.   Beam Balance, Set Up.

The slide is moved up to the bottom of the spring again, and a reading is taken, say $6\frac{1}{4}''$. As the measure is in inches and eighths, these readings must be converted to a common unit, in this case eighths, which gives 85 for the first reading and 50 for the second. Subtracting these we have 35. This divided into 85 gives 2.43 which is the specific gravity of the specimen.

This illustration shows the very simplest form, but many refinements may be made, such as using a pair of pans instead of the thread, a sliding support for holding the glass of water, a vernier for more accurate readings, and a specially wound spring which may be purchased from a chemical supply house.

The crudely constructed Jolly balance illustrated will give results accurate to 1/10. With refinements, one may easily be built to read accurately to 1/100.

The **beam** balance illustrated in Fig. 4 is probably the most generally useful of the various types, as a properly constructed one may be used for making weighings as well as the simple determination of specific gravity. Because of this, detail construction drawings are given in Figs. 4, 5, 6, 7, and 8.

The critical parts of this type of balance are the beam, which must be graduated accurately, and the type and location of the knife edges. These have been carefully worked out, and if the details of the drawings are followed a first class piece of equipment should result.

The drawings show the beam notched with 20 divisions to the inch. This was done on a metal shaper by setting it to move 1/20" to each stroke and

9

having the bit ground to 60°. If this is not available it is not absolutely necessary and the constructor may leave the top of the beam smooth, and using an engineer's scale accurately mark it on the side into inches and tenths. The beam may be made of almost any material, such as hard wood, aluminum, brass or iron, but must be of uniform thickness and weight.

The knife edges are made of a three cornered file with the serrations ground off and one edge very smooth. The supporting knife edge must be in exactly the right place, for if it is too low it will be below the center of gravity and the balance will be unstable, the beam tending to go either up or down and not balance. If too high, the sensitivity of the balance is greatly reduced.

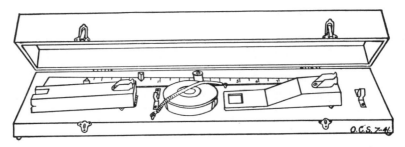

FIG. 5.   Beam Balance, Folded.

The knife edge carrying the pans is exactly three inches from the supporting knife edge; in other words, the reading "3" on the beam is the same distance from the supporting knife edge as the pan support, and the beam is graduated uniformly through its whole length. This makes it possible to take fairly accurate weighings by using a set of three riders weighing 30 grams, 3 grams and 3/10 grams respectively. They are used as follows: with the scale in balance, if the 30 gram rider is placed on reading "1," it will balance 10 grams on the pan; if at "10," it will balance 100 grams. The same is true of the other riders, except that they read 1 gram and 1/10 gram respectively. If, then, one wishes to weigh 23.27 grams, the large rider would be placed on reading "2," the medium rider on reading "3" and the small rider on reading "2 7/10." In making weighings as above both pans should be in air and not have one pan submerged in water as when taking specific gravity, or a special single pan may be used for weighings only.

To make these riders it is best to have standard weights for use on the pan. A standard 50 gram, 5 gram and 5/10 gram weight will be sufficient. With the 50 gram weight on the pan, the large rider is made so that when it is hung at reading "5" on the beam it exactly balances; the other riders are made the same way, using the smaller weights. If it is not possible to obtain standard weights, then approximate ones may be made by measuring accurately 50 milliliters of distilled water at 39°F. into a container on the balanced scale.

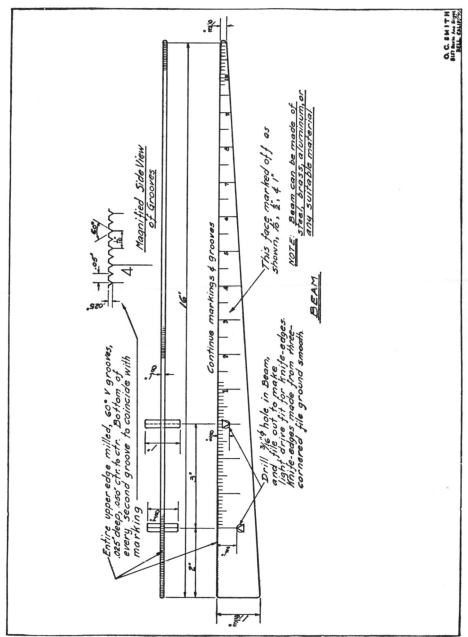

FIG. 6. Beam Balance, Drawing of Beam.

11

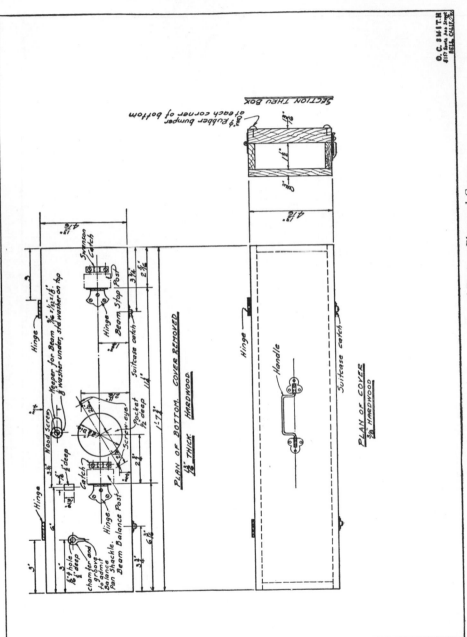

FIG. 7. Beam Balance, Drawing of Bottom Plan and Cover.

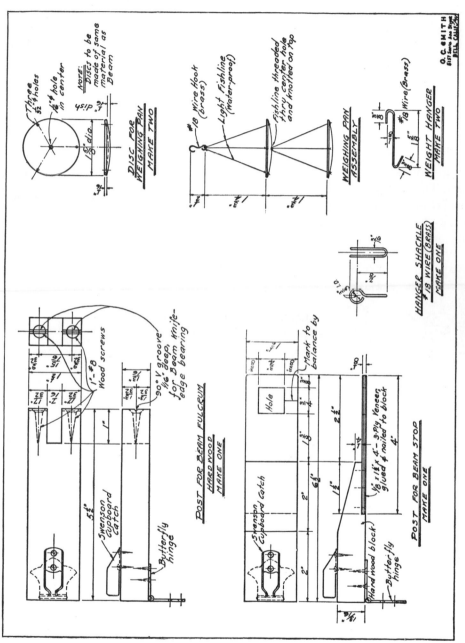

FIG. 8.   Beam Balance, Drawing of Accessories.

This will weigh 50 grams, for 1 milliliter of water at 39°F. weighs 1 gram. Due to the fact that it is difficult to measure accurately small volumes of water without special equipment, this method should not be used unless it is impossible to make riders using standard weights.

The riders of definite weight described above can be used for both weighings and specific gravity determinations, but for taking the specific gravity only they are not necessary, as anything may be used. The drawings show a set of common iron washers for this purpose. The operation using these is as follows: the cup is filled with water deep enough so that when the specimen is placed in the bottom pan it will be covered, but the water must not reach the top pan. With the pans hanging freely in the water, rider "A" is placed so that the beam is in balance. *This rider must not be disturbed or moved during the weighings.* The specimen is placed on the upper pan and rider "C" is placed so that the beam is again in balance, and the reading is taken, say 8. This is the weight in air. The specimen is now removed from the top pan and placed in the lower one, where it is covered with water. Rider "C" is again placed so that the beam is again in balance and the reading is taken, say 6. This is the weight in water. The specific gravity is calculated by the formula:

$$\text{Sp. Gr.} = \frac{(\text{weight in air})}{(\text{weight in air}) - (\text{weight in water})}.$$

Substituting the above readings we have:

$$\text{Sp. Gr.} = \frac{8}{8-6} = \frac{8}{2} = 4.$$

Relatively small samples may be used satisfactorily by adjusting the weight of the rider to give readings near the end of the beam. This balance may be improved in sensitivity and accuracy by making the knife edges and supports of agate, enclosing it so as not to be affected by air currents, etc.

The **pycnometer** method is not used much by amateurs, as it requires special equipment and a very accurate balance. It is used to some extent by analytical laboratories on very small samples, where great accuracy is desired. With this method, the pycnometer is first weighed empty (weight "A," say 5.0 grams). The particles of mineral are then introduced into the pycnometer and another weighing (weight "B," say 5.2 grams) is made. The difference between these weights is the weight of the sample. The pycnometer is then filled with water and weighed again (weight "C," say 10.15 grams), care being taken that all air bubbles are removed from the mineral. This may require boiling. If this is done the apparatus must be cooled before weighing. All water and mineral are then removed from the pycnometer and it is refilled with water and weighed again (weight "D," say 10.00 grams). The specific gravity of the sample is calculated as follows:

$$\text{Sp. Gr.} = \frac{(B - A)}{D + (B - A) - C}$$

Substituting, we have:

$$\frac{(5.2 - 5.0)}{10.0 + (5.2 - 5.0) - 10.15} = \frac{.20}{.05} = 4.$$

The **Berman density** balance is a torsion micro-balance developed by the late Dr. Harry Berman of Harvard University. It has great accuracy and is designed to handle very small samples. The capacity is 5 to 75 milligrams and the sensitivity is such that a vernier scale will read to 0.000001 gram. The specific gravity is determined in the same manner as with the beam balance, using the two pan system and weighing in air and in liquid. Toluene is recommended instead of water for submersion of the specimen, as the surface tension is only $\frac{1}{3}$ that of water, the ratio being 29 to 73. By using a 25 milligram sample, the balance is accurate to 0.2% and a determination can be made in about five minutes, the results checking very closely with the theoretical.

With the **heavy liquid** method, methylene iodide (CH_2I_2), Braun's solution, with a specific gravity of 3.3, may be mixed with benzol, specific gravity 0.98, for intermediate gravities or potassium mercuric iodide (KI,HgI), Thoulet's solution, with a specific gravity of 3.19 may be mixed with water. Other heavy liquids are Klein's, borotungstate of cadmium, Clerici's thallium formate and malonate and silver thallium nitrate. The procedure with these liquids is to make dilutions until the particles of mineral neither sink nor float, then determine the specific gravity of the liquid with a Westfall balance or pycnometer, or a definite volume of the liquid may be measured out and weighed.

As potassium mercuric iodide is a strong irritant, producing painful blisters, and as some of the other heavy liquids, such as silver thallium nitrate, specific gravity 4.5, are very poisonous, and since special equipment must be used to determine the density of the liquids after the test, this method has been used only for special samples, such as gems and minute particles.

Recently, however, the Cargille Heavy Liquid line has been developed and put on the market. These liquids are graduated in steps and have a specific gravity span of 1.48 to 7.5. They are considered to be non-hazardous. Sets can be obtained with the difference in specific gravity between each liquid in the series at any desired increment. This is a great advance over previous usage as it is not necessary to determine the density of the liquid which is found to correspond to that of the sample; also the range of liquid specific gravities is much greater than formerly. In using these liquids, the sample is placed in one after another, removing the adhering liquid in between, until one is found in which it neither sinks nor floats; or if it floats in one and sinks in the next, the specific gravity of the sample is in between these two. The specific gravity is then read from the label on the bottle.

Commercial systems have been developed using the sink or float principle by which light and heavier materials can be separated. In the coal industry the coal as mined is freed of slate by this method.

An **ordinary spring scale,** such as is used around the home, may be used on fairly large pieces by hanging the piece by a string to the scale in the same way as described under the Jolly balance, taking the weight in air, say 1 pound 4 ounces, then lowering it in a bucket of water and reading the weight, say 15 ounces. These readings must be converted to ounces, which gives 20 for the first reading and 15 for the second. These subtracted give five, which divided into the first reading (20) gives 4 as the specific gravity of the sample.

All the above descriptions and directions have been given using water for the submersion of the sample. However, some minerals are soluble in water and therefore some other liquid must be used. Toluene, also known as toluol, gives excellent results. In fact, much more accurate results are obtained by using toluene instead of water on *all* substances, as the surface tension of toluene is much lower than that of water and thus does not have the restraining action or damping effect on the balance. If it is used, however, the results obtained must be corrected; since the specific gravity of toluene is 0.866 at 68°F. the results obtained will be high, and it is necessary to multiply the result by the specific gravity of the liquid (0.866) to obtain the correct specific gravity of the sample.

Sometimes it is desired to determine the specific gravity of sand, gravel, ground mineral, concentrates, etc. This can be done by weighing out a sample and placing it in a graduated container and determining the volume in milliliters displaced by it. For instance, if a sample of sand or concentrate weighed 10 grams and on placing it in a burette containing water it raised the liquid level 2 milliliters, the volume of the sample would be 2 milliliters, and since 1 milliliter weighs 1 gram, the weight of the water displaced weighs 2 grams. This divided into the weight of the sample (10) gives 5 as the specific gravity. In this determination, care must be used to see that all air is removed from the sample grains, or the volume recorded will be erroneous and an incorrect result will be obtained.

Uses of Specific Gravity. Specific gravity and the difference in specific gravity of various minerals and substances are used in a number of ways by mineralogists, mining engineers and in the arts.

One of the important uses is assisting in the *identification of minerals.* The specific gravity is one of the most constant of the physical properties of minerals and a classification based on it is one of the very few that can satisfactorily include all the minerals. In the tables of this book the minerals are

16

divided into 13 specific gravity groups and in each group they are arranged according to their decreasing hardness.

In identifying a mineral by this method, the specific gravity is first determined, throwing the mineral into one or more of these groups, thus eliminating all minerals in the other groups. The hardness is next found and, by running down the table to this hardness, it is seen that the specimen must be one of a few minerals, as *all known minerals of that specific gravity and hardness are found together in that group.* By a comparison of the other properties, such as fusibility, solubility in hydrochloric acid, color, streak, luster, cleavage, fracture, crystal system and index of refraction, which are all conveniently listed across the page, the identification can usually be made. Simple blowpipe and chemical tests and the chemical composition are also given and may be used if necessary.

Most of the more common minerals and many of the rarer ones can be identified by this method, but one should not get the mistaken impression that absolutely all minerals can be identified by their physical properties or even by qualitative analysis, for some of them vary from each other by only slight differences in chemical composition, index of refraction, etc. Where this is the case, complete equipment for quantitative analysis and the determination of the optical properties and molecular structure is necessary.

In using the table, one should bear in mind that the specific gravity and other data are on the *pure minerals* and that the specimen under investigation should be observed for uniformity of texture, etc., to make sure it is not a mixture. It must also be remembered that although the specimen may be a crystal there is the possibility that it may be altered somewhat or may not be absolutely pure, with the result that its specific gravity and other properties may vary slightly from those of the pure mineral. For this reason it is always well to compare the groups immediately before and after the one into which the mineral falls.

Another important use of specific gravity is in the determination of the *percentage composition* of an ore or mixture of two minerals. With an ore, the procedure is as follows:

Assume, for example, that the ore in question is a sulfide carried in quartz as the gangue mineral. To arrive at the percentage of sulfide we must know three things, namely, the specific gravity of the sulfide, or concentrate (X), of the gangue (Y), and of the ore (Z). These can be determined by one of the methods already described. If we let X, Y and Z represent these gravities, then the percentage of the heavier mineral (sulfide) in the ore is found by the formula:

$$\text{Percentage by weight of the heavier mineral} = \frac{100 \times X \times (Z - Y).}{Z \times (X - Y)}$$

As a concrete example, take a sample of "picture rock" gold quartz, similar

17

to one that most mineralogists have (or wish they had) in their collections, and determine the gold content.

The specific gravity of the gold is taken as $18.00(X)$.
The specific gravity of the quartz is taken as $2.65(Y)$.
The specific gravity of the ore is taken as $4.65(Z)$.

Substituting in the above equation we have:

$$\frac{100 \times 18.00 \times (4.65 - 2.65)}{4.65 \times (18.00 - 2.65)} = \frac{100 \times 18.00 \times 2}{4.65 \times 15.35} = \frac{3600}{71.38}$$
$$= 50.43\% \text{ gold by weight}$$

The percentage composition of any other mixture of two minerals or substances is determined in the same manner.

The same determination can also be made by using the formula $W = VD$, i.e., $V = W/D$, where W is the weight, V the volume in milliliters and D the density or specific gravity. This method is more complicated and requires the use of weights. The following is an example, the ore consisting of gold-bearing pyrite in rock.

The specific gravity of the pyrite is 5.
The specific gravity of the rock is 3.
The specific gravity of the ore is 4.
The weight of the sample is 100 grams.

Let X be the weight of the pyrite in grams.
Let Y be the weight of the rock in grams.
Then $X + Y = 100$ grams (weight of the sample).
From the formula $V = W/D$ we find the volume of each thus: $X/5$, $Y/3$ and $100/4$. From these we derive the equation: $X/5 + Y/3 = 100/4 = 25$. Clearing fractions, we have:

$$3X + 5Y = 25(3 \times 5) = 375.$$

Solving for X in the two equations, we have:

$$5X + 5Y = 500$$
$$3X + 5Y = 375$$
$$\overline{2X \qquad\quad = 125}$$
$$X \qquad\quad = 62.5$$

The ore contains 62.5 grams of pyrite in the 100 gram sample, which is 62.5% by weight and a ton contains 1250 pounds.

Another use for the difference in specific gravity is utilized in **panning**. Panning is usually thought of in connection with gold, but any heavy material may be separated from a lighter one by this method. In carrying out a separation, a gold pan or other flat container is filled with the gravel or crushed ore and thoroughly wet with water by stirring and mixing. All large rock is washed and discarded. The pan is then submerged in water and given a rotary motion with a sidewise movement to agitate the contents and loosen them so that the heavier particles will settle to the bottom. After shaking for a short time the very top of the contents of the pan will be freed of the heavier substance and by a little more violent motion the water is made to wash some of this top material over the side of the pan; or one may scrape the top off by hand or dip the pan under water, then raise it out, allowing the water to run off one side, thus carrying the top away. After this removal the pan is again submerged, rotated and shaken to allow the heavier parts to settle further, and the top is again washed off. This cycle is repeated until nothing but the heavier material remains in the pan. When most of the lighter material has been removed it is better to transfer it to a smaller pan and, when near the end, to use a still smaller one for the final separation. By using 16″, 12″ and 6″ pans, excellent separations can be made with a little practice.

If water is not available, as is often the case in the desert, the separation may be made by **dry panning.** This is carried out in much the same way, except that the lighter material must be removed by blowing with the mouth or pouring from one pan to another and allowing the wind to carry it away.

Still another method of separation is achieved by **jigging.** Jigging uses the same principle as panning, but the operation is different. Using this method, the gravel, sand or crushed ore is placed in a sieve, pan, or box with a fine screen bottom. This is submerged in a tub or basin of water and is raised and lowered with enough force to cause the water to flow first upward then down through the sand or ore. This loosens it and with each succeeding cycle the heavier particles move toward the bottom and are finally concentrated on the screen. After allowing to drain, a board is placed over the top and the entire apparatus is quickly turned upside down. By tapping the screen, all of the material is loosened from it and deposited on the board, and on removal of the screen or sieve the concentrate will be found on top and may be taken off with a knife or spatula. Some of the fines will have passed through the screen and these must be examined separately, possibly by panning.

These are only a few of the many uses to which specific gravity and the difference in specific gravity may be put by the mineralogist and mining engineer. In mining and ore dressing many of the methods and much equipment for separation and concentration, such as jiggs, concentrating tables, and gravity settlers, depend on specific gravity for their success. Nature is continually making use of it and it is only through the sorting action of water that we have our placer deposits of gold, tin, black sands, and many of the important deposits of minerals and gems.

HARDNESS

By hardness is meant the resistance of a mineral to abrasion. Mohs' scale is generally used for the measurement of this property, utilizing the numbers 1 to 10 to designate the various degrees of hardness. A number of common articles greatly assist in this determination. These are included with the typical minerals used as the standards listed below.

1. **Talc:** easily scratched by the finger nail.
2. **Gypsum:** scratched with difficulty by the finger nail. Will not scratch a copper coin.
Finger nail: will scratch gypsum; will not scratch calcite. Hardness abolt 2.5.
3. **Calcite:** scratches copper and is scratched by copper. Not scratched by the finger nail.
Copper: scratches calcite; will not scratch fluorite. Hardness about 3.
4. **Fluorite:** does not scratch apatite or glass. Scratches copper.
5. **Apatite:** scratches glass with difficulty and is scratched by glass with difficulty.
Glass: scratches apatite but does not scratch feldspar. Hardness about 5–5.5.
6. **Feldspar** (orthoclose): scratches glass easily; scratched with difficulty by a knife blade.
Knife blade: will scratch feldspar; will not scratch quartz. Hardness 5.5–6.
7. **Quartz:** not scratched by a knife blade; scratched with difficulty by a file.
File: will scratch quartz with difficulty; will not scratch topaz. Hardness about 7.
8. **Topaz:** will scratch quartz; will not scratch corundum; is scratched by corundum.
9. **Corundum:** will scratch topaz; will scratch silicon carbide with difficulty and is scratched by silicon carbide with difficulty.
Silicon carbide: will scratch corundum; will not scratch diamond. Hardness about 9.
10. **Diamond:** not scratched by any known substance; will scratch all other substances.

The determination of the hardness is best made by scratching the sample with a knife blade to arrive at its approximate hardness and then determined exactly by means of the test minerals. With a little practice, hardness of 5 and below can usually be determined quite well with the knife blade only.

If a sample scratches feldspar and in turn is scratched by feldspar, they both have the same hardness, which is 6. If, however, it will not scratch feldspar but will scratch apatite and is not scratched by apatite, it has a hardness of 5.5.

In making the test, care must be taken to be sure the scratch is a distinct groove and not merely a chalk mark.

On some minerals the hardness of the various faces varies. Kyanite, for instance, has a hardness of 4–5 along the length of the crystal but 6–7 across it. In the tables the hardest face is given as the hardness of the mineral.

FUSIBILITY

The ease with which minerals melt or become plastic in a flame is designated by the numbers 1-7. All determinations are made with the mouth blowpipe, using no artificial air supply. Typical minerals and their approximate fusion points are given below.

1. **Stibnite:** fuses easily in the luminous flame, in a closed tube and in a match or candle flame; about 525°C. (977°F.).
2. **Chalcopyrite:** fuses easily in the blowpipe flame but with difficulty in the luminous flame or closed tube; about 800°C. (1472°F.).
3. **Almandite:** fuses easily in the blowpipe flame but is not fused in the closed tube or luminous flame. Finest splinters only rounded on the point in the gas flame; about 1050°C. (1922°F.).
4. **Actinolite:** thin edges fuse easily in the blowpipe flame but larger masses are difficult to fuse; about 1200°C. (2192°F.).
5. **Orthoclase:** fuses on the edges with difficulty in the blowpipe flame; larger masses are not fused, only rounded; about 1300°C. (2372°F.).
6. **Enstatite: Bronzite:** fused and rounded only on the thinnest edges and points of small pieces; about 1400°C. (2552°F.).
7. **Quartz:** infusible even on the thinnest edges and points of small pieces; over 1400°C. (2552°F.).

In using this scale, the hottest or oxidizing flame is used and the thinnest possible splinter of the mineral is tested. These should be held in the tip of the forceps or tweezers, so as to conduct away as little heat as possible. If the

APPROXIMATE MELTING POINT OF VARIOUS METALS

Metal	°C.	°F.	Metal	°C.	°F.
Mercury	−39	−38.2	Gold	1063	1945.6
Tin	232	449.6	Copper	1083	1981.4
Bismuth	271	519.8	Nickel	1455	2651.0
Cadmium	321	609.8	Cobalt	1480	2696.0
Lead	327	620.6	Iron	1535	2795.0
Zinc	419	786.2	Platinum	1774	3225.2
Antimony	630	1166.0	Molybdenum	2520	4568.0
Magnesium	650	1202.0	Tungsten	3370	6130.0
Aluminum	660	1220.0	(Approximate limit of blowpipe flame, 1500°C.)		
Silver	961	1761.8			

sample decrepitates so that splinters can not be used, it should be ground to a powder, mixed with a little water to form a paste, spread in a thin layer on charcoal and heated slowly then strongly until it forms a thin coherent mass that can be held in the forceps and tested in the oxidizing flame.

If a substance fuses easily in the blowpipe flame, but is infusible in the luminous flame or closed tube, it is said to have a fusibility of 3; if it is barely affected by the luminous flame it has a fusibility of 2.5.

SOLUBILITY IN HYDROCHLORIC ACID

In the column headed HCl is recorded whether the mineral is soluble or insoluble in the acid and also its general reactions.

Sol., indicates that it is completely soluble.

Pt. Sol., indicates that it is partially soluble or soluble with difficulty.

Gelat., indicates that the mineral is decomposed with the formation of a gelatinous precipitate of silica.

Dcpd., indicates that the mineral is soluble with decomposition, such as evolution of gas.

Ins., indicates that the mineral is insoluble in either hot or cold acid.

In making the test, place a small piece of the specimen in a test tube and add diluted HCl. Note whether there is any reaction, such as effervescence; if there is an odor, such as chlorine or bromine; whether the rate of solution is slow or rapid; the color of the liquid, etc. If there is no reaction or only a very slight one, heat gently and observe the results. If no solution or reactions occur, repeat, using concentrated HCl.

COLOR

The color of some minerals often varies a great deal as in fluorite and scheelite. These variations are frequently due to the different amounts and kinds of impurities present or to changes in composition. In these cases the range of colors is covered as completely as possible in the tables.

These impurities very often give value to an otherwise valueless mineral. For instance, colorless corundum is worth very little, but the clear red (ruby) and blue (sapphire) are precious gems. Quartz in the pure state is colorless, but the violet, rose, smoky, yellow and other colors are used for the cheaper jewelry. Tourmaline often has unusual colors and combinations, varying from black to brown, red, green, yellow, gray and white. A crystal may also have a red core and green outer part (watermelon tourmaline) or vice versa, and it is not uncommon for a crystal to be a beautiful green at one end and red at the other with a very sharp demarcation between them as though two separate, distinct crystals had been cemented together. Other minerals which vary much in color are topaz, spinel, garnet, zircon, opal, etc.

In many minerals, however, the color is a characteristic of the mineral and is not dependent on any foreign substance. In these cases, the color is a valuable diagnostic tool. Most of the so-called metallic minerals, such as galena, chalcopyrite and other sulfides, as well as magnetite and the other irons, and the coppers, have fairly uniform colors and usually can be recognized at a glance. Often the surface color is different from the fresh break because of oxidation. This *tarnish* is useful in mineral identification, for it is a characteristic of certain minerals as in chalcocite, bornite and chalcopyrite.

The color of the mineral should always be determined on a freshly broken piece and the color recorded in the tables is on the fresh, unweathered material.

STREAK

The powder of a mineral often has a color which is different from that of the solid, which aids greatly in its identification. This color is called the streak and may be obtained by noting the color of the ground mineral, by scratching the surface or by drawing the specimen over a piece of unglazed porcelain known as a **streak plate.** This leaves a streak or chalk-like mark of the mineral powder. An example of the value of the streak is found with the mineral hematite, which may be steel gray, red or black in color but in which the streak is always red or brownish-red.

LUSTER

The luster of minerals depends on their ability to reflect light and is a valuable aid in their identification. The designations for luster, with the symbols as used in the tables, are as follows:

Metallic, M: has the appearance of metal; as with galena.
Sub-metallic, Sm: not as brightly metallic in appearance.
Adamantine, A: appears hard and brilliant; as diamond.
Sub-adamantine, Sa: not as brilliant as adamantine.
Vitreous, V: looks like glass; as quartz.
Sub-vitreous, Sv: not as glassy appearing as vitreous.
Resinous, R: looks like resin; as sphalerite, often called "rosin jack."
Pearly, P: iridescent like the inside of sea shells.
Greasy, G: appears to be covered with a thin film of grease or oil.
Silky, S: looks as though made of silk threads; as satin spar (gypsum).
Dull, D and **Earthy,** E: are degrees of luster and are usually applied to such substances as kaoline, chalk and clay.

There are a number of other phenomena of light reflections which are produced either by peculiarities in the reflecting surface or by the fact that reflection takes place from surfaces in the interior of the substance. Among these are the following:

Opalescence is a peculiar milky or cloudy reflection from the interior of a mineral. It is seen in some opal and moonstone.

Chatoyancy is a changeable, banded luster or silky sheen. Chatoyant stones, such as chrysoberyl ("cat's eye"), when suitably cut, flash out light bands which shift their position according to the position in which the stone is held. This phenomenon is the result of a fibrous structure.

Asterism is the phenomenon displayed by certain varieties of ruby, sapphire, garnet, mica, quartz, etc. It is due to the intersection of two or three systems of striations and causes the production of star-like effect of four or six prominent rays of reflected light.

Change or *Play of Colors* is obtained when, on turning, several spectral colors are obtained. This is a phenomenon of diffraction produced at the surface of a mineral by a very fine lineation. Labradorite is a good example.

Iridescence refers to the prismatic colors produced by the interference of light in the interior or at the surface of a subtance. It is due to the presence of minute fissures or a thin superficial film.

CLEAVAGE

Cleavage is the tendency of a mineral to break along certain planes yielding a relatively smooth surface. The planes are always parallel to possible faces and usually correspond to a common form of the mineral. They are separations parallel to molecular planes composing the mineral (not necessarily the existing faces) and are due to the fact that molecular attraction is weaker in some directions than in others.

The minerals of the different crystal systems often exhibit characteristic cleavage forms and appearance. Thus galena and halite which crystallize in the isometric system often cleave in three directions, yielding cubes or square-cornered pieces. This type of cleavage is called *cubical*. Fluorite, also isometric, although it is ordinarily found as cubes, usually cleaves so as to produce all or part of an eight-sided solid (octahedron) which is composed of two four-sided pyramids, base to base, the sides of which are equilateral triangles. This is known as *octahedral* cleavage. Sphalerite, also isometric, cleaves to produce rhombic faces (distorted squares) which, if carried to completion, would form a twelve-sided solid. This type of cleavage is called *dodecahedral.*

In the hexagonal system, cleavage parallel to the basal face (at right angles to the C axis) is called *basal,* while if it is parallel to this axis (usually lengthwise of the crystal) parallel to the side faces, it is *prismatic.* This system is also characterized by distinct cleavage in some minerals by which rhombohedrons (solids like a box that has been deformed by pushing in one corner) are formed. Calcite is an excellent example, for no matter what the crystal shape may be, cleavage will always produce rhombohedrons. The cleavage is *rhombohedral* in this system. Basal cleavage is represented by beryl, while apatite illustrates both the *basal* and *prismatic* types.

In the tetragonal system, basal and prismatic cleavage occurs as illustrated in apophyllite, rutile and scheelite. The *basal* cleavage is across the C axis, parallel to the terminal face, and the *prismatic* is parallel to the C axis on one or more of the prisms.

In the orthorhombic and monoclinic systems, cleavage is basal, prismatic and pinacoidal. The *pinacoidal* type is where the cleavage is in one direction parallel to the pinacoids. (Pinacoids are two faces parallel to two of the axes). Examples of these cleavages are represented by anhydrite, barite, topaz and stibnite in the orthorhombic and orthoclase, mica, gypsum, stilbite and epidote in the monoclinic system.

In the triclinic system the cleavage is basal and pinacoidal, there being no prismatic. Examples are the plagioclase feldspars, microcline, and kyanite.

The perfection of the cleavage is designated as follows, and the types recorded in the tables occur on at least one of the faces and is the best on any face.

Eminent, E: is applied only to such cleavage as is obtained with the micas.

Perfect, Perf: is obtained very easily, as in calcite.

Distinct, Dist. or **Good:** is obtained readily but not as easily as Perfect. Arsenopyrite is an example.

Imperfect, Imperf. or **Fair:** are more difficult to obtain than Distinct. Pyrrhotite is an example.

Difficult, Diff. or **Poor:** are obtained with difficulty and are usually evident only in traces as in bornite.

Parting or **pseudo-cleavage** is not uncommon in some of the minerals and may be mistaken for cleavage. This property is caused by stress, foreign material, etc., which develop planes or structural weakness along which a solid may easily break. Twin crystals often break along their twinning plane. Parting is distinguished from cleavage by the fact that all similar specimens of a mineral will not separate, and that there are a limited number of planes along which the mineral will break. Magnetite, which shows very poor cleavage, often has a highly developed octahedral parting which is easily mistaken for cleavage.

FRACTURE

The fracture is the type of surface obtained by breaking other than along a cleavage plane. Under this heading in the tables will be found the fracture characteristics in most cases, but as this is not reported in many minerals, other descriptive properties, such as brittle, granular, fibrous, etc., are also included in this column.

The designations for fracture and the abbreviations as used in the tables are as follows:

Conchoidal, Conch: the surfaces are curved like the inside of a shell, as in quartz and glass.

Sub-Conchoidal, Subconch: somewhat curved but not as distinctly as conchoidal, as in wulfenite and argentite.

Even: the break is smooth and quite flat, as in galena.

Uneven: the surfaces are even for only small spaces, as in arsenopyrite.

Hackley: the surface is pointed and rough, as in silver and copper.

Splintery: breaks into splinters and fibers, as in jadite.

Earthy: breaks to pieces, as dirt or clay.

TENACITY

The tenacity of a mineral is the resistance it offers to being broken, crushed, bent or torn apart. The usual designations for the types found in minerals are as follows:

Brittle: can be easily broken or powdered. Examples: galena and quartz.

Sectile: will cut with a knife, producing shavings. Examples: gypsum and chalcocite.

Malleable: when hammered, it clings together but gets thinner. Examples: gold, copper, etc.

Ductile: can be drawn out into wire. Examples: gold, copper, etc.

Flexible: thin layers can be bent without breaking and remain bent when released. Examples: some of the micas and foliated talc.

Elastic: thin layers can be bent without breaking, but resume their original shape when released. Examples: some of the micas.

TASTE

Substances soluble in water or the saliva usually have a characteristic taste. The designations used in connection with minerals are as follows:

Acid: sour, like vinegar.

Alkaline: tastes like washing soda.

Astringent: the puckery taste of alum.

Bitter: like Epsom salts.

Cooling: the taste of sodium nitrate.

Saline: the taste of common salt.

ODOR

Most minerals in the dry, unaltered state have no odor, but some do produce odors when scratched, rubbed, breathed on, wetted, struck, or treated with acids. Some of the designations used for the odors of minerals are as follows:

Argllaceous: like wet soil after a rain or clay that has been wetted or breathed on.

Bituminous: the odor of bituminous matter which is obtained by striking asphalt with a hammer.

Fetid: the odor of hydrogen sulfide and rotten eggs. Obtained from the sulfides.

Garlic: obtained from arsenical minerals.

Horse-radish: obtained from selenium minerals.

Sulfurous: from burning sulfur.

FEEL

The impression that one gets from handling substances is characteristic of some minerals and is designated as follows:

Greasy: slippery like soap. Talc is an example.

Harsh or **Meager:** rough like chalk.

Smooth: without projections or irregularities as with sepiolite.

Unctuous: some minerals adhere to the tongue. Among these are chalk, kaoline, and diatomaceous earth.

CRYSTAL SYSTEMS

All crystalline substances form solids with definite molecular arrangements. The minerals crystallize from vapors, water solutions and fusions and, if these processes continue unhindered, bodies form with faces having definite relationships to one another and to hypothetical lines known as *axes*. The number of these and their relationship to each other form the basis of the crystal systems which are divided into six main subdivisions, depending on the number, length and inclination of these axes. They are the **isometric, tetragonal, hexagonal, orthorhombic, monoclinic,** and **triclinic.** These are further divided into a total of thirty-two sub-groups. The distinguishing characteristics of each group are as follows:

The **isometric** system has three axes of equal length intersecting one another at right angles. Examples: galena, garnet.

The **tetragonal** system has three axes intersecting one another at right angles. Two, which are of equal length, are considered the lateral axes; the third is the vertical axis and may be either longer or shorter than the other two. Examples: zircon, rutile.

The **hexagonal** system has four axes. The three lateral ones are equal, intersect one another at 60°, and are at right angles to the vertical axis, which is of a different length. Examples: quartz, beryl.

The **orthorhombic** system has three axes intersecting one another at right angles, but no two are the same length. Examples: sulfur, barite.

The **monoclinic** system has three axes. The vertical one and one lateral axis (the one running from the front to the back) are oblique to each other, but the transverse lateral axis is at right angles to both the others. Examples: gypsum, orthoclase.

The **triclinic** system has three axes, all oblique to one another. Crystals of this system are symmetrical to a central point only. Examples: chalcanthite, albite.

The field of crystallography is a study of its own and cannot be covered here. For further information consult any good textbook on the subject.

INDEX OF REFRACTION

The index of refraction for a substance is the ratio of the velocity of light in a vacuum to its velocity in the substance. It is a function of the substance and the light source and is a constant.

The minerals are divided into the following three general classes:

The **isotropic** group, which has only one value (n) for the index of refraction. This group includes those minerals which crystallize in the isometric system and the amorphous substances.

The **uniaxial** group, which has two values (omega, ω and epsilon, ϵ). This group includes minerals of the hexagonal and tetragonal systems.

The **biaxial** group, which has three values (alpha, a, beta, β, and gamma, γ). This group includes the minerals which crystallize in the orthorhombic, monoclinic, and triclinic systems.

The index of refraction given in the table is n for the isotropic group, *omega* for the uniaxial group, and *beta* for the biaxial group. In those cases where there was a variation in the reported value, the $\pm$ was added.

CHAPTER II

The Blowpipe and Its Uses

HISTORY OF BLOWPIPING *

* The following data regarding the early uses and developments of the blowpipe have been gleaned from Plattner's "Probirkunst mit dem Loethrohre," Mitchell's "Manual of Practical Assaying" and several other books, all of which are out of print.

The mouth blowpipe has been used for centuries for glassblowing and by artisans of gold, silver, and copper as a means of soldering and working these materials, but it was not until 1670 that Erasmus Barthilin first mentioned its use with minerals. In his treatise on doubly-refracting spar, he states that this mineral is burned to lime before the blowpipe. In all probability, the instrument was in use by mining men and chemists many years before this, for only nine years after the above reference to its use, J. Kunckel, in his "Ars vitaria experimentalis," Part II, states that a table arranged for glass blowing may be useful to the chemist in many ways. He says "for it is only necessary in testing metallic calx, to hollow out a coal, put it in this and blow on it with the flame of a powerful lamp."

About the year 1733, Anton Schwab made use of the blowpipe in the regular analysis of mineral substances and, in 1739, John Andreas Cramer published his "Elementis artis domesticae" in which he recommends the blowpipe (which according to him should be made of copper and provided with a hollow sphere at the bend in order to retain moisture resulting from blowing) for melting small bits of metal or for quickly testing other grains in small quantities.

Since blowing with the mouth seemed troublesome, there were, even at that time, proposals for the use of an artificial blast, and great ingenuity was exhibited in devising means and methods to accomplish this end.

The blowpipe gained especial attention in Sweden, regarded as the cradle of blowpipe analysis. From the middle of the 18th century through the first half of the 19th century are found a series of celebrated men who busied themselves much with blowpipe tests and looked upon this instrument as an essential aid to their mineralogical and chemical labors.

Cronstedt sought to base a classification of the minerals on their chemical composition and used the blowpipe in order to detect quickly their composition, fusibility, etc. According to Engestroem, Cronstedt was the first who tried to bring into a compact form all of the utensils and reagents necessary for the blowpipe tests and to construct a portable blowpipe apparatus, a so-called portable laboratory.

In 1765 Von Engestroem published a translation of Cronstedt's "System of Mineralogy" and added a "Treatise on the Blowpipe" in which he brought together the methods developed and used by Cronstedt. Soda, borax, and salt of phosphorus were already in use and considered as most excellent reagents.

This work attracted the attention of research workers to this valuable instrument and its use became more general. Bergman extended the use of the blowpipe beyond the bounds of minerology, and in his hands this instrument became an invaluable agent for the detection of minute amounts of many metallic substances. He verified and extended Cronstedt's tests and submitted his results in the treatise "Commentatio de tubo ferrumentoria, Etc." which was printed in 1779. Bergman treated the greater number of the minerals known in his time with the reagents employed by Cronstedt, described their reactions and improved many of the instruments necessary for the performance. In these experiments he was assisted in his mineralogical studies by Gahn, who became particularly expert in the use of the blowpipe. An example of the utility of this instrument in practiced hands is given by the following incident. "Ekeberg asked Gahn his opinion of the then newly discovered mineral, the oxide of tantalum, and Gahn immediately discovered that it contained tin, although it did not amount to more than 1 per cent."

Berzelius, after Gahn, was particularly famed for his skill with the blowpipe and for his improvements in the form of the various pieces of accessory apparatus. We also must thank Berzelius that the excellent work of Gahn was not lost, as might easily have happened since Gahn never published anything about his methods or results. Berzelius reported Gahn's methods and experiences in his "Textbook of Chemistry," which appeared in 1812, but did not stop with Gahn's experiments. He took up the subject himself with especial zeal and in 1820 published his "Anwendung des Loethrohrs" which lived through four German editions and was translated into several languages.

B. de Saussure also made use of the blowpipe for the same purpose as Cronstedt, to study and distinguish minerals and although he introduced several improvements in the use of the apparatus, Berzelius states that he remained far behind Gahn in the results obtained with the instrument. Among other things, de Saussure endeavored to estimate the temperature necessary to melt certain substances by measuring the size of the globule which could be fused with the blowpipe.

After the first edition of Berzelius' work had appeared, the use of the blowpipe spread more and more and was variously enriched, partly by Berzelius himself, partly by Le Baillif, Smithson, Turner, Harkort, Plattner, Th. Richter, von Kobell and others.

During his studies at Freiberg in 1826, Harkort hit on the idea of using the blowpipe for quantitative as well as qualitative determinations. He occupied himself primarily with the silver test and described his method in a volume "Probirkunst mit dem Loethrohr," printed at his expense in 1827. Plattner completed what Harkort had begun and extended the quantitative blowpipe assay to gold, copper, lead, bismuth, tin, nickel and cobalt. The quantitative determination of these latter, however, are not practical by blowpipe methods as they are too easily oxidized and altered. Gold, silver and the platinum metals alone having enough resistance to enable them to be treated at the temperature and conditions which are necessary for their separation as beads of pure metal.

Bunsen has also furnished valuable additions to blowpipe analysis through his publications "Flamenreactionen" and "Loethrohrversuche."

An adequate scheme of analysis using blowpipe methods only has never been developed. A number have been attempted but they all are full of "if's" and cover only the more common elements. The scheme devised by Prof. T. Egeleston and included in Plattner's "Blowpipe Analysis" (out of print) is about as good as any, but lacks much in the way of completeness and sharp separations.

Blowpipe tests are well suited for determinations of simple substances or very simple mixtures, but many complications and much uncertainty arises when complex mixtures are tested, due to the interference of different elements.

The early blowpipe analyst had many difficulties to overcome. He had to devise his blowpipe, burner or other source of flame and even his charcoal slabs were so difficult to obtain that methods were devised for moulding blocks and crucibles out of a mixture of ground charcoal with cooked starch, ground together until no more charcoal would be taken up; then kneaded by hand until the mass was stiff and plastic. This was then moulded into small dishes, crucibles and slabs in suitable moulds, allowed to dry thoroughly, and then heated to dull redness in a closed container to prevent oxidation. Clay crucibles were also made by pressing a plastic mixture of elutriated fire-clay and water into moulds (the sides of which had been oiled), allowing to dry and baking at a red heat.

As most of the general reagents of the blowpipe tests are common household substances, the early analysts used many of those now in use and developed a good number of the tests still used. Among these are sodium carbonate and bicarbonate, borax, salt of phosphorus, potassium bisulfate, cobalt nitrate and the acids, hydrochloric, nitric and sulfuric. They were familiar with and developed most of the tests using these reagents. They understood the use of the closed and open tube, the formation of sublimates, the bead tests, the use of fusibility, flame color, fusions and the formation of metallic globules on charcoal.

Besides the qualitative tests, quantitative analysis was also attempted and methods were worked out for the quantitative determination of silver, gold, copper, lead, cobalt, nickel and mercury. All but gold and silver are easily oxidized, and special methods, apparatus and precautions were necessary which made the determinations quite complicated and unreliable, with the result that gold, silver and the platinum metals are practically the only ones attempted at the present time.

The Flame and Its Use in Blowpiping

An ordinary flame such as a candle or gas burner consists of three parts. Just above the wick or burner is the transparent zone "A," composed of gas or volatilized fuel that has not yet fired. Outside of this is zone "B," composed of burning gas. In the luminous flame it is rendered yellow by minute particles of incandescent carbon produced in the thermal decomposition of some of the hydrocarbons in the fuel. In the nonluminous flame this region is bluish as sufficient air is present to oxidize these compounds without the formation of particles of free carbon. Covering the entire outside is the faint bluish, hardly visible mantle, zone "C," composed of the products of complete combustion. See Fig. 9.

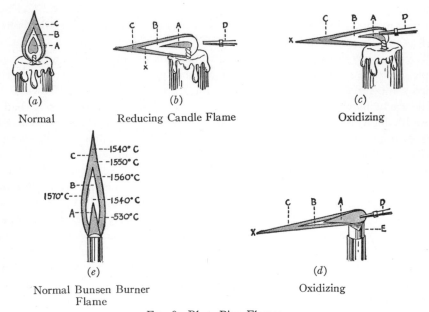

(a) Normal   (b) Reducing Candle Flame   (c) Oxidizing

(e) Normal Bunsen Burner Flame   (d) Oxidizing

Fig. 9. Blow Pipe Flames.

Flame Sources. Any convenient flame may be used for blowpiping, but for practical purposes only three sources will be considered here. They are the gas burner, alcohol lamp, and the candle.

For use in a permanent laboratory, domestic gas and a Bunsen burner (Fig. 10) equipped with a blowpipe tip (Fig. 9(d)) is most convenient. With this arrangement excellent oxidizing and reducing flames can be produced and a large amount of heat is available when desired.

For field use or where gas is not available, the alcohol or spirit lamp (Fig. 11) or candle may be used. The alcohol lamp does not produce a very good reducing flame but otherwise is quite satisfactory. The candle does give a good reducing flame but has the objection of not supplying much heat and tends to melt down quickly. Plumber's candles are probably best for general use as they are made from a higher melting point wax than the ordinary candle.

FIG. 10.
Bunsen Burner.

FIG. 11.
Alcohol Lamp.

A **blowpipe** (Fig. 12) is a tube, usually of brass, so arranged that a fine jet of air may be delivered from the mouth of the operator, at right angles to his line of vision, into or through a flame, thus directing and controlling the amount of heat and type of flame applied.

Learning the proper use of the blowpipe is somewhat difficult; a novice is inclined to blow with his lungs, which is incorrect. Good blowpiping can be accomplished only after the proper method has been learned. The success of blowpiping as a means of making qualitative tests depends on its proper manipulation, as it is necessary that the operator be able to produce a strong, steady oxidizing or reducing flame for an indefinite period. Considerable practice may be required before this can be accomplished.

The blowpipe is held in any convenient manner, with the mouth piece held firmly between the lips or firmly pressed against them. The cheeks are filled with air and the passage between the throat and mouth is closed with the tongue in the same manner as one puffs out one's cheeks. If this is done the cheeks will remain full of air and breathing through the nose can be carried on without in any way disturbing the air held in the mouth. This accomplished, the air in the mouth is expelled by the cheek muscles through the blowpipe. As the air is depleted, a fresh supply is taken in through the nose without interrupting the flow through the blowpipe. In this way a steady flame is produced and breathing is carried on normally through the nostrils.

The production of the oxidizing flame by the candle and Bunsen burner is illustrated in *c* and *e* of Fig. 9. The Bunsen burner has slipped over it a blowpipe tip ("E") which gives a flat flame and provides a support for the blowpipe.

In producing the **oxidizing flame** (O.F.), the tip of the blowpipe is inserted about ⅛″ into the flame (Fig. 9 (c) and (d)). A steady current of air will elongate the flame into a narrow cone with a point almost as definite as a

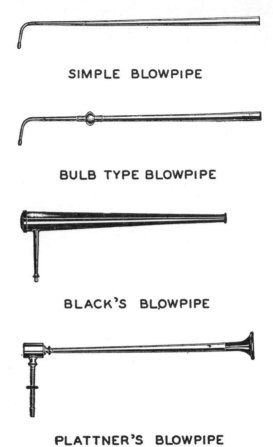

SIMPLE BLOWPIPE

BULB TYPE BLOWPIPE

BLACK'S BLOWPIPE

PLATTNER'S BLOWPIPE

Fig. 12. Types of Mouth Blowpipes.

needle, and the luminous part will disappear if sufficient air is used. An oxidizable substance, if held at the point "X" or even further in toward the tip of the cone "B," will be rapidly oxidized. Flame tests are made by holding the material being tested at this place. Since the flame of the Bunsen burner just above the tip of the inner cone "B" ((e) of Fig. 9) is the hottest, fusions can be made here also.

In general, **oxidation** proceeds best when the substance is kept at a dull red heat. The blue cone must be kept free from straggling yellow rays of the reducing flame. If the analysis is carried out on charcoal, the blast of air should not be too strong, as much of the coal will be converted to carbon monoxide, which has a strong reducing action and will tend to retard the oxidation. The oxidizing flame requires a steady current of air, so as to keep the blue cone constantly of the same length. Practice in producing this flame may be carried out by melting a little molybdic acid with some borax, on a platinum wire, about $\frac{1}{16}''$ from the point of the cone. In the pure oxidizing flame, a clear yellow glass is formed; but as soon as the reducing flame touches it, the color of the bead changes to brown, which finally, after a little blowing, becomes quite dark and loses its transparency. The cause of this is that the molybdic acid is very easily reduced to a lower degree of oxidation. The pure oxidizing flame will again convert this dark bead into a clear one, and this conversion is a good test of the progress of the student in the use of the blowpipe. An easily oxidizable substance may be separated from one which is more resistant by careful use of the oxidizing flame.

The **reducing flame** (R.F.) is illustrated in (b) of Fig. 9. This flame is produced by holding the tip of the blowpipe *outside* of the flame a short distance above the wick or burner top. A jet of air blows the entire flame into a horizontal cone, but not to a fine point as in the oxidizing flame. The air used is not sufficient to destroy the luminosity, but does oxidize much of the free carbon, thus giving a higher temperature. A reducible substance held at "X" in the yellow tip of the cone "B" will be rapidly deoxidized or **reduced.**

If the oxide of a metal is brought into the luminous part of the flame produced as above, so that the flame envelops the substance completely, the access of air is prevented. The partially consumed gases now have a strong affinity for oxygen, under the influence of the intense heat of that part of the flame. The substance is thus deprived of a part or all of its oxygen and becomes reduced according to the relative affinity which the substance has for oxygen. If the reduction of a substance is attempted on platinum, by fusion with a flux, or if the oxide is difficult to reduce, the reduction will be completely effected only in the luminous flame. But if a substance be reduced on charcoal, the reduction will take place in the blue part of the flame, as long as the excess of air is cut off. However, it is the luminous part of the flame which possesses the greatest reducing power.

For the purpose of practice, the student may fuse the oxide of manganese with borax on a platinum wire in the oxidizing flame. A violet-red glass should be obtained. If too much of the oxide is used, an opaque glass of a dark color will result. By submitting this glass to a reducing flame, it will become colorless in correspondence to the perfection with which the flame is produced. Also a piece of metallic tin may be fused on charcoal and kept in this state for a considerable time, while it presents the appearance of bright metal on the surface. This will require dexterity of the operator, for if the oxidizing flame should chance to touch the bright metal for only a moment, it will be coated with an infusible oxide.

Many of the elements give very characteristic reactions when subjected to different treatments under the blowpipe.

Uses of the Blowpipe

The principal operations with the blowpipe consist of oxidation, reduction, fusion, sublimation, and ignition and may be explained briefly as follows:

Oxidation. Increasing the proportion of oxygen or acid-forming elements or removal of hydrogen from a substance is termed oxidation. In blowpipe work, it usually consists of converting the substance to an oxide or changing it from a lower to a higher degree of oxidation by treatment with the oxidizing flame. As these oxides have properties which are usually quite different from the unoxidized material, oxidation is often a great help in determining the elements present. The conditions necessary for efficient oxidation are high temperatures, with free admission of air to the substance or the presence of a compound which releases oxygen. Potassium nitrate, potassium chlorate, sodium peroxide, hydrogen peroxide, nitric acid and sulfuric acid are often used as oxidizers and will be met with in the analytical and blowpipe procedures.

Examples of oxidation are the burning of carbonaceous matter with the formation of water vapor and the carbonic oxides; the formation of white vapors of arsenic oxides on treating arsenic with the oxidizing blowpipe flame; the formation of the blue-green potassium manganate on fusion of a manganeze mineral with soda and potassium nitrate on platinum; and the conversion of iron, cobalt, nickel, chromium, etc. into a higher valence state by treatment with potassium chlorate in solutions. (See Iron Group, page 184.)

Reduction. Increasing the proportion of hydrogen or base-forming elements or removal of oxygen from a substance is termed reduction. In blowpipe work it usually consists of the formation of the free metal by the complete removal of the combined oxygen or of changing the substance to a lower degree of oxidation by treatment with the reducing flame. As these reduced substances usually have properties which are quite different from the unreduced materials, reduction is often a great aid in determining the elements present.

The conditions necessary for efficient reduction are high temperatures with the exclusion of air from the substance or the presence of a compound which consumes oxygen or releases hydrogen. Common reducing agents are charcoal, hydrogen, potassium cyanide, potassium oxalate and base metals, such as tin, zinc, iron and copper in acids, usually hydrochloric.

Examples of reduction are: the treatment of base metal oxides in the reducing flame resulting in the formation of the free metals; the action of flour in the fluxes used in gold-silver assaying resulting in the liberation of free metallic lead; the action of hydrogen sulfide in reducing cobalt, nickel, iron, chromium, etc. to a lower valence condition; and the action of metallic zinc or tin with tungsten and columbium resulting in a blue color, as well as the color changes of many other metals as indicated in the table on "Reactions with Metallic Zinc in Acid Solutions."

Fusion. The difference between the meaning of the terms fusion and melting is rather difficult to define, as they both indicate changes from the solid to a liquid or plastic state. However, fusion is usually applied to materials or mixtures in which there is a blending or melting together which becomes plastic or forms viscous fluids, while melting is applied to pure substances and those which become quite mobile.

With minerals, the fusion point is the designation applied to the temperature at which the points or edges of small splinters are rounded.

Fusion in chemical analysis usually consists of the treatment of a refractory or insoluble material with a chemical or mixture which, on heating, melts and reacts with the refractory substance, giving a final product which is fluid and in which desirable combinations are formed. Some of the reagents most often used in making fusions are sodium and potassium carbonates, potassium bisulfate, borax and salt of phosphorus (sodium ammonium hydrogen phosphate).

Some of the common fusions made in blowpipe and other analytical procedures are as follows:

Soda Fusions. Many of the silicates are insoluble in the common acids and must be decomposed by fusion with soda or potassium carbonate before solution can be obtained. On heating a mixture of an excess of soda with the ground silicate, the soda melts and a reaction takes place whereby the silica is converted to sodium silicate with the evolution of carbon dioxide, and the metallic elements present are usually left in such a form that they are easily soluble in the common acids. A similar reaction occurs when an insoluble mineral, such as barite, is fused with soda in that barium carbonate and sodium sulfate are formed, or if a metallic sulfide is fused with soda, sodium sulfide and the free metal are usually produced. If the barite fusion above is dissolved in water (no acid) and filtered, the greater part of the sulfate will pass through the filter paper as sodium sulfate and a corresponding amount of the barium will be retained on the paper as barium carbonate which is easily soluble in acids.

Potassium Bisulfate Fusions. When potassium bisulfate, $KHSO_4$ (also called potassium acid sulfate), is heated, it melts and loses water (causing frothing) and is converted into the pyrosulfate, $K_2S_2O_7$. This conversion is complete when frothing ceases. On further heating at a higher temperature, $K_2S_2O_7$ gives off sulfur trioxide, SO_3, with the formation of potassium sulfate, K_2SO_4, which melts at a much higher temperature than the pyrosulfate. This change is evidenced by the solidification of the melt. The SO_3 evolved at the high temperature is a very powerful reagent and converts many difficultly soluble substances to easily soluble sulfates.

Fusion with potassium bisulfate is necessary when a very refractory ore is encountered. This treatment is actually an acid digestion at a high temperature. The fusion should be made at a dull red heat so as to give a slow evolution of sulfur trioxide and allow sufficient time to react with the sample.

Fusions with $KHSO_4$ should be made in a porcelain crucible or dish. Platinum is attacked, and charcoal and plaster cannot be used, because of their porosity.

Borax and Salt of Phosphorus Fusions. These compounds have the property of absorbing and dissolving many oxides and other substances when in the molten state. A number of the metallic oxides impart characteristic colors, and this property is utilized in the bead tests.

Sublimation. The passage of a substance from a solid to a vapor state, or vice versa, without passing through a liquid phase, is termed sublimation. If crystals of iodine are heated, they pass directly into vapor and recondense as crystals in the cooler part of the tube or apparatus.

There are many examples of sublimation in blowpipe procedure, and a number of excellent tests depend on this phenomenon. For example, all of the coatings obtained on charcoal and plaster are due to sublimation, as are also many of the open and closed tube reactions.

Ignition. Ignition in analytical procedures means the subjection of a mineral, precipitate, or other substance to a high temperature, usually red heat, for the purpose of ridding it of carbonaceous material, changing its composition by oxidation, or driving off moisture or combined water.

Precipitates are often ignited to burn the filter paper or to convert them from hydroxides to oxides by driving off the water content. Some minerals change character on ignition, such as many iron ores which are non-magnetic but which become magnetic on ignition. The residue of the sodium group is ignited in order to drive off all ammonia salts and thus make it easier to test for the members of this group.

Auxiliary Equipment

It is necessary in operating with such minute quantities of substances as are used in blowpipe analysis that they should have some appropriate support. In order that no false results be obtained, the supports must be of such a nature that they will not form a chemical combination with the substance while it is exposed to the severe treatments under the blowpipe. A discussion of the supports for the various blowpipe tests, such as charcoal, platinum equipment, etc., is given below.

Charcoal. It is most convenient to purchase this item from chemical supply houses. There are two types available. The kind ordinarily used is about 1″ x ¾″ x 4″ and is untreated. Because it is untreated, the charcoal is consumed quite rapidly, although many tests can be made on a single piece. The other style is about 2″ x 1″ x 4″ and is given a special treatment which makes it fire resistant, with the result that these sticks give a much longer service than the untreated. They are, however, much more expensive than the former.

The best kind of charcoal is that of pine, linden, willow, alder, or other softwood. Coal from fir sparks freely, while that from many of the hardwoods is coarse grained and may contain too much iron in the ash. Smooth pieces, free from knots, should be used. The wood should be thoroughly carbonized, and the annual rings of growth should be as close together as possible.

If the charcoal is in masses, it should be sawed into pieces about 4″ long, 1″ wide and ¾″ thick in such a manner that the annual growth rings run perpendicular to the broadest side, since the uneven structure of the annual rings and spaces between them cause uneven burning.

In order that the substance under examination may not be carried off by the blast of air, small conical depressions should be made in the broad side of the charcoal between the growth rings. They can be made by using a knife blade, a piece of tin, or similar tool, about ¼″ to ½″ from one end of the block.

In general, the charcoal support is used where it is desired to reduce metallic oxides, to prevent oxidation, make fusions, or to test the fusibility of a substance. It is worth remembering that those metals which are volatile in the reducing flame usually appear as oxides in the oxidizing flame. These oxides normally form sublimates on the charcoal close to the assay or where it originally was, and by their color or distribution indicate fairly well the element which is the source of the sublimate. (See color plates 1 to 6.)

White Blowpipe Slabs. These are very useful in carrying out tests in which colored sublimates are formed. In making examinations on the plaster tablet, one volume of the finely ground sample is mixed with 3 to 4 volumes of flux and this mixture is placed in a little heap near one end of the slab. When the blowpipe flame is played on this, a colored coating is produced on the slab in many instances. The color and type of a number of these sublimates are characteristic of certain elements, and this is an easy, simple method of their identification as illustrated in color plates 1 to 6.

The normal slab is white, but a black surface may be produced by holding the slab over a candle or other luminous flame. The results obtained on smoked plaster are often quite different from those produced on the white slab or on charcoal and this can also be used to good advantage in blowpipe analysis. (See color plate 6.)

White blowpipe slabs are easily made by wetting plaster of Paris with water to a paste, spreading it about ¼″ thick on a sheet of glass and cutting into 1″ x 4″ sections before it hardens.

Platinum Supports. Metallic platinum is infusible in the blowpipe flame and is such a poor conductor of heat that it may be held close to the portion of it which is red hot without the least inconvenience to the fingers. Metals should not be treated in platinum apparatus, nor should the easily reducible metallic oxides, sulfides, or chlorides; these substances will form free metals, alloy with the platinum, and thus render it unfit for further use in analysis. Platinum is expensive; take care of it.

Platinum Wire. The wire should be of about No. 28 gage and 2″ to 2½″ in length. For convenient handling, one end is inserted into a piece of glass rod about 4″ long by heating the rod to redness and then inserting the wire into it while it is still plastic. On the other end of the wire, a small loop is made by coiling the end around the lead of a pencil (Fig. 13).

In making the **bead tests** the loop of wire is heated in the flame, then dipped into the borax or other reagent and again held in the flame until the flux has

FIG. 13.   Platinum Wire Mounted in Glass Rod.

melted and become a quite molten mass. The bead, before the addition of the sample, must, of course, be clear and colorless; if it is not, the bead must be removed from the wire. This is easily accomplished by heating it to a fluid condition and then quickly striking the hand which is holding the wire onto the other one. This sharp blow will cause the bead to drop off the wire. Another bead is then made as above and, should this one also be not clear and colorless, the operation is repeated until such a bead is obtained. The presence of color or a cloudy bead indicates that contaminating substances are present. The above procedure will remove them and give an uncontaminated wire and bead.

The clear, colorless bead is touched to a speck of the sample powder to be tested and again subjected to the action of the flame until the bead is a uniform mass or it is evident that all reaction has ceased. The result of treatment in both the O.F. and R.F., both hot and cold and as the bead cools, should be noted, for often a decided difference is apparent under these conditions. (See color plate 7.)

At the end of the test the bead should be removed from the wire, as above, thus leaving the wire in condition for the next experiment.

For the determination of the **flame coloration** the platinum wire is often used, although plain iron wire will give results just as good. In making this test a different procedure is employed in that usually no fluxing material is used, the substance being treated directly. In order, however, to obtain the best results, the substance should be quite volatile, for it is the volatilization of the elements which causes them to color the flame. To accomplish this, the finely divided mineral or precipitate is usually moistened with concentrated hydrochloric acid, since the chlorides of most of the elements are among the most easily volatile compounds.

In carrying out the flame color tests, the loop of the platinum wire is held in the non-luminous flame to see that no contaminating substance is present. Sodium is a very common element, and the yellow color is seen in most flames (not the luminous flame which is yellow due to the presence of incandescent carbon). If the non-luminous flame is colored by the wire, it is necessary to clean the wire before making a test. Cleaning cannot be accomplished by simply wiping it or washing with water. The wire must be dipped into pure concentrated hydrochloric acid, then held in the flame. This volatilizes the material present, but the cleaning operation is usually not complete in a single treatment. The dipping

40

and heating are repeated until none or at least very little color is developed when the loop is heated in the non-luminous flame.

After the loop has been cleaned, the flame color test is made by touching the flame to the sample powder which is moist with concentrated hydrochloric acid or by supporting a speck of the sample on the loop and holding it in the non-luminous flame.

The platinum wire can be used in all tests except where reducing conditions are likely to produce a free metal or with metals which will alloy with it. In general, these are the metals of the hydrogen sulfide groups.

Platinum Foil. When fusions or special heatings are desired and reduction or the presence of charcoal is undesirable, the platinum foil is used as a support. This foil should be about 0.002″ thick and can be either about 1″ square or about 2″ long and ½″ wide. In use it is held, preferably, in platinum-tipped forceps. Fusions on platinum allow any color that is developed to be better seen. The test for manganese with soda and niter is best carried out on the foil. (Color plate 3.) Many of the cobalt nitrate tests are better seen if made on platinum instead of charcoal. If the sample is a silicate and is free of the hydrogen sulfide group elements, it is well to make the soda fusion of it on platinum, since a clean, carbon-free, unreduced product is obtained.

Platinum Spoon. The platinum spoon is used primarily for soda fusions of larger quantities than can be handled on the foil. It is quite convenient but is expensive, and the student, in most cases, can make the necessary fusions on charcoal. Those which must be made on platinum can be made on the foil.

Platinum Forceps. Platinum-tipped forceps, Fig. 14, should be used for holding the small fragments or splinters of mineral being tested for fusability

Fig. 14.   Platinum Tipped Forceps.

and treatment in the flame. As platinum is not affected by heat and is a poor conductor, it gives much better results than other metals such as iron. The platinum foil should be held in the platinum tips of these forceps when being heated.

Crucible Tongs. (Fig. 15). This equipment is used for holding the charcoal blocks and plaster slabs during blowpipe tests and for handling hot dishes, crucibles, or other articles. The ordinary type, made of steel or brass, are not the best for handling platinum ware. In order to use this cheaper type and still protect platinum, platinum sleeves which fit over the jaws of the tongs are often used in the larger laboratories. Thus, the platinum ware is never touched by any metal but platinum. Although these sleeves are useful, they are not essential in the operations required in blowpiping. They are quite expensive.

Iron Spoon. (Fig. 16). For preliminary examinations and for fusions where the presence of iron is not objectionable, the iron spoon serves as well as platinum and, of course, is much cheaper. With the iron spoon soda fusions can be made with metallic ores, thus recovering a larger amount of the metal than if they were carried out on coal. Platinum cannot be used for fusions where free

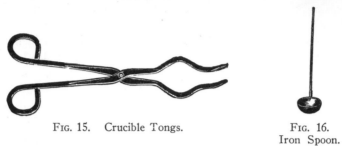

FIG. 15.   Crucible Tongs.

FIG. 16.
Iron Spoon.

metals are produced. The spoon bowl should be about $\frac{5}{8}''$ to $\frac{3}{4}''$ in diameter and the handle about 6″ to 8″ long. If the bowl is of stainless steel, Monel metal, chromium, nickel, etc., it may also contaminate the fusions as well as iron, and this situation must be considered in analytical work where the iron spoon is used.

Iron Wire. Iron wire will serve as well as platinum for making flame color determinations; iron itself has no effect on the color of the flame. It can also be used for making the sodium and lithium fluoride bead tests. It is used in the same manner as platinum wire. As it is very cheap, it should be used only once. After a determination has been made, the end is cut off, giving a new clean part on which to make the next test. The wire should be of about 24-26 gage since coarse wire heats too slowly for good results.

Iron wire should not be used for the borax and salt of phosphorus bead tests.

Open Tubes. These are made of Pyrex glass tubing about 5-7 mm ($\frac{3}{16}''$-$\frac{1}{4}''$) diameter and about 15 cm (6″) long and are open at both ends. The tube is heated about 4 cm ($1\frac{1}{2}''$) from one end and bent to an angle of about 30 to 40 degrees (Fig. 17).

In using these tubes, the powdered material is placed in the tube at the bend ((a) Fig. 17). The part containing the sample is heated while holding the long arm of the tube so that it slopes upward and the shorter part is approximately level. This allows a current of air to circulate over the assay, causing oxidation to take place, and any volatile matter or sublimate travels up the long arm and will deposit in the cooler parts. Many substances give characteristic sublimates or decomposition products by this treatment.

Closed Tubes. Closed tubes are those having one end closed. Although they can be home made, the ordinary small Pyrex test tube (Fig. 18) is more convenient and not very expensive.

Closed tubes are used where a substance is to be heated with little or no oxidation. They give an excellent method of testing for the presence of water or volatile matter. In using them, the ground substance is placed in the bottom

FIG. 17.
Open tube, assayed at "a."

FIG. 18.
Closed Tube.

of the tube and this part is then held over the flame in a sloping position so that only the part containing the assay is heated, thus leaving the top part cool. Any volatile matter that is vaporized will condense and redeposit in this cool part and may readily be examined.

Wash Bottle. This piece of apparatus is an arrangement whereby a fine stream of water may be played on to a desired location by blowing air into the bottle with the mouth (Fig. 19). Its use is primarily for washing precipitates from filter papers. In using it for this purpose, the filter paper is lifted carefully from the funnel with the aid of a knife blade and carefully unfolded; it is held by the part that was folded under, over the vessel into which the precipitate is to be washed. A fine stream of distilled water is then played on the paper at the upper edge of the precipitate, thus washing it into the vessel. A minimum amount

FIG. 20.
Porcelain Mortar and Pestle.

FIG. 19.   Wash Bottle.

FIG. 21.   Magnifying Glass.

of water should always be used. Sometimes, if there is a very large amount of the precipitate, it is advisable to spread the paper on a piece of clean glass plate and scrape the greater part of the precipitate off, then wash the paper as above.

Other Equipment. Other pieces of apparatus which aid in handling and studying minerals are *mortar and pestle* (Fig. 20), *magnifying glass* (Fig. 21), *steel mortar* (Fig. 22), *magnet* (Fig. 23), *test tube clamp* (Fig. 24), and a *hammer*. The test tube clamp is used for holding hot test tubes. A pincer-type clothespin will serve very well for small tubes. The steel mortar and pestle and the hammer are used for breaking the larger pieces of rock before grinding in the agate or porcelain mortar. A prospector's hammer and a piece of steel will take the place of the steel mortar for field work.

FIG. 23.   Horseshoe Magnet.

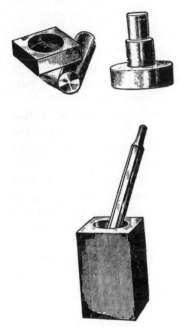

FIG. 22.
Types of Steel Mortars.

FIG. 24.   Test Tube Clamp.

Folding Filter Papers. The filter papers are round disks. To prepare one for use, first fold it in half, then take the corners of the straight edge and bring them together, creasing them lightly, thus forming a three-cornered figure. Now divide the folds by placing a finger between them so there are three layers on one side and one on the other. Place the paper in the funnel, holding it down to the bottom with the finger, and wet with water. Throw out the excess water and gently press and smooth the paper so that it fits the funnel snugly. There should be no cracks or openings down which the liquid can run to the bottom of the funnel. The paper is now ready to receive the liquid to be filtered.

CHAPTER III

Blowpipe Reactions

THE COLOR PLATES

The color plates show the films and sublimates formed and the various color reactions obtained by treatment of compounds containing the different elements, on charcoal slabs, plaster of Paris tablets, and platinum foil, both per se and with different reagents; also the bead tests and representative specimens of minerals.

The list of blowpipe tests has been made as complete as possible, even including several tests which are of a negative nature. A great number of these tests were made, and the ones selected for reproduction were chosen because it was thought they represented the average results obtained. It must, however, always be remembered that no two tests will be exact duplicates. The sublimates will vary in amount, degree of color and location, depending on the size of the sample used, the amount and intensity of the flame, etc. The sublimates on smoked plaster are more pronounced and definite than those on charcoal, probably due to the greater porosity of the coal. The bottom row of Plate 6 shows a few of the per se reactions on smoked plaster.

The bead tests shown are of the cold beads. Several beads of each are shown so as to give the different degrees of color and in some instances the different colors obtained by varying the amount of metal and flame treatment. These tests were especially difficult to reproduce, for, while most of the colors are seen by transmitted light, some of the beads are opaque or nearly so and are viewed with reflected light. The color reproduction is therefore a combination of both, with the result that some of the beads show the reflected color, when ordinarily that with transmitted light is the usual one, and vice versa.

The minerals shown in the color plates were selected in order to show the typical representative specimens rather than the outstanding and spectacular ones. They are intended to serve as an aid to those who wish to identify the unknown. When one knows and is able to identify a mineral, he will have very little difficulty in recognizing a spectacular specimen of it.

It is extremely difficult to describe adequately a color, for saying that a film, bead, or mineral is yellow or green really tells very little, as there are many shades and degrees of color; when these are modified by other colors, the task is almost impossible. The color reproductions are as accurate as it is

45

possible to obtain, taking into consideration the limitations of color photography and printing.

Per Se Reactions on the Plaster Tablet

(Sample treated by itself; no flux or reagents used. Use oxidizing flame.)

Antimony, Sb: The white coat of Sb_2O_3 and Sb_2O_4 is hardly visible; slightly yellowish around the assay.

Arsenic, As (Metal): Gives a white, very volatile coating of As_2O_3 over brownish-black metallic arsenic. The odor of garlic (arsine gas, AsH_3) is often present.

Arsenic Sulfides: yield a yellowish to reddish-brown, volatile coat of AsS and As_2S_3. If heated too rapidly, brownish-black metallic arsenic is deposited.

Bismuth, Bi: near the assay the coat is orange-yellow while hot and lemon-yellow when cold, with bluish-green far away. The coating is not very prominent.

Cadmium, Cd: a reddish-brown to greenish-yellow or iridescent, non-volatile sublimate of CdO is formed near the assay.

Carbon, C: carbonaceous materials form a brownish-black non-volatile coat.

Copper, Cu: no coating is formed.

Germanium, Ge: no reactions.

Gold, Au: with high heat, gold forms near the assay a slightly purplish to rose color that is best seen when cold.

Indium, In: slight coating that is orange-yellow while hot and lemon-yellow when cold is formed near the assay. The assay is lemon-yellow.

Iron, Fe: no coating is formed.

Lead, Pb: the coating is dark yellow while hot and lighter yellow when cold.

Mercury, Hg: forms a drab-gray, extremely volatile sublimate of metallic mercury that may be formed into larger globules by rubbing.

Molybdenum, Mo: the O.F. produces near the assay a yellowish-white crystalline coat of MoO_3, with red MoO_2, which when touched with the R.F. immediately changes to a deep blue.

Selenium, Se: forms a cherry-red to crimson volatile sublimate or metallic selenium and SeO_2 and the odor of decayed horseradish. Where the coat is very thick, it is black.

Silver, Ag: with intense heat, silver produces a non-volatile yellow coating of the oxide near the assay, which when touched with the R.F. becomes brownish and mottled.

Tellurium, Te: forms a volatile brown to black coat of Te and TeO_2 with sometimes a narrow blue fringe near the assay. Treated with conc. H_2SO_4 and heated gently it yields an evanescent pink color. Touched with the R.F., the flame is colored bluish-green.

Thallium, Tl: the white coating of the oxide is hardly visible.

Tin, Sn: the white coating of SnO_2 is hardly visible. Treated with cobalt nitrate solution and heated, gives a bluish-green color.

Zinc, Zn: the white coating of ZnO is hardly visible. Treated with cobalt nitrate solution and heated, gives a grass-green color.

(Many of the reactions that are listed under the tests on charcoal may be carried out to good advantage on smoked plaster in the O.F. and R.F.)

Reactions with Iodide Flux

(On Plaster.)

Mix 1 part of the powdered mineral or precipitate with 3 parts of iodide flux and treat on the plaster tablet with the oxidizing flame.

COLOR OF COAT	REMARKS
Antimony, Sb. Orange to peach-red coat that disappears when subjected to ammonia fumes.	A drop of $(NH_4)_2S_x$ on the coat forms an orange-red ring that is *not dissolved* by a drop of NH_4OH.
Arsenic, As. Lemon-yellow to orange-yellow coat which disappears if subjected to ammonia fumes.	A drop of $(NH_4)_2S_x$ on the coat forms a yellow ring that is *completely dissolved* by a drop of NH_4OII.
Bismuth, Bi. Chocolate-brown coat with underlying crimson and yellowish on the outer edge.	Subjected to NH_4OH fumes, the brown coating changes to orange-yellow, then cherry-red.
Cadmium, Cd. Orange-yellow coat near the assay.	$(NH_4)_2S_x$ gives a slight yellowish-gray spot with a lemon-yellow border.
Copper, Cu. Very slight yellow coat.	$(NH_4)_2S_x$ gives a light brown ring and darkens the coat around it.
Germanium, Ge. Very slight yellow film.	
Indium, In. Small dark ring near assay. Light yellow coating at some distance from assay. Assay is yellow to brown.	
Lead, Pb. Chrome-yellow coat, darker while hot, often covering the entire tablet.	A drop of $(NH_4)_2S_x$ applied to the film yields a black spot, often surrounded by a reddish cloud.
Mercury, Hg. If heated gently a bright scarlet very volatile coat with yellow fringes is formed.	If heated quickly, the coat is pale yellow or greenish-yellow and black.

REACTIONS WITH IODIDE FLUX—(*Continued*)

COLOR OF COAT	REMARKS
Molybdenum, Mo. A slight volatile yellowish coat is formed.	$(NH_4)_2S_x$ forms a slight brown ring. The R.F. does not turn the coat blue.
Selenium, Se. Gives a reddish-brown to scarlet coat. Reddish fumes are given off.	The flame is colored indigo-blue. $(NH_4)_2S_x$ dissolves the coat and forms a ring of deeper color.
Silver, Ag. Slightly yellowish coat near the assay. Requires intense heat.	When touched with the R.F. it becomes pinkish-brown and somewhat mottled.
Tellurium, Te. Gives a purplish-brown to black coat. The flame is colored pale green.	$(NH_4)_2S$ dissolves the coat. $(NH_4)_2S_x$ has no effect. A drop of conc. H_2SO_4 added to the coat and heated gently, yields an evanescent pink color.
Thallium, Tl. Orange-yellow film near the assay, with purplish-black band far away. Entire coat finally becomes yellow.	$(NH_4)_2S_x$ changes the coat to chocolate-brown.
Tin, Sn. The coat is canary-yellow and brownish near the assay.	The coat is obtained by treatment of the sulfide.
Zinc, Zn. Nothing.	

REACTIONS WITH BROMIDE FLUX

(On Plaster.)

Mix 1 part of the powdered mineral or precipitate with 3 parts of bromide flux and treat on the plaster tablet with the oxidizing flame.

COLOR OF COAT	REMARKS
Antimony, Sb. Forms a faint yellow coat far away, with reddish-yellow near the assay.	$(NH_4)_2S_x$ forms an orange ring and develops the coat around it to orange-yellow. The coat and ring are *not dissolved* by NH_4OH.
Arsenic, As. Gives only a faint yellow coat that is very volatile.	A drop of $(NH_4)_2S_x$ forms a ring of slightly darker color. NH_4OH *dissolves* both the ring and coat.

REACTIONS WITH BROMIDE FLUX—(*Continued*)

COLOR OF COAT	REMARKS
Bismuth, Bi. Near the assay a brownish-black to red coat. Farther away the coat is canary-yellow and at a distance a brown border develops.	A drop of $(NH_4)_2S_x$ forms a black spot surrounded by a brownish haze. NH_4OH has no effect.
Cadmium, Cd. Gives a lemon-yellow coat near the assay.	$(NH_4)_2S_x$ gives a slight grayish spot.
Copper, Cu. Gives a brownish to yellow coat near the assay, with a slight purplish band far away.	The assay is greenish and the flame is colored blue. $(NH_4)_2S_x$ gives a brown ring.
Germanium, Ge. Trace of yellow and brown film.	
Indium, In. Small brownish coating near assay and a slight yellow one far away. Assay is yellow to brown.	
Iron, Fe. Gives a blackish coat around the assay, with a brownish band far away.	$(NH_4)_2S$ vapors turn the coat green and develop spots where no coat was seen before.
Lead, Pb. Forms a small quite volatile canary-yellow film.	$(NH_4)_2S_x$ placed beyond where the film is visible gives a black spot surrounded by a reddish cloud.
Mercury, Hg. Only a faint yellow very volatile coat.	A drop of $(NH_4)_2S_x$ gives a black spot.
Molybdenum, Mo. Gives a bluish-green coat with traces of blue and yellow on the edges and sometimes brown near the assay.	A drop of $(NH_4)_2S_x$ gives a brown spot. The R.F. *does not turn the coat blue,* but makes it a deeper brown.
Selenium, Se. Gives a brownish-red to yellow coat covering most of the tablet. Reddish fumes are given off.	The flame is indigo blue. $(NH_4)_2S$ and $(NH_4)_2S_x$ dissolve the coat and form a ring of deeper color.
Silver, Ag. Gives an indistinct, slightly yellowish coat near the assay. Requires intense heat.	Treated with the R.F., the coat becomes mottled yellowish-brown and may be developed over a considerable part of the tablet. $(NH_4)_2S_x$ causes no change.

REACTIONS WITH BROMIDE FLUX—(*Continued*)

COLOR OF COAT	REMARKS
Tellurium, Te. Gives a coat, covering most of the tablet, that is dark gray to black near the assay, grading into reddish-brown through canary-yellow, with brown far away. The flame is colored pale green.	$(NH_4)_2S$ dissolves the coat. $(NH_4)_2S_x$ applied to the lighter portions, forms a ring of darker color. H_2SO_4 added to the coat and warmed, yields an evanescent pink color.
Thallium, Tl. Gives a reddish-orange coat at some distance from the assay, surrounded by a light lemon-yellow film. The reddish coat disappears on standing, leaving only the lemon-yellow film. Both coats are quite volatile.	A drop of $(NH_4)_2S_x$ gives a brown spot with a darker border. NH_4OH dissolves both coats.
Tin, Sn. The treatment of the sulfide yields only a slight darkening of the tablet around the assay.	No sublimate is formed. Very unsatisfactory.
Zinc, Zn. Nothing.	

REACTIONS WITH CHROMATE FLUX

(On Plaster.)

Mix 1 part of the powdered mineral or precipitate with 3 parts of chromate flux and treat on the plaster tablet with the oxidizing flame.

COLOR OF COAT	REMARKS
Antimony, Sb. The coat is dark brown near the assay, grading into orange-yellow far away.	Yellow ammonium sulfide does not form a ring.
Arsenic, As. The coat is orange-yellow near the assay and lemon-yellow far away.	Yellow ammonium sulfide forms an orange-yellow ring.
Bismuth, Bi. The coat is dark brown near the assay and light brown far away.	Yellow ammonium sulfide [$(NH_4)_2S_x$] forms a deeper brown spot.

REACTIONS WITH CHROMATE FLUX—(*Continued*)

COLOR OF COAT	REMARKS
Cadmium, Cd. Near the assay a coat that is red while hot and lemon-yellow when cold.	Yellow ammonium sulfide gives a light yellow spot.
Copper, Cu. Nothing.	
Germanium, Ge. No reactions.	
Indium, In. Slight yellowish and brownish coat near the assay.	
Iron, Fe. Nothing.	
Lead, Pb. The coat is black near the assay and brown far away. Traces of white may show in some places.	$(NH_4)_2S_x$ gives a black spot and reddish cloud where no coat was visible before.
Mercury, Hg. The coat is shiny black near the assay, with a small brownish yellow band next and gray far away. The coat is volatile.	A drop of $(NH_4)_2S_x$ gives a ring of darker color.
Molybdenum, Mo. Nothing.	
Selenium, Se. Cherry-red to crimson coat very similar to that from the treatment per se.	$(NH_4)_2S_x$ dissolves the coat and forms a ring of deeper color.
Silver, Ag. The coat is brown to yellowish and near the assay. It requires high heat.	Treated with the R.F., it becomes more prominent. $(NH_4)_2S_x$ causes no change.
Tellurium, Te. Brown to black, volatile coat very similar to that from the per se treatment.	
Thallium, Tl. The coat is reddish-brown to greenish yellow and near the assay. It is quite volatile. The flame is colored green.	A drop of $(NH_4)_2S_x$ gives a shiny blackish brown spot with a darker border.
Tin, Sn. Nothing.	
Zinc, Zn. Nothing.	

SUBLIMATES ON CHARCOAL

PER SE	WITH THE FLUXES
Antimony, Sb. Dense white coat of Sb_2O_4 and Sb_2O_3 near the assay. Bluish far away. The coat is less volatile than that from As. Fumes continue after flaming is stopped. The flame is colored pale yellowish-green.	**Iodide flux.** Gives a white coat near the assay with yellow far away. **Bromide flux.** The coat is white. **Chromate flux.** Gives a slight whitish coat with traces of brown near the assay.
Arsenic, As. A white, very volatile coating of As_2O_3 is formed. This is sometimes tinted with brown or yellow from volatilized sulfides. The coating consists of a octahedral crystals of As_2O_3 and deposits mostly at a distance from the assay. Often the garlic odor of arsine gas, AsH_3.	**Iodide flux.** Gives a volatile coat that is white near the assay, with a canary-yellow border and a slight yellow coat beyond. **Bromide flux.** Gives a slight white volatile coat with a faint yellow border **Chromate flux.** Gives a very volatile slight white coat with a faintly yellow tinge. It is far from the assay.
Bismuth, Bi. The coat of Bi_2O_3 is dark, orange-yellow while hot and lemon-yellow when cold. It is greenish-white far away. Volatile in both flames. In both the O.F. and R.F. a brittle, metallic button is formed and the flame is colored a pale greenish-white.	**Iodide flux.** The coat is chocolate-brown with underlying scarlet. NH_4OH fumes change it to orange-yellow. **Bromide flux.** The coat is white near the assay and greenish far away. **Chromate flux.** Gives a slight whitish coat near the assay.
Cadmium, Cd. The coating of CdO is black to reddish brown near the assay and yellowish green far away. Thin coats show peacock colors. The coat is volatile in both flames.	**Iodide flux.** Gives a slight whitish to greenish coat. **Bromide flux.** The coat is gray and some distance from the assay. **Chromate flux.** The coat is near the assay, reddish while hot and canary-yellow to greenish yellow when cold.
Copper, Cu. In the R.F., the Cu minerals are reduced to globules of red malleable metal and the flame is colored emerald-green, or azure-blue.	**Iodide flux.** Slight grayish-white coating. **Bromide flux.** Very slight gray coat. The flame is a brilliant blue. **Chromate flux.** None.

Sublimates on Charcoal—(*Continued*)

PER SE	WITH THE FLUXES
Germanium, Ge. Bluish white coat near assay. White fused droplets.	**Iodide flux.** Coat is white and assay is brown. **Bromide flux.** White ring around assay. Not much of a coating. **Chromate flux.** White coating.
Gold, Au. All gold compounds give a yellow malleable button of free gold if treated with soda on coal.	**Iodide, Bromide, Chromate flux.** Nothing.
Indium, In. Coating that is orange-yellow while hot and whitish yellow when cold is formed near the assay with a bluish black, somewhat iridescent ring beyond.	**Iodide flux.** Coating is white near assay with a darker ring beyond and is bluish far away. **Bromide flux.** Shiny black near assay with bluish white next followed by a darker area and light bluish far away. **Chromate flux.** Slight yellowish and brownish coat near the assay.
Lead, Pb. In either flame, lead compounds (except the phosphates which require a flux) are reduced to metallic lead and yield, near the assay, a dark yellow coat which becomes sulfur yellow when cold and has a bluish-white border. Touched with the R.F., the coating disappears, tinging the flame azure blue.	**Iodide flux.** The coat is greenish yellow, darker while hot, brown near the assay; the flame is colored azure blue. **Bromide flux.** The coat is whitish gray, volatile, and some distance from the assay. Touched with the R.F., the coat disappears, tinging the flame azure blue. **Chromate flux.** The coat is yellowish-white and volatile. It is not very prominent and is formed at some distance from the assay. Treated with the R.F., it disappears, tinging the flame azure blue.
Mercury, Hg. Some mercury compounds volatilize without decomposition but most of them are reduced and decomposed and yield a grayish white coat that is very volatile. It consists of metallic mercury and will collect into globules if rubbed.	**Iodide flux.** Yields only a faint yellow coat. **Bromide flux.** A slight yellowish white, very volatile coat a considerable distance from the assay. **Chromate flux.** Gives a very slight extremely volatile gray coat.

Sublimates on Charcoal—(*Continued*)

PER SE	WITH THE FLUXES
Molybdenum, Mo. Very near the assay copper-red MoO_2 is deposited. Beyond this but still near the assay is deposited a coating of MoO_3, pale yellow while hot and white when cold. Bluish far away. It is sometimes crystalline. Touched with the R.F., it becomes azure blue and volatilizes. Volatile in the O.F. The flame is colored yellowish green.	**Iodide flux.** Gives a white coat near the assay. Touched with the R.F., it is volatilized but does not turn blue. **Bromide flux.** A very volatile yellowish green coat is first deposited far from the assay then, on longer flaming, a white one near. Treated with the R.F., it volatilizes but does not turn blue. **Chromate flux.** Nothing.
Selenium, Se. Steel gray very volatile coat near the assay. At some distance white SeO_2, tinged red with metallic Se, and beyond a red border of metallic selenium is deposited. Red fumes are given off; characteristic decayed horseradish odor. The flame is colored blue by the coating.	**Iodide flux.** Small white coat near the assay, with a yellowish green border and traces of reddish brown. Yellowish fumes are given off. Characteristic odor. **Bromide flux.** Small white coat and yellowish fumes with a characteristic odor. **Chromate flux.** Mixed red and yellow fumes with a characteristic odor. The coating is very slight, white near the assay, yellowish beyond, traces of red far away.
Silver, Ag. All silver compounds are reduced to a white malleable bead of the metal. On long treatment with the O.F., a faint reddish brown coat of the oxide is formed.	With the fluxes no special coating is formed but on long, intense heating with the O.F. a faint reddish brown coat of silver oxide is produced.
Tellurium, Te. Dense white volatile coat of TeO_2 near the assay. Far away a gray to brownish-black coat of metallic Te. Treated with the R.F., the coat colors the flame green and volatilizes. The coat somewhat resembles that from antimony.	**Iodide flux.** Gives a white to gray coat. The flame is colored pale green. **Bromide flux.** White near the assay, with brownish black far away. The flame is colored pale green. **Chromate flux.** White near the assay, with brownish black far away. The flame is colored pale green.

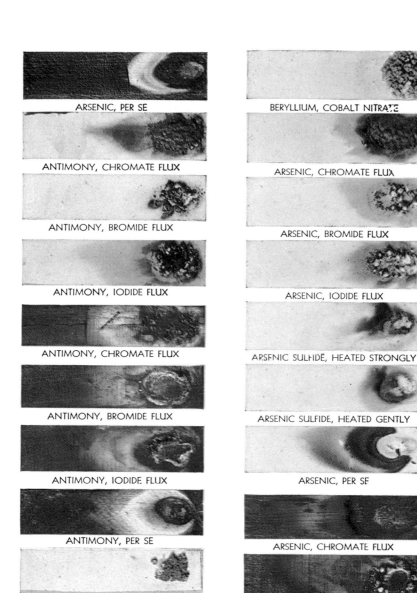

ARSENIC, PER SE

BERYLLIUM, COBALT NITRATE

ANTIMONY, CHROMATE FLUX

ARSENIC, CHROMATE FLUX

ANTIMONY, BROMIDE FLUX

ARSENIC, BROMIDE FLUX

ANTIMONY, IODIDE FLUX

ARSENIC, IODIDE FLUX

ANTIMONY, CHROMATE FLUX

ARSENIC SULFIDE, HEATED STRONGLY

ANTIMONY, BROMIDE FLUX

ARSENIC SULFIDE, HEATED GENTLY

ANTIMONY, IODIDE FLUX

ARSENIC, PER SE

ANTIMONY, PER SE

ARSENIC, CHROMATE FLUX

ALUMINUM, COBALT NITRATE

ARSENIC, BROMIDE FLUX

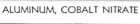

ALUMINUM, COBALT NITRATE

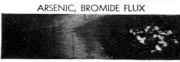

ARSENIC, IODIDE FLUX

Copyright by O. C. Smith, 1945

PLATE I

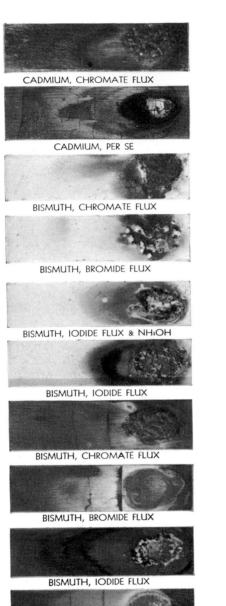

CADMIUM, CHROMATE FLUX

CADMIUM, PER SE

BISMUTH, CHROMATE FLUX

BISMUTH, BROMIDE FLUX

BISMUTH, IODIDE FLUX & NH₄OH

BISMUTH, IODIDE FLUX

BISMUTH, CHROMATE FLUX

BISMUTH, BROMIDE FLUX

BISMUTH, IODIDE FLUX

BISMUTH, PER SE

IRON, BROMIDE FLUX

GOLD, PER SE

COPPER, BROMIDE FLUX

COPPER, IODIDE FLUX

COPPER, IODIDE FLUX

COPPER, PER SE

CHROMIUM, SODIUM CARBONATE

CARBON, PER SE

CADMIUM, CHROMATE FLUX

CADMIUM, PER SE

PLATE 2

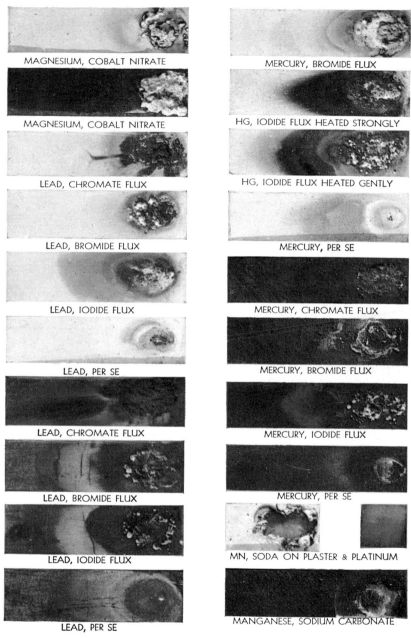

MAGNESIUM, COBALT NITRATE

MAGNESIUM, COBALT NITRATE

LEAD, CHROMATE FLUX

LEAD, BROMIDE FLUX

LEAD, IODIDE FLUX

LEAD, PER SE

LEAD, CHROMATE FLUX

LEAD, BROMIDE FLUX

LEAD, IODIDE FLUX

LEAD, PER SE

MERCURY, BROMIDE FLUX

HG, IODIDE FLUX HEATED STRONGLY

HG, IODIDE FLUX HEATED GENTLY

MERCURY, PER SE

MERCURY, CHROMATE FLUX

MERCURY, BROMIDE FLUX

MERCURY, IODIDE FLUX

MERCURY, PER SE

MN, SODA ON PLASTER & PLATINUM

MANGANESE, SODIUM CARBONATE

PLATE 3

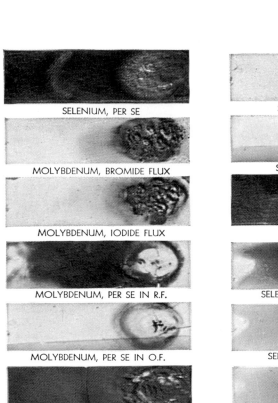

SELENIUM, PER SE

MOLYBDENUM, BROMIDE FLUX

MOLYBDENUM, IODIDE FLUX

MOLYBDENUM, PER SE IN R.F.

MOLYBDENUM, PER SE IN O.F.

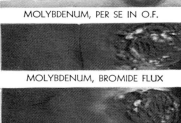

MOLYBDENUM, BROMIDE FLUX

MOLYBDENUM, IODIDE FLUX

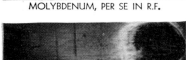

MOLYBDENUM, PER SE IN R.F.

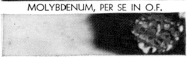

MOLYBDENUM, PER SE IN O.F.

MERCURY, CHROMATE FLUX

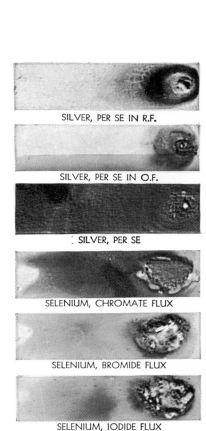

SILVER, PER SE IN R.F.

SILVER, PER SE IN O.F.

: SILVER, PER SE

SELENIUM, CHROMATE FLUX

SELENIUM, BROMIDE FLUX

SELENIUM, IODIDE FLUX

SELENIUM, PER SE

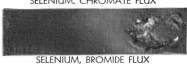

SELENIUM, CHROMATE FLUX

SELENIUM, BROMIDE FLUX

SELENIUM, IODIDE FLUX

PLATE 4

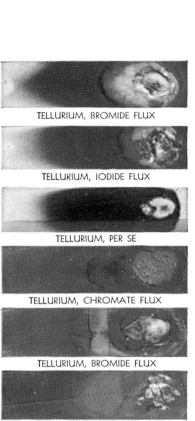

TELLURIUM, BROMIDE FLUX

TELLURIUM, IODIDE FLUX

TELLURIUM, PER SE

TELLURIUM, CHROMATE FLUX

TELLURIUM, BROMIDE FLUX

TELLURIUM, IODIDE FLUX

TELLURIUM, PER SE

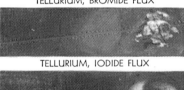

SILVER, CHROMATE FLUX

SILVER, BROMIDE FLUX

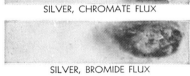

SILVER, IODIDE FLUX

TIN, COBALT NITRATE

TIN, PER SE

THALLIUM, CHROMATE FLUX

THALLIUM, BROMIDE FLUX

THALLIUM, IODIDE FLUX

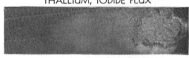

THALLIUM, CHROMATE FLUX

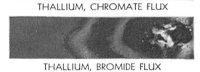

THALLIUM, BROMIDE FLUX

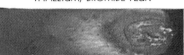

THALLIUM, IODIDE FLUX

THALLIUM, PER SE

TELLURIUM, CHROMATE FLUX

PLATE 5

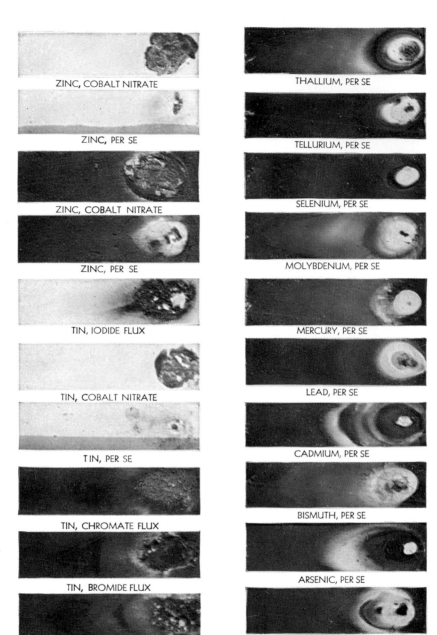

ZINC, COBALT NITRATE

ZINC, PER SE

ZINC, COBALT NITRATE

ZINC, PER SE

TIN, IODIDE FLUX

TIN, COBALT NITRATE

TIN, PER SE

TIN, CHROMATE FLUX

TIN, BROMIDE FLUX

TIN, IODIDE FLUX
(On Charcoal)

THALLIUM, PER SE

TELLURIUM, PER SE

SELENIUM, PER SE

MOLYBDENUM, PER SE

MERCURY, PER SE

LEAD, PER SE

CADMIUM, PER SE

BISMUTH, PER SE

ARSENIC, PER SE

ANTIMONY, PER SE
(On Smoked Plaster)
Copyright by O. C. Smith, 1945

PLATE 6

Sᴜʙʟɪᴍᴀᴛᴇꜱ ᴏɴ Cʜᴀʀᴄᴏᴀʟ—(*Continued*)

PER SE	WITH THE FLUXES
Thallium, Tl. The O.F. yields a white, very volatile coat of Tl_2O that is mostly distant from the assay with sometimes a brown coating near the assay. Treated with the R.F., the sublimate volatilizes, coloring the flame emerald-green.	**Iodide flux.** The coat is lemon-yellow and is darker and brownish near the assay. **Bromide flux.** Yields a yellowish coat at a considerable distance from the assay, with a slight whitish film beyond and a faint white one near the assay. The flame is colored green. **Chromate flux.** Gives a small yellowish white coat near the assay, with a faint white one beyond. The flame is colored green.
Tin, Sn. The coat of SnO_2 is near the assay and is faint yellow and luminous while hot and white when cold. If moistened with $Co(NO_3)_2$ solution and heated strongly, the coat becomes bluish green. Not volatile in the O.F. The addition of sulfur and soda increases the amount of the coat. In the R.F. a slight coat is formed.	The reactions with the fluxes are obtained by treatment of the sulfide. **Iodide flux.** White coat with patches and streaks of yellow through it. **Bromide flux.** White coat. **Chromate flux.** White coat.
Zinc, Zn. The coat of ZnO is near the assay and is canary-yellow while hot and white when cold. When moistened with cobalt nitrate solution and heated strongly, the coat becomes grass green. Not volatile in the O.F.	No reaction with the fluxes.

BEAD TESTS

Borax and **Salt of Phosphorus (Microcosmic Salt)** have the property of absorbing the oxides of metals, yielding, in many cases, pronounced colors. This is made use of in the bead tests, which for a number of the elements are characteristic and are a useful aid in identification and analysis of minerals.

The test is carried out with a small loop, about the size of a pinhead, at the end of a platinum wire which has been sealed in a 3″-4″ piece of glass rod or tubing by heating the glass till soft, then inserting the platinum wire. The loop is easily made by bending the end of the wire around the tip of a lead pencil. (See Fig. 13.)

In making the bead, the loop is touched while hot to the borax or salt of phosphorus powder, which causes some of it to adhere. On heating, this will form into a small ball or bead. If the bead is not large enough, the hot bead is touched to the borax or salt of phosphorus again and reheated. The operation is repeated until the bead is of the desired size. Making the borax bead is quite simple, but on heating the microcosmic salt to form the salt of phosphorus bead there is quite an effervescence so that at first it froths badly and is likely to drop off the wire. However, if heated gently and carefully at first, the foaming soon ceases and the bead remains on the wire. The heating of the microcosmic salt ($HNaNH_4PO_4 \cdot 4H_2O$) decomposes it with the formation of sodium metaphosphate ($NaPO_3$). If this latter substance is used in the formation of the salt of phosphorus bead, no difficulty from frothing is encountered.

The bead must be clear and colorless both hot and cold; if it is not, the bead is heated red hot and then thrown off the wire by striking the hand holding the wire on the other hand. Another bead is then made, and, if necessary, another one, until a colorless one is obtained. The color is due to some foreign substance which is removed by this procedure, thus cleaning the loop.

In making bead tests the clear, colorless bead is heated and, while hot, is touched to the powder of the substance to be tested. A small amount of the substance adheres and, on reheating, is absorbed in the bead. For absorption, the powder tested should consist of oxides; however, if the bead is heated in the oxidizing flame, most compounds will be changed to oxides, and yield the desired test result (color of bead).

In examining the bead, the color should be noted while the bead is still hot after removal from the flame, while it is cooling, and after it is cold (cold) by transmitted light. Opaque beads, of course, must be viewed by reflected light. The colors by artificial light are usually different from those by sunlight, so that daylight should be used wherever possible. It is well to heat the bead in the O.F. a second time to be sure the reactions are complete; then it is retreated with the reducing flame and carefully examined both hot and cold after each heating.

If a bead does not develop sufficient color, a little more of the substance

56

being tested is added, but care must be taken that too much is not used or the bead will become so dark in color that light will not pass through it or it is unable to absorb all of the solid.

Flaming is the process of alternate treatment of the bead with the O.F. and R.F. for some time. If the bead is nearly saturated, some of the elements such as calcium, barium, strontium, yttrium, beryllium, etc., which give beads that are clear and colorless, both hot and cold, will become opaque and enamel-like on flaming. Others like uranium may change color. If the bead becomes completely saturated, the opaque, enamel-like effect may be obtained without flaming. For this reason, the smallest possible amount which will produce the color should be used.

As the substance is dissolved in the bead, note should be made as to whether the absorption is rapid or slow, complete or leaves a residue, such as silica in the salt of phosphorus bead, and whether it occurs quietly or with effervescence.

See also reactions with sodium thiosulfate.

Borax Bead Tests

	OXIDIZING FLAME		REDUCING FLAME	
	Hot	Cold	Hot	Cold
Antimony	Pale yellow.	Colorless to white.	Pale yellow.	Colorless.
Bismuth	Pale yellow.	Colorless to white.	Gray.	Gray.
Cadmium	Pale yellow.	Colorless to white.	Pale yellow.	Colorless.
Cerium	Yellow.	Greenish yellow.	Colorless.	Colorless.
Chromium	Yellow.	Green.	Green.	Green.
Cobalt	Blue.	Blue.	Blue.	Blue.
Copper	Green.	Blue.	Colorless to green.	Brownish, opaque red with much oxide.
Didymium	Pale rose.	Pale rose.	Pale rose.	Pale rose.
Iron	Yellow to orange.	Greenish to brown.	Bottle-green.	Pale bottle-green.
Lead	Pale yellow.	Colorless to white.	Pale yellow.	Colorless.
Manganese	Violet.	Brownish to reddish violet.	Colorless.	Colorless.
Molybdenum	Pale yellow.	Colorless to white.	Brown.	Brown to black and opaque.
Nickel	Violet.	Reddish brown.	Opaque gray.	Opaque gray.
Titanium	Pale yellow.	Colorless to white.	Grayish or yellowish.	Brownish.
Tungsten	Pale yellow.	Colorless to white.	Yellow.	Brownish.
Uranium	Yellow to orange.	Yellow to, brown. Can be flamed enamel-yellow.	Pale green.	Green. Can be flamed black.
Vanadium	Yellow.	Green.	Brownish to dirty green.	Yellow to green.

BORAX BEADS

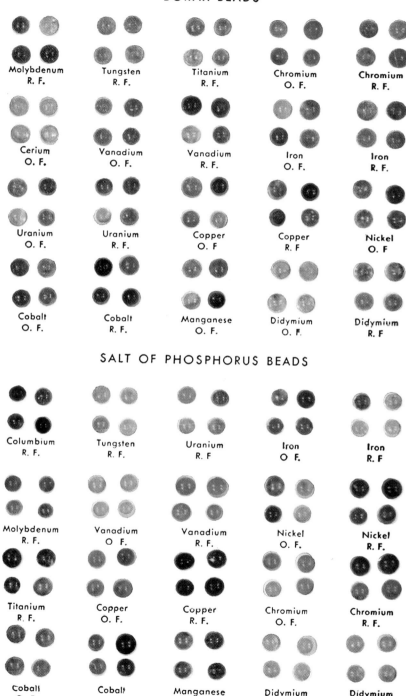

Molybdenum R. F.   Tungsten R. F.   Titanium R. F.   Chromium O. F.   Chromium R. F.

Cerium O. F.   Vanadium O. F.   Vanadium R. F.   Iron O. F.   Iron R. F.

Uranium O. F.   Uranium R. F.   Copper O. F   Copper R. F   Nickel O. F

Cobalt O. F.   Cobalt R. F.   Manganese O. F.   Didymium O. F.   Didymium R. F

SALT OF PHOSPHORUS BEADS

Columbium R. F.   Tungsten R. F.   Uranium R. F   Iron O F.   Iron R. F

Molybdenum R. F.   Vanadium O F.   Vanadium R. F.   Nickel O. F.   Nickel R. F.

Titanium R. F.   Copper O. F.   Copper R. F.   Chromium O. F.   Chromium R. F.

Cobalt O. F.   Cobalt R. F.   Manganese O. F.   Didymium O. F.   Didymium R. F.

Copyright by O. C. Smith, 1945

PLATE 7

SALT OF PHOSPHORUS BEADS

	OXIDIZING FLAME		REDUCING FLAME	
	Hot	Cold	Hot	Cold
Antimony	Pale yellow.	Colorless.	Gray.	Gray.
Bismuth	Pale yellow.	Colorless.	Gray.	Gray.
Cadmium	Pale yellow.	Colorless.	Pale yellow.	Colorless.
Cerium	Brownish yellow.	Light yellow.	Light yellow, opaque.	Colorless, opaque.
Chromium	Reddish to dirty green.	Yellowish green to green.	Red to dirty green.	Green. If not completely reduced it is brown to red.
Cobalt	Blue.	Blue.	Blue.	Blue.
Columbium	Pale yellow.	Colorless.	Brown.	Red-brown.
Copper	Dark green.	Greenish blue.	Brownish green.	Opaque red.
Didymium	Pale rose.	Pale rose.	Pale rose.	Pale rose.
Iron	Yellow to brownish red.	Brownish yellow.	Red or yellow to greenish yellow.	Pale violet.
Lead	Pale yellow.	Colorless.	Gray.	Gray.
Manganese	Grayish violet.	Violet.	Colorless.	Colorless.
Molybdenum	Yellowish green.	Colorless.	Dirty green.	Yellowish green.
Nickel	Reddish to brownish red.	Yellow to brownish.	Reddish to brownish red.	Yellow to brownish.
Silica	Insoluble skeleton.	Insoluble skeleton.	Insoluble skeleton.	Insoluble skeleton.
Tantalum	Pale yellow.	Colorless.	Pale yellow.	Colorless.
Titanium	Pale yellow.	Colorless.	Yellow.	Delicate violet.
Tungsten	Pale yellow.	Colorless.	Greenish to dirty blue.	Greenish blue.
Uranium	Yellow.	Yellowish green to colorless.	Pale dirty green.	Green.
Vanadium	Yellow.	Greenish yellow.	Brown to dirty green.	Green.

FLUORESCENT BEADS

Borax and Salt of Phosphorus Beads. The only minerals which respond to the short-wave ultra-violet light are the uranium, O.F. (greenish) and copper, R.F. (pinkish) of the borax beads and the uranium, R.F. (greenish), copper, R.F. (reddish) and tungsten, R.F. (pinkish) of the phosphorous beads.

Sodium Fluoride and Lithium Fluoride Beads. These are made in the same manner as the borax and phosphorous beads using the O. F. It is not absolutely necessary to use the platinum wire for these beads, as an iron wire may also be used. However, the Pt wire gives the most reliable results, as the beads may absorb iron from the iron wire and this may dull or even quench the fluorescence. No distinctive color is imparted to the fluoride beads by the elements. However, a pronounced response to ultra-violet light is obtained with certain elements present and in the case of uranium, this constitutes a quite sensitive field and laboratory test. The presence of thorium and/or the rare earths may interfere with the test. The beads, subjected to both the short wave (2540 Angstrom units) and the long wave (3660 Angstrom Units) Mineralight, give the response listed below.

SODIUM FLUORIDE

Element	Short wave	Long wave
Bismuth	Blue-white	Yellow
Columbium	Blue-white	none
Titanium	Light green	none
Tungsten	Light bluish yellow	none
Uranium	Brilliant lemon-yellow	Bright yellow

LITHIUM FLUORIDE

Element	Short wave	Long wave
Bismuth	Orange	Dark orange
Columbium	none	none
Titanium	Dark green	none
Tungsten	Light blue	none
Uranium	Brilliant blue	Blue-green

REACTIONS WITH HYDROBROMIC ACID

Place the ground mineral on the plaster tablet, add a drop or two of HBr and heat with the oxidizing flame.

Bismuth: a volatile, reddish green or yellow coating is formed.

Copper: the flame is colored green and a volatile, purplish coating mottled with black is formed. This frequently changes to yellow.

Iron: rust-colored, non-volatile spots are formed near the assay. If copper is present in the sample the coating from it may obscure the iron spots; these will become visible if the flame is applied directly to the coating near the assay.

Lead: the coating is canary yellow in color.

Mercury: the coat formed is yellow and volatile.

Molybdenum: the coat formed is blue to bluish green and volatile.

COLOR CHANGES ON HEATING IN THE CLOSED TUBE

	ORIGINAL COLOR	COLOR AFTER HEATING	
		Hot	Cold
Bismuth minerals	White or colorless.	Dark yellow to brown.	Pale yellow to white.
Cobalt minerals	Pink.	Black.	Black.
Copper minerals	Blue or green.	Black.	Black.
Iron minerals	Green, brown or red.	Black.	Black or dark red.
Lead minerals	White or colorless.	Dark yellow to brown.	Pale yellow to white.
Manganese minerals	Pink.	Black.	Black.
Zinc minerals	White or colorless.	Pale canary-yellow.	White.

(The changes cited above usually occur when the oxides of the metals are produced during the heating.)

REACTIONS WITH COBALT NITRATE

The ground mineral is heated slowly with the oxidizing flame on the plaster tablet or charcoal slab, allowed to cool, cobalt nitrate added, and again heated intensely with the O.F. The mineral should be light in color and infusible, for best results.

Antimony oxide gives a bluish to dirty green color. The result is better if applied to the coat.

Aluminum compounds give an ultramarine blue. **Zinc silicates** give a similar color.

Beryllium oxide gives a lavender, rather indistinct color.

Magnesium minerals give a pink or flesh color which is best seen when cold.

Silica gives a rather indistinct violet color.

Titanium oxide gives a rather indistinct yellowish green color.

Tin oxide gives a bluish to dirty green color. The results are better if the test is carried out on the coating.

Zinc oxide gives a beautiful grass-green color which is very characteristic. The test is good whether carried out on small pieces, on the ground mineral, or on the zinc oxide coating.

FLAME COLORS

The flame color test should be carried out on a platinum loop that has been thoroughly cleaned. This is accomplished by repeatedly dipping the loop into conc. HCl and holding in the flame until no coloration appears. Iron wire will serve as well as platinum for this test.

A small amount of the mineral powder or precipitate to be tested is placed in a watch glass and moistened with conc. HCl. The clean platinum loop is dipped into this and held in the non-luminous part of the oxidizing flame and the color produced is noted. As the alkalies Na, K and Li are more volatile than the alkaline earths, Ca, Ba and Sr, by heating the loop gently and then strongly, a differentiation can often be obtained, as the alkalies will show first, and are later followed by the color from the alkaline earths.

	WITH NAKED EYE	WITH MERWIN SCREEN	REMARKS
Antimony	Pale green. Especially evident when treated on charcoal.		
Arsenic	Livid blue.		Odor of garlic.
Barium	Yellowish green.	Through 1, bright green. Through 2, faint green. Through 3, faint green.	
Bismuth	Pale greenish white.		
Boron	Yellowish green.	Through 1, bright green. Through 2, faint green. Through 3, faint green.	If a borate is decomposed with HSO_4 and added to alcohol and the alcohol ignited, it will burn with a yellowish green color.

FLAME COLORS—(*Continued*)

	WITH NAKED EYE	WITH MERWIN SCREEN	REMARKS
Calcium	Yellowish red.	Through 1, flash of greenish yellow. Through 2, invisible. Through 3, flash of crimson.	The color is obtained very readily.
Copper Chloride and Bromide	Azure-blue.	Through 1, bright green. Through 2, bluish green. Through 3, bluish green.	The flame is tinged emerald green.
Copper Iodide	If treated per se, the flame is emerald green; with HCl, the color is azure blue.		
Copper Oxide	If treated per se, the flame is emerald green; with HCl, the color is azure blue.		
Erbium	Green.		
Indium	A corn-flower blue, tinged on the outer edges with green.		
Lead	Pale azure-blue, tinged with green on the edges.		
Lithium	Carmine.	Through 1, Invisible. Through 2, Invisible. Through 3, crimson.	If $BaCl_2$ is added, the red of the Li will appear before the green of the Ba.
Molybdenum	From oxides and sulfides, a faint yellowish green is developed.		
Phosphorous	Pale bluish green.	Through 1, green. Through 2, Invisible. Through 3, red violet.	Better results are obtained if H_2SO_4 is used instead of HCl.
Potassium	Pale violet.	Through 1, blue violet. Through 2, deep red violet. Through 3, red violet.	Purplish red through cobalt glass. Rubidium and caesium give similar colors and a spectroscope is necessary to distinguish between them.

FLAME COLORS—(*Continued*)

	WITH NAKED EYE	WITH MERWIN SCREEN	REMARKS
Selenium	Indigo blue.		Has a characteristic odor.
Sodium	Intense yellow.	Through 1, invisible. Through 2, invisible. Through 3, invisible.	Viewed through cobalt glass the yellow of Na is invisible but if K is present the purplish red will show.
Strontium	Crimson.	Through 1, invisible. Through 2, invisible. Through 3, crimson.	If $BaCl_2$ is added the red of the Sr will last longer than the green of the Ba.
Tellurium	Grass green.		
Thallium	Grass green.		
Zinc	Bluish green which usually appears as bright streaks in the flame.		

CLOSED TUBE SUBLIMATES

Place a small amount of the powder of the mineral in a closed tube and heat the bottom portion carefully. Heating with but very little oxidation is thus obtained and many substances react characteristically. The list below gives some of the sublimates formed and their derivation.

Antimony Oxide. Sb_2O_4: a white fusible sublimate of needle-like crystals.

Antimony Oxysulfide, Sb_2S_2O: difficultly volatile sublimate which is black while hot and reddish brown when cold. Obtained from antimony sulfantimonates and sulfides of antimony.

Ammonia Salts: a very volatile, white sublimate.

Arsenic, As: a brilliant, black sublimate, which is often gray and crystalline near the heated part of the tube. Obtained from metallic arsenic and some arsenides.

Arsenic Oxide, As_2O_3: a white, volatile sublimate consisting of octahedral crystals.

Arsenic Sulfides, AsS, and As_2S_3: easily volatile, deep red to almost black liquid while hot and a reddish yellow solid when cold. Obtained from realgar, orpiment and sulfarsenites.

Lead Chloride, $PbCl_2$: a white sublimate which fuses to yellow drops.

Mercury, Hg: minute, gray, metallic globules which coalesce when rubbed with a match stick. Obtained from metallic mercury and amalgams.

Mercuric Chloride, $HgCl_2$: a white *fusible* sublimate that is yellow while hot, white when cold.

Mercurous Chloride, HgCl: a white *infusible* sublimate that is yellow while hot, white when cold.

Mercuric Sulfide, HgS: a brilliant black solid which turns to red powder when rubbed. Obtained from cinnabar.

Sellenium, Se: fusible black globules which become red when rubbed. Often also there are small gray crystals of the oxide SeO_2. Obtained from selenium and the selenides. A high temperature is required.

Sulfur, S: a dark yellow to red liquid while hot and yellow to white solid when cold. Easily volatile. In small amounts it is nearly white. Obtained from sulfur and a few of the sulfides.

Tellurium, Te: fusible, black globules which are formed only at high temperatures. Fused globules of the oxide, TeO_2 are often present. Obtained from tellurium and the tellurides.

Tellurous Oxide, TeO_2: pale yellow to colorless globules which are volatile with difficulty. Obtained from metallic tellurium and a few of its compounds.

Water, H_2O: a colorless, volatile liquid which collects in the upper, cooler part of the tube. It is usually neutral but may be either acid or alkaline. Obtained from minerals containing water of crystallization.

OPEN TUBE REACTIONS

A study should be made of both the gases evolved and the sublimates formed in the open tube tests. The results obtained by treating certain substances in the open tube are given below.

Antimony: forms dense white fumes which partly escape and partly condense as a white powder which is straw-yellow while hot. This powder is composed of crystalline, slowly volatile Sb_2O_3 and amorphous, non-volatile Sb_2O_4.

Antimony Sulfides: the results are the same as for antimony except that fumes of SO_2 are also evolved.

Arsenic: yields a white, volatile sublimate of octahedral crystals, As_2O_3. If complete oxidation has not taken place, a black mirror of metallic arsenic may also result. Garlic odor.

Arsenides: same as arsenic. Garlic odor (Arsine AsH_3).

Arsenic Sulfides: same as arsenic but also if the heating has been too rapid, an orange or yellow deposit of sulfur or the arsenic sulfides may result. SO_2 is formed. May have garlic odor.

Bismuth: yields a fusible sublimate of Bi_2O_3 that is brown while hot and yellow when cold.

65

Bismuth Sulfide: a white, non-volatile powder, $Bi_2(SO_4)_3$, is formed. This is fusible to yellow drops.

Lead Chloride: gives a white, partially volatile deposit of $PbOCl_2$ which fuses to yellow drops.

Lead Sulfide: yields white, non-volatile $PbSO_4$ near the assay which fuses to drops that are yellow while hot and white when cold.

Mercury and Amalgams: yield a sublimate of minute, volatile metallic droplets which coalesce when rubbed with a match stick.

Mercury Sulfide: if heated rapidly a deposit of brilliant, black sulfide is formed; if slowly, gray, metallic globules of mercury are formed and SO_2 evolved. Rubbing causes the droplets to coalesce.

Molybdenum Oxide and **Sulfide:** yield a delicate network of crystals of MoO_3 which are yellow while hot and white when cold.

Selenium Compounds: forms a steel-gray, volatile coating of radiating needles of SeO_2 near the assay and the characteristic odor of rotten horse-radish is evident. A reddish deposit of metallic selenium may form at some distance from the assay.

Sulfides: careful heating yields SO_2 but heated too rapidly or with an insufficient amount of air decomposition results with the deposition of sulfur which eventually disappears.

Tellurium and **Tellurides:** form a white, non-volatile deposit of TeO_2 which fuses into pale yellow or colorless drops.

FUSION WITH SODIUM CARBONATE

(On Charcoal.)

Make a mixture of 1 part of the powdered mineral or precipitate to be tested with 3 parts of sodium carbonate and heat on the charcoal slab with the reducing flame. Note the color of the melt, the sublimates formed and any metallic globules that may appear. Some of the elements react characteristically. The sublimates formed are in general the same as when the substance is treated per se and will be found under the heading of Sublimates on Charcoal.

FREE METALS FORMED

Antimony: gray brittle buttons or beads.

Bismuth: a reddish white somewhat malleable button with brittle edges.

Cobalt: gives magnetic particles.

Copper: gives a red, malleable bead which usually becomes black when the reducing flame is withdrawn or if touched with the oxidizing flame.

Gold: yellow malleable beads.

Iron: gives magnetic particles.

Lead: yields gray, malleable beads.

Nickel: gives magnetic particles.

Silver: yields white, malleable beads.

Tin: white malleable beads which oxidize easily.

Fusion Colors

Chromium: yellow color due to the formation of the chromate, Na_2CrO_4. Better if the O.F. is used.

Copper: bluish green color, somewhat similar to that from manganese.

Manganese: bluish green color due to the formation of Na_2MnO_4.

These color reactions are better obtained on platinum than charcoal as they depend on oxidation for their production. If done on platinum, add a little KNO_3 as this assists in the oxidation. If KNO_3 is used on charcoal small explosions take place.

SODIUM CARBONATE BEAD REACTIONS

Make a bead of soda and touch the hot bead to a speck of the mineral. Fuse in the O.F. and note the reactions which indicate the following:

Manganese, Mn. Bluish-green, opaque bead. This reaction may not be obtained unless potassium nitrate is also present in the soda bead.

Chromium, Cr. Yellow, opaque bead.

Silica, SiO_2, is indicated by effervescence and solution to a clear colorless bead unless colored by one of the metals.

Sulfur, S as **Sulfate,** SO_4. If the fusion has been made on Pt in the O.F., and is crushed, moistened with water and placed on a bright silver, no discoloration should result. If the fusion has been made in the strong R.F. or on coal, and is crushed and placed on bright silver, it will turn black. By this treatment sulfates are reduced to sulfides.

Sulfur, S as **Sulfides.** If fusion has been made on Pt in the O.F. and turns bright silver black when crushed and moistened with water, S is present as sulfides or sulfo salts. **Selenium** and **tellurium** show this also and must be tested separately.

Reactions with Sodium Thiosulfate

When sodium thiosulfate ($Na_2S_2O_3 \cdot 5H_2O$) is heated, hydrogen sulfide and free sulfur are liberated. If any of the elements which react with these are present, they are converted to sulfides, many of which have characteristic colors.

BEAD TESTS

These bead tests may be carried out by the usual procedure of making the bead tests, noting the colors as usual, in the O.F. and R.F., both hot and cold, then touching the hot bead to sodium thiosulfate and reheating in the R.F. The objectionable features of this test are that easily volatile metals, such as arsenic and mercury, are liable to give no reaction and also that it is sometimes difficult to distinguish the color formed by the sulfide. However, it also has the distinct advantage in that beads containing such elements as antimony, bismuth, cadmium, etc., which have no very positive color in the borax and salt of phosphorus beads, are easily differentiated by the sodium thiosulfate treatment. In general, borax gives the best results.

CLOSED TUBE TESTS

The disadvantages encountered with the bead tests are obviated if the tests are carried out in the closed tube.

Grind together 1 volume of the sample with about 10 volumes of sodium thiosulfate, place the mixture in a closed tube, and heat. (The presence of a little oxalic acid generally improves the test.) At first, considerable water is driven off and to prevent this from condensing, running back down the tube and breaking it, the tube must be kept warm to the top. Heat for only a short time after the boiling has ceased, allow to cool and note the color of the fusion.

If too strongly heated, the sodium thiosulfate itself is changed to dark brown which appears black while hot.

| | | COLD BORAX BEAD COLORS | |
Metal	Reaction with $Na_2S_2O_3$	Oxidizing Flame	Reducing Flame
Antimony	orange	colorless	colorless
Arsenic	yellow, lemon	....	....
Bismuth	black	colorless	gray
Cadmium	yellow, orange	colorless	colorless
Chromium	green	green	green
Cobalt	black	blue	blue
Copper	black	blue	brown
Iron	black	green to brown	pale bottle green
Lead	black	colorless	colorless
Manganese	light green	reddish violet	colorless
Mercury	black	....	....
Molybdenum	brown	colorless	brown to black
Nickel	black	reddish brown	gray
Thallium	black	colorless	colorless
Tin	brown	....	....
Uranium	black	yellow to brown	green
Zinc	white	colorless	gray

If the sample has a distinctive color, this must be taken into consideration in judging the results. There are substances which will not be decomposed by this treatment and with these the sulfide of the metal will probably not be formed.

The foregoing table gives a list of the sodium thiosulfate reactions along with the comparable borax bead tests.

REACTIONS WITH POTASSIUM BISULFATE

In the Closed Tube

Mix the powdered mineral with an equal volume of potassium bisulfate ($KHSO_4$) and heat in the C.T. The indications are as follows:

Nitrates and **Nitrites.** Reddish-brown vapors (NO_2, N_2O_5) with a pungent odor.

Chlorates. Yellowish-green fumes (ClO_2) with the odor of chlorine.

Iodides. Violet, choking vapors and a brown to black sublimate (free iodine).

Bromides and **Bromates.** Brown irritating vapors. Free bromine is liberated and the tube may be filled with a heavy brown gas.

Chlorides. Colorless gas (HCl) which forms white fumes if the mouth of the ammonia bottle is held near.

Fluorides. The colorless gas (HF) etches the glass.

Sulfides. The gas (H_2S) has the odor of rotten eggs. Turns lead acetate paper black.

Acetates. Smells like vinegar.

Carbonates. Colorless gas (CO_2) which causes a drop of lime water, if subjected to it in the Pt loop, to become turbid.

Oxalates. Colorless gas (CO) which burns with a blue flame.

In the Crucible

The $KHSO_4$ fusion also gives indications of the presence of certain elements by its color as follows:

Element	Color While Hot	Color When Cold
Antimony	brown	light lemon-yellow
Cerium	red-brown	orange-yellow
Chromium	dark purple	yellowish green
Cobalt	dark purple	purple (magenta)
Copper	olive-green	blue
Didymium	bluish gray	lilac
Iron	red-brown	very light yellow

Element	Color While Hot	Color When Cold
Manganese	dark brown	dirty greenish gray
Nickel	brown-black	orange-yellow
Molybdenum	brownish-yellow	clear, colorless
Selenium	light yellow	very light brown
Thorium	very light yellow	white, yellow tint
Uranium	orange-yellow	bright lemon-yellow
Vanadium	red-brown	yellowish brown

ASSAY OF GOLD AND SILVER WITH THE BLOWPIPE

Materials Required. Approximate quantitative determination of gold and silver can easily be made by blowpiping with the aid of a few simple pieces of apparatus.

Since an accurate balance is not available to many, a method using a volume of ore and the volume of the final bead of metal has been worked out. At first consideration this might seem to lack much in the way of quantitative results but in practice, checking against assayed samples, it has been found to be quite reliable. Most gold ores are primarily quartzes or silicates with varying amounts of gold and sulfides. These vary somewhat in specific gravity and this will necessarily change the weight of a measured amount of ore, but this difference in weight is in most cases not over 10% and in the majority will not be over or under the average to anything like this extent. If the gold or silver occurs as scales or relatively large pieces, it may be very difficult to obtain a representative sample.

The **sampler** (ore measurer) shown in *A* of Fig. 25 was made of the bulb from the bottom of a thermometer. It has a volume of 2/10 milliliter and holds approximately 0.2 grams (not packed) of average, finely ground ore. The entire method is based on the treatment of this quantity.

The other materials and equipment required for this determination are as follows:

Flux. A good general-purpose low-melting flux is made by grinding and mixing together thoroughly the following materials in the proportions designated:

Sodium bicarbonate (baking soda)	5 parts by weight.
Potassium carbonate	4 parts by weight.
Borax glass	2 parts by weight.
Flour (wheat)	1 part by weight.
Litharge	6 parts by weight.

Charcoal Slab. It is best to use the large 4″ x 2″ x 1¼″ slabs which are specially treated to retard their burning. They will give long service and many assays can be run with one slab.

Borax Glass. This may be purchased from a chemical supply house or made by heating ordinary borax in an iron crucible until it is fused, then grinding. Porcelain must not be used for the fusion, as the glaze will be dissolved.

Bone Ash. This may be purchased from a chemical supply house or made by burning ordinary bones until all the organic matter is removed, then grinding.

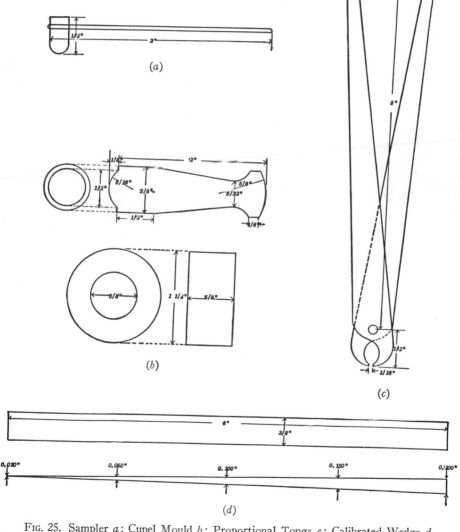

FIG. 25. Sampler *a*; Cupel Mould *b*; Proportional Tongs *c*; Calibrated Wedge *d*.

Cupels. In making these, a mould should be used. A very satisfactory one is shown in the detail drawing of *B* in Fig. 25. It is easily made from steel on a lathe. The cupels are made by thoroughly mixing together the ground bone ash with 10% of flour, then moistening with strong sal soda (ordinary washing soda) solution until it will stick together when pinched between the fingers. If too wet, the cupel will be dense and will crack in use, while if not wet enough, it will not hold together well. After moistening, it should be sifted through a flour sieve to break up all lumps.

To make the cupels, the ring is placed on a smooth block of wood or iron and is filled with the moistened bone ash. The pestle is then inserted and pressed down with the hand, then given a sharp blow or two with a mallet. On raising the ring from the board the cupel is easily forced out. The thickness of the cupel is governed by the amount of bone ash used and the texture by the moisture content and the pressure exerted.

Proportional Tongs. The final beads are spheres. Those from rich ores are small and those from poor ones are *very tiny*. In order to measure these, special equipment must be used. Proportional dividers may be purchased from a dealer in drafting materials, but they are not as satisfactory as the proportional tongs shown in *c* of Fig. 25. These may be made from any convenient material, such as a folding steel rule, by grinding and filing into the shape shown. If one is made by the analyst, it is not necessary to have the long arms open exactly 10 times as wide as the short arms, but the *exact relationship between the two* must be accurately determined with machinists' feelers, a calibrated wedge, or a micrometer.

Calibrated Wedge. This may be purchased from a machinists' supply house or made with a little patience and care. The one illustrated in *d* of Fig. 25 was made from a ⅜" wood chisel by grinding and honing on a new perfectly straight oil stone, then calibrating with a micrometer, and marking.

Assay Procedure. The approximate quantitative determination of gold and silver by the blowpipe is carried out as follows: Mix 1 measure (approximately 0.2 grams) of the finely ground ore with 2 volumes of flux. Hollow out a shallow depression in one end of the charcoal block and place the mixture in it. Holding the block with a pair of crucible tongs, play the blowpipe flame on it gently until the material has fused, then strongly. On heating, small globules of lead will appear. As heating continues, these will gradually coalesce into larger ones. The assay must be turned and flamed from all sides so as to force the small lead particles around the edge into the center, or wherever the large globule is, so that all the lead is finally in one mass. This button of molten lead contains the gold, silver and any other precious metals.

When the assay has been completely liquefied and the lead all collected into a single ball it is brought to the edge, the assay and coal heated strongly, and the lead globule allowed to run off into a crucible, iron mortar, or other container. After cooling, the slag on the coal is removed with a knife blade and a small amount of borax glass is put in its place. The lead button is then added and **scorification** started. By playing a strong oxidizing flame over the lead, it is oxidized and the lead oxide along with the oxide of any other base metal is absorbed by the borax glass. As scorification continues, the bead is seen to become gradually smaller. When it has been reduced in size until it has a diameter of about $\frac{1}{32}''$ (about $\frac{1}{2}$ the size of a pin head) it is removed from the coal and flux as before.

It is now ready for **cupellation.** This is carried out by placing the bead in a cupel, placing the cupel on a slab of charcoal and playing a strong oxidizing flame over the lead bead. As strong a blast with as much air and as little flame as is consistent with keeping the bead molten, should be used. As the bead is oxidized, the lead oxide is absorbed by the cupel, with the result that when all the lead has finally been burned off, a sphere of the precious metal remains. On removing the flame there will be a flash or "blick" when the metal solidifies. Sometimes a bright bead is not obtained, because of the presence of copper or other metals. In this case it must be melted with additional lead (gold and silver free), then be again scorified with borax glass, and re-cupelled. On very refractory ores it may be necessary to repeat this process several times.

The beads of gold and silver obtained from lean ores are very small, sometimes with a diameter of only 1/1000 of an inch. A bead of this size can barely be seen with the naked eye. In order to measure a bead it is picked up with the small jaws of the proportional tongs, using a hand lens. Holding the tongs very carefully, the wedge is inserted between the jaws of the long end and a reading of this width taken. For example, if this width is found to be 0.025″ the bead has a diameter of 0.0025″. Referring to the graph, Fig. 26, it is seen that this is equivalent to about 0.35 ounces of gold per ton, or if it is silver, 0.35 × 0.544, or 0.19 ounces per ton.

The bead may consist of pure gold or silver or a mixture of these, or it may contain any of the precious metals. If it is white, it is principally silver; if yellow, principally gold. With small amounts of lead, copper, platinum or paladium, the bead it not as bright as pure gold or silver. With rhodium, iridium, ruthenium, osmium or osmiridium present, the bead does not brighten at all.

If it is thought that the bead is a mixture of gold and silver, the amount of each may be determined by **parting.** A mixture of $\frac{2}{3}$ or more of silver and $\frac{1}{3}$ of gold by weight will dissolve in nitric acid. If the bead does not have this great a silver content, it is remelted with a piece of silver at least twice the size of the bead. This is then treated with nitric acid, which dissolves the silver. It is then filtered, the filter paper containing the gold carefully burned, the gold taken up with lead and re-cupelled. This bead will be pure gold and the difference between it and the original is the silver content of the ore.

The method herein described makes no claim to being absolutely exact, but

73

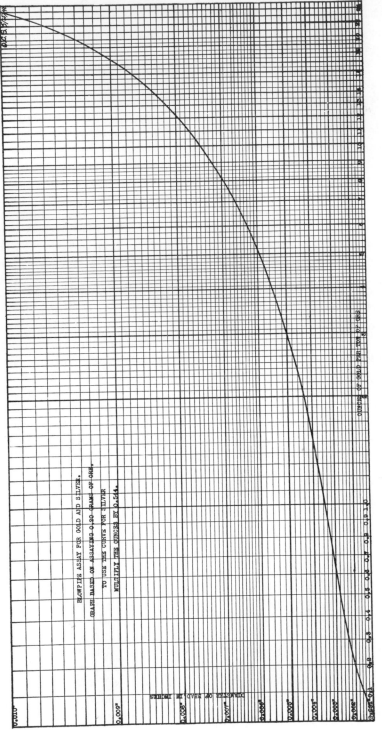

FIG. 26. Assay Graph.

74

by its use we can determine whether the ore under examination carries values of $1.00, $5.00, $10.00 or $1000.00 per ton, which in many cases will give the information we are after—namely, whether or not the ore is commercial and carries values that warrant further examination and expense.

It is remarkable that with ores carrying as little as $1.00 per ton, which is 1 part by weight in about 1,000,000 parts of rock, a bead of gold will always be obtained. Sometimes it gets into a tiny crack and is lost or cannot be picked up and measured, but it is always there, and when it is considered that a bead with a diameter of 1/1000" has a volume of only 0.000,000,000,523,6 cubic inch and weighs only 0.000,000,165,6 gram it becomes still more astonishing. Due to the fact that these beads are spheres, their weight by measurement is more accurate than that obtained by using the most delicate assay balance, which is accurate to 0.000,005 gram. It takes 30 beads 1/1000" in diameter to make a mass large enough to weigh on an assay balance.

REACTIONS WITH HYDROGEN PEROXIDE
(Use a 3% solution.)

The precipitate or mineral is dissolved in acid or, if insoluble, fused with soda or potassium acid sulfate and the melt dissolved in water and acid.

Chromium: H_2O_2 added to a solution of a chromatic acid with HCl or better H_2SO_4, and heated, gives a blue, then green color. In a *cold alkaline* solution of a chromate, H_2O_2 produces a red color that slowly disappears.

Titanium: H_2O_2 added to a solution slightly acid with H_2SO_4 or HCl produces a yellow to orange-red color. HF or the addition of a fluoride *destroys* the color. H_2O_2 prevents the precipitation of Ti by Na_2HPO_4 from weak acid solutions (difference from Zr).

Vanadium: nearly neutralizes the solution with NH_4OH, take 1 ml, add 5 drops of conc. HNO_3 and 1 or 2 drops of H_2O_2 to the cold solution. A reddish-brown color results. The color is *not destroyed* by the addition of HF or a fluoride.

Uranium: H_2O_2 added to a solution acid with HCl precipitates yellowish uranium tetroxide (UO_4) that is insoluble in HCl but soluble in $(NH_4)_2CO_3$ solution giving a deep yellow color. Sulfate ion hinders the precipitation.

Molybdenum: evaporate to dryness carefully so as not to overheat; treat the residue with conc. NH_4OH then with H_2O_2. A pink or red color is formed. On evaporating to dryness again and treating the residue with HNO_3 or H_2SO_4, yellow permolybdic acid ($HMoO_4$) is formed.

Manganese, Cobalt, Nickel: NH_4OH in the presence of NH_4Cl does not precipitate these metals. If H_2O_2 is added to the strongly ammoniacal solution and boiled, Mn and Co are precipitated as Mn_3O_4 and Co_2O_3. Both are brown and indistinguishable. Nickel is thrown down as apple-green nickelous hydroxide [$Ni(OH)_2$]. This procedure serves to separate these elements from Fe, Al and other metals that form hydroxides that are insoluble in ammonia.

Columbium, Tantalum: when dilute HCl and H_2O_2 are added to the freshly precipitated pentoxides and heated, Cb goes completely into solution and Ta is partially dissolved, giving a yellow to orange color. By boiling to decompose the H_2O_2, the white Cb_2O_5 and Ta_2O_5 are precipitated.

Gold: from alkaline solutions, H_2O_2 gives a precipitate of finely divided metal, brownish-black by reflected light but bluish-green by transmitted light. In dilute solutions a reddish coloration with a bluish shimmer is obtained.

Cerium: H_2O_2 added to an acid solution reduces ceric to cerous salts. If a cerous salt is precipitated with NH_4OH and an excess of H_2O_2 added, a reddish-brown precipitate of perceric hydroxide ($CeO_3 \cdot nH_2O$) is precipitated, which on boiling is changed to pure yellow $Ce(OH)_4$.

Zirconium: when H_2O_2 is added to a slightly acid solution, the voluminous peroxide is precipitated. If this is warmed with conc. HCl, chlorine is evolved. H_2O_2 does not prevent the precipitation of Zr by Na_2HPO_4 from weak acid solutions (difference from Ti).

Thorium, H_2O_2 added to a hot neutral solution or one faintly acid with HNO_3 or H_2SO_4 or to an ammonium carbonate solution, causes all the Th to be precipitated as white hydrated thorium peroxide.

Scandium, H_2O_2 prevents the precipitation of Sc by Na_2HPO_4 from weak acid solution. Destroying the H_2O_2 by adding Na_2SO_3 causes the scandium phosphate to be precipitated (similar to Ti).

Yttrium: H_2O_2 added to an alkaline solution precipitates gelatinous, unstable, hydrated peroxide $Y(O \cdot OH)(OH)_2$.

Copper: in a 5% NaOH solution Cu usually gives a blue color, due to cupric salts, before the addition of H_2O_2. H_2O_2 oxidizes cuprous to cupric compounds. Cuprous hydroxide is yellow, cupric hydroxide blue.

Osmium, Ruthenium, Palladium: H_2O_2 added to a solution of these elements in 5% NaOH, yields yellowish colors similar to chromium. The color is destroyed by adding NH_4Cl to the cold solution.

Platinum: the color is similar to Os, Ru, and Pd, but is not destroyed by NH_4Cl.

REACTIONS WITH METALLIC ZINC IN ACID SOLUTIONS

Titanium: Zn added to an HCl solution gives a violet color. The color is green if fluoride is present.

Tungsten: Sn added to an HCl solution of a tungstate or suspended oxide, and boiled, yields a beautiful blue color; Zn gives a purple then reddish-brown color. Dilution with water *does not destroy* the color (difference from columbium).

Columbium: Zn added to an acid solution and boiled gives a blue to black color. The color *disappears* on dilution with water (difference from tungsten).

Tantalum: gives no color reactions.

Vanadium: an acid solution heated with metallic Zn becomes blue, green, then bluish-violet.

Molybdenum: a solution acid with HCl or H_2SO_4, when treated with metallic Zn, becomes blue, green, then brown.

Ruthenium: metallic Zn and HCl solution produces an azure-blue color which disappears with the precipitation of metallic Ru.

Uranium: Zn in acid solutions reduces the yellow uranyl to green uranous compounds; when all the acid has been used up, a yellow precipitate or coating will form on the residual zinc.

Selenium: red metallic Se is precipitated by Zn in acid solution and the zinc becomes coated with the Se and looks as if coated with copper. On warming, the red Se is changed to brown or gray to black.

Tellurium: from acid solutions Zn precipitates gray to black metallic tellurium.

Thallium: is precipitated as the metal in tiny black crystals.

Indium: is precipitated as the metal in white lustrous flakes.

Osmium, Rhodium, Ruthenium, Iridium, Palladium, Platinum, Copper, Silver, Gold, Cadmium, Mercury, Indium, Thallium, Germanium, Tin, Lead, Bismuth, Selenium, Tellurium, Polonium, and **Antimony:** are all precipitated as metals by metallic zinc.

Silver, Lead, Tin, Thallium and **Indium:** are precipitated on the zinc from neutral or faintly acid solutions as silvery dendrites or "trees" with a metallic luster. They are usually large and loosely branched. The precipitation of the metal does not take place until the zinc has used all the free acid.

Antimony, Bismuth, Copper, Tellurium, Gold and **Palladium:** form dendrites more in form of moss and are shorter and more compact than those from the metals above. Some long slender "trees" may be formed. The dendrites usually have the characteristic color of the metal. Some of these metals will not be deposited on the zinc until all the free acid has been consumed.

Manganese, Nickel, Ruthenium, Platinum, Iridium, Vanadium, Uranium, Tellurium, Selenium, and possibly **Antimony** and **Bismuth:** will form a yellow to brown or black stain on the zinc, but no dendrite or "tree" is formed. Some of these metals will not be deposited until all the free acid has been consumed by the zinc.

Mercury: is precipitated as minute silvery white globules. These are black by transmitted light.

Antimony and **Arsenic:** may yield a gas, stibine SbH_3 and arsine AsH_3. If these gases are allowed to escape through a tube along with hydrogen and burned, and a piece of glazed porcelain is held directly over the flame, metallic antimony and arsenic are deposited. Treated with sodium hypochlorite, this will dissolve the arsenic, but the antimony will be unaffected.

77

Antimony and **Tin:** if a drop or two of an HCl solution of Sb and Sn are placed on a piece of platinum and bright metallic zinc is then placed in the solution so that the two metals touch, a gray or black stain will be deposited on the platinum. On removal of the zinc, if the stain is due to antimony, it will not disappear; if due to tin, it will be dissolved if some free acid remains.

Cadmium: is precipitated only from neutral solutions.

REACTIONS OF BLOWPIPE TESTS TO ULTRA-VIOLET LIGHT

The blowpipe tests were subjected to ultra-violet light from a model No. V-41 Mineralight cold quartz lamp, with the following fluorescent and phosphorescent effects (those not listed gave no noticeable response):

Antimony: Per se on coal: small blue and green spots.
I flux on coal: blue and pink areas at assay.
Br on coal: assay is brownish and pink with a red border.
Cr flux on coal: assay is green with light orange around it.
Per se on plaster: blue-white ring at assay.
I flux on plaster: pink around assay.
Br flux on plaster: pink around assay.
Cr on plaster: slight brown around assay.

Arsenic: I flux on coal: assay is bluish white and pink.
Br on coal: assay is pink to red.
Sulfide heated gently on plaster: brownish red around assay.
Sulfide heated strongly on plaster: brownish red around assay.
I flux on plaster: pink around assay. Coating is brownish red.
Br flux on plaster: coating is brownish red.
Cr flux on plaster: coating is brownish red.

Bismuth: Per se on coal: assay is orange with a brilliant red border.
I flux on coal: assay is bright blue. Coating is brilliant red.
Br flux on coal: pink around assay.
Cr flux on coal: assay glows as though on fire.
Per se on plaster: blue white at assay.
I flux on plaster: greenish spots at assay and coating is brownish red.
Cr flux on plaster: red orange through assay.

Cadmium: Per se on coal: the coating is brownish orange.
Cr flux on coal: orange at assay, reddish just beyond.
Per se on plaster: coating is red to deep brownish orange with sometimes brilliant ivory and green.
Cr flux on plaster: brilliant red at some distance from assay.

Chromium: Soda fusion on coal: green spot at assay; assay is phosphorescent.

Copper: Per se on coal: cream yellow at assay.
I flux on coal: green with tinges of red.
I flux on plaster: assay is green.
Br flux on plaster: assay is green.

Iron: Br flux on plaster: greenish white spots around assay.

Lead: I flux on coal: green and orange near assay with green streaks radiating outward.
Br flux on coal: bright ivory and blue green at assay.
Cr flux on coal: bright ivory and green around assay and covering considerable portion of slab.
I flux on plaster: yellow at assay with greenish yellow film at some distance.
Br flux on plaster: orange at assay.
Cr flux on plaster: pink at assay with brown at some distance.

Manganese: Soda fusion on coal: green spot at assay; assay is phosphorescent.
Soda fusion on plaster: phosphorescent but not fluorescent.

Mercury: I flux on coal: deep blue and brilliant red areas.
Br flux on coal: assay is bright brownish orange.
Cr flux on coal: bright deep brownish orange at assay.
I flux on plaster heated gently: brownish red on edge of film.
I flux heated strongly on plaster: brownish red on edge of film.
Br flux on plaster: blue and deep orange at assay.

Molybdenum: Per se O.F. on coal: greenish and brownish at assay.
Per se R.F. on coal: greenish and reddish brown at assay.
I flux on coal: greenish yellow and red around assay.
Per se O.F. on plaster: the assay is brilliant yellow.
Per se R.F. on plaster: the assay is brilliant yellow.
I flux on plaster: the assay is yellow.
Br flux on plaster: assay is yellow with brown at some distance.

Selenium: I flux on coal: green around assay with sometimes deep blue areas.
Br flux on coal: assay has a yellowish brown color.

79

Cr flux on coal: assay is reddish orange like glowing coals of fire.

I flux on plaster: reddish orange at assay; coating is dark brown.

Br flux on plaster: assay is reddish orange; coating is dark brown.

Cr flux on plaster: assay is deep brilliant red; coating is dark brown.

Silver: Per se on coal: orange at assay.

Tellurium: I flux on coal: bluish white and pink around assay.

Br flux on coal: bluish white at assay with brown around it.

Cr flux on coal: assay is brownish orange.

Thallium: I flux on coal: brilliant blue, green, and ivory at assay and around it.

Br flux on coal: brilliant yellow with blue-white and orange around assay.

Cr flux on coal: bright brownish red at assay.

I flux on plaster: bright bluish green and brilliant blue at assay.

Br flux on plaster: assay is bright yellow with blue.

Cr flux on plaster: orange through the assay.

Tin: Per se on coal: orange-red at assay.

Per se with cobalt nitrate on coal: light orange red with green at assay.

I flux on coal: assay is green to blue.

Br flux on coal: assay and coating is yellow orange with sometimes green.

Per se on plaster: orange red spots at assay.

SMOKED PLASTER TABLETS (ALL PER SE TESTS)

Antimony: green with pink spots.

Arsenic: slight blue and whitish blue coloration.

Cadmium: bright blue at assay with yellowish brown ring beyond and light blue farther away.

Lead: slight greenish at assay.

Mercury: small whitish blue at assay.

Molybdenum: brilliant yellow at assay.

Tellurium: bright red spot at assay.

Bead Tests. The only beads which responded to the ultra-violet light were the uranium O.F. (greenish) and copper R.F. (pinkish) of the Borax beads and uranium R.F. (greenish), copper R.F. (reddish), and tungsten R.F. (pinkish), of the salt of phosphorus beads.

FLUORESCENCE OF SODIUM FLUORIDE FUSIONS

A small amount of the oxide or salt of various elements was fused with about 10 times its volume of sodium fluoride (NaF) on a charcoal slab in the O.F. After cooling, these were subjected to ultra-violet light from a model No. V-41 Mineralight lamp with the following fluorescent effects:

(Aluminum, barium, beryllium, calcium, didyminum, lead, magnesium, manganese, molybdenum, tellurium, tin and vanadium gave no response.)

COLOR

	ORDINARY LIGHT	ULTRA–VIOLET LIGHT
Antimony	Gray.	Blue and green.
Arsenic	Gray.	Blue and green.
Bismuth	Dark brown.	Greenish ivory.
Cerium	Gray; yellow while hot.	Red.
Cadmium	Red.	Light blue and green.
Cobalt	Dirty blue.	Deep blue.
Columbium	Pinkish white.	Greenish white.
Copper	Brown.	Ivory.
Lanthanum	White.	Blue with traces of pink and yellow.
Lithium	Gray.	Blue with pink and greenish areas.
Mercury	White.	Blue.
Nickel	Dirty blue.	Deep blue.
Selenium	Brown.	Light blue.
Silicon	White.	Pinkish blue.
Silver	Salmon.	Green.
Strontium	Light brown.	Yellow.
Tantalum	Pinkish.	Bluish white.
Thallium	Brown.	Dark green.
Thorium	White.	Bright blue.
Titanium	White.	Light blue.
Tungsten	Brown.	Yellow.
Uranium	Gray.	Brilliant greenish yellow.
Yttrium	White.	Pinkish blue.
Zinc	White.	Pink; sublimate is blue.
Zirconium	Salmon.	Light blue and yellow.

CHAPTER IV

Ultra-Violet Light in Mineral Fluorochemistry*

Ultra-violet rays, also known as "black light," have found a very definite place in the mineral sciences during the past several years. The branch of science which treats of the relationships between ultra-violet and other kinds of radiation and minerals is known as mineral fluorochemistry. Theoretical and academic interest along this line began to develop before the turn of the century. However, this branch of knowledge has only recently been widely recognized as of the greatest importance in almost every type of earth science.

Ultra-violet rays cause certain minerals to glow or release their own light — a phenomenon called fluorescence — and this emission of "cold light" has proven of decided value in the detection and identification of many minerals and ores. Though there are limitations in the use of ultra-violet light, as only a few important, economic minerals fluoresce, the simplicity and expediency of this agent have demonstrated that a fluorescence test is essential in all prospecting as well as in mining, sorting, grading and milling of certain ores. Its greatest usefulness is in the identification of scheelite, zircon, hydrozincite, willemite, mercury and petroleum. Other minerals which may or may not fluoresce are agate, albite, aragonite, barite, benitoite, calcite, chalcedony, colemanite, fluorite, hyalite, manganapatite, semi-opal, powellite, selenite, sphalerite, wernerite, etc.

There are many instances of undiscovered values in mining properties that have been worked for certain ores, such as gold and silver, and the rock which did not carry the gold and silver values was thrown on the dump. In a number of cases the supposedly worthless rock has been proven to contain greater values in scheelite, an ore of tungsten, than the gold values actually contained in the ore which was milled.

In the Chuckawalla Mountains near the Imperial Valley of California some miners tunneled into the side of a mountain for 350 feet. The gold values did not prove profitable and the property was abandoned. During the rush for new tungsten deposits, which occurred during the war, the dump at this property was examined by a prospector with an ultra-violet lamp. He found a section which contained many specimens of high grade scheelite. Inside the tunnel he found that an 8 foot vein, which carried from 1 to 2% of scheelite, had been cut 105 feet from the entrance. Further investigation disclosed that

*Written by Thomas S. Warren, president of Ultra-Violet Products, Inc., Los Angeles, Calif. The plates used in illustrating this chapter were furnished through the courtesy of that company.

the vein reached the surface above the tunnel. Possession of the property was secured and profitable operations commenced.

There is another story of a man who brought in a truck load of attractive rock from the desert for garden decoration. Several years after the rock had been installed in his garden he examined them with ultra-violet light and found they contained profitable percentages of scheelite. He immediately retraced his steps to the location from which the rock came and laid out his claims.

The largest producer of tungsten in the United States during the war was the Yellow Pine Mine in Idaho. This property has been worked for gold, and vanadium and further development was being investigated by the U. S. Geological Survey. It was while extensive core drilling was going on that scheelite was discovered by fluorescent analysis of the cores. Further work by means of core drilling disclosed a tremendous ore body and this was developed into the big producer.

In Montana there is the record of a mine which was a marginal producer of copper. A U. S. Government engineer was investigating the property and as a matter of routine inspection used an ultra-violet lamp for examination of the walls of the various tunnels. He unexpectedly discovered scheelite in several veins which had been cut. This information was given to the owner and a profitable tungsten producer was developed.

A great many other properties have been opened up in the United States after prospecting with an ultra-violet lamp. The listing of such properties would be very extensive. The more important locations include those near Essex, California; Beaver, Utah; Shoshoni, Wyoming; Winnemucca, Nevada; the Fresno-Porterville section of the Sierra Nevada Mountains in California; Bishop, California, and Yellow Pine, Idaho.

SOURCES OF ULTRA–VIOLET RADIATION

One natural source of ultra-violet rays is sunlight. Ultra-violet rays are invisible and are shorter than the visible ones. When the sun's rays are passed through a quartz prism, the white light is separated into the various colors of the spectrum: red, orange, yellow, green, blue, violet and indigo. There are rays still longer than the red, which are invisible, and are the wave lengths responsible for heat effects. They are termed "infra-red" rays. At the other end of the visible spectrum are the invisible "ultra-violet" rays. They are "cold" (have no appreciable heating effect) and have a chemical action (actinic effect) on the cells of the body. They form Vitamin D and create tan.

The wave lengths of light rays are not measured in yards, feet or inches, but by a very small unit of measurement known as the Angstrom Unit, which is about four billionths of an inch. This unit is not one of intensity or amount, but is a measurement of the wave length; and the wave length determines the nature and effects of the radiation. The infra-red rays of the sun lie between 25000 and 8000 Angstrom units. The visible rays are between 8000 and 4000

Angstrom units in length. The ultra-violet rays are between 4000 and 3000 Angstrom units. The rays at 8000 Angstrom units have a red color; longer ones are invisible. Rays at 4000 Angstrom units are violet and shorter ones are invisible. Rays at 3000 Angstrom units are chemically active. They also excite a fluorescent effect on some minerals. They are called the "long" ultra-violet rays. The "short" ultra-violet rays are not found in sunlight which reaches the earth, but can be produced only from artificial sources such as the quartz lamps which emit short, energetic rays located at about 2500 Angstrom units. They form vitamin D, cause sunburn, kill bacteria and excite fluorescence in a wide range of minerals. It is this ability of short ultra-violet rays to create fluorescence which makes them so valuable in the mining industry.

There are several sources of ultra-violet radiations. The quartz lamp equipped with a special filter, which screens out the visible light and permits transmission of the short rays, the iron arc, the germicidal lamps, and some others.

Some prospectors have attempted to construct an ultra-violet lamp from an ordinary flashlight by using a special filter in front of the bulb. While this filter may be successful in screening out visible radiations, it does not produce the short waves necessary for the detection of certain important minerals. The result is the complete inability to fluoresce the minerals for which search is being made. The long ultra-violet rays will not cause fluorescence of any mineral of commercial importance, except certain uranium ores, fluorite and petroleum.

Figure 27 shows the wave length range for the cold quartz, black light lamp. Inside the quartz tube there is a mixture of the rare gases argon, helium and neon. A small drop of mercury is also added. When the gas is ionized by an electric discharge, the mercury radiations at 2540 Angstrom units greatly predom-

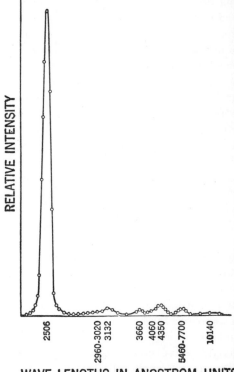

FIG. 27. Ultra-Violet Wave Length, Graph.

inate over all other wave lengths. Actually 89.8% of the total emission is located at this particular wave band. It is this high efficiency in the short ultra-violet wave length region which accounts for the ability of the quartz lamp to produce fluorescence of scheelite and other valuable ores. The Mazda lamp bulbs and many other sources do not produce ultra-violet wave lengths short enough to be effective for the fluorescent analysis of minerals. It is, therefore, easy to understand that even with the filter placed in front of such lamps the results are negative, since the filter does not generate the correct wave length but only screens out conflicting visible light. In general it may be said that a filter is only as good as the light source it is designed to be employed upon. Hence, a filter which passes short wave lengths is useless if the lamp to which it is attached does not create the short waves.

These are two long-wave bulb-type lamps which produce a flourescent effect on certain minerals. These are the Argon bulb and the so-called 50-hour black light lamp. The ultra-violet radiations from these are of the long wave length type which cause the fluorescence of a few minerals. The use of the home-made flashlight with filter or either of the bulbs is ineffective when searching for economic minerals. Those using these long wave lengths will find them of no value at all in the search for tungsten ore. Their value lies only in the fluorescence of such minerals as wernerite, dakeite, curtisite, a few semi-opals, calcites, some willemites, fluorite and hackmanite.

The wave lengths of the ultra-violet radiations emitted by the spark between iron electrodes lies between 4270 and 2100 Angstrom units. Scheelite will fluoresce brilliantly under light from this source, but for best results a filter is required to shut out the large amount of visible light.

FLUORESCENCE AND PHOSPHORESCENCE

Ultra-violet and other forms of light are ordinarily thought of as a continuous stream of energy. The undulatory characteristic, which the mind usually associates with light, has another attribute which must be considered before a true explanation of fluorescence can be developed. This other property is the real connecting link between all forms of light energy and the manner in which atoms capture or absorb, and give out or emit energy. It is known that light energy can be absorbed or emitted only in small though discrete packets called quanta; not, however, as a continuous and unbroken stream of light waves, as is commonly believed. These packets, or quanta, exhibit the properties of a wave, hence the convenient method of measuring them by their wave length.

All minerals, like all other matter, are composed of atoms, each of which consists of a core with one or more electrons revolving about it, as in a miniature solar system. The electrons are particles having a negative charge. The core or nucleus, which is made up of one or more heavier particles, has a positive charge. Ultra-violet quanta entering this atom strike in some instances the cloud of electrons, and the packets of light energy are taken up by the individual electrons. Those which take up this energy of the light quanta have their total energy content increased and jump outward from their normal orbits. Usually they remain away for only a minute fraction of a second and then release their excess, previously captured energy and return to their normal state.

The act of capturing quanta of light energy by electrons is called excitation. In this case the ultra-violet light is the excitant. The act of releasing quanta is called luminescence, or light emission. When the release of packets of energy occurs immediately after they have been taken up or absorbed, the luminescence is known as fluorescence. In fluorescence, the glow or light emission takes place only as long as the ultra-violet light is on the mineral and ceases as soon as the lamp is shut off. If the electrons have taken up much energy and have been driven completely away from the parent atom, they may wander about for considerable periods of time before dropping into the normal orbit of some atom, not necessarily their own, and may in addition be subject to a number of other influences peculiar to the matter itself. Wandering electrons, however, eventually drop back into their normal energy state, releasing energy as light. This is called phosphorescence, for it is a light release which goes on for some time after the ultra-violet light has been removed.

The cause of fluorescence in many minerals is due to some impurity. For instance, most forms of calcite do not fluoresce, but if a small amount of manganese is present it will serve as an activator and cause the calcite to fluoresce red. The hue and brilliance of the color will vary with the percentage of the manganese present. The calcite from Franklin, New Jersey will fluoresce red when amounts of manganese are present, varying from 1 to 5%, with 3.5% giving the most brilliant result. More or less does not act as an activator and there is no decided fluorescence. Uranium salts in various rocks will have the effect of an activator, but in such cases the fluorescence will be green or yellow-green.

There are many instances where it is difficult to determine the cause of mineral fluorescence. Not all activators have been identified. In some cases the fluorescence may be due to a variable molecular arrangement or peculiar crystallinity. The entire subject of mineral fluorescence is so new that in only a few cases are the reasons for the response to ultra-violet light fully understood. A mineral may be listed as fluorescent, while actually the fluorescent part may be only a coating of a fluorescent nature, or a responsive mineral may be present as a mixture or disseminated inclusions through the mass. Mineral species from one locality may fluoresce, while identical ones from another locality may not. Variations may also appear in minerals from the same locality. General characteristics, however, usually remain the same.

PROSPECTING AND MINING

Scheelite, *Ore of Tungsten.* As scheelite may vary considerably in color, and may be white, gray, yellow, green, orange, reddish or brown, in ordinary white

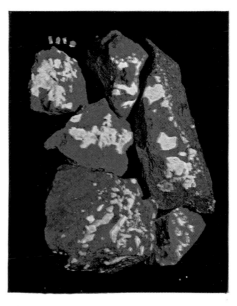

Overlooked in ore examined under ordinary light, crystals of valuable scheelite . . .

PLATE 8

fluoresce clearly, distinctly and brilliantly under ultra-violet rays.

PLATE 9

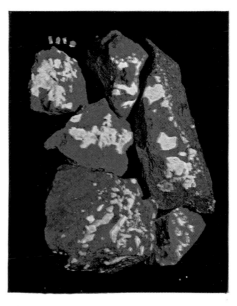

Crystals of calcium tungstate. Yellow indicates impurities. (California and Nevada.)

PLATE 10

These rocks illustrate large Scheelite crystal formations in characteristic colors. (Montana, Idaho, California.)

PLATE 11

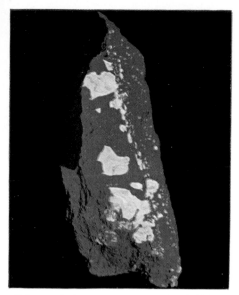

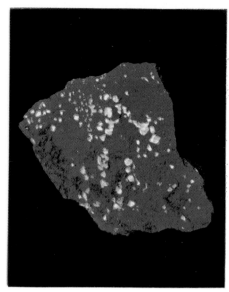

Color variations may appear in individual crystals of Scheelite as illustrated below. (Drum Valley, California.)

PLATE 12

Excellent example of large blue-white Scheelite crystals. (Little McGee Creek, Bishop, California.)

PLATE 13

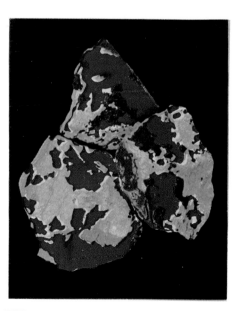

This specimen shows the most common appearance of Scheelite — small, evenly disseminated crystals. (Nevada.)

PLATE 14

Willemite — green fluorescence and calcite — red fluorescence. (Franklin, New Jersey.)

PLATE 15

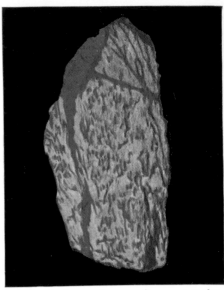

A valuable sample containing Willemite (zinc silicate) — green and calcite — red. (Franklin, N. J.)

PLATE 16

Typical specimen of wernerite — a complex silicate rock. (Ontario, Canada.)

PLATE 17

Calcite sample, which "glows like live coals of fire." (Arizona.)

PLATE 18

light it is very difficult to distinguish from certain gangue minerals such as quartz, epidote, carbonates and some lime silicates. Under the influence of the shorter wave lengths of ultra-violet light all scheelite will fluoresce. Without the help of the ultra-violet lamp it is extremely difficult to locate because of the wide variety of rock in which it occurs. This is illustrated in plates 8 and 9. Ordinarily it is found close to a limestone-granite contact, but because it is so similar in appearance to the rock in which it may be found every type of ore should be carefully examined with a lamp.

The fluorescent colors which indicate the presence of scheelite are blue, blue-white, cream and golden yellow, as shown in plates 10, 11, and 12. The pure form fluoresces a bright blue, plate 13. The crystals are hard and the edges well defined. The appearance of the ore in daylight may be white or orange-gray, but the blue-white color under ultra-violet light indicates the lack of impurities.

Scheelite usually forms in small crystals disseminated through the rock. These vary in size from that of a pin head to a silver dollar. Sometimes it forms in solid veins, stringers or chunks, but the small disseminated spots are the most common, as shown in plate 14. Some types fluoresce a white color. This ore contains a very small amount of molybdenum, and if the fluorescent areas are hard and well defined the ore can usually be considered of good commercial quality. If the crystals are soft and can be powdered with the fingernail, it usually indicates a high percentage of lime and the assay for tungsten will probably be low.

The golden yellow fluorescence is a definite indication of some impurity. Usually this is molybdenum, but it may be copper (cupro-scheelite), iron, manganese or other elements. The combination of calcium tungstate and calcium molybdate is most frequently found. This ore contains Powellite and may or may not have commercial value. If calcium tungstate predominates, the crystals will be hard, with well defined edges and apparent depth. If the fluorescent spots smear upon rubbing or powder under the pressure of the thumb nail or are more of a coating than well defined crystals, it is likely that the amount of tungsten present is small or lacking. All scheelite which fluoresces yellow should be checked by assay much more carefully than that which is blue or blue-white. A great many profitable mines are operating on golden yellow scheelite because the amount of the impurity is small, but the yellow color does indicate an impurity which must be carefully checked and analyzed before development of the property.

The U. S. Geological Survey has developed a scheelite fluorescence analyzer card by which it is possible to determine the percentage of molybdenum on a comparative basis with known samples. This card, Fig. 28, provides a simple and relatively accurate means of making this determination. They are manufactured and sold under a licensing agreement.

Occasionally a form of calcium carbonate will fluoresce a blue-white and resemble scheelite closely, but it is usually pale and does not have the same luster. It is often in the form of a coating, has the appearance of a fine-grained substance and lacks crystal structure. Sometimes it is phosphorescent and this definitely proves it cannot be scheelite. In a few rare cases calcium carbonate has a golden yellow color which is similar to some scheelite, but in these cases it is soft and smears upon rubbing.

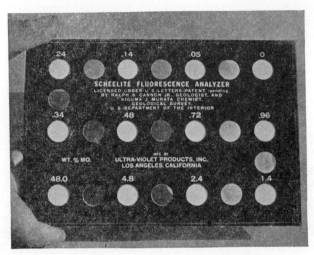

Fig. 28. Scheelite Fluorescence Analyzer Card.

The filter on the ultra-violet lamps passes a very small amount of blue-purple light. This is reflected from the rock that is being examined and will be a dark purple or blue that varies according to the natural color of the rock. A white one will reflect blue; a dark one will reflect purple. This reflection should not be confused with fluorescence. Scheelite never fluoresces green, red or pink. Also it has no apparent phosphorescence; fluorescence disappears instantly when the ultra-violet light is turned off.

Other Valuable Ores and Minerals. Another valuable ore which fluoresces is hydrozincite. This is frequently associated with smithsonite. It always fluoresces a soft blue but can easily be distinguished from scheelite as it is a soft, lightweight mineral, and the fluorescent ore is usually, but not always, in the form of a coating.

Black sand very often contains small bright orange fluorescent grains. These are zircon. They are a brighter orange than scheelite and usually appear as grains, so are easily distinguishable. Zircon is one of the most frequently overlooked of all fluorescent values. It is rather easy to distinguish because of its weight and orange fluorescence. Whenever found it can be confirmed by chemical tests and its value should be carefully checked by assay.

In a number of mining properties that are being worked for gold, silver, etc., it has been found that there is a fluorescent hyalite associated with the valuable ore. The hyalite itself is not of commercial value, but because of its association with the values in these particular properties the miners have found the lamp of very great assistance in enabling them to stay on the vein where the non-fluorescent but valuable ores are located.

In some properties it is advisable to use the fluorescent lamps which produce the long wave lengths as well as those giving the short ones. There are fluorite deposits which respond to either of these wave lengths, and in such cases the fluorescent analysis of the ore has proven very profitable, as by the use of these two types of ultra-violet light differentiation is obtained.

SORTING ORES

The sorting lamp is suspended over a conveyor belt in a darkened room, Fig. 29. By means of the fluorescence the ores are easily sorted so that only those of a pre-determined value reach the mill. Waste rock and pieces with a high amount of impurities are discarded. The ultra-violet light is of value at scheelite mines and in sorting willemite, zircon, hydrozincite, tremolite and steatite talc.

FIG. 29. Sorting Ore.

BLACK LIGHT FOR MINERALOGISTS AND COLLECTORS

The most vivid and beautiful fluorescent minerals in the world are the willemite and calcite rocks of New Jersey, shown in plates 15 and 16.

Willemite is a zinc silicate and has a bright green fluorescence. It is mined extensively for its zinc content. The calcite is frequently a gorgeous red. These brilliant colors are unsurpassed for beauty and their most beautiful shades are brought out fully by the quartz ultra-violet lamps. Another mineral which fluoresces beautifully is wernerite, shown in plate 17.

The most frequent fluorescent response found in mountains and deserts of the United States is green. The green glow may be bright or dull. Usually it is in seams or as a coating and is generally a hyalite opal, chalcedony or altered quartz, or a calcite that is stained with a small amount of a uranium salt. None of these rock have a commercial value and may be passed over when searching for valuable ores.

Many forms of calcite fluoresce. The colors are usually orange or red, some bright, some pale in color. Plate 18 illustrates the brilliant red fluorescence of the Arizona calcite, which is a mixture of calcite and a manganese salt and "glows like live coals of fire." A few calcites fluoresce blue. Many will phosphoresce and hold their glow for a considerable time after the ultra-violet light has been turned off. In one or two rare instances they have resembled scheelite, but by a careful examination for crystal structure and hardness the difference can usually be determined. If there is doubt, chemical tests and an assay are always advisable.

Fluorescent microscopy offers inviting and worthwhile results in many fields of research. New applications for the short ultra-violet rays are opening up in the study of micro-crystals, mineral slabs and polished surfaces of all sorts. An entire new field in chemical microscopy is opened when ultra-violet examination is used. Many specific crystalline substances upon which identification is based in microchemical reactions are fluorescent or react characteristically in ultra-violet light.

Testing for Mercury. The presence of extremely small amounts of mercury in cinnabar or other ore can very easily be determined with the short ultra-violet rays, a willemite screen, and small flame for heating the substance to be tested.

The willemite screen is made by grinding pure willemite to a very fine powder and painting it on a wooden board by means of a suitable binder. The result is a surface which is very sensitive to the short ultra-violet wave lengths, Fig. 30.

The quartz lamp is practically a monochromatic source of ultra-violet light. This radiation is the wave length of 2540 Angstrom units, called "mercury resonance radiation." Willemite is particularly sensitive to this wave length and fluoresces brilliantly under its action.

The simple directions for testing for mercury are as follows:

1. The sample of rock to be tested should be in small pieces or ground.

2. Place these half way between the ultra-violet lamp and the willemite screen. (The space between each should be three or four inches.)

3. Heat the ore over a flame. An alcohol or gas flame is suitable in the laboratory. In the field a blowtorch is best, but in many cases a candle or stove will suffice.

As the sample is heated, the mercury will be driven off as an invisible vapor. This vapor, however, completely absorbs the ultra-violet rays creating dark shadows on the otherwise brilliantly fluorescent willemite screen. Very small quantities of mercury will completely absorb the rays and cause dense shadows. The appearance is that of black clouds of billowing smoke similar to that from

Fig. 30. Willemite Screen.

a heavy oil fire. If ordinary smoke passes in front of the screen it is visible to the eye and casts only a slight shadow, as ultra-violet light will partially pass through it. The mercury vapor cannot be seen and the shadow is very dark.

Since very small quantities of mercury vapor will completely absorb the rays and cause dense shadows on the screen, the test is not reliable for quantitative work. Many operators, however, have worked out relationships between ore samples and the volume of shadows so that for these particular mines they can approximate the different percentages in the ore. This can come only from experience. The test is so sensitive that quantities as small as 1/1000th of 1% of mercury can be detected. This method is reliable, for no other vapor absorbs ultra-violet rays as effectively as mercury vapor under comparable conditions.

Examination of ore in place can be carried out by using a blowtorch and willemite screen. The blowtorch generates enough heat to vaporize the mercury and the screen will show the shadows. Many tunnels, as well as outcrops, have been tested by this method. Use should be made of the high degree of sensitivity of this test to determine leaks in retorts and milling equipment.

In many cases the leaks may not be of commercial importance. However, as mercury vapor is quite poisonous, they can all be found and, if serious, the proper steps instituted to correct them.

Ultra-Violet Rays in Bead Tests. Most of the rare earths and many elements of high atomic order produce fluorescence of a comparatively high degree of brightness in inert bases, even in exceedingly small amounts. This is especially true of uranium salts. As little as 0.001 microgram of some elements is detectable by their fluorescence. The spectroscope is needed for the fullest appreciation of such a test. Manganese, chromium, nickel and some other elements may exert an activating effect on many compounds and the fluorescence produced contains characteristic bands which can lead to identification of small amounts of these salts.

In bead testing certain elements may suppress the fluorescence and others may promote it. As little as 0.2 parts per million of nickel in zinc-sulfide-copper-phosphor reduces the emission characteristics appreciably. Copper is universally present as an activator in zinc sulfide. Thulium in sodium fluoride has a yellow fluorescence, while in calcium oxide it has a slightly different fluorescent response. Europium in Salt of Phosphorus beads fluoresces a deep red. The presence of uranium salts causes the bead to fluoresce a strong vivid lemon-yellow. This is particularly true of the sodium or potassium fluoride beads on a platinum wire. Borax bead tests can also be used but are not as satisfactory as with the fluorides.

Fluorescent Minerals

The use of the short wave quartz ultra-violet "black light" lamp will cause fluorescence or phosphorescence in the following minerals. In some cases the activating factor has been identified, but in many it is still unknown.

Agate: Widely distributed, but specimens from only a few localities fluoresce. The activator in the green fluorescent specimens is probably some uranium salt.

Albite: The kaolinized form found at Crestmore, California, fluoresces a bright green.

Alunite: That from Marysville, Utah, has a grayish white fluorescence. This is probably due to an activator of some kind which is peculiar to this locality, as alunite from other districts does not fluoresce.

Amazonstone: Specimens from New York and Virginia show a pale grayish-green fluorescence, but specimens from other districts fail to react.

Amber: Amber in lignite from Texas fluoresces yellow and a specimen from Prussia is yellow-green.

Amethyst: Usually does not fluoresce, but specimens from North Carolina and Madagascar fluoresce a deep blue.

Anglesite: From Black Hills, South Dakota, and Leadhills, Scotland, fluoresces yellow.

Anorthoclase: From Franklin, N. J., fluoresces blue.

Apatite: Is usually non-fluorescent, but specimens from certain localities respond (yellow to orange).

Aragonite: Like calcite, is widely distributed and has a wide variety of fluorescent responses. (Greenish, bluish-white or yellow). The colors are undoubtedly due to the type of impurity or activator present.

Autunite: Has a very strong yellowish green flourescence. Autunite is often seen as yellow coatings on granite pegmatites which carry uranium bearing minerals.

Axinite: From Franklin, N. J., fluoresces red.

Barite: Has a better phosphorescence than fluorescence. Should be examined in a thoroughly darkened room. The afterglow is usually pale bluish green. Samples from Palos Verdes, California, have a yellowish white fluorescence and phosphorescence, while specimens from England have only a bluish green phosphorescence.

Bauxite: From Nadine, Georgia, has a whitish phosphorescence which is probably due to some special activator peculiar to the locality, as most other specimens fail to react.

Benitoite: These crystals are found in only one locality in the world. This is an isolated section of San Benito County, California. They are blue, but the short ultra-violet rays cause a deep and brilliant blue fluorescence that is very distinctive.

Beryl: Cannot be classed as a fluorescent ore. A few cases have been reported where there were varying shades of green fluorescence, but these are not fully corroborated. The fluorescence may be due to some impurity disseminated throughout the mineral.

Borax: Often has a greenish blue phosphorescence though very rarely fluorescent.

Calcite: One of the most spectacular and widely distributed of all fluorescent minerals. Not all fluoresce by any means, but certain impurities and activators cause almost every possible shade of fluorescent color. The calcites of New Jersey have a brilliant red color with a transitory deep red phosphorescence. Those from Texas are pink and blue and phosphoresce blue. A great variety of colors characterize the California calcites as well as those from most of the Western States. In some instances their appearance is very similar to scheelite but it is never as brilliant as scheelite, and usually the granular appearance distinguishes it from the more crystalline structure of the latter. There is a wide variation in the color responses of calcite.

Calcium Larsenite: A rare mineral from Franklin, N. J., fluoresces a bright yellow.

Calamine: That from Superior, Arizona, fluoresces a cream color.

Celestite: From Clay Center, Ohio, has a blue-white phosphorescence, while specimens from Gembeck, Germany, have a definite blue color.

Chalcedony: Is fluorescent only when an activator is present. This is usually a trace of some uranium salt which gives a green fluorescence.

Clinohedrite: From Franklin, N. J., has an orange and yellow fluorescence.

Colemanite: From the Calico Hills and Death Valley regions of California, fluoresces white and phosphoresces blue-white.

Copalite: From Zanzibar, fluoresces green.

Crocoite: From Dundas, Tasmania, and the Ural Mountains of Russia, fluoresces a dark brown.

Cupro-Scheelite: Usually fluoresces a yellow with a faint tinge of green. It is a calcium tungstate with copper present and is usually quite hard. Cupro-scheelite from Milford, Utah, and Plumas County, Calif., fluoresces yellow.

Curtisite: Appears in the seams in the quicksilver mines at Skaggs Springs, Calif. The fluorescence is a very bright yellow, cream and green.

Daketite: The correct mineralogical name is Schroekingerite, but it is more readily known to collectors by the former name. It is a hydrated uranium, calcium carbonate which fluoresces a strong yellow-green. A large deposit is located near Wamsutter, Wyoming, and a small one in Europe.

Diamond: Less than 15% of those tested shows fluorescence. The cause of fluorescence is unknown and definitely has no relation to the quality of the crystal. They may be pale blue, pale green, orange or reddish, and these fluorescent colors are probably due to the presence of a very minute amount of some hydrocarbon. Diamonds from Brazil display a higher percentage of fluorescence.

Diaspore: From Chester, Mass., fluoresces pale yellow.

Dolomite: From several localities, has a fluorescent response which is probably due to a hydrocarbon or metallic impurity, giving it an orange, cream or blue color.

Dumortierite: From San Diego County, Calif., and Oreana, Nevada, fluoresces purple.

Elaterite: From Utah, has a brown phosphorescence.

Emeralds: Usually do not fluoresce, but a few stones from Muzo, Columbia, Minas Geraes, Brazil, and Emerald Mines, Ural Mountains, Russia, show a pale fluorescence.

Epsomite: From Death Valley, Calif., has a pale blue phosphorescence.

Fluorite: The first fluorescent mineral studied; gave its name to the whole subject. It is not particularly fluorescent under the short rays, although the brown variety from Clay Center, Ohio, fluoresces a cream yellow and from Cumberland, England, it fluoresces bright blue. From other localities there is a wide variation in the response, most specimens being more vivid under the long wave lengths.

94

Glauberite: From Borax Lake, Calif., phosphoresces bluish gray.

Gypsum: From the saline lakes of the desert regions of Southwestern United States, has marked green fluorescence due to some type of activator. From the Grand Rapids, Michigan, area it shows a deep green. From most other areas there is a lack of fluorescence.

Gyrolite: From Bohemia, fluoresces and phosphoresces white.

Hackmanite: From Dungannon Township, Ontario, Canada, fluoresces a reddish purple with the short ultra-violet wave lengths and a brilliant orange with the long ones. This mineral has the peculiar property known as reversible photosensitivity. It is dull gray in ordinary light but after exposure to the short ultra-violet wave lengths the mineral changes color to a deep purple. On exposure to sunlight this purple color fades away and the mineral regains its original color. No other mineral will change its actual color on exposure to ultra-violet light.

Halite: The dry lake at Amboy, Calif., contains a halite that has a beautiful red fluorescence. Some fluorescent material has precipitated from solution along with the halite and causes it to fluoresce these brilliant red shades. Halite from a dry lake in San Diego County, Calif., gives the same reaction as that from Amboy.

Hanksite: From Searles Lake, Calif., phosphoresces a light blue.

Hexagonite: From Edwards, N. Y., fluoresces red.

Howlite: From Lang, Calif., fluoresces brown and yellow.

Hyalite Opal: Is so closely associated with opal that it is described under that heading.

Hydromagnesite: From Lodi, N. J., phosphoresces a light blue.

Hydrozincite: All true hydrozincites floresce a strong blue, but in a few cases this may fade to a cream color with certain impurities. The mineral has a comparatively light weight and is soft and powdery.

Inyoite: From Death Valley, Calif., phosphoresces a pale white.

Kunzite: (Pink spodumene.) From near Pala, Calif., fluoresces a pale yellow to strong reddish brown. It frequently phosphoresces for long periods of time.

Lepidolite: From Keystone, South Dakota, fluoresces a pale green.

Mangan-Apatite: From Strickland Quarry, Portland, Conn., and also from Grafton Center, N. H., fluoresces a beautiful creamy golden color; from St. Mary's Lake, B. C., and Valyermo, Calif., it fluoresces a bright orange similar to wernerite, but lighter in color.

Mercury: Is not fluorescent, but its presence is readily determined with the quartz ultra-violet lamp and a willemite screen as previously described.

Meyerhofferite: From Death Valley, Calif., phosphoresces a yellow-white.

Nasonite: From Franklin, N. J., fluoresces blue.

Opal: The green fluorescent hyalite opal is probably the most common fluorescent mineral found in the United States and Canada. It is usually colorless or white in ordinary light and fluoresces various shades of green under the short ultra-violet light. It is generally found in cleavages and crevices. It sometimes is seen as green spots scattered through granite, lime and other types of rock. The response of hyalite opal is usually due to a slight trace of some uranium salt. This explains why the common opal from some localities fluoresces and others do not. The best hyalite opal for display purposes comes from Stone Mountain, Georgia, and from various Mexican localities. Less spectacular specimens are found in almost every mine in the country. The best common opal comes from Virgin Valley, Nevada, and some beautiful pieces of opalized wood come from Goldfield, Nevada.

Ozocerite: From Brazil and Persia, fluoresces a yellow-brown.

Pearls: Often fluoresce, but the fluorescence has no apparent relationship to their value. Artificial pearls as a rule do not respond, only the native and cultured ones. The activator is manganese.

Pectolite: Has only a slight fluorescence but a very striking phosphorescence. Specimens from Paterson, N. J., Magnet Cove, Ark., and Lake County, Calif., show bright splashes of orange, yellow and green.

Petroleum: Most petroleums show a fluorescent response. Oils from different strata have different shades of color and the color varies with the gravity. Petroleum products, such as kerosene, paraffin, vaseline, medical ointments and lubricating oils, also fluoresce.

Phosgenite: From Monte Poni, Sardinia, has a brownish red or orange phosphorescence.

Powellite: The U. S. Bureau of Mines and Geological Survey state that the term "Powellite" shall be given to the mineral calcium molybdate and to the double salts calcium molybdate and calcium tungstate as long as the amount of calcium tungstate does not exceed the amount of the molybdate. The division point between powellite and scheelite, therefore, is the 50-50 point of tungsten and molybdenum. Powellite fluoresces yellow, usually is soft and powdery. Often it appears as a film over the face of crystals of other molybdenum minerals. It is frequently associated with scheelite and sometimes mistaken for it. Powellite is yellow to greenish yellow under ultra-violet light.

Priceite: From Death Valley, Calif., fluoresces yellowish.

Quartz: Usually does not fluoresce, but quartz tubing made from Brazilian quartz has a white phosphorescence. Smoky quartz sometimes shows a brownish yellow response, but the average quartz is negative, except in the cases of the varieties of chalcedony and agate already mentioned.

Rubellite: (Pink Tourmaline.) From Pala, Calif., and Newry, Maine, fluoresces lavender.

Ruby: (Red Corundum.) Varies in fluorescent quality. Specimens from Siam give a weak red, and those from Burma and North Carolina a strong red glow. Synthetic rubies are much more brilliant in their fluorescence than the natural ones.

Sassolite: From Tuscana, Italy, fluoresces blue.

Satin Spar: (Silky Gypsum.) May fluoresce due to the presence of an activator. This will vary in districts as well as in specimens. The usual fluorescence and phosphorescence is bluish green.

Scapolite: Is more commonly known as wernerite. For further description see Wernerite.

Scheelite: (Calcium tungstate.) is an ore of tungsten, a metal used in hardening steel for innumerable purposes. Scheelite flouresces a bright vivid blue. It may appear as small crystals scattered through a matrix or as large massive chunks and even as vein material varying in thickness from a knife blade to several feet. The pure scheelite that fluoresces blue is hard and frequently has definite structural lines. The mineral varies in color due to the impurities, which are usually varying amounts of molybdenum, 0.05% of which changes the color to a faint blue; 0.48 gives a white fluorescence, and from 0.96 to 4.8% gives an increasingly yellow appearance. Amounts of molybdenum above 4.8% do not cause an appreciable variation in the color of the fluorescence.

The presence of molybdenum in the scheelite has a tendency to soften it. Scheelite that fluoresces yellow will be hard if the amount of molybdenum is low, but if the percentage is high it will be soft, crumble easily and powder under the pressure of the fingernail.

All scheelite fluoresces blue, white or golden yellow. It is never red or green and has no apparent phosphorescence.

The other ores of tungsten do not fluoresce. Wolframite very often has scheelite associated with it as a coating around the wolframite or along cleavage lines.

Selenite: (Clear crystallized gypsum.) Usually has a better phosphorescence than fluorescence. An activator is present as an impurity and causes the color which varies as to the locality and specimen.

Sapphire: (Blue corundum.) Frequently has a yellow-orange to red fluorescence. This is true of both the natural and synthetic stones, especially of the colorless varieties.

Sodalite: From Moultonboro, N. H., fluoresces orange-red.

Sphalerite: From Tsumeb, Africa, has a bright orange fluorescence and phosphorescence. This type is also found at Medford, Utah and Bisbee, Ariz. The presence of Wurtzite is thought to be responsible for the fluorescence of sphalerite.

Spinel: The red variety has a bright red fluorescence. Other shades of the mineral usually do not respond. The red spinel from Ceylon usually gives a vivid color.

Spodumene: From Portland, Conn., sometimes phosphoresces a deep red which is quite persistent.

Strontianite: From California, Germany and England, has a slight bluish-green fluorescence and phosphorescence.

Terlinguaite: From Terlingua, Texas, fluoresces yellow.

Thaumasite: From Paterson, N. J., phosphoresces white.

Topaz: Does not usually react, but a few specimens have shown fluorescence. Specimens from Schneckenstein, Germany, give a slight green color.

Trona: From Searles Lake, Calif., fluoresces blue and phosphoresces a light blue.

Tourmaline: Only the light yellow shades exhibit fluorescence and these in only a slight degree.

Uranium Salts and **Minerals:** Uranium is responsible for the fluorescence of a great many minerals. The characteristic color produced by uranium salts is a lemon yellow or light green. It is probably the salts of this element, acting as activators, which cause the fluorescence of most hyalite opals, many forms of chalcedony and some calcites.

The following list of the better known uranium minerals show practically identical fluorescent qualities. They are all secondary uraninites with little or no commercial value but may appear as a coating on more valuable ores, and this may be used in locating and mining the other ores.

MINERAL	FLUORESCENCE
Autunite.	Yellow-green.
Beta-Uranopilite.	Yellow-green.
Beta-Uranotil.	Yellowish.
Chalcolite.	Yellow-green.
Gummite (variable).	Violet.
Johannite (variable).	Yellow-green.
Meta-Torbernite.	Yellowish-blue
Schroeckingerite (dakeite).	Green.
Torbernite.	Yellow-green.
Uranocircite.	Yellow-green.
Uraniferous hyalite.	Yellow-green.
Uranophane.	Yellow-green
Uranopilite.	Yellow-green.
Uranospathite.	Yellow-green.
Uranothallite.	Green.
Uranotil.	Yellowish.
Zippeite.	Yellowish.

Wavellite: From Mt. Holly, Pa., has a blue fluorescence and phosphorescence.

Wernerite: Has a bright yellow fluorescence. It is popular specimen material.

Willemite: Is one of the brightest and most spectacular of all fluorescent minerals. It is one of the many zinc ores mined in New Jersey. Willemite fluoresces because of the presence of manganese which serves as an activator; when this impurity is absent it does not react. Various amounts of the activating material create different shades of green. Some specimens also phosphoresce brilliantly.

Witherite: From Hexam, England, fluoresces yellow; but from Cave in Rock, Ill., the fluorescence is white.

Wollastonite: Is occasionally responsive to the short ultra-violet rays. This is due to an activator. The ore from quarries near Riverside, Calif., has a beautiful blue-green fluorescence and golden-yellow phosphorescence. Specimens from Pennsylvania and Alaska show the same response. Franklin, N. J., speci-mens fluoresce bright orange.

Zippeite: A mineral formed by the alteration of pitchblende. Gives a strong yellowish-green fluorescence.

Zircon: Is variable in its response to ultra-violet rays. It is found in the black placer sands of California, Oregon, and Idaho, as small, clear crystals which fluoresce a bright orange. Samples of sand from Montana, North Carolina, Wyoming and Ontario, Canada, also show the presence of zircon crystals. Specimens from Brazil have shown the same bright orange color. The effect is believed to be due to the presence of the rare element hafnium.

THE GEIGER COUNTER

The Geiger-Mueller counter, usually referred to as the Geiger counter, is an instrument which responds to and measures the intensity of nuclear radiations (Fig. 30A). Geiger tubes are made in a variety of shapes and sizes, but they all consist essentially of a tube filled with a gas which yields positive and negative ions when irradiated. The tube wall is the cathode or negative electrode, and a wire suspended in the center of the tube is the anode or positive electrode. An electric potential is maintained between these terminals. As long as the gas in the chamber is un-ionized there is no discharge. When, however, rays from a radioactive source pass through the chamber, some of the atoms of gas are ionized into positive and negative ions. These at once migrate to the electrodes where they give up their electric charge. This disturbs the balance of the cell and causes a current to flow between the cathode and anode. This flow is recorded by the instrument as flashes of a lamp, by a scale reading, or by clicks in earphones, and since each ray causes a separate discharge, the reading of the scale or the number of clicks and flashes is a measure of the radiations which enter the Geiger tube.

The radiations are of three principal types: namely, alpha, beta, and gamma rays. The **alpha** particles have a low penetrating power; a few sheets of paper will stop them and they can travel but a few inches through the air. The **beta** particles have more penetrating ability; a sheet of aluminum $\frac{1}{8}''$ thick is required to stop them and they can travel about 12 feet through the air. The

gamma rays have much greater penetrating power; they can travel several miles through the air and will penetrate several feet of concrete or other dense

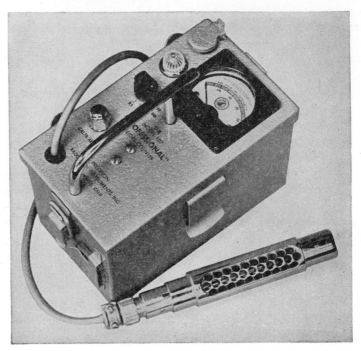

FIG. 30A.   Portable Geiger Counter.
(Courtesy Precision Radiation Instruments)

material. *Cosmic* rays should also be mentioned, as they are always present and affect the Geiger counter. These are rays from the stars and outer space and have tremendous power, being able to penetrate several miles into the earth even after traveling many millions and probably billions of miles. None of these radiations can be seen, felt, heard, or tasted. The human body cannot sense them in any way.

Whenever a counter is in operation, the cosmic rays cause it to click or flash with no radioactive substance near it. The number of clicks per minute is known as the "background" count and this must be taken into consideration in any work. As the cosmic rays vary in intensity from time to time and also from place to place, the "background" count must be determined every hour or so if one is prospecting.

In using the Geiger counter for prospecting, the geigerman must first determine the "background" count for the locality. Then prospecting is carried out by slowly and systematically covering the area, pausing occasionally to check the count and holding the probe as near the ground or rock as convenient, say within a foot or two. The distance from the source of radiation has a pronounced effect on the response of the counter. For example, if a net count (the count exclusive of the "background" count) of 100 were obtained with the probe 1 foot from the source, the net count would be only about one fourth as many, or 25, if the distance were increased to 2 feet. The intensity of radiation varies inversely as the square of the distance.

In order to be detectable, most ores must be on the surface, for a very rich vein would probably be overlooked if covered by 3 or 4 feet of overburden, and low grade ores can be concealed by a few inches of soil. For this reason, bare rock surfaces such as mountain sides, road cuts, quarries and mines are excellent for prospecting. Pegmatites often have small amounts of radioactive minerals in them.

In using the Geiger counter for mineral identification the same general principles apply. If a mineral containing uranium or thorium is brought near a counter, an increase in the count rate is observed. There are no means of determining whether the emanations are from thorium or uranium, but this can be ascertained by the bead tests, or by chemical means. In general, uranium is the more active of the two.

The approximate percentage content of uranium or thorium may be determined by comparison of the unknown sample with one of known content under controlled conditions. The conditions are that the known and unknown samples must contain only one of the elements, be of the same size, and be tested at the same distance from the probe or sensitive tube of the counter. As equal amounts of the elements should give practically the same amount of radiation, a comparison of the net count from the two pieces under the above conditions should give an idea of the amount of the element present. For instance, if the unknown uranium sample gave only half the net count of the known sample, it could be assumed that the uranium content was half that of the standard sample. However, this is at best only a rough estimate and ores should be assayed for accurate results.

While uranium in small amounts causes marked fluorescence in many minerals, the rich ores—such as uraninite, pitchblende, and carnotite and the rare earth minerals, euxenite, samarskite, and furgusonite—do not respond to the ultra-violet light. The Geiger counter is a valuable diagnostic tool and, in combination with the ultra-violet light, is a great aid in the determinaton of many minerals. If a fluorescent or radioactive mineral is found, it is always well to run chemical tests and, if the indications from these are promising, have the sample assayed.

All uranium minerals affect the Geiger counter, but a number of them do not have a uniform response to ultra-violet light, as some specimens of a mineral fluoresce, while others do not. A list of those which ordinarily respond is given on page 98. The following list gives the more common uranium- and thorium-bearing minerals which do not usually show fluorescence.

Betafite	Microlite	Thorite
Brannerite	Monazite	Thorianite
Carnotite	Pitchblende	Tyuyamunite
Euxenite	Pyrochlore	Uraninite
Fergusonite	Samarskite	Uranothorite

CHAPTER V
Mineral Chemistry

Some elements occur in the earth's crust in much greater amounts than others. Oxygen is the most abundant, composing 46.46% of all rocks. Silicon is next, with 27.61%. Since silicates contain both of these elements, we can naturally expect the great majority of the minerals to be silicates. Aluminum, 8.07%, and iron, 5.06%, are the most plentiful of the metallic elements and since the silicate radical is acid in character and iron and aluminum are basic, the result is that the great majority of silicates contain iron or aluminum, or both. Next in abundance comes calcium, 3.64%; sodium, 2.75%; potassium, 2.58%; magnesium, 2.07%; titanium, 0.62% and hydrogen, 0.14%. These 10 elements comprise 99% of all the minerals and rocks of the earth's crust. As there are 98 chemical elements, this means that the other 88 (some not of natural occurrence) comprise only 1% of the rocks and minerals.

There are only a few naturally occurring acids which form compounds stable enough to persist for any length of time, so that, in general, minerals consist of a relatively few classes, most of which are listed below.

Classes of Minerals

Silicates: As pointed out above, silicates are the most abundant of all rock forming minerals and are encountered almost everywhere. The great majority contains the more plentiful metals mentioned above, but silicates of all but a few of the metals exist in nature and with the combinations possible it is easily realized that the number and forms of this type of mineral must be very great. According to Clarke, *Data of Geochemistry,* silica, SiO_2, comprises about 60.0% of the earth's crust.

Carbonates: These come next in abundance, carbon dioxide, CO_2, comprising about 0.70% of the lithosphere. As with silica, the great majority of it is combined with the most plentiful metals, of which calcium and magnesium are the most common and abundant. Great masses of limestone and dolomite are found at many places on the earth.

Sulfides: This class of compounds differs from the two above in that few of the very abundant elements form stable compounds with sulfur. Iron is the only exception. The great majority of the metallic ore minerals such as galena and sphalerite belong to this class.

Oxides: This class of minerals consists of a combination of a metal with oxygen. Many of the ore minerals are of this nature. Iron in the form of hematite, magnetite and limonite are good examples.

Halides: Halides are those minerals in which the metal is combined with chlorine, bromine, iodine, or fluorine. The chloride is the most common and abundant and is best represented by sodium chloride (halite) which is very common, especially in arid regions.

Sulfo Compounds, Sulfates, and **Phosphates:** These are compounds encountered quite frequently in nature, with **chromates, vanadates, tungstates, titanates,** etc., representing relatively few minerals. There are, of course, other rare compounds and combinations, but the great majority of the minerals fall into one of these classes.

Elements: A few of the elements occur uncombined, especially those known as the noble metals, gold, silver, platinum, etc. Others, however, not of this class, are also found in the free state as, for instance, sulfur.

CHEMICAL FORMULA

The **chemical formula** of a substance can be determined from the chemical analysis. Thus, if one knows the percentage composition, he will be able to write the formula. This is best illustrated by examples. We will assume that a substance has been analyzed and found to contain 63.52% of iron and 36.48% of sulfur. The next step is to find how many symbol weights of each element are present. This is done by dividing the percent of iron by the atomic weight of iron, which is 55.84; thus: $63.52/55.84 = 1.137$. The same is done with sulfur, with the result that: $36.48/32.06 = 1.137$. By dividing the answers obtained by the lowest one we get the number of each symbol or atomic weights represented in the compound. In the above example it is 1 in both, so the atoms of the elements are in the ration of 1 to 1, and the formula is FeS.

Another example is as follows. Chemical analysis gave: 27.09% Na, 16.50% N and 56.41% O. By dividing these results by their respective atomic weights we get: $27.09/23.00 = 1.175$, $16.50/14.00 = 1.175$, and: $56.41/16.00 = 3.526$. Dividing these results by the lowest number we get: $1.175/1.175 = 1$; $1.175/1.175 = 1$; $3.526/1.175 = 3$. Thus it is seen that there is 1 atom of sodium, 1 of nitrogen and 3 of oxygen, so the formula must be $NaNO_3$. These numbers do not always come out exact integers, due to the inaccuracies of the analysis, but they are close enough so there is no doubt of the number of atoms of each element present.

The **percentage composition** of a substance may be determined by reversing the above process. If, for instance, we wish to know the theoretical percentage of copper in chalcopyrite we proceed as follows. The chemical formula is $CuFeS_2$, which means that there is 1 atomic weight of copper, 1 of iron and 2 of sulfur in each molecule. Referring to the table of chemical elements we find that the atomic weight of copper is 63.57, of iron 55.84, and of sulfur 32.06. Adding these together in the proportion they exist in the molecule we have:

$$1 \times 63.57 = 63.57$$
$$1 \times 55.84 = 55.84$$
$$2 \times 32.06 = 64.12$$
$$\text{Weight of molecule} = 183.53$$

Dividing the weight of copper by the weight of the entire molecule and multiplying the result by 100 we get the percent of copper, thus: $63.57/183.53 = .3463 \times 100 = 34.63\%$ copper.

REAGENTS FOR QUALITATIVE CHEMICAL ANALYSIS AND BLOWPIPING

A number of the chemicals listed are for special tests and are not necessary for a field kit. The term *dry reagent* means it can be carried as a solid.

Acetic Acid, $HC_2H_3O_2$: purchased in the concentrated state and diluted as required, 1 volume to $2\frac{1}{2}$ volumes of water.

Acetone, CH_3COCH_3: used as purchased.

Alcohol, C_2H_5OH: 95% ethyl alcohol.

Alkacid Test Paper: This test paper enables the analyst to determine not only whether the solution is alkaline or acid but also the degree of each by the different colors formed. Strongly alkaline is blue, weakly alkaline is green, *very* strongly acid is red, medium acidity is orange and weakly acid is lemon. To test a solution, place a drop on a piece of alkacid paper with a glass rod and note the color produced.

Ammonium Acetate, $NH_4C_2H_3O_2$: use a saturated solution.

Ammonium Carbonate, $(NH_4)_2CO_3$, (ordinary smelling salts): dry reagent, dissolve 20 grams in 35 ml of conc NH_4OH and dilute to 100 ml with water.

Ammonium Chloride, NH_4Cl (salammoniac): dry reagent, dissolve 27 grams in 100 ml of water.

Ammonium Hydroxide, NH_4OH: purchased in the concentrated state and diluted as required, 1 volume to 2 of water.

Ammonium Molybdate, $(NH_4)_2MoO_4$, reagent: mix 10 grams of MoO_3 with 40 ml of distilled water and 8 ml of conc NH_4OH. When solution is complete, pour slowly with constant stirring into a mixture of 40 ml of conc HNO_3 and 60 ml of water. Let stand in a warm place for several days. Decant or filter before using.

Ammonium Oxalate, $(NH_4)_2C_2O_4 \cdot 2H_2O$: dry reagent, dissolve 4 grams in 100 ml of water (saturated solution).

Ammonium Phosphate, $(NH_4)_2HPO_4$: dissolve 5 grams in 100 ml of water.

Ammonium Phosphomolybdate Paper: made by impregnating filter paper with the phosphomolybdic acid reagent, holding over the ammonia bottle for a time, drying and cutting into strips. The paper will keep well in a stoppered bottle in the dark.

Ammonium Sulfide, (Light) $(NH_4)_2S$: saturate 60 ml of conc NH_4OH with H_2S gas and dilute to 100 ml with conc NH_4OH.

Ammonium Sulfide [(yellow) also known as (dark)], $(NH_4)_2S_x$: dissolve 5 to 7 grams of sulfur in 100 ml of the colorless ammonium sulfide.

Ammonium Sulfocyanate (Thiocyanate), NH_4SCN: dry reagent, dissolve 4 grams in 100 ml of water.

Ammonium Tartrate, $(NH_4)_2C_4H_4O_6$: 20% solution, dissolve 16 grams of tartaric acid in water, make alkaline with NH_4OH, boil to remove the excess NH_4OH and make up to 100 ml with water. Used in testing for scandium.

Aqua Regia: make as required by mixing 3 volumes of conc HCl and 1 volume of conc HNO_3.

Barium Chloride, $BaCl_2 \cdot 2H_2O$: dry reagent, dissolve 6 grams in 100 ml of water.

Barium Hydroxide, $Ba(OH)_2 \cdot 8H_2O$: dry reagent, dissolve 6 grams in 100 ml of water.

Benzidine Reagent: dissolve 0.05 grams of benzidine base or hydrochloride in 10 ml of conc acetic acid, dilute with water to 100 ml and filter.

Bismuth Flux: same as iodide flux.

Bone ash: ground, calcined bones, used in making cupels for gold and silver assaying.

Borax, $Na_2B_4O_7 \cdot 10H_2O$: dry reagent, used for fusions and bead tests.

Borax Glass: made by fusing borax in an iron crucible and grinding. Used in assaying.

Boric Acid, H_3BO_3: use a saturated solution.

Boric Acid Flux: made by grinding together 4 parts, by weight, of $KHSO_4$ and 1 part of CaF_2.

Bromide Flux: Grind together 1 part by weight of KBr, 1 part of $KHSO_4$ and 2 parts of sulfur.

Bromine, Br_2: Used for making HBr. Handle with care. Very corrosive and causes bad burns.

Cacotheline, $C_{21}H_{21}N_7O_3$: dry reagent, use a freshly made saturated water solution.

Calcium Carbonate, $CaCO_3$: use the precipitated form. Sodium group test.

Calcium Hydroxide, (slaked lime), $Ca(OH)_2$: dry reagent. Use a saturated solution.

Carbon Disulfide, CS_2: used as a sulfur solvent.

Chlorine Water: made by dropping conc HCl on potassium permanganate $(KMnO_4)$ crystals and passing the resultant chlorine gas through water to saturation.

Chromate Flux: grind together 1 part by weight of K_2CrO_4, 1 part of $KHSO_4$ and 2 parts of sulfur.

Cobalt Nitrate, $Co(NO_3)_2 \cdot 6H_2O$: dry reagent. Dissolve 7 grams in 100 ml of water. Used in charcoal and plaster tests.

Cupric Oxide (copper oxide), CuO: dry reagent, powdered malachite will serve instead.

Di-ammonium Phosphate: see ammonium phosphate.

Dimethylgloxime: dissolve 1 gram in 100 ml of ethyl alcohol.

Di-sodium Phosphate: see sodium acid (Di-sodium) phosphate.

Ferric Chloride, $FeCl_3 \cdot 6H_2O$: dissolve 1 gram in 100 ml of water.

Ferrous Sulfate (copperas) $FeSO_4 \cdot 7H_2O$: dry reagent, use a saturated solution. Add a few scraps of metallic iron and a few drops of sulfuric acid from time to time.

Hydrobromic Acid, HBr: made by passing H_2S through a water solution of bromine till the red color of the bromine disappears.

Hydrochloric Acid, HCl: purchased in the concentrated state and diluted as required, 2 volumes to 3 of water.

Hydrofluoric Acid, HF: in ceresin bottles. Difficult to carry as it dissolves glass and dangerous as it attacks the flesh causing bad burns and sores that heal slowly.

Hydroiodic Acid, HI: made by passing H_2S through water containing iodine crystals till they disappear.

Hydrogen Peroxide, H_2O_2: use the 3% solution as purchased.

Hydrogen Sulfide. H_2S; The charge for dry H_2S generators can be made by grinding together 1 part by weight each of rosin, sulfur and shredded asbestos. A generator is made of a Pyrex test tube fitted with a delivery tube. To operate, lightly pack the tube about ½ full of the charge and heat gently. Evolution of the gas ceases when the heating is stopped and the delivery tube must be withdrawn at once from the liquid being treated else it may be drawn into the apparatus thus breaking it. Dry charges and liquid H_2S generators may be purchased from chemical supply houses.

Hydrogen Sulfide Water: this may be made by passing H_2S through water to saturation. It should be kept in a tightly stoppered bottle. Used for drop tests where only a small amount of H_2S is required.

Iodide Flux: made by grinding together 1 part by weight of KI, 1 part of $KHSO_4$ and 2 parts of sulfur.

Iodine, I_2: crystals, used in making HI and alcoholic iodine.

Iodine, Alcoholic: dissolve 5 grams of iodine in 100 ml of ethyl alcohol.

Lead Acetate, $Pb(C_2H_3O_2)_2 \cdot 3H_2O$: dry reagent, dissolve 10 grams in 100 ml of water.

Lead Acetate Paper: made by moistening strips of filter paper in the lead acetate solution and drying. Keep in a stoppered bottle. Used for the detection of H_2S which turns it brown to black.

Lithium fluoride, LiF: dry reagent, for fluorescent bead tests.

Magnesium Ribbon, Mg: a handy form of metallic magnesium.

Manganese Dioxide, MnO_2: dry reagent.

Mercury (metallic), Hg: used in amalgamation tests.

Nitric Acid, HNO_3: purchased in the concentrated state and diluted as required, 1 volume to 2 of water.

Oxalic Acid, $H_2C_2O_4 \cdot 2H_2O$: dry reagent, use a saturated solution.

Paraffin: ordinary para wax that is used for sealing fruit jars.

Phosphomolybdic Acid: dissolve 1 gram of phosphomolybdic acid in 100 ml of water.

Potassium Bicarbonate, $KHCO_3$: dry reagent.

Potassium-Bismuth Iodide Reagent: heat to boiling 1 gram of Bi_2O_3 and 5 grams of KI in 5 ml of water and add this a little at a time to 25 ml of glacial acetic acid.

Potassium Bisulfate (Potassium Acid Sulfate), $KHSO_4$: dry reagent.

Potassium Chlorate, $KClO_3$: dry reagent.

Potassium Chloride, KCl: dry reagent.

Potassium Chromate, K_2CrO_4 or **Potassium Dichromate,** $K_2Cr_2O_7$: dry reagent, dissolve 5 grams in 100 ml of water.

Potassium Cyanide, KCN: dry reagent, dissolve 5 grams in 100 ml of water. *Very poisonous.*

Potassium Ferricyanide-Lead Acetate Reagent: mix 10 ml of a saturated solution of potassium ferricyanide with 10 ml of a saturated solution of lead acetate and filter.

Potassium Ferrocyanide, $K_4Fe(CN)_6$: solid reagent, use a saturated solution.

Potassium Hydroxide, KOH: solid reagent, dissolve 28 grams in 100 ml of water.

Potassium Iodate, Reagent: dissolve 10 grams of KIO_3 in a mixture of 33 ml of conc HNO_3 and 66 ml of water.

Potassium Iodide, KI: dry reagent, dissolve 8 grams in 100 ml of water.

Potassium Nitrate, KNO_3: solid reagent.

Potassium Nitrite, KNO_2: solid reagent.

Potassium Permanganate, $KMnO_4$: solid reagent, used in producing chlorine gas.

Potassium Thiocyanate (Potassium Sulfocyanate), KSCN: dissolve 10 grams in 100 ml of water.

Quinalizarine: use a saturated solution in ethyl alcohol (0.020 grams in 100 ml).

Salt of Phosphorous (Microcosmic Salt), $HNaNH_4PO_4 \cdot 4H_2O$: solid reagent used in bead tests.

Silver Nitrate, $AgNO_3$: dissolve 4 grams in 100 ml of water. Keep in a dark colored bottle.

Slaked Lime (Calcium Hydroxide), $Ca(OH)_2$: dry reagent.

Sodium Acid (Di-sodium) Phosphate, $Na_2HPO_4 \cdot 12H_2O$: dry reagent, dissolve 6 grams in 100 ml of water.

Sodium Carbonate, Na_2CO_3, or **Bicarbonate** (baking soda) $NaHCO_3$: both referred to as "Soda"; used for fusion and bead tests.

Sodium Chloride (common salt), $NaCl$: dry reagent, used in assaying and bead tests.

Sodium Fluoride, NaF: dry reagent, for fluorescent bead tests.

Sodium Hydroxide (ordinary lye), $NaOH$: dissolve 20 grams in 100 ml of water.

Sodium Hypochlorite, $NaOCl$: made by passing chlorine gas through a solution of sodium hydroxide.

Sodium Meta-Phosphate, $NaPO_3$: dry reagent.

Sodium Peroxide, Na_2O_2: dry reagent; keep in a tightly sealed can.

Sodium Phosphate, see sodium acid (Di-sodium) phosphate.

Sodium Sulfate, Na_2SO_4: dry reagent.

Sodium Sulfide Reagent, $Na_2S—Na_2S_2$: made by dissolving 48 grams of $Na_2S \cdot 9H_2O$ and 4 grams of $NaOH$ in water, adding 1.6 grams of sulfur, shaking till the sulfur is dissolved and diluting to 100 ml with water.

Sodium Sulfite, Na_2SO_3: dry reagent.

Sodium Thiosulfate, $Na_2S_2O_3 \cdot 5H_2O$ (ordinary photographers "hypo"): dry reagent. Dissolve 12.4 grams in 100 ml of water. Also for bead tests.

Stannous Chloride, $SnCl_2$: dissolve 11.5 grams of $SnCl_2 \cdot 2H_2O$ in 17 ml of conc HCl and make to 100 ml with water. Keep in bottles containing a strip of metallic tin.

Starch Paper: make by moistening strips of filter paper in starch boiled in water.

Sulfur, S: finely ground or flowers of sulfur; dry reagent.

Sulfur Dioxide, SO_2: prepared by dropping a mixture of 1 part conc H_2SO_4 and 3 parts water into a concentrated solution of Na_2SO_3.

Sulfuric Acid, H_2SO_4: purchased in the concentrated state and diluted as required, 1 volume to 6 of water. In making this dilution pour the *acid into the water* and not vice versa.

Tannic Acid, $C_{12}H_{10}O_9$, dry reagent, use a freshly made solution.

Tartaric Acid, $H_2C_4H_4O_6$: dissolve 50 grams in water and make up to 100 ml.

Test Lead, Pb: pure granulated or filings. Used in assaying.

Tin, Sn: pure granulated, or tin foil will serve. Used as a reducing agent.

Turmeric Paper: Used in testing for boron and zirconium.

Zinc, Zn: pure granulated, or the metal parts of flashlight batteries will serve. Reducing agent.

CONCENTRATED REAGENTS

	SP. GR.	PER CENT BY WEIGHT	APPROXIMATE CONCENTRATION
Acetic acid, glacial	1.06	99.5	17 N
Acetic acid	1.07	80.0	15 N
Hydrochloric acid	1.19	37.9	12 N
Nitric Acid	1.42	69.8	16 N
Phosphoric acid	1.7	85.0	15 N
Sulfuric acid	1.85	96.0	36 N
Ammonium hydroxide	0.90	28.0	15 N

APPARATUS

The list below contains a number of items that are convenient but not absolutely essential. If a field kit is being prepared, the larger and less important pieces may be omitted.

Anvil: a small block of steel, 2″ x 2″ x 1″, for breaking samples.

Asbestos Thread: a piece from asbestos string or rope packing will serve.

Beakers: a nest of 100 ml down to 5 ml is very convenient.

Bunsen Burner: if gas is available; a **Candle** or an **Alcohol Lamp** will serve.

Charcoal Slabs: these come in sizes of 4″ x 1″ x ¾″ and 4″ x 2″ x 1″.

Color Screen (Merwin): can be used instead of the Smith Flame Analyzer.

Filter Paper: to fit the funnels.

Filter Stand: if working in a laboratory.

Flask: about 250 ml, fitted with a 2 hole rubber stopper; for a wash bottle.

Flame Analyzer (Smith): can be used instead of the Merwin Color Screen.

Forceps: a platinum tipped and another cheap iron pair are needed.

Funnels: 2 short-stemmed, about 1½″ in diameter.

Glass Rod: several pieces about 6″ long and 3/16″ in diameter.

Glass Tubing: a piece of hard glass 5/16″ in diameter for open tube tests, and a piece of ⅛″ diameter soft glass for making the wash bottle, H_2S generator, etc.

Graduated Cylinders: 1—50 ml and 1—10 ml.

Hammer: a small one for breaking samples.

Iron Spoon: with ¾″ diameter bowl for making fusions which would damage platinum.

Iron Wire: about 24-26 gauge can be used instead of platinum for flame color tests.

Lens: one of about 1″ to ¾″ focal length and a magnification of about 15 diameters, gives good results.

Magnet: or magnetized knife-blade.

Measure: 1 ml: This is quite handy and can be made by measuring 1 ml of water into a ⅜″ diameter test tube, cutting off at the top of the water and mounting as illustrated on page 71.

Mortar and Pestle.

Plaster Tablets: made by making a paste of Plaster-of-Paris with water, smoothing it out on glass in a layer about ¼″ thick and cutting it into 4″ x 1″ pieces before it hardens.

Platinum Foil: a thin piece about 1″ x 1″ is a convenient size.

Platinum Wire: about 27 gauge and 3″ long. This is fused into a piece of glass tubing or rod and is used for making bead tests.

Porcelain, or better, **Silica Dish:** about 2″ in diameter.

Ring Stand: if working in a laboratory.

Sampler: see gold-silver assay, page 70.

Spot Plate: of white glazed porcelain.

Streak Plate: a piece of unglazed porcelain will serve.

Test Tubes: about six 3″ x ⅜″ for general use and one 6″ x ⅝″, fitted with a one-hole rubber stopper, for an H_2S generator.

Test Tube Holder or **Clamp:** for holding test tubes over the flame. Ordinary spring clip clothespins do very well.

Test Tube Rack: can be made by boring holes in a block of wood and cutting away a portion of the front so the tubes can be seen.

Tongs, Crucible: of steel or brass.

Triangle: nichrone, about 1¼″ across.

Watch Glasses: 3 or 4 about 2″ in diameter; old spectacle lenses will serve very well.

Wire Gauze: about 4″ x 4″.

CHARCOAL STICKS

The charcoal blocks purchased from chemical supply houses are consumed quite rapidly but may be made to give much longer life by soaking them in sal soda (ordinary washing soda, $Na_2CO_3 \cdot 10H_2O$). This leaves the sticks white, but, on heating, the soda soaks into the charcoal and does not interfere with the reactions. If these blocks of charcoal are not available, charcoal sticks may be made by taking a small splinter of wood, such as a match stick, soaking it in a melted crystal of sal soda and holding in the flame until the soda has penetrated the wood. A charcoal stick made in this way will give long service and most of the oxidizing and reducing reactions on charcoal can be carried out on it very satisfactorily.

THE PORTABLE LABORATORY

Those who wish to make mineral analyses where laboratory facilities are not available should have a carrying case in which most of the essential reagents and apparatus can be kept and transported. To assist in the construction of this, a set of detail drawings, Figs. 31–37, of a portable laboratory is given. The laboratory portrayed is quite convenient and has been found very satisfactory after several years of use. The general idea in its design is to have reagents and equipment available in a convenient form for complete tests. This does not mean, however, that everything one may use occasionally can be included, for no matter how large the kit is made there will always be something else that will be desired for some special purpose.

To those accustomed to reading construction blueprints, the drawings will be self-explanatory, but to others they may seem quite a puzzle. An endeavor will, therefore, be made to interpret them and to give advice and suggestions as to the best method of carrying on the work.

The blocks for the trays must first be built. This is done by glueing the boards together with the grain of each succeeding one running at right angles to its neighbor. This gives a block of wood that will not warp and has great strength. The drawings show these blocks built of basswood. However, if basswood is not available, a good grade of soft pine, free from knots, may be used. The covering of plywood gives an excellent finish to the blocks and also strengthens the outer edge. A waterproof or water-resistant glue, such as casein glue, should be used, and the glueing should be done with heavy pressure. Before starting to drill the holes, the glueing of the blocks for all the trays should be completed, except that the layer of *plywood on the bottom of #1 tray is not put on until after the drilling has been done.*

In laying out the holes, the figures inside the circles are used. These designate the distance of the center from the left side in the "X" direction and from the bottom in the "Y" direction. The center of hole "A" at the lower left-hand corner of tray #1 is $1\frac{9}{16}''$ from the bottom and also $1\frac{9}{16}''$ from the left side. The first line of "D" holes at the left of the drawing is $\frac{7}{8}''$ from the left side and the lowest one is $4\frac{1}{16}''$ from the bottom, the next $5\frac{3}{16}''$ from the bottom, etc. The row of "B" holes at the extreme right are $9\frac{1}{16}''$ from the left side of the drawing and the first one is $3\frac{5}{8}''$ from the bottom, the next $5\frac{3}{8}''$ from the bottom, etc.

The hole-centers are laid out on the bottom side of the block for the #1 tray, *the bottom layer of plywood having been left off.* The blocks for trays #2, #3 and #4 are complete with all plywood glued on. The block for tray #2 is placed upside down and the one for #1 tray is placed upside down on it. This puts the side with the hole layout on it facing upward. The two blocks are carefully lined up and firmly clamped together. Three or four of the "F" holes ($\frac{7}{16}''$) are drilled through both blocks until the point of the bit starts through the #2 block. They are then turned over and the holes finished from the opposite side. This procedure is used on all holes that pass completely through a block, as a smoother hole and less tearing of the wood results. Seven sixteenth inch dowels (rods of wood) are inserted through these holes and are used to keep

111

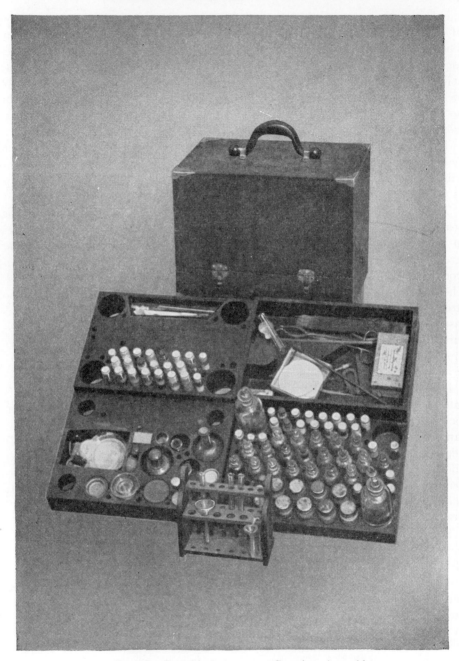

FIG. 31. Portable Laboratory, Complete Assembly.

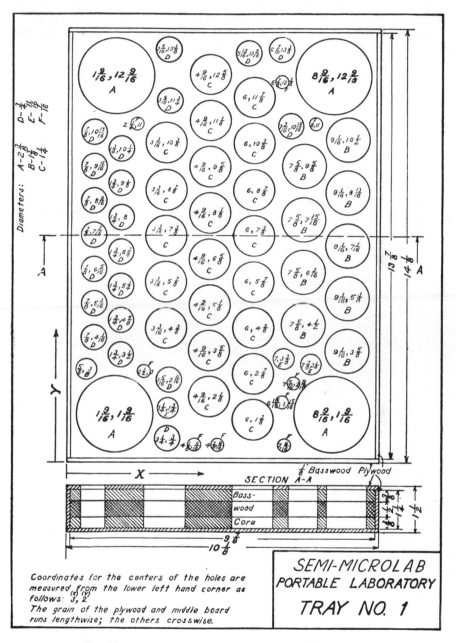

FIG. 32. Portable Laboratory, Drawing of Tray No. 1.

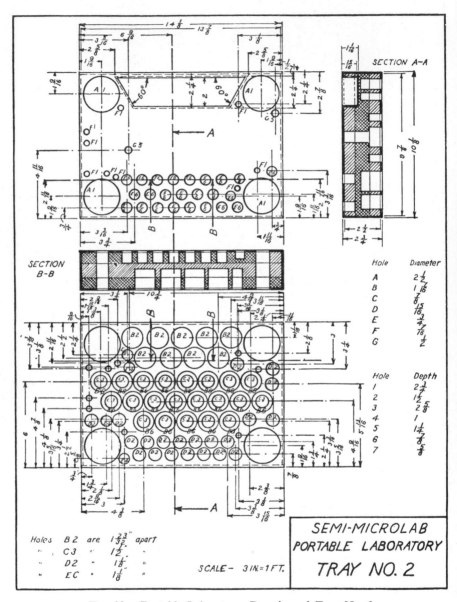

FIG. 33.   Portable Laboratory, Drawing of Tray No. 2.

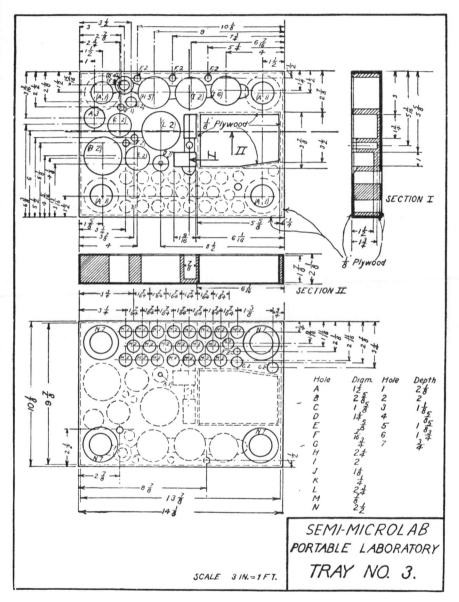

FIG. 34. Portable Laboratory, Drawing of Tray No. 3.

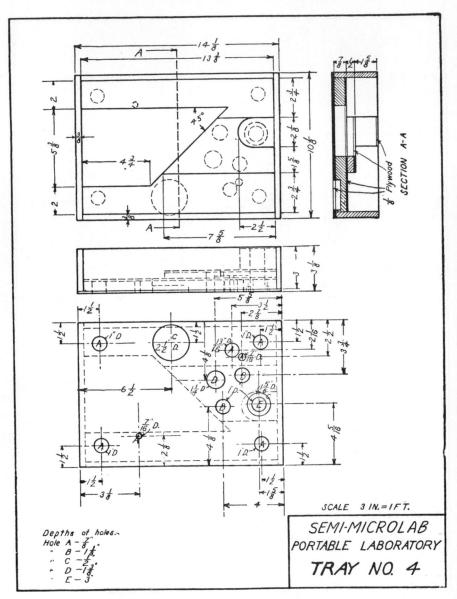

FIG. 35. Portable Laboratory, Drawing of Tray No. 4.

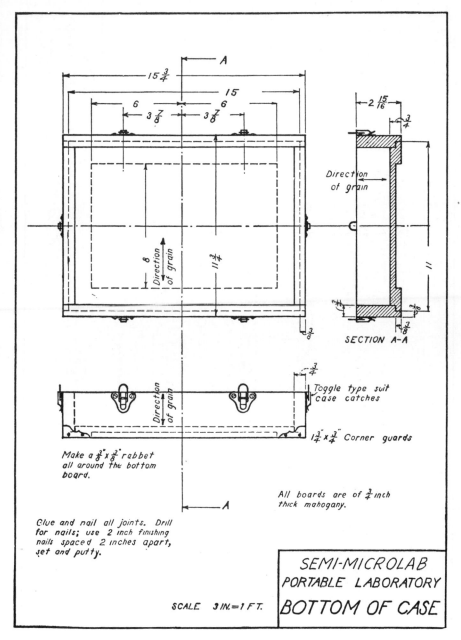

FIG. 36.   Portable Laboratory, Drawing of Bottom of Case.

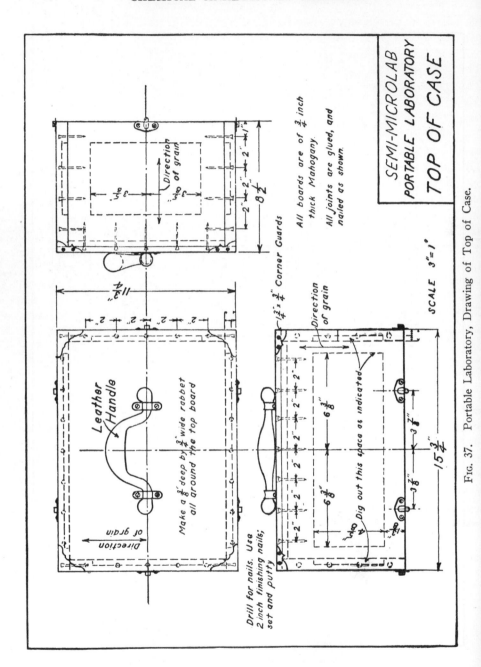

Fig. 37. Portable Laboratory, Drawing of Top of Case.

the blocks in line during the remainder of the drilling. The guide holes should pass through all four trays.

With the blocks lined up and the dowels in place, the holes can be bored. The diameter of the various holes, "A," "B," "C," etc. is given on the drawing. *The trays are designed to carry specific equipment, and as glass containers vary considerably in size it is best to have at least a few of each type at hand and to try for size, depth, etc. before boring the holes.*

The drilling is carried out as before, except that the bit is allowed to barely pass through the first block and to mark the hole-center on the block below. The holes are finished from the opposite side as directed above and are carried on into the second block as required. After all the holes in the #1 tray are completed, the bottom plywood, which forms the bottom of the tray may be glued on. In drilling the holes, a much better job can be done if a drill press is used, as it is very difficult to make perpendicular, parallel holes by hand.

The #2 tray has holes on the lower side, the centers of which exactly correspond to those in tray #1 and will be marked if the operations were carried out as outlined above. These are drilled to the depth designated in the drawing of tray #2. In the center of the sketch at the bottom of the drawing, which is a view of the underside of the tray, there are concentric circles, "C3" the inner one, and "B6" the outer one. The "B6" part is first drilled $1\frac{7}{16}''$ diameter and $\frac{7}{8}''$ deep, then continued with a $\frac{7}{8}''$ bit to a total depth of $2\frac{5}{8}''$. The other holes are bored the size and depth designated in the drawing. The upper sketch of the drawing of tray #2 gives the layout for the top of the tray.

In the drawing of tray #3 the lower sketch is of the bottom of the block and shows the extensions of the holes from the block below. The sketch above is of the top of the tray and shows, along with the hole arrangement, the box-like recess that is made by gouging and chiseling out the block. Tray #2 also has one of these, shown at the upper edge of the top sketch.

In the drawing of tray #4 the same scheme is carried out, the lower sketch portraying the bottom and the upper one the top view. In this tray most of the wood has been removed to give a box effect, it being left as indicated only where the equipment in the tray below extends up into the bottom of tray #4.

After all drilling and chiseling has been completed, all parts are thoroughly sanded and the blocks are ready for finishing, the first step of which is to make the wood as acid and chemical resistant as possible. A good acid resistant wood

SOLUTION #1	SOLUTION #2
125 grams of copper sulfate. 125 grams of potassium chlorate. 1000 milliliters of water.	150 grams of fresh aniline oil. 180 grams of concentrated hydrochloric acid. 1000 milliliters of water.

stain, in common use on wooden tops of laboratory tables, is made and applied as shown above.

To the clean, sanded wood apply two coats of #1 solution boiling hot, with a paint brush, allowing each coat to dry thoroughly. Then apply two coats of solution #2 in the same way. When the wood has completely dried, wash off the excess chemicals with hot soapsuds and again allow to dry. The blocks can then be finished by giving them several coats of linseed oil or lacquer. The carrying case is now built and finished in conventional manner.

As glass bottles and jars are to be carried, it is best to have a cushion effect on both the bottom and top of the liquid containers. Corrugated rubber matting, such as is commonly used in aisles and hallways, cut to fit, makes a very good pad for the bottom, and sponge rubber is excellent for the top of the glass stoppered bottles, for it can be made of such thickness as to keep the stoppers in place without fear of breakage.

The contents and location of the equipment of the Microlab, all on a small scale, are as follows:

Tray #1

HOLE	NUMBER OF ARTICLES	SIZE AND DESCRIPTION
A	4	8 oz glass stoppered bottles.
B	9	1 oz screw top bottles.
C	21	1 oz glass stoppered bottles.
D	21	4 dram vials.
E	4	2 dram vials.

Tray #2

E6	23	4 dram vials.

Tray #3

A1		Note that these are 2½″ in diameter for a depth of ⅞″ on the bottom of the block and 1½″ through the remainder of the block. They receive the top of the bottles in the "A" holes of tray #1.
A3	4	Porcelain crucibles, #00000, #000, #0 and 1 iron crucible, made of stainless steel, for fusions which cannot be made in porcelain (not a purchased item).
B2	1	125 ml flat bottomed flask for a wash bottle.
C2	2	25 ml Erlenmeyer flasks.
D7	1	Funnel 1″ top diameter. Note that the hole for this is the diameter of the top of the funnel only deep enough to receive it, the remainder of the hole being the size of the stem.
E2 & D4	1	Cupel mould as shown in the drawing under "Assay of Gold and Silver."
F2	6	Test tubes ⅜″ diameter by 3″ long. The tops of the holes should be widened enough to allow the flange of the tube to go down flush.
G2	1	Iron pestle to go with the mortar which goes into the rectangular opening at 1 (not a purchased item).
H5	1	3 oz tin sample cup to hold small filter paper.
I6	6	Low form Griffin beakers with lip. 5, 10, 20, 30, 50 & 100 ml. These beakers all fit one within another forming a "nest."
J6	1	Push top type can for sodium peroxide. A small paint or similar can may be used but should be well coated with paraffin in and out and kept tightly closed.
L2	1	2 oz alcohol lamp.

TRAY #4

This tray, as well as the box-like recesses in trays #2 and #3, is used to carry such miscellaneous equipment as Merwin screen, streak plate, small casserole, evaporating dishes, tweezers, crucible tongs, set of hardness minerals, larger filter papers, plumbers candle, plaster and charcoal slabs, and magnet.

The set is designed to use the ordinary glass stoppered bottles for liquids. Drops from these can be readily obtained by first loosening the stopper, grasping the body of the bottle in the hand and the stopper between the first and second finger. By tilting the bottle and working the stopper in and out with the fingers, drops are obtained as desired, using only the one hand. Regular dropping bottles may be obtained. Three or four of them for strong acids and ammonia are quite convenient and can be kept at the permanent place where most of the work is done.

The portable hydrogen sulfide generator gives good results and is used quite extensively. (Cartridges are supplied by chemical houses.) However, it is not quite as convenient as one using ferrous sulfide and hydrochloric acid in which the gas is always readily available. Hydrogen sulfide is used a great deal, and the liquid type generator should be used where most of the work is carried on. One may be devised, or the Kipp generator may be purchased from chemical supply houses. However, they are somewhat expensive, the smaller size costing about ten dollars.

A suggested list of reagents to be carried in the kit is given below.

IN THE EIGHT OUNCE BOTTLES

Distilled water.
Alcohol.
Hydrochloric acid (conc).
Ammonium hydroxide (conc).

IN THE ONE OUNCE SCREW TOP BOTTLES

Sodium carbonate.	Gold, silver flux.
Salt of phosphorous.	Borax glass.
Iodide flux.	Potassium bisulfate.
Bromide flux.	Ammonium chloride.
Chromate flux.	Borax.

IN THE TWENTY–ONE GLASS STOPPERED BOTTLES

Hydrochloric acid (conc).	Ammonium hydroxide (conc).
Nitric acid (conc).	Ammonium molybdate reagent.
Sulfuric acid (conc).	Ammonium oxalate reagent.
Acetic acid (conc).	Ammonium sulfide.

Ammonium sulfide (yellow).	Oxalic acid.
Barium chloride.	Potassium chromate.
Cobalt nitrate.	Potassium iodide.
Dimethylglyoxime.	Sodium hydroxide (use a rubber
Di-ammonium phosphate.	stopper).
Hydrogen peroxide.	Sodium sulfide reagent.
Lead acetate.	Silver nitrate.

In the 48 vials most of the other reagents can be carried in sufficient quantities for a great many analyses.

All glass stoppers should be coated with Vaseline or stop-cock grease; strong caustics such as sodium and potassium hydroxide solutions should be kept closed with a rubber stopper, as the glass is likely to stick. The top tray, and spaces in trays #2 and #3 provide ample room for all the remaining equipment. A one-half size specific gravity balance may be included if desired.

The containers may be labeled in a number of ways, but using the ordinary adhesive label is probably the simplest. If these are used it is necessary to protect them. They should be written on in India ink, pasted on, and after thoroughly drying, coated with melted paraffin, a saturated solution of paraffin in benzene, or a solution of ordinary tooth brush handles in acetone. If well protected, they are very satisfactory and give long service.

THE CHEMICAL ELEMENTS

September 1951

	Symbol	Atomic Number	Atomic Weight *		Symbol	Atomic Number	Atomic Weight *
Actinium	Ac	89	227	Neodymium	Nd	60	144.27
Aluminum	Al	13	26.98	Neon	Ne	10	20.183
Americium	Am	95	[241]	Neptunium	Np	93	[237]
Antimony	Sb	51	121.76	Nickel	Ni	28	58.69
Argon	A	18	39.944	Niobium			
Arsenic	As	33	74.91	(Columbium)	Nb	41	92.91
Astatine	At	85	[210]	Nitrogen	N	7	14.008
Barium	Ba	56	137.36	Osmium	Os	76	190.2
Berkelium	Bk	97	[243]	Oxygen	O	8	16.0000
Beryllium	Be	4	9.013	Palladium	Pd	46	106.7
Bismuth	Bi	83	209.00	Phosphorus	P	15	30.975
Boron	B	5	10.82	Platinum	Pt	78	195.23
Bromine	Br	35	79.916	Plutonium	Pu	94	[239]
Cadmium	Cd	48	112.41	Polonium	Po	84	210
Calcium	Ca	20	40.08	Potassium	K	19	39.100
Californium	Cf	98	[244]	Praseodymium	Pr	59	140.92
Carbon	C	6	12.010	Promethium	Pm	61	[147]
Cerium	Ce	58	140.13	Protactinium	Pa	91	231
Cesium	Cs	55	132.91	Radium	Ra	88	226.05
Chlorine	Cl	17	35.457	Radon	Rn	86	222
Chromium	Cr	24	52.01	Rhenium	Re	75	186.31
Cobalt	Co	27	58.94	Rhodium	Rh	45	102.91
Copper	Cu	29	63.54	Rubidium	Rb	37	85.48
Curium	Cm	96	[242]	Ruthenium	Ru	44	101.7
Dysprosium	Dy	66	162.46	Samarium	Sm	62	150.43
Erbium	Er	68	167.2	Scandium	Sc	21	44.96
Europium	Eu	63	152.0	Selenium	Se	34	78.96
Fluorine	F	9	19.00	Silicon	Si	14	28.09
Francium	Fr	87	[223]	Silver	Ag	47	107.880
Gadolinium	Gd	64	156.9	Sodium	Na	11	22.997
Gallium	Ga	31	69.72	Strontium	Sr	38	87.63
Germanium	Ge	32	72.60	Sulfur	S	16	32.066 †
Gold	Au	79	197.2	Tantalum	Ta	73	180.88
Hafnium	Hf	72	178.6	Technetium	Tc	43	[99]
Helium	He	2	4.003	Tellurium	Te	52	127.61
Holmium	Ho	67	164.94	Terbium	Tb	65	159.2
Hydrogen	H	1	1.0080	Thallium	Tl	81	204.39
Indium	In	49	114.76	Thorium	Th	90	232.12
Iodine	I	53	126.91	Thulium	Tm	69	169.4
Iridium	Ir	77	193.1	Tin	Sn	50	118.70
Iron	Fe	26	55.85	Titanium	Ti	22	47.90
Krypton	Kr	36	83.80	Tungsten			
Lanthanum	La	57	138.92	(Wolfram)	W	74	183.92
Lead	Pb	82	207.21	Uranium	U	92	238.07
Lithium	Li	3	6.940	Vanadium	V	23	50.95
Lutetium	Lu	71	174.99	Xenon	Xe	54	131.3
Magnesium	Mg	12	24.32	Ytterbium	Yb	70	173.04
Manganese	Mn	25	54.93	Yttrium	Y	39	88.92
Mercury	Hg	80	200.61	Zinc	Zn	30	65.38
Molybdenum	Mo	42	95.95	Zirconium	Zr	40	91.22

* A value given in brackets denotes the mass number of the most stable known isotope.

† The Atomic Weights Commission recommends that a range of ±0.003 be attached to the official value of 32.066.

CHAPTER VI
Tables of Chemical Reactions

It is often possible to make a few simple chemical tests that give indications as to the chemical nature of the mineral, thus greatly assisting in making the final identification. To simplify this procedure as much as possible, tables of a number of the more common minerals have been prepared. There are four of these tables, based on the solubility of the minerals in acids. These tables are intended for use in conjunction with the mineral identification tables as outlined below.

Table A includes those minerals which are partially or completely **soluble in hydrochloric acid.**

Table B includes those minerals which are not soluble in hydrochloric acid but **dissolve in nitric acid.**

Table C includes those minerals which are not soluble in hydrochloric or nitric acids but are at least partially decomposed and **dissolved by sulfuric acid.**

Table D includes minerals **not attacked by any of the common acids.** In order to make chemical tests on these, fusion with soda or potassium bisulfate is necessary.

The use of this method of grouping the minerals tends to throw substances of a similar nature together. In table A will be found the water soluble and most of the carbonate, phosphate, sulfate and borate minerals, and a great number of the less stable silicates. In Table B are the majority of the heavy metallic sulfides, while Tables C and D consist mostly of silicates.

After making the specific gravity and hardness determinations and referring to the mineral tables, it will be seen that the specimen can be one of only a few minerals. The chemical nature of these different possible minerals should be noted and kept in mind during the chemical testing that follows. All tests should be made on fresh, unweathered material.

Soluble in Hydrochloric Acid. A small amount of the finely ground mineral is placed in a test tube and a few drops of water added. If solution does not occur, add an equal amount of concentrated hydrochloric acid and boil if necessary. If still insoluble, double the volume by adding concentrated hydrochloric acid, and boil. If complete or partial solution is obtained by any of these treatments, the mineral belongs in Table A. Dilute the concentrated acid treatment with an equal volume of water, filter off any residue, and test the clear filtrate.

Soluble in Nitric Acid. If solution was not obtained in the treatment with hydrochloric acid, a fresh sample is treated in a test tube with concentrated nitric acid, boiled if necessary. Solution even with the deposition of a substance places the mineral in Table B. Dilute with twice its volume of water, filter off any residue or precipitate and make the tests on the clear filtrate.

Soluble in Sulfuric Acid. If the mineral was not dissolved by either the hydrochloric or nitric acid treatments a fresh sample is treated with concentrated sulfuric acid, boiled if necessary. Solution with the deposition of silica, or only partial decomposition, places the mineral in Table C.

Not Attacked by Acids. In this group are the minerals that are unaltered by treatment with the common acids. In order to test these for their chemical constituents they must be put into solution by means of fusions.

Fuse the finely ground mineral with four times its volume of soda on charcoal. Note any metallic beads formed, color and character of any sublimates, and color of the fusion. Dissolve the fusion in nitric acid, evaporate to dryness, moisten with concentrated nitric acid, add water, boil and filter. The silica is left behind on the filter paper and the metals pass through into the filtrate. This treatment will decompose the silicates, sulfides, chlorides and sulfates, converting the latter into sulfides. On treatment of the soda fusion with acid it will be seen if the mineral is still unaffected. If this is apparent it is probably one of the oxides, corundum, chromite, cassiterite, or bauxite, etc.

CHEMICAL TESTS

The few simple tests applied indicate the acid radicals and some of the common metals in groups, and are carried out as follows:

(Note any reaction during the process of solution. Carbonates effervesce; gases are given off by some manganese and sulfur compounds; certain elements give colored solutions, such as iron, copper, nickel, manganese, chromium, cobalt, vanadium and uranium.)

1. **Sodium Carbonate Bead Test.** Treat a speck of the mineral in the soda bead on the platinum loop with the oxidizing flame. Effervescence indicates a silicate; manganese will color it green; chromium colors it yellow. Crush the bead on a silver coin and moisten with water. A darkening of the coin indicates sulfide, selenide or telluride.

2. **Ammonium Molybdate Test.** Add 1 ml. of the solution to a mixture of 1 ml. of ammonium molybdate reagent and 1 ml. of concentrated nitric acid, and warm. A yellow precipitate indicates phosphate or arsenate.

3. **Barium Chloride Test.** Add a few drops of barium chloride solution to the acid solution of the mineral. A white, insoluble precipitate indicates sulfate. This test cannot be applied to Table C.

4. **Turmeric Paper Test.** Nearly neutralize the solution of the mineral with ammonium hydroxide, moisten a piece of turmeric paper in it and dry

carefully on a test tube of hot water. A reddish-brown color that turns blue to black when treated with ammonia, indicates borates. (Titanium, columbium, molybdenum, tantalum and zirconium also color it brown.)

5. **Hydrochloric Acid Test.** (a.) This test is applicable only to Tables B and D. Add a few drops of hydrochloric acid, or a little common table salt, to the nitric acid solution of the mineral. A white precipitate indicates silver, lead, or mercury. If the precipitate is silver it will be dissolved by making alkaline with ammonia; if lead, it will dissolve in hot water and recrystallize on cooling. Only monovalent mercury is precipitated by the above. The divalent form may be present but gives no indication here.

(b.) Boil some of the powdered mineral with concentrated hydrochloric acid in a porcelain dish and add a little zinc. Tungsten, titanium, columbium, vanadium, molybdenum, uranium and ruthenium give characteristic color reactions. For interpretations of the results, see **Reaction of Metallic Zinc in Acid Solutions, Chapter VI. III.** *Pg 76*

6. **Ammonium Hydroxide Test.** Add solid ammonium chloride equal to 1/10 of the volume of the test solution, then make alkaline with ammonium hydroxide, heat to boiling, and filter. Iron gives a brown, uranium a yellow, chromium a gray-green, mercury a black precipitate. Bismuth, titanium, zirconium, thorium, aluminum, beryllium, tin, lead, and antimony all give white precipitates. Molybdenum and vanadium may also be partially precipitated here.

Copper colors the filtrate blue, nickel is blue-green and cobalt is yellowish. A small amount of iron will color a white precipitate, thus obscuring that from aluminum, beryllium, etc. If it is desired to test for these elements, the precipitate is washed from the filter paper, dissolved in hydrochloric acid, made strongly alkaline with sodium hydroxide, boiled for a minute or two and filtered. Iron, chromium, mercury, bismuth, uranium, titanium, zirconium and thorium remain on the filter paper. Make the filtrate acid with hydrochloric acid, then alkaline with ammonium hydroxide. Aluminum, beryllium, tin, lead, and antimony are precipitated.

7. **Ammonium Oxalate Test.** To the clear filtrate from the treatment with ammonia add a little ammonium oxalate solution. A white precipitate indicates calcium, barium or strontium.

8. **Ammonium Phosphate Test.** To the clear filtrate from the ammonium oxalate test add a little di-ammonium phosphate. Magnesium and manganese are precipitated. That from magnesium is pure white, while the one from manganese is pinkish.

9. **Miscellaneous Tests.** The filtrate from the ammonium phosphate test will contain any sodium, potassium, lithium, and also copper, cobalt, nickel, molybdenum, vanadium, etc. By evaporating to dryness and heating carefully to drive off all volatile ammonia salts, flame and bead tests may be applied to this residue.

The operations listed above will give an excellent indication of the probable composition of the sample. If, however, on inspection of the possible minerals as obtained from the tables doubt still remains, such other tests as flame, bead, charcoal, and the complete analytical procedure should be applied.

These simple tests will in most cases enable the common minerals to be identified. Tests of only a few specific elements are obtained, but acid radicals and groups of elements are indicated, and as the physical properties of the various compounds of members of a chemical group have considerable variation, it is not difficult to determine which metal is present. Consider the following example: The sample has a specific gravity of 2.9 and a hardness of 3.5. Referring to the tables under this specific gravity and hardness, it is seen that of the common minerals it may be either margarite, ankerite, aragonite, dolomite or alunite. Treatment with hydrochloric acid gives complete solution with effervescence showing that it is carbonate, and so it must be either ankerite, aragonite or dolomite. It is a member of Table A. Tests with the soda bead, ammonium molybdate and turmeric paper are negative. On making alkaline with ammonia, a brown precipitate and colorless filtrate is obtained, showing the presence of iron. The addition of ammonium oxalate gives a white precipitate, indicating calcium, barium or strontium. As none of the possible minerals contain barium or strontium, the test indicates calcium. The addition of di-ammonium phosphate to this clear filtrate gives a precipitate indicating magnesium or manganese, but as none of the possible minerals contain manganese, the test indicates magnesium. It is therefore seen from these tests that the mineral contains calcium, magnesium, iron, and that it is a carbonate. It is evident that it is ankerite.

These few tests are for assistance in mineral identification and are not intended to take the place of a thorough chemical analysis. For a complete chemical test for impurities carried by a mineral (gold, silver, vanadium, etc.), and for testing for the rarer elements, the complete qualitative scheme should be followed.

It should always be kept in mind that the physical and chemical properties reported for a mineral are on the pure substance and that there are very often alterations and substitutions of one element for another. Iron may partially replace aluminum, aluminum replace iron, calcium partially replace magnesium or magnesium partially replace calcium and lead may partially replace antimony, or vice versa. It is very often the relative amounts of the various constituents which determine the mineral. *Proportions* of the various elements must therefore always be considered in arriving at the final result.

Spot Tests

A great deal of time can often be saved by making a few preliminary tests on the sample before beginning the routine qualitative analysis. Some of the blowpipe reactions may be applied and, after the mineral is in solution, spot or drop tests can be used to great advantage. Virtually all of the different specific reactions of the elements and many group tests can be carried out by using drops of the solution and reagents.

Drop tests are made on a glass slide or a piece of window glass which has been coated with paraffin, vaseline, or oil, then wiped off so as to leave a thin film which causes the drops to cling together and prevents them from spreading over the glass; or a spot plate may be used. This is a piece of white or black glazed porcelain containing a number of small depressions for holding the liquids. Spot tests are made on paper by placing the drops of solution and reagents on a piece of filterpaper or spot test paper.

In making a test by this method, a drop or two of the solution is placed on the slide or spot plate and a drop of the reagent placed near it. With a clean glass rod these are then brought together and the results observed, using a hand lens if necessary. Reactions giving white or light colored precipitates are best carried out on the black plate, while those which give dark or colored ones should be made on the white plate. If glass is used, white or black paper can be placed under it. Testing for a group before adding the reagent to the entire solution can easily be done this way. For instance, if a drop or two of the solution of the mineral is treated with a drop of dilute HCl and no precipitate forms, the silver group is absent and it is not necessary to treat the entire solution with HCl. The same procedure may be carried out with many of the other group tests.

The value of drop or spot tests is illustrated in the following table which requires only three drops of the solution of the unknown and the addition to each of these of a drop of a different reagent.

TABLE FOR DETERMINING SOME OF THE COMMON ELEMENTS BY DROP TESTS

Metal	Ammonium Carbonate	Ammonium Sulfide	Potassium Iodide
Aluminum	white	white	....
Antimony	white	orange-red (S)*	....
Arsenic	....	yellow (S)	red from hot solutions
Bismuth	white	dark brown	dark brown (S)
Cadmium	white	yellow to orange	....
Chromium	green	green	....
Cobalt	reddish or amethyst	black	....
Copper.................	green to blue	black	white changing to pink, green or reddish yellow
Ferric iron	brown	black	....
Ferrous..............	dirty white	black	....
Lead	white	black	bright yellow
Manganic manganese..	brown	brown to black	....
Manganous	white	flesh colored	....
Mercuric mercury	white	black	red (S)
Mercurous...........	black	black	olive green (pS)*
Nickel	apple green (S)	black	....
Silver.................	white (S)	black	curdy yellow
Tin	white	yellow to brown	....
Zinc	white (S)	white	....

(S) indicates that the precipitate formed is soluble in an excess of the reagent.
(pS)* means that it is partly soluble.

TABLE A. MINERALS PARTIALLY OR COMPLETELY

	Soluble with separation of	Gas evolved	SODIUM CARBONATE BEAD		Ammonium molybdate gives a yellow precipitate	Barium chloride gives a white precipitate	Turmeric paper turns brown on drying	AMMONIUM HYDROXIDE		Ammonium oxalate gives a white precipitate	Ammonium phosphate gives a white precipitate
			A silver coin is blackened	Effervesces during fusion				Color of precipitate	Color of filtrate		
1						x				x	x
2						x					
3						x					x
4						x		Wht			
5						x			Blue		
6						x					
7						x					x
8						x		Brwn			
9						x		Brwn			
10											
11											
12											x
13											
14											
15							x				
16							x			x	
17							x				
18							x				
19		CO_2									
20		CO_2									
21		CO_2									
22		CO_2								x	
23		CO_2							Blue		
24		CO_2						Brwn			
25		CO_2							Blue		
26		CO_2								x	
27		CO_2									x
28		CO_2							Blue		
29		CO_2									x
30		CO_2						Brwn		x	x
31		CO_2								x	x
32		CO_2								x	
33		CO_2								x	
34		CO_2									x
35		CO_2								x	
36		CO_2									
37		CO_2		x				Wht		x	
38		Cl_2						Brwn			x
39		Cl_2									x
40		Cl_2									x

DISSOLVED BY HYDROCHLORIC ACID

	NAME	COMPOSITION	REMARKS
1	Polyhalite	$K_2SO_4 \cdot CaSO_4 \cdot MgSO_4 \cdot 2H_2O$	Pt sol in water.
2	Thenardite	Na_2SO_4	Sol in water.
3	Kainite	$MgSO_4 \cdot KCl \cdot 3H_2O$	Sol in water.
4	Kalinite	$K_2SO_4 \cdot Al_2(SO_4)_3 \cdot 24H_2O$	Sol in water.
5	Chalcanthite	$CuSO_4 \cdot 5H_2O$	Sol in water.
6	Mirabilite	$Na_2SO_4 \cdot 10H_2O$	Sol in water.
7	Epsomite	$MgSO_4 \cdot 7H_2O$	Sol in water.
8	Melanterite	$FeSO_4 \cdot 7H_2O$	Sol in water.
9	Copiapite	$Fe_4(OH)_2(SO_4) \cdot 18H_2O$	Sol in water.
10	Halite	$NaCl$	Sol in water.
11	Sylvite	KCl	Sol in water.
12	Carnallite	$KMgCl_3 \cdot 6H_2O$	Sol in water.
13	Niter	KNO_3	Sol in water.
14	Soda niter	$NaNO_3$	Sol in water.
15	Borax	$Na_2B_4O_7 \cdot 10H_2O$	Sol in water.
16	Ulexite	$Na_2O \cdot CaO \cdot 5B_2O_5 \cdot 16H_2O$	Pt sol in water.
17	Sassolite	$B_2O_3 \cdot 3H_2O$	Sol in water.
18	Kernite	$Na_2B_4O_7 \cdot 4H_2O$	Slowly sol in cold water.
19	Trona	$Na_2CO_3 \cdot NaHCO_3 \cdot 2H_2O$	Sol in water.
20	Natron	$Na_2CO_3 \cdot 10H_2O$	Sol in water.
21	Smithsonite	$ZnCO_3$	Cobalt sol on coal gives a green coat.
22	Witherite	$BaCO_3$	Sulfuric acid gives insoluble ppt.
23	Malachite	$CuCO_3 \cdot Cu(OH)_3$	Sol deposits Cu on bright iron.
24	Siderite	$FeCO_3$	Potassium ferrocyanide gives blue.
25	Azurite	$2CuCO_3 \cdot Cu(OH)_3$	Sol deposits Cu on bright iron.
26	Strontianite	$SrCO_?$	Colors flame intense red.
27	Rhodochrosite	$MnCO_3$	S.Ph. bead in O.F. is amethyst.
28	Aurichalcite	$2(Zn,Cu)CO_3 \cdot 3(Zn,Cu)(OH)_2$	Copper and zinc tests.
29	Magnesite	$MgCO_3$	
30	Ankerite	$2CaCO_3 \cdot MgCO_3 \cdot FeCO_3$	
31	Dolomite	$CaCO_3 \cdot MgCO_3$	
32	Aragonite	$CaCO_3$	
33	Calcite	$CaCO_3$	
34	Hydromagnesite	$3MgCO_3 \cdot Mg(OH)_2 \cdot 3H_2O$	
35	Gay-Lussite	$CaCO_3 \cdot Na_2CO_3 \cdot 5H_2O$	
36	Hydrozincite	$ZnCO_3 \cdot 2Zn(OH)_2$	
37	Cancrinite	$4Na_2O \cdot CaO \cdot Al_2O_3 \cdot 2CO_2 \cdot 9SiO_2 \cdot 3H_2O$	
38	Franklinite	$(Fe,Mn,Zn)O \cdot (Fe,Mn)_2O_3$	Gives manganese bead tests.
39	Psilomelane	$MnO_2 \cdot 2H_2O$	S.Ph. bead in O.F. is amethystine.
40	Pyrolusite	MnO_2	S.Ph. bead in O.F. is amethystine.

TABLE A. MINERALS PARTIALLY OR COMPLETELY

	Soluble with separation of	Gas evolved	SODIUM CARBONATE BEAD		Ammonium molybdate gives a yellow precipitate	Barium chloride gives a white precipitate	Turmeric paper turns brown on drying	AMMONIUM HYDROXIDE		Ammonium oxalate gives a white precipitate	Ammonium phosphate gives a white precipitate
			A silver coin is blackened	Effervesces during fusion				Color of precipitate	Color of filtrate		
41		Cl_2									x
42		Cl_2									x
43	$PbCl_2$	H_2S	x					Wht			
44	$PbCl_2$	H_2S	x					Wht			
45	$PbCl_2$	H_2S	x					Wht			
46		H_2S	x					Wht			
47		H_2S	x					Brwn			
48			x					Wht			
49		H_2S	x								
50		H_2S	x								x
51		H_2S	x								
52	SiO_2	Cl_2		x							x
53	$PbCl_2$	H_2S	x					Wht			
54					x			Brwn			x
55					x			Wht			
56					x					x	
57					x					x	
58					x					x	
59					x					x	
60					x			Brwn			
61					x			Wht	Blue		
62					x			Wht			
63					x			Wht			
64					x			Brwn			
65					x				Blue	x	
66					x				Grnsh		
67					x				Ylwsh		
68								Ylw			
69	$PbCl_2$							Wht			
70	Ylw WO_3									x	
71	$PbCl_2$						x	Wht			
72						x			Blue		
73						x		Brwn			
74						x				x	
75						x			Blue		
76						x				x	
77						x				x	
78									Blue		
79							x			x	
80						x					x
81											x

DISSOLVED BY HYDROCHLORIC ACID (*continued*)

	NAME	COMPOSITION	REMARKS
41	Manganite	$Mn_2O_3 \cdot 2H_2O$	S.Ph. bead in O.F. is amethystine.
42	Hausmannite	Mn_3O_4	S.Ph. bead in O.F. is amethystine.
43	Boulangerite	$5PbS \cdot 2Sb_2S_3$	Sb separates out on dilution.
44	Jamesonite	$Pb_4FeSb_6S_{14}$	Sb separates out on dilution.
45	Zinkenite	$PbS \cdot Sb_2S_3$	Sb separates out on dilution.
46	Greenockite	CdS	On coal in R.F., a reddish-brown coat.
47	Pyrrhotite	Fe_xS_y	Potassium ferrocyanide gives blue.
48	Stibnite	Sb_2S_3	Fuses in a match flame.
49	Sphalerite	ZnS	Has a resinous luster.
50	Alabandite	MnS	Manganese beads. Not common.
51	Wurtzite	ZnS	Not common.
52	Braunite	$3Mn_2O_3 \cdot MnSiO_3$	Manganese bead tests.
53	Galena	PbS	$PbCl_2$ is soluble in hot water.
54	Triphylite-Lithiophyllite	$Li(Fe,Mn)PO_4$	Flame test for lithium.
55	Amblygonite	$LiF \cdot AlPO_4$	Gives flame test for lithium.
56	Fluorapatite	$9CaO \cdot 3P_2O_5 \cdot CaF_2$	Gives test for fluorine.
57	Chlorapatite	$9CaO \cdot 3P_2O_5 \cdot CaCl_2$	Gives tests for calcium.
58	Apatite	$3Ca_3(PO_4)_2 \cdot Ca(F,Cl)_2$	
59	Collophanite	$Ca_3(PO_4)_2 \cdot H_2O$	
60	Vivianite	$Fe_3(PO_4)_2 \cdot 8H_2O$	Potassium ferrocyanide gives blue.
61	Turquoise	$CuO \cdot 3Al_2O_3 \cdot 2P_2O_5 \cdot 9H_2O$	
62	Wavellite	$4AlPO_4 \cdot 2Al(OH)_3 \cdot 9H_2O$	
63	Monazite	$(Ce,La,Di)PO_4$	Tests for the Rare Earths.
64	Scorodite	$FeAsO_4 \cdot 2H_2O$	Gives arsenic tests.
65	Conichalcite	$8(Cu,Ca)As_2O_3 \cdot 3H_2O$	Copper and arsenic tests.
66	Annabergite	$3NiO \cdot As_2O_3 \cdot 8H_2O$	Nickel and arsenic tests.
67	Erythrite	$Co_3(AsO_4)_2 \cdot 8H_2O$	The solution is rose-red.
68	Carnotite	$K(UO_2)_2(VO_4)_2 \cdot 8H_2O$	The solution is yellowish.
69	Vanadinite	$3Pb_4(VO_4)_2 \cdot PbCl_2$	
70	Scheelite	$CaWO_4$	Reacts for tungsten. Fluorescent.
71	Wulfenite	$PbMoO_4$	Gives molybdenum reactions.
72	Brochantite	$CuSO_4 \cdot 3Cu(OH)_2$	Sol deposits Cu on bright iron.
73	Jarosite	$K_2O \cdot Fe_2O_3 \cdot 4SO_3 \cdot 6H_2O$	
74	Anhydrite	$CaSO_4$	
75	Antlerite	$3CuO \cdot SO_3 \cdot 8H_2O$	Sol deposits Cu on bright iron.
76	Glauberite	$Na_2SO_4 \cdot CaSO_4$	
77	Gypsum	$CaSO_4 \cdot 2H_2O$	
78	Atacamite	$CuCl_2 \cdot 3Cu(OH)_2$	Sol deposits Cu on bright iron.
79	Colemanite	$2CaO \cdot 3B_2O_3 \cdot 5H_2O$	
80	Boracite	$MgCl_2 \cdot 6MgO \cdot 8B_2O_3$	
81	Brucite	$Mg(OH)_2$	

TABLE A. MINERALS PARTIALLY OR COMPLETELY

	Soluble with separation of	Gas evolved	SODIUM CARBONATE BEAD		Ammonium molybdate gives a yellow precipitate	Barium chloride gives a white precipitate	Turmeric paper turns brown on drying	AMMONIUM HYDROXIDE		Ammonium oxalate gives a white precipitate	Ammonium phosphate gives a white precipitate
			A silver coin is blackened	Effervesces during fusion				Color of precipitate	Color of filtrate		
82									Blue		
83											
84								Brwn			
85								Brwn			
86								Brwn			
87								Brwn			
88							x	Brwn			
89	SiO$_2$			x				Wht		x	
90				x				Wht			
91				x				Wht		x	
92				x				Wht		x	
93				x				Wht		x	
94				x							
95				x				Brwn			x
96				x						x	x
97				x				Wht		x	
98		CO$_2$		x				Wht		x	
99				x				Wht			
100				x		x		Wht		x	
101		H$_2$S	x	x				Wht			
102				x					Blue		
103	SiO$_2$	Cl$_2$		x							x
104	Res			x				Brwn			x
105	Res			x				Brwn			
106	Res			x							x
107	SiO$_2$			x						x	
108	SiO$_2$			x						x	
109	SiO$_2$			x				Wht			
110	Res			x				Wht		x	
111	Res			x				Wht		x	
112	SiO$_2$			x			x			x	
113	Res			x				Brwn		x	
114	SiO$_2$			x				Brwn		x	
115	SiO$_2$			x				Brwn		x	
116	SiO$_2$			x							
117	SiO$_2$			x						x	
118	SiO$_2$			x				Wht		x	

DISSOLVED BY HYDROCHLORIC ACID (*continued*)

	NAME	COMPOSITION	REMARKS
82	Cuprite	Cu_2O	Sol deposits Cu on bright iron.
83	Zincite	ZnO	
84	Hematite	Fe_2O_3	Slowly soluble.
85	Magnetite	$FeO \cdot Fe_2O_3$	Slowly soluble.
86	Goethite	$Fe_2O_3 \cdot H_2O$	
87	Limonite	$Fe_2O_3 \cdot 3H_2O$	Sometimes leaves a residue of silica.
88	Ilmenite	$FeO \cdot TiO_2$	Slowly soluble. Titanium tests.
89	Anorthite	$CaO \cdot Al_2O_3 \cdot 2SiO_2$	
90	Leucite	$K_2O \cdot Al_2O_3 \cdot SiO_2 \cdot 5H_2O$	Decomposed without gelatinization.
91	Heulandite	$(Ca,Na_2)O \cdot Al_2O_3 \cdot 6SiO_2 \cdot 5H_2O$	Decomposed without gelatinization.
92	Stilbite	$(Na_2,Ca)O \cdot Al_2O_3 \cdot 6SiO_2 \cdot 6H_2O$	Decomposed without gelatinization.
93	Harmotome	$(K_2,Ba)Al_2Si_5O_{14} \cdot 5H_2O$	Decomposed without gelatinization.
94	Willemite	$ZnSiO_4$	Dissolved without gelatinization.
95	Chrysolite	$2(Mg,Fe)O \cdot SiO_2$	Dissolved without gelatinization.
96	Monticellite	$CaO \cdot MgO \cdot SiO_2$	Dissolved without gelatinization.
97	Prehnite	$2CaO \cdot Al_2O_3 \cdot 3SiO_2 \cdot H_2O$	Decomposed slowly without gelatinization.
98	Cancrinite	$4Na_2O \cdot CaO \cdot Al_2O_3 \cdot 2CO_2 \cdot 9SiO_2 \cdot 3H_2O$	Dissolves without gelatinization.
99	Sodalite	$3NaAlSiO_4 \cdot NaCl$	Dissolves without gelatinization.
100	Hueynite	$3NaAlSiO_4 \cdot CaSO_4$	Dissolves without gelatinization.
101	Lazurite	$3NaAlSiO_4 \cdot Na_2S$	Dissolves without gelatinization.
102	Chrysocolla	$CuSiO_3 \cdot 2H_2O$	Dissolves without gelatinization.
103	Braunite	$3Mn_2O_3 \cdot MnSiO_3$	Gives manganese reactions.
104	Hypersthene	$(Fe,Mg)SiO_3$	Only partially decomposed.
105	Acmite	$Na_2O \cdot Fe_2O_3 \cdot 4SiO_2$	Only slightly acted on by acids.
106	Rhodonite	$MnSiO_3$	Only slightly acted on by acids.
107	Wollastonite	$CaSiO_3$	
108	Pectolite	$Na_2O \cdot 4CaO \cdot 6SiO_2 \cdot H_2O$	Partly decomposed.
109	Nephelite	$NaAlSiO_4$	
110	Wernerite	Ca,Na,Al,SiO_2	Imperfectly decomposed.
111	Vesuvianite	$12CaO \cdot 3(Al,Fe)_2O_3 \cdot 10SiO_2 \cdot 2H_2O$	Partially decomposed.
112	Datolite	$2CaO \cdot B_2O_3 \cdot 2SiO_2 \cdot H_2O$	Reacts for boron.
113	Epidote	$4CaO \cdot 3(Al,Fe)_2O_3 \cdot 6SiO_2 \cdot H_2O$	Only partially decomposed.
114	Allanite	$4(Ca,Fe)O \cdot 3(Al,Ce,Fe,Di)_2O_3 \cdot 6SiO_2 \cdot H_2O$	Tests for the Rare Earths.
115	Ilvaite	$2CaO \cdot 4FeO \cdot Fe_2O_3 \cdot 4SiO_2 \cdot H_2O$	
116	Calamine	$2ZnO \cdot SiO_2 \cdot H_2O$	
117	Apophyllite	$K_2O \cdot 8CaO \cdot 16SiO_2 \cdot F \cdot 16H_2O$	
118	Laumontite	$CaO \cdot Al_2O_3 \cdot 4SiO_2 \cdot 4H_2O$	

TABLE A. MINERALS PARTIALLY OR COMPLETELY

	Soluble with separation of	Gas evolved	SODIUM CARBONATE BEAD		Ammonium molybdate gives a yellow precipitate	Barium chloride gives a white precipitate	Turmeric paper turns brown on drying	AMMONIUM HYDROXIDE		Ammonium oxalate gives a white precipitate	Ammonium phosphate gives a white precipitate
			A silver coin is blackened	Effervesces during fusion				Color of precipitate	Color of filtrate		
119	SiO$_2$			x				Wht		x	
120	SiO$_2$			x				Wht		x	
121	SiO$_2$			x				Wht		x	
122	SiO$_2$			x				Wht			
123	SiO$_2$			x				Wht			
124	SiO$_2$			x				Wht		x	
125	SiO$_2$			x				Wht		x	
126	Res			x				Wht			
127	Res			x				Wht		x	
128	Res			x				Brwn			x
129	SiO$_2$			x							x
130	SiO$_2$			x							x
131	SiO$_2$			x				Wht			
132	SiO$_2$			x							x
133	SiO$_2$			x					Grnsh		x
134	Res			x							x
135	Res			x				Brwn			x
136	SiO$_2$			x				Brwn		x	
137				x				Brwn			x
138	SiO$_2$			x							x
139	Res			x				Wht		x	
140	SiO$_2$			x							x
141	Res			x			x			x	

DISSOLVED BY HYDROCHLORIC ACID (*continued*)

	NAME	COMPOSITION	REMARKS
119	Phillipsite	$(K_2,Ca)O \cdot Al_2O_3 \cdot 4SiO_2 \cdot 4\frac{1}{2}H_2O$	
120	Chabazite	$(Na_2,Ca)O \cdot Al_2O_3 \cdot 4SiO_2 \cdot 6H_2O$	
121	Gmelinite	$(Na_2,Ca)O \cdot Al_2O_3 \cdot 4SiO_2 \cdot 6H_2O$	
122	Analcite	$Na_2O \cdot Al_2O_3 \cdot 4SiO_2 \cdot 2H_2O$	
123	Natrolite	$Na_2O \cdot Al_2O_3 \cdot 3SiO_2 2H_2O$	
124	Scolecite	$CaO \cdot Al_2O_3 \cdot 3SiO_2 \cdot 3H_2O$	
125	Thomsonite	$(Ca,Na_2)O \cdot Al_2O_3 \cdot 2SiO_2 \cdot 2\frac{1}{2}H_2O$	
126	Lepidolite	$(K,Li)_2O \cdot Al_2O_3 \cdot 3SiO_2$ with F	Not completely decomposed.
127	Margarite	$CaO \cdot 2Al_2O_3 \cdot 2SiO_2 \cdot H_2O$	Only partially decomposed.
128	Penninite	$5(Mg,Fe)O \cdot Al_2O_3 \cdot 3SiO_2 \cdot 4H_2O$	Only partially decomposed.
129	Sepiolite	$2MgO \cdot 3SiO_2 \cdot 2H_2O$	
130	Serpentine	$3MgO \cdot 2SiO_2 \cdot 4H_2O$	
131	Halloysite	$Al_2O_3 \cdot 2SiO_2$	
132	Antigorite	$3MgO \cdot 2SiO_2 \cdot 2H_2O$	
133	Chrysotile	$3MgO \cdot 2SiO_2 \cdot 2H_2O$	Silica separates out in fibers.
134	Garnierite	$(Ni \cdot Mg)O \cdot SiO_2 \cdot nH_2O$	Partially decomposed. Ni tests.
135	Cordierite		
	(Iolite)	$4(Mg,Fe)O \cdot 4Al_2O_3 \cdot 10SiO_2 \cdot H_2O$	Only partially decomposed.
136	Andradite	$3CaO \cdot Fe_2O_3 \cdot 3SiO_2$	Difficultly soluble.
137	Olivine	$(Mg,Fe)_2SiO_4$	Slowly soluble.
138	Forsterite	Mg_2SiO_4	
139	Clinozoisite	$4CaO \cdot 3Al_2O_3 \cdot 6SiO_2 \cdot H_2O$	Only partially decomposed.
140	Chondrodite	$4MgO \cdot 2SiO_2 \cdot Mg(F,OH)_2$	
141	Titanite (Sphene)	$CaO \cdot TiO_2 \cdot SiO_2$	Partially decomposed.

TABLE B. MINERALS

	Soluble with separation of	Gas evolved	SODIUM CARBONATE BEAD		Ammonium molybdate gives a yellow precipitate	Barium chloride gives a white precipitate	Hydrochloric acid gives a white precipitate	AMMONIUM HYDROXIDE		Ammonium oxalate gives a white precipitate	Ammonium phosphate gives a white precipitate
			A silver coin is blackened	Effervesces during fusion				Color of precipitate	Color of filtrate		
1							x				
2		Red							Blue		
3							x	Blk			
4			x					Wht			
5	Wht		x								
6	Wht		x				x	Wht			
7	Wht		x				x				
8	S	Red	x						Blue		
9			x					Brwn	Grnsh		
10			x				x	Blk			
11	S		x					Brwn	Blue		
12	S		x					Brwn	Blue		
13	S		x					Brwn			
14			x						Ylw		
15	S		x						Ylw		
16	S		x					Brwn			
17	S		x					Brwn			
18	Wht		x				x	Wht	Blue		
19	Wht		x				x	Wht			
20	Wht		x					Wht			
21	Wht		x				?	Wht			
22	S		x				x				
23	Wht		x				x	Wht	Blue		
24	Wht		x				x	Wht			
25	Wht		x				x	Wht			
26	SnO$_2$		x					Brwn	Blue		
27		CO$_2$					x	Wht			
28	Wht	CO$_2$					x	Wht			
29	Wht				x		x	Wht			
30	Wht				x		x	Wht			
31	Wht						x	Wht			
32					x				Blue		
33							x	Ylw			
34	Wht						x	Wht			
35			x						Blue		
36			x						Blue		
37	S		x								
38	S		x								
39	Gold		x				x				

SOLUBLE IN NITRIC ACID

	NAME	COMPOSITION	REMARKS
1	Silver	Ag	
2	Copper	Cu	Gives a green solution.
3	Mercury	Hg	
4	Bismuthinite	Bi_2S_3	Gives a wht ppt on dilution.
5	Molybdenite	MoS_2	Gives turmeric paper test.
6	Dyscrasite	Ag_3Sb	May give a wht ppt on dilution.
7	Argentite	Ag_2S	
8	Chalcocite	Cu_2S	Gives a green solution.
9	Pentlandite	$(Fe,Ni)S$	Gives a green solution.
10	Cinnabar	HgS	
11	Bornite	$3Cu_2S \cdot Fe_2S_3$	Sol deposits Cu on bright iron.
12	Chalcopyrite	$CuFeS_2$	Green sol.
13	Pyrite	FeS_2	S is deposited on heating the sol.
14	Smaltite	$(Co,Ni)As_2$	Gives a rose-red solution.
15	Cobaltite	$CoS_2 \cdot CoAs_2$	
16	Marcasite	FeS_2	
17	Arsenopyrite	$FeS_2 \cdot FeAs_2$	
18	Bournonite	$2PbS \cdot Cu_2S \cdot Sb_2S_3$	Gives a blue sol.
19	Galena	PbS	
20	Stibnite	Sb_2S_3	May give a wht ppt on dilution.
21	Pyrargyrite	$3Ag_2S \cdot Sb_2S_3$	May give a wht ppt on dilution.
22	Proustite	$3Ag_2S \cdot As_2S$	
23	Tetrahedrite	$(Cu,Fe,Zn,Ag)_{12}Sb_4S_{13}$	Green sol.
24	Stephanite	$5Ag_2S \cdot Sb_2S_3$	
25	Polybasite	$9Ag_2S \cdot Sb_2S_3$	
26	Stannite	$Cu_2S \cdot FeS \cdot SnS_2$	Blue sol
27	Cerussite	$PbCO_3$	
28	Phosgenite	$PbCO_3 \cdot PbCl_2$	
29	Pyromorphite	$3Pb_3(PO_4)_2 \cdot PbCl_2$	
30	Mimetite	$Pb_3(AsO_4)_2 \cdot PbCl_2$	
31	Vanadinite	$3Pb_3(VO_4)_2 \cdot PbCl_2$	
32	Olivenite	$4CuO \cdot As_2O_5 \cdot H_2O$	
33	Uraninite	$U_3O_8,PbO,etc.$	
34	Anglesite	$PbSO_4$	Soluble with difficulty.
35	Covellite	CuS	Green sol.
36	Enargite	Cu_3AsS_4	
37	Orpiment	As_2S_3	
38	Realgar	AsS	
39	Sylvanite	$(Au,Ag)Te_2$	

TABLE C. MINERALS

| | Soluble with separation of | Gas evolved | SODIUM CARBONATE BEAD | | Ammonium molybdate gives a yellow precipitate | Barium chloride gives a white precipitate | Turmeric paper turns brown on drying | AMMONIUM HYDROXIDE | | Ammonium oxalate gives a white precipitate | Ammonium phosphate gives a white precipitate |
			A silver coin is blackened	Effervesces during fusion				Color of precipitate	Color of filtrate		
1		F_2								x	
2		F_2						Wht			
3								Wht			x
4								Wht			
5								Wht			
6	SiO_2			x			x	Wht			
7	Res			x				Brwn			
8	SiO_2			x				Brwn			x
9	SiO_2			x				Brwn			x
10	SiO_2			x				Wht			x
11	Res			x				Wht			
12	SiO_2			x			x	Wht		x	
13	Res						x	Brwn			x
14	Res						x	Brwn		x	
15						x		Wht			
16	Res			x				Wht			
17	SiO_2			x				Wht			x
18	SiO_2			x				Wht			x
19			x								

SOLUBLE IN SULFURIC ACID

	NAME	COMPOSITION	REMARKS
1	Fluorite	CaF_2	The gas etches glass.
2	Cryolite	$3NaF \cdot AlF_3$	The gas etches glass.
3	Spinel	$MgO \cdot Al_2O_3$	Difficultly soluble.
4	Gahnite	$ZnO \cdot Al_2O_3$	Difficultly soluble.
5	Gibbsite	$Al_2O_3 \cdot 3H_2O$	
6	Zircon	$ZrSiO_4$	Only fine powder effected by conc sulfuric.
7	Staurolite	$2FeO \cdot 5Al_2O_3 \cdot 4SiO_2 \cdot H_2O$	Only partly decomposed.
8	Biotite	$(K,H)_2O \cdot 2(Mg,Fe)O \cdot (Al,Fe)_2O_3 \cdot 3SiO_2$	Silica remains in thin scales.
9	Penninite	$5(Mg,Fe)O \cdot Al_2O_3 \cdot 3SiO_2 \cdot 4H_2O$	
10	Clinochlore	$5MgO \cdot Al_2O_3 \cdot 3SiO_2 \cdot 4H_2O$	
11	Pyrophyllite	$Al_2O_3 \cdot 4SiO_2 \cdot H_2O$	Partly decomposed.
12	Perovskite	$CaTiO_3$	
13	Columbite-Tantalite	$(Fe \cdot Mn)O \cdot Cb_2O_5 \cdot Ta_2O_5$	
14	Samarskite	$3(Fe,Ca,UO_2,etc.)O \cdot (Ce,Y,etc.)_2O_3 \cdot (Cb,Ta)_2O_5$	Only partially soluble.
15	Alunite	$K_2O \cdot 3Al_2O_3 \cdot 4SO_3 \cdot 6H_2O$	
16	Topaz	$Al_2(F,OH)_2SiO_4$	Only partially decomposed.
17	Phlogopite	$2K_2O \cdot 10(Mg,Fe)O \cdot 3Al_2O_3 \cdot 12SiO_2 \cdot 3H_2O$	Gives a milky sol with con acid.
18	Chlorite	$9MgO \cdot 3Al_2O_3 \cdot 5SiO_2 \cdot 8H_2O$	
19	Calaverite	$AuTe_2$	Hot sulfuric gives a deep red color.

141

TABLE D. MINERALS NOT

	Soluble with separation of	Gas evolved	SODIUM CARBONATE BEAD		Ammonium molybdate gives a yellow precipitate	Barium chloride gives a white precipitate	Turmeric paper turns brown on drying	AMMONIUM HYDROXIDE		Ammonium oxalate gives a white precipitate	Ammonium phosphate gives a white precipitate
			A silver coin is blackened	Effervesces during fusion				Color of precipitate	Color of filtrate		
1											
2											
3								Blk			
4											
5				x							
6				x							
7								Wht			
8								Brwn	Pink		
9								Wht			
10											
11							x	Wht			
12								Wht			
13								Wht			
14				x				Wht			
15				x				Wht			
16				x				Wht			
17				x							x
18				x				Brwn		x	x
19				x				Wht			
20				x				Wht			
21				x				Brwn			x
22				x				Brwn		x	x
23				x				Wht			
24				x				Brwn		x	x
25				x				Wht			
26				x			x			x	
27				x				Wht			
28				x				Wht			
29				x				Wht			
30				x				Wht			
31				x				Wht		x	
32				x				Brwn		x	x
33				x			x	Brwn			x
34				x				Wht			
35				x				Wht			
36				x							x
37				x				Brwn			x
38						x				x	
39						x				x	
40											
41			x								

142

ACTED UPON BY ACIDS

	NAME	COMPOSITION	REMARKS
1	Diamond	C	
2	Gold	Au	
3	Calomel	HgCl	Soda fusion on coal gives Hg coat.
4	Cerargyrite	AgCl	Soda on coal gives a bead of silver.
5	Quartz	SiO_2	
6	Opal	$SiO_2 \cdot nH_2O$	
7	Corundum	Al_2O_3	
8	Chromite	$FeO \cdot Cr_2O_3$	In R.F. gives green beads.
9	Chrysoberyl	$BeO \cdot Al_2O_3$	
10	Cassiterite	SnO_2	See tests for cassiterite.
11	Rutile	TiO_2	H_2O_2 gives reddish-yellow color.
12	Diaspore	$Al_2O_3 \cdot H_2O$	
13	Bauxite	$Al_2O_3 \cdot 2H_2O$	
14	Orthoclase	$K_2O \cdot Al_2O_3 \cdot 6SiO_2$	Flame test for potassium.
15	Microcline	$K_2O \cdot Al_2O_3 \cdot 6SiO_2$	Flame test for potassium.
16	Albite	$Na_2O \cdot Al_2O_3 \cdot 6SiO_2$	
17	Enstatite	$MgO \cdot SiO_2$	
18	Pyroxene	$Ca,Fe,Mg,SiO_2,etc.$	
19	Jadeite	$Na_2O \cdot Al_2O_3 \cdot 4SiO_2$	
20	Spodumene	$Li_2O \cdot Al_2O_3 \cdot 4SiO_2$	Flame test for lithium.
21	Anthophyllite	$(Mg,Fe)SiO_3$	
22	Amphibole	Ca,Fe,Mg,Al,K,Na,SiO_2	
23	Beryl	$3BeO \cdot Al_2O_3 \cdot 6SiO_2$	
24	Garnet	Ca,Mg,Fe,Al,Cr,SiO_2	Andradite is pt sol in HCl.
25	Phenacite	$2BeO \cdot SiO_2$	
26	Danburite	$CaO \cdot B_2O_3 \cdot 2SiO_2$	
27	Topaz	$Al_2O_3 \cdot (OH,F) \cdot SiO_2$	Slightly sol in sulfuric.
28	Andalusite	$Al_2O_3 \cdot SiO_2$	
29	Sillimanite	$Al_2O_3 \cdot SiO_2$	
30	Kyanite	$Al_2O_3 \cdot SiO_2$	
31	Zoisite	$4CaO \cdot 3Al_2O_3 \cdot 6SiO_2 \cdot H_2O$	
32	Axinite	$6(Ca,Fe,Mn)O \cdot 2Al_2O_3 \cdot 8SiO_2 \cdot H_2O$	
33	Tourmaline	Borosilicate of K, Li, Mg, Fe and Al	
34	Muscovite	$K_2O \cdot 3Al_2O_3 \cdot 6SiO_2 \cdot 2H_2O$	
35	Kaolinite	$Al_2O_3 \cdot 2SiO_2 \cdot 2H_2O$	
36	Talc	$3MgO \cdot 4SiO_2 \cdot H_2O$	
37	Lazulite	$(Fe,Mg)O \cdot Al_2O_3 \cdot P_2O_5 \cdot H_2O$	
38	Barite	$BaSO_4$	Flame tests for barium.
39	Celestite	$SrSO_4$	Flame test for strontium.
40	Graphite	C	
41	Sulfur	S	

TABLE D. MINERALS NOT

	Soluble with separation of	Gas evolved	SODIUM CARBONATE BEAD		Ammonium molybdate gives a yellow precipitate	Barium chloride gives a white precipitate	Turmeric paper turns brown on drying	AMMONIUM HYDROXIDE		Ammonium oxalate gives a white precipitate	Ammonium phosphate gives a white precipitate
			A silver coin is blackened	Efferves-ces during fusion				Color of precipitate	Color of filtrate		
42				x				Wht		x	
43									Blue		
44				x						x	x
45				x				Brwn		x	x
46				x						x	x
47				x				Brwn		x	x
48				x				Brwn			x
49				x				Brwn			x
50					x			Wht			
51					x			Wht			
52								Wht			
53				x				Brwn		x	
54				x				Brwn			x

ACTED UPON BY ACIDS (*continued*)

	NAME	COMPOSITION	REMARKS
42	Clinozoisite	$4CaO \cdot 3Al_2O_3 \cdot 6SiO_2 \cdot H_2O$	
43	Niccolite	$NiAs$	
44	Diopside	$CaO \cdot MgO \cdot 2SiO_2$	
45	Augite	$CaO \cdot 3(Fe,Mg)O \cdot Al_2O_3 \cdot 4SiO_2$	
46	Tremolite	$2CaO \cdot 5MgO \cdot 8SiO_2 \cdot H_2O$	
47	Hornblend	$mCa(Mg,Fe)_3 \cdot (SiO_3)_4$ $n(Al,Fe)(F,OH)SiO_3$	
48	Glaucophane	$Na_2O \cdot Al_2O_3 \cdot 4SiO_2 \cdot 2(Mg,Fe)O \cdot 2SiO_2$	
49	Glauconite	$K_2(Mg,Fe)_2Al_6(Si_4O_{10})(OH)_{12}$	
50	Amblygonite	$LiF \cdot AlPO_4$	Lithium flame test.
51	Wavellite	$4AlPO_42Al(OH)_3 \cdot 9H_2O$	
52	Lepidolite	$(Li,K)_2O \cdot Al_2O_3 \cdot 3SiO_2$ with F	
53	Arfvedsonite	$4Na_2O \cdot 3CaO \cdot 14FeO \cdot (Fe,Al)_2O_3 \cdot 21SiO_2$	
54	Staurolite	$2(Fe,Mg)O \cdot 5Al_2O_3 \cdot 4SiO_2 \cdot H_2O$	

TABLE E. ANALYTICAL SCHEME

BASIC CONSTITUENTS

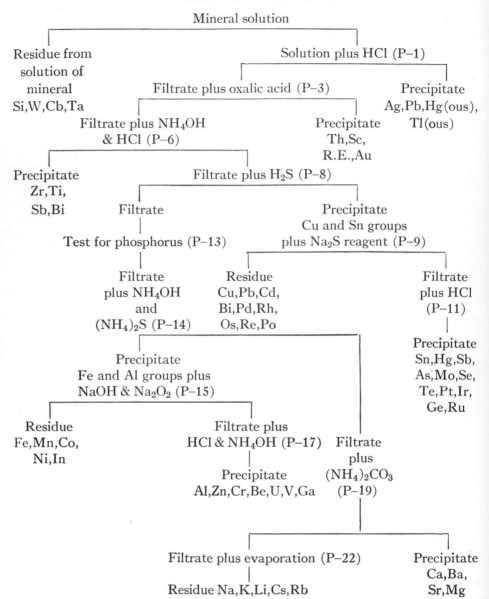

Mineral solution

Residue from solution of mineral Si,W,Cb,Ta

Solution plus HCl (P–1)

Filtrate plus oxalic acid (P–3)

Precipitate Ag,Pb,Hg(ous), Tl(ous)

Filtrate plus NH$_4$OH & HCl (P–6)

Precipitate Th,Sc, R.E.,Au

Precipitate Zr,Ti, Sb,Bi

Filtrate plus H$_2$S (P–8)

Filtrate

Test for phosphorus (P–13)

Precipitate Cu and Sn groups plus Na$_2$S reagent (P–9)

Filtrate plus NH$_4$OH and (NH$_4$)$_2$S (P–14)

Residue Cu,Pb,Cd, Bi,Pd,Rh, Os,Re,Po

Filtrate plus HCl (P–11)

Precipitate Sn,Hg,Sb, As,Mo,Se, Te,Pt,Ir, Ge,Ru

Precipitate Fe and Al groups plus NaOH & Na$_2$O$_2$ (P–15)

Residue Fe,Mn,Co, Ni,In

Filtrate plus HCl & NH$_4$OH (P–17)

Precipitate Al,Zn,Cr,Be,U,V,Ga

Filtrate plus (NH$_4$)$_2$CO$_3$ (P–19)

Filtrate plus evaporation (P–22)

Residue Na,K,Li,Cs,Rb

Precipitate Ca,Ba, Sr,Mg

CHAPTER VII

Qualitative Chemical Tests

In the following directions, 20 drops from a dropping bottle are taken as equal to 1 ml and the amount of acid or other reagent added is on this basis. Since the size of the drops depends on both the character of the liquid and the point from which it falls, the label on each reagent bottle should record the number of drops required to make 1 ml: thus, hydrochloric acid, conc, 18 drops ml. The analyst should determine how many drops from the apparatus at hand are required to make 1 ml and regulate the amounts added according to these results. The size of the drops depends in a large measure on the size of the tip from which they fall and may vary from 20 to 30 or more per milliliter.

The ore sampler described under gold-silver assay makes an excellent sample measure. This measure, ½ full of the finely ground, unpacked mineral, is the amount used in the analytical work.

LABORATORY PROCEDURE

SOLUTION OF THE SAMPLE

In the following procedures 0.10 gram is used as the basic assay, but this may be varied according to the desires of the analyst. If a substance is being tested for a trace of an element, a much larger sample should be used so that the precipitate containing the element sought will be in sufficient quantity for testing.

The sample is tested first for its solubility in water. If solution is complete, test the solution by Procedure 1 (P-1). If the sample is not soluble in water, add a little nitric acid (HNO_3) and boil if necessary. (If tests show that the sample is soluble in hydrochloric acid (HCl), this solution should be used, which eliminates P-1.) If the substance does not dissolve completely, add conc HNO_3 and boil. If still insoluble, evaporate nearly to dryness, add a mixture of 3 volumes of conc HCl and 1 volume of conc HNO_3 (aqua regia) in a porcelain or silica dish and heat gently. (Rapid, strong heating drives off the chlorine formed without giving it time to react with the assay.) Repeat two or three times if necessary, then evaporate to dryness, treat with conc HNO_3 and evaporate to dryness; again add conc HNO_3 and evaporate to dryness to drive off all excess acid and complete the removal of the HCl, thus converting the metals to nitrates. Dissolve the residue in water and filter. This treatment will dissolve

147

all of the metallic sulfides and many of the silicates, leaving the silica as a white or gray residue.

If a residue other than silica (SiO_2) remains (usually indicated by the presence of colored particles of the undecomposed sample), incinerate the filter paper, or remove the residue from it, and treat as follows: mix the dried residue with 4-5 volume of anhydrous Na_2CO_3 and heat until quiet fusion is obtained. If the HCl and H_2S groups are *absent,* platinum ware may be used, but if they are present, it is necessary to make the fusion in a nickel or iron crucible or on charcoal. Cool, dissolve in the smallest amount of water and HNO_3; evaporate to dryness, add conc HNO_3, and evaporate to dryness, redissolve in water and filter. This procedure decomposes the silicates, putting the metals into solution as nitrates, leaving the SiO_2 as an insoluble residue.

Insoluble sulfates, such as barite, will not be dissolved on treatment with acid if the fusion has been made in platinum. If made on charcoal or mixed with a reducing substance, the sulfate is reduced to sulfide, which dissolves, with the liberation of hydrogen sulfide.

If the fusion is made in platinum, then treated with water (no acid) and filtered, the majority of the sulfate passes into the filtrate as sodium sulfate and the greater part of the barium is converted to barium carbonate which is easily soluble in HCl. This method may also be used to remove other objectionable radicals, such as phosphate.

If gold or the platinum metals are present, it is necessary to acidify the fusion with HNO_3, evaporate to practical dryness, then digest the residue with aqua regia to put them into solution.

A few substances are not decomposed completely and dissolved by the above treatments. If this is apparent, incinerate the filter paper at a low red heat, mix the residue with 2-3 volumes of dry potassium bisulfate ($KHSO_4$), and heat to quiet fusion at a low red heat for several minutes in a porcelain crucible. Allow to cool, add a few drops of conc sulfuric acid (H_2SO_4), and reheat until the fusion has melted (red heat). Cool, dissolve the melt in *cold water,* and filter. Wash the residue from the filter paper with a small amount of water, add about 1 ml of conc HCl, and heat to near boiling for a few minutes. Filter, and add the *cold filtrate* to that from the other operations.

Mix the clear filtrates from all of the solution operations together and treat by P-1, or, if it is seen that the sample is a mixture, the solutions obtained by the various treatments may be analyzed separately, which will aid in the identification of the various constituents.

If the Na_2CO_3 fusion is made on the original substance before other treatments, it should be observed for color reactions and metallic globules which indicate certain metals by their color, tenacity, and malleability as follows:

Malleable: silver and tin, white; lead, gray; gold, yellow; copper, red.

Brittle: antimony, white; bismuth, reddish white.

The **color** of the fusion indicates the following: manganese, bluish green; chromium, yellow.

Silica is indicated by effervescence during the soda fusion.

The potassium bisulfate fusion also gives indications of the presence of certain elements by its color as follows:

	Color While Hot	*Color When Cold*
Antimony	brown	light lemon-yellow
Cerium	red-brown	orange-yellow
Chromium	dark purple	yellowish green
Cobalt	dark purple	purple (magenta)
Copper	olive-green	blue
Didymium	bluish gray	lilac
Iron	red-brown	very light yellow
Manganese	dark brown	dirty greenish gray
Nickel	brown-black	orange-yellow
Molybdenum	brownish yellow	clear, colorless
Selenium	light yellow	very light brown
Thorium	very light yellow	white, yellow tint
Uranium	orange-yellow	bright lemon-yellow
Vanadium	red-brown	yellowish brown

If it is evident that the sample is a silicate, treatment with the acids may be omitted and the analyst may proceed directly with the Na_2CO_3 fusion.

The addition of the filtrate from the $KHSO_4$ fusion to that from the previous operations will precipitate lead, barium, and strontium as sulfates. Calcium will be partially precipitated in neutral or alkaline solutions, and antimony and bismuth may be partly precipitated by hydrolysis on dilution of the solution. Therefore, if the $KHSO_4$ fusion is used, it is well to test for and, if present, precipitate the silver group from the solution of the other operations before adding the filtrate from the $KHSO_4$ fusion. If this is done, any precipitate formed will be only Ba, Sr and Ca sulfates and Sb and Bi oxychlorates and/or oxynitrates.

The undissolved residue may still contain small amounts of Sb, Sn, Cr, Ti, V and Mo, but they are not tested for here as they will appear in much greater quantities at other points in the analytical procedures. Cassiterite, however, may be only partially decomposed and dissolved.

Solution of the Platinum Metals. Treatment with aqua regia dissolves platinum and palladium readily; compact rhodium and iridium with difficulty, although the finely divided form is quite soluble; osmium not at all in the compact form, but fairly readily in the finely divided state; and ruthenium not at all. Gold is easily soluble.

The $KHSO_4$ fusion attacks palladium readily; platinum slightly; rhodium slowly; and iridium, osmium and ruthenium not at all. Gold is not attacked.

Fusion with Na_2O_2 converts all of the platinum metals into forms that are soluble in water or HCl, except that platinum is changed to the yellow oxide which is soluble with difficulty in concentrated acid. Gold is not attacked.

The colors of the various platinum metal solutions obtained by extracting the Na_2O_2 fusion with water and also treatment with an excess of HCl are as follows: *platinum,* pale yellow—with acid, deep yellow; *palladium,* pale yellow—with acid, brown; *rhodium,* yellow—with acid, orange-yellow to red; *iridium,* pale yellow—with acid, dark blue turning to dark red; *osmium,* orange-yellow—with acid, yellow to red; *ruthenium,* dark orange-red—with acid, yellow to brown.

Tungsten, Columbium and Tantalum, if present, remain with the silica as acid insoluble residues.

Tungsten, W, remains in the residue as acid insoluble canary-yellow WO_3. On treatment of this residue with conc. NH_4OH, warming and filtering, tungsten goes into solution and passes into the filtrate.

Make a portion of this solution acid with HCl, add metallic tin and boil. In the presence of W, the solution becomes blue, then green. If zinc is used, the colors are purple, then reddish brown.

Make a second portion acid with HCl and boil. A yellow precipitate (WO_3), which is soluble in NaOH and NH_4OH, indicates tungsten. The addition of metallic tin and boiling gives a blue, then brown color.

Another portion is evaporated nearly to dryness and a drop of stannous chloride added. Tungsten gives a flocculent, blue precipitate of $W_2O_5 \cdot XWO_3$.

On three different pieces of filter paper, place a drop of the NH_4OH solution. Add to one a drop of HCl. Tungsten gives a yellow coloration.

To another add a drop of $SnCl_2$. Tungsten gives a blue color.

Add to a third a drop of $(NH_4)_2S$. In the cold there is no evident reaction, but on warming, if W is present, the spot becomes green or blue.

If a mineral is fused with Na_2CO_3 and extracted with water (no acid), tungsten will go into solution as Na_2WO_4. (Mo will also go into solution as Na_2MoO_4.)

Place a little of the finely ground sample in a porcelain dish, add a little conc HCl, boil for a few minutes, add a piece of metallic tin and again boil. The presence of W is indicated by the development of a purple, then reddish brown color. A ring around the dish may be formed with small amounts. Dilution does not destroy the color. (The blue from columbium is destroyed on dilution.) Ti, Cb, V, Mo, Ru, and U also give color reactions with this test.

The sodium and lithium fluoride beads containing tungsten fluoresce under ultra-violet light. (See Fluorescent Bead Tests.)

Tungsten, with borax in the O.F. (oxidizing flame), gives a bead that is colorless to yellow while hot, and colorless when cold; in the R.F. (reducing flame) it is colorless while hot, and yellowish brown when cold.

The salt of phosphorus (S. Ph.) bead, in the O.F., is pale yellow while hot, and colorless when cold; in the R.F., it is dirty blue while hot, and fine blue when cold, and becomes blood-red when a little $FeSO_4$ is added, or dark green on long blowing with tin on coal.

Make several S.Ph. beads with the residue and dissolve in HCl. Add metallic tin and heat. If tungsten is present, the solution will become dark blue. Dilute with water. If the color is due to tungsten it will persist; if due to columbium, it will disappear. If zinc is used instead of tin, the color will be purple, then reddish brown.

By treating the insoluble residue with NH_4OH, warming, filtering and washing with water, the tungsten is dissolved, leaving the Cb and Ta with the silica.

Columbium, Cb, (**Niobium,** Nb,) and **Tantalum,** Ta. Mix a small amount of the finely ground sample or dried acid insoluble residue with 1 ml of dry $KHSO_4$, bring to quiet fusion in a porcelain crucible, cool and dissolve the melt in 10 ml of saturated ammonium oxalate solution by boiling. Dissolve 2/10 gram (about 1″ in a ⅜″ diameter test tube) of tannic acid powder in 1 ml of water (about ¾″ in a ⅜″ diameter test tube) by boiling. Add some of this solution to the hot oxalate solution. Columbium gives a brown to vermilion color or precipitate and tantalum gives a sulfur-yellow color or precipitate. If no precipitate forms, add NH_4OH carefully until one is obtained or the solution is alkaline. Titanium gives a color similar to that from columbium, but if this test is carried out on the acid insoluble residue, no Ti should be present.

The acid insoluble residue may be freed of tungsten and silica by fusing with solid NaOH in an iron crucible, dissolving in water (no acid) and filtering or centrifuging. The sodium silicate and tungstate are soluble, but the sodium columbate and tantalate are insoluble in the excess sodium hydroxide.

Treat the acid insoluble residue, after the removal of tungsten, with about 2 ml of conc H_2SO_4 and heat to strong fuming for several minutes. Columbium and tantalum go into solution. Cool, carefully decant the solution from the undissolved residue, and slowly dilute to about 25 ml with cold water, allowing time to keep relatively cool. Tantalum is precipitated by the dilution and may be filtered off, but columbium remains in solution and may be precipitated on boiling or by the addition of NH_4OH or NaOH. An idea of the relative amounts of each element may be obtained by this procedure. Tannic acid solution (see above), added to these precipitates and boiled, will cause the columbium to become vermillion and the tantalum, sulfur-yellow. Titanium gives a color similar to that from columbium, but there should be none present in this residue.

The freshly precipitated, hydrous oxide of columbium is practically insoluble in boiling conc HCl, but on decanting off the acid and adding water to the moist residue, it passes into solution. Tantalum is only partly soluble.

On treatment of the freshly precipitated, hydrous oxides with *dilute* acid and an equal volume of H_2O_2 and boiling, columbium is dissolved to a clear solution, tantalum is only partly soluble, and tungsten is insoluble.

Place a little of the finely ground sample in a porcelain dish, treat with conc H_2SO_4, evaporate to dryness, then add a little conc HCl and metallic tin and boil for a few minutes. In the presence of columbium a deep blue color will develop. The color may appear as a ring around the dish if only a small amount is present. Dilution with water destroys the color. (If the color is due to tungsten, it will not be destroyed on dilution.) Tantalum gives no color reaction. Tungsten, Ti, V, Mo, Ru, and U also give color reactions with this test.

Columbic acid (Cb_2O_5) and tantalic acid (Ta_2O_5) are infusible.

On treatment of the $KHSO_4$ melt with hot 30% tartaric acid solution, columbium and tantalum dissolve. Boiling with $\frac{1}{3}$ of its volume of conc HCl precipitates the elements as the white infusible oxides. Tungsten is precipitated (yellow) only from concentrated solutions.

Columbium in the residue is soluble in hot conc H_2SO_4, and the cold solution remains clear on being diluted with *cold water* slowly enough so that it remains relatively cool. (Ta is precipitated.) On boiling, a white precipitate is formed.

Treat the residue, after the removal of the tungsten, with conc H_2SO_4, heat to fuming, cool, dilute with water, add metallic zinc and heat. If a deep blue color develops, dilute with water. If the color is due to columbium it will disappear; if due to tungsten it will persist. The original color produced by both elements is quite similar. Tantalum gives no color reactions.

The NaF bead containing columbium fluoresces a blue-white under the short wave U-V light. The LiF bead does not fluoresce. Tantalum causes no fluorescence in either fluoride bead.

Columbium in the S.Ph. bead in the O.F. is pale yellow while hot, and colorless when cold; in the R.F., it is blue-violet or brown, according to the amount present, and is changed to blood-red on the addition of $FeSO_4$.

Tantalum gives no color to the S.Ph. bead in either flame and the addition of $FeSO_4$ does not cause a color to develop. The bead containing Ti also becomes blood-red on the addition of $FeSO_4$.

PROCEDURE 1

Precipitation of the Silver Group

On the addition of a few drops of HCl to the solution of the sample, if any of the **silver group** [Ag, Hg(ous), Pb, Tl(ous)] are present, a white precipitate will develop. If no precipitate or cloudiness is produced, all are absent Treat the solution by P–3.

If a precipitate is formed, add HCl to complete precipitation and filter. Trea the precipitate by P–2 and the filtrate by P–3, or if the **rare earth** and **zirconium groups** are not to be tested for, by P–8.

Silver is completely precipitated, but divalent mercury and trivalent thallium are not thrown down. A very small amount of thallous thallium and lead may also not be indicated.

Bismuth and antimony may be partly precipitated on dilution of strong acid solutions and give false indication of the silver group.

A separation of the common elements of this group may be made by washing the precipitate from the filter paper into a beaker, adding 10 ml of water, heating to boiling and filtering. Lead chloride is soluble in hot water and will pass into the filtrate from which it will recrystallize on cooling. Wash the residue from the paper and treat with 5 ml of conc. ammonia. Filter. Silver chloride is dissolved and passes into the filtrate from which it may be precipitated by acidifying with nitric acid. The mercury remains as a black residue.

Procedure 2

Silver Group Tests

Mix 1 part of the dried residue or precipitate from P–1 with 3 parts of the fluxes and heat gently with the oxidizing flame on the plaster tablet. The various members of the group give the following reactions:

IODIDE FLUX	
Color of Coat	Remarks
Lead, Pb. Chrome-yellow coat, darker while hot, often covering the entire tablet.	A drop of yellow ammonium sulfide $[(NH_4)_2S_x]$ applied to the film, yields a black spot, often surrounded by a reddish cloud.
Mercury, Hg. If heated gently, a bright scarlet, very volatile coat with yellow fringes is formed.	If heated too strongly, the coat is pale yellow or greenish-yellow and black.
Silver, Ag. Slightly yellowish coat near the assay. Requires intense heat.	When touched with the R.F., it becomes pinkish-brown and somewhat mottled.
Thallium, Tl. Orange-yellow film near the assay, with purplish, black band far away. The entire coat finally becomes yellow.	Yellow ammonium sulfide $[(NH_4)_2S_x]$ changes the coat to chocolate brown.

153

BROMIDE FLUX

Color of Coat	Remarks
Lead, Pb. Small canary-yellow film. Quite volatile.	A drop of $(NH_4)_2S_x$ placed beyond the point where the film is visible gives a black spot surrounded by a reddish-brown cloud.
Mercury, Hg. Gives a faint yellow, very volatile coat.	A drop of $(NH_4)_2S_x$ applied to the film gives a black spot.
Silver, Ag. Gives an indistinct, slightly yellowish coat near the assay. Requires intense heat.	Treated with the R.F., the coat becomes mottled yellowish-brown and may be developed over a considerable part of the tablet. $(NH_4)_2S_x$ causes no change.
Thallium, Tl. Gives a reddish-orange coat at some distance from the assay; surrounded by a slight lemon-yellow film. The reddish coat disappears on standing, leaving only the lemon-yellow film. Both are quite volatile.	A drop of $(NH_4)_2S_x$ gives a brown spot with a darker border. NH_4OH dissolves both coats.

CHROMATE FLUX

Color of Coat	Remarks
Lead, Pb. Black near the assay and brown far away. Some traces of white may show.	A drop of $(NH_4)_2S_x$ gives a black spot and reddish cloud where no coat was visible before.
Mercury, Hg. The coat is shiny black near the assay, with a small brownish-yellow band next and gray far away. The coat is volatile.	A drop of $(NH_4)_2S_x$ gives a dark ring.
Silver, Ag. The coat is brown to yellowish and near the assay. Requires high heat.	Treated with the R.F. it becomes more prominent. $(NH_4)_2S_x$ causes no change.
Thallium, Tl. The coat is reddish-brown to greenish-yellow, and near the assay. Quite volatile. The flame is colored green.	A drop of $(NH_4)_2S_x$ gives a shiny blackish-brown spot with a darker border.

REACTIONS ON CHARCOAL

Per se	With the Fluxes
Lead, Pb. In either flame, lead compounds (except the phosphates which require a flux) are reduced to metallic lead and yield, near the assay, a dark yellow coat which becomes sulfur-yellow when cold and has a bluish-white border. Touched with the R.F., the coating disappears, tinging the flame azure-blue.	**Iodide flux.** The coat is greenish-yellow, darker while hot, brown near the assay. The flame is colored azure-blue. **Bromide flux.** The coat is whitish-gray, volatile and some distance from the assay. Touched with the R.F., the coat disappears, tinging the flame azure-blue. **Chromate flux.** The coat is yellowish-white and volatile. It is not very prominent and is formed at some distance from the assay. Treated with the R.F., it disappears, tinging the flame azure-biue.
Mercury, Hg. Some mercury compounds volatilize without decomposition but most of them are reduced and decomposed and yield a grayish-white coat that is very volatile. It consists of metallic mercury and will collect into globules if rubbed.	**Iodide flux.** Yields only a faint yellow coat. **Bromide flux.** A slight yellowish-white, very volatile coat is developed at considerable distance from the assay. **Chromate flux.** Gives a very slight, extremely volatile gray coat.
Silver, Ag. All silver compounds are reduced to a white malleable bead of the metal. On long treatment with the O.F., a faint reddish-brown coat of the oxide is formed.	With the fluxes no special coating is formed. On long intense heating with the O.F., a faint reddish-brown coat of silver oxide is formed.
Thallium, Tl. The O.F. yields a white, very volatile coat of Tl_2O that is mostly distant from the assay. Treated with the R.F., the sublimate volatilizes, coloring the flame emerald-green.	**Iodide flux.** The coat is lemon-yellow and is darker and brownish near the assay. **Bromide flux.** Yields a yellowish coat at a considerable distance from the assay, with a slight whitish film beyond and a faint white one nearer the assay. The flame is colored green. **Chromate flux.** Gives a small yellowish-white coat near the assay, with a faint white one beyond. The flame is colored green.

ADDITIONAL TESTS

Lead, Pb. With borax and S.Ph. the beads in the O.F. are yellow while hot and colorless when cold. They can be flamed opaque. With the R.F. the borax bead becomes clear and the S.Ph. bead cloudy.

The precipitate formed by HCl ($PbCl_2$) is soluble in hot water but recrystallizes on cooling to acicular crystals with an adamantine luster.

K_2CrO_4 precipitates yellow $PbCrO_4$ from neutral or faintly acetic acid solutions, soluble in mineral acids and alkalies. Silver gives a red precipitate.

Potassium iodide (KI) precipitates yellow PbI_2.

H_2SO_4 gives a white precipitate of $PbSO_4$ very sparingly soluble in weak acids but soluble in hot HNO_3.

Mercury, Hg. To confirm mercury, mix a small amount of the precipitate or powdered mineral with an equal amount of soda and heat gently in the C.T. If Hg is present, a mirror-like sublimate of metallic mercury will be formed, which will collect in small globules if rubbed with a match stick.

Most Hg compounds, if rubbed on bright copper in the presence of HCl, will coat the copper with mercury, forming a white amalgam.

Mercuric iodide heated in the C.T. yields a yellow sublimate that turns red on being rubbed.

In the open tube, a crystal of iodine just above the sample will form a bright red sublimate of mercuric iodide if mercury is present.

Silver, Ag. If there is an indication of silver, treat a small amount of the precipitate with NH_4OH in the cold and filter. To the clear filtrate add HNO_3 until acid. A white, curdy precipitate that will redissolve on making alkaline with NH_4OH shows the presence of silver.

Potassium iodide (KI) precipitates yellow AgI soluble in NH_4OH.

K_2CrO_4 gives a red precipitate of Ag_2CrO_4. Lead gives a yellow precipitate.

Treat the precipitate with NH_4OH; filter, place a drop of the filtrate on filter paper or the spot plate and add a drop of stannous chloride ($SnCl_2$) solution. A black coloration or spot will be formed if silver is present.

Thallium, Tl, occurs in nature very sparingly.

Only the (ous) thallium is precipitated by HCl, thallic chloride ($TlCl_3$) being soluble but decomposes at 100°C to TlCl and chlorine so that if the solution is boiled after adding HCl, all but very small amounts of the thallium is precipitated.

The S.Ph. bead is colorless in both flames and the addition of $FeSO_4$ does not cause the formation of a blood-red color (difference from Ti and Cb).

KI precipitates yellow thallous iodide (TlI) which becomes green on standing, from even the most dilute solutions. This is the most sensitive test for thallium. Use an H_2SO_4 solution.

Alkali chromates precipitate yellow $TlCrO_4$ insoluble in cold dilute HNO_3 and H_2SO_4.

Place a drop of the solution on filter paper which has been previously treated with a drop of NH_4OH and follow this with a drop of benzidine reagent. A blue ring or coloration is formed according to the amount of thallium present.

Alkali carbonates cause precipitation only in very concentrated solutions (5 parts of Tl_2CO_3 dissolving in 100 parts of water). If it is desired to test for Tl it is best to use a separate portion of the solution of the sample and add $(NH_4)_2CO_3$ to complete precipitation; filter, make the filtrate slightly acid with HCl and boil. This removes all but a very small amount of the other members of the silver group and the precipitate with HCl will be principally TlCl.

PROCEDURE 3

Precipitation of Th, Sc and the R.E. Groups

The filtrate from P–1 is made nearly neutral by adding NH_4OH drop by drop till the precipitate formed barely dissolves, or by testing for neutrality with litmus paper, then adding 1 ml. of conc. HCl. The total volume should be about 25 ml., which gives an approximately 0.5N HCl solution.

To 1 ml. of this slightly acid solution add 5 drops of saturated solution of oxalic acid ($H_2C_2O_4$), heat to nearly boiling and allow to stand for some time. If no precipitation forms, heat again and let stand. If a positive test is obtained, add to the remainder of the solution 5 ml. of the saturated oxalic acid solution. *Do not boil* but keep quite warm for about 1 hour and let stand, overnight if possible. A precipitate indicates the **oxalic acid group** (Th, Sc, the R.E. groups and Au) and any one or all may be present. *If no precipitate forms, all are absent.*

If large quantities of the calcium group are present, Ca and to a lesser extent, Sr and Ba may be partially precipitated, thus giving a false indication of the group. Zinc and cobalt may also be precipitated in small amounts if a considerable amount is present.

Sb and Bi may be partly precipitated on dilution of strong acid solutions and give a false indication of this group.

If a positive test was *not obtained* and the entire solution *has not been treated* with the oxalic acid, treat the solution by P–6.

If a precipitate forms, filter, treat the precipitate by P–4, and the filtrate by P–5.

PROCEDURE 4

Reprecipitation of Th, Sc and the R.E. Groups

The precipitate from P–3 is washed from the filter paper, treated with a few drops of conc. HNO_3, evaporated to dryness and gently ignited to destroy the oxalate radical; treated with conc. HCl, evaporated to dryness, again

157

treated with conc. HCl and evaporated *almost to dryness,* dissolved in a small amount of water and a few drops of conc. HCl.

Any gold in the precipitate will not be dissolved by this treatment but will remain as a brown or black residue. If Au is indicated, the solution is filtered, the filter paper incinerated, the ash treated as under the cupellation test in chapter six and the gold recovered as a bright bead, or it may be put into solution and tested for as directed below.

The clear filtrate or solution is made alkaline with NH_4OH. A precipitate indicates **thorium, scandium** and the **rare earths,** as the members of the Ca group are not precipitated and Zn and Co hydroxides are soluble in an excess of ammonia and ammonium chloride. *If no precipitate forms, all are absent.*

If a precipitate formed, filter. The filtrate may be tested for Ca, Ba, Sr, Co and Zn if desired, then rejected. Wash the precipitate from the filter paper, dissolve in a small amount of water and HCl, then add NH_4OH until the solution is almost neutral. To the *very weakly acid solution* add sodium thiosulfate $(Na_2S_2O_3)$, and boil. A precipitate indicates **thorium and scandium.** Either or both may be present. *If no precipitate forms, both are absent.*

Strongly ignited thorium oxide is not soluble in HCl or HNO_3 and is soluble in conc. H_2SO_4 only after long boiling.

On treatment with $Na_2S_2O_3$, sulfur is often liberated, which may be mistaken for the Th, Sc precipitate.

If a precipitate forms, filter, and saturate the filtrate with sodium sulfate (Na_2SO_4). A white or light colored precipitate indicates the **cerium group** (Ce, La, Pr, Nd, Sm) and any one or all may be present. *If no precipitate forms, all are absent.*

If a precipitate was formed, filter and make the filtrate alkaline with NH_4OH. A precipitate indicates the **yttrium group** (Y, Eu, Tb, Ho, Dy, Gd, Er, Tm, Yb, Lu) and any one or all may be present. *If no precipitate forms, all are absent.*

A few tests for some of the members of the oxalic acid group are given below, but as there are no simple tests for the various members of the rare earth groups, for further identification consult texts on advanced qualitative analysis.

ADDITIONAL TESTS

Thorium, Th. Dissolve a portion of the Th, Sc precipitate in HNO_3 and a little water (there must be no HCl present), evaporate to dryness carefully, add 1 ml. of water and 2 ml. of the potassium iodate reagent and heat to boiling. Thorium is thrown down as a white, bulky precipitate. Scandium remains in solution, from which it may be precipitated by making alkaline with NH_4OH.

Dissolve a portion of the Th, Sc precipitate in HCl and a little water. Place a drop of this solution and 2 drops of quinalizarine on the spot plate and mix, then add 1 drop of 20% NaOH solution. Thorium gives a blue color or precipitate quite distinct from the blue-violet of the blank which should be run at the same time. The quinalizarine reagent is decomposed by the iodate precipitate.

H_2O_2 added to a hot neutral solution or one only faintly acid with HNO_3 or H_2SO_4 or to an ammonium carbonate solution, causes all of the thorium to be precipitated as white, hydrated thorium peroxide.

Scandium, Sc. Dissolve a portion of the Th, Sc precipitate in HCl and carefully evaporate to dryness. Take up with 1 ml. of water and add dropwise to 1 ml. of boiling 20% ammonium tartrate [$(NH_4)_2C_4H_4O_6$] solution. Boil for several minutes, adding NH_4OH occasionally. Allow to stand and cool. Scandium gives a crystalline precipitate; thorium remains in solution.

H_2O_2 prevents the precipitation of Sc by Na_2HPO_4 from weakly acid solutions. Destroying the H_2O_2 by adding Na_2SO_3 causes the scandium phosphate to be precipitated (similar to titanium).

Scandium forms a highly fluorescent complex with morin.

Cerium, Ce. Dissolve a portion of the precipitate of the cerium group in the minimum amount of HCl and water.

Place a drop of this solution on filter paper or the spot plate; add a drop of water, a drop of dilute NaOH and a drop of benzidine solution. Cerium gives a blue coloration. Mn, Co, Cu, Ag, Tl and the chromates give the same reaction, but as these should not be present the test indicates cerium.

To another drop of the HCl solution of the precipitate on filter paper or the spot plate add a drop of phosphomolybdic acid, then a drop of 20% NaOH. Cerium gives a blue color or precipitate. None of the other members of the R.E. groups give this reaction.

H_2O_2 added to an acid solution reduces ceric to cerous salts. If a cerous salt is precipitated with NH_4OH and an excess of H_2O_2 added a reddish-brown precipitate of perceric hydroxide ($CeO_2 \cdot nH_2O$) is obtained, which on boiling is changed to pure yellow $Ce(OH)_4$.

The borax and S.Ph. beads in the O.F. are dark brown while hot and light yellow when cold; in the R.F. the bead is colorless both hot and cold but if heated strongly CeO_2 will remain suspended in the bead and give it a turbid, yellowish appearance.

Lanthanum, La, **Neodymium,** Nd, **Praseodymium**, Pr, and **Cerium,** Ce, all give a blue lake with quinalizarine.

Place a drop of an HCl solution of the Ce group precipitate and 2 drops of quinalizarine on the spot plate and then add 1 drop of 20% NaOH. A blue color or precipitate indicates La, Nd, Pr, or Ce. A blank should be run at the same time. The blue of these elements is quite distinct from the blue-violet of the blank. If cerium *has not been found* by the foregoing tests, this test indicates La, Nd or Pr.

Didymium, (a mixture of praseodymium and neodymium). With borax and S.Ph., in both the O.F. and R.F., either hot or cold, the beads are pale rose.

Erbium, Er. Colors the flame a distinct green.

The color of the solutions of the rare earths give some indication of their identity. La. Ce(ous), Gd, Tb, Y, Yb and Lu solutions are colorless. Eu gives a very light pink solution, Er gives a deeper pink, Nd is reddish-violet, Sm and Ho give yellow solutions, Ce(ic) is deep reddish-orange, and Pr, Dy, and Tm give green solutions.

Ce, La, Nd, Y, Pr, Sm and Er occur in greater abundance, decreasing approximately in this order.

Gold, Au. To test the residue after the re-solution of the precipitate in the first part of P–4, dissolve in aqua regia, evaporate to a small volume, add conc. HCl and again evaporate until only a drop or two remains, and add a few drops of water.

Place a drop of this solution on filter paper or the spot plate and add a drop of benzidine reagent. A blue color indicates gold.

Place another drop on filter paper or the spot plate and add $SnCl_2$ reagent. Dark brown metallic gold or the "purple of cassius" is formed if Au is present.

Another drop is placed on the spot plate and treated with a drop of NaOH and a drop or two of H_2O_2. If Au is present a precipitate of finely divided metal is thrown down. This appears brownish-black by reflected light and bluish-green by transmitted light. With very dilute solutions the liquid is reddish with a bluish shimmer.

Evaporate a drop of the solution on the end of a very small glass rod or tube, then fuse into a small ball. Gold will give a red color to the glass.

Zinc, iron, copper and the other base metals precipitate gold from solution.

All gold compounds give a yellow malleable button of free gold if treated with soda on coal.

Gold treated per se on the plaster tablet, with high heat, gives a purplish to rose colored coat near the assay.

Touch Stone (hard, black basalt or flinty jasper) is used for determining the value of gold alloys by comparing the streak formed on it with standardized streaks. The metallic streaks are removed by smearing the stone with oil, rubbing with charcoal and wiping off with a cloth.

Mercury, if ground with an ore containing free gold or used in the pan while panning, will form an amalgam with it. The gold may be separated from the mercury in the amalgam by dissolving the Hg in dilute HNO_3 or by straining through a chamois skin, placing the solid that remains in a crucible and heating. The old miners used their frying pans. As Hg vapors are poisonous, a half potato, turnip or onion, hollowed out to allow for the amalgam, is placed over it during heating. This condenses and holds the mercury and leaves the gold as a yellow, spongy mass.

A solution of iodine (4 grams) and potassium iodide (2 grams) in 100 ml. of water will dissolve gold. From this solution it is precipitated as free gold on careful evaporation.

If an ore contains only a small amount of gold or is in a very fine state, the *cupellation test* (fire assay) should be used. This is given in Chapter III.

PROCEDURE 5

The oxalic acid in the filtrate from P–3 must be destroyed before proceeding with the analysis. Evaporate to dryness; treat the residue with conc. HNO_3, evaporate to dryness and ignite. Moisten the residue with conc. HCl, evaporate to dryness; again moisten with conc. HCl, evaporate *almost to dryness,* and dissolve in water.

The solution and residues are treated together by P–6.

To ignite a substance, place it in a porcelain dish or crucible and heat over a flame to dull redness.

Complete solution may not be obtained, for titanium may be converted to $Ti(OH)_4$, and antimony and bismuth may be changed to the oxychlorides or oxides, all of which are difficultly soluble in weak acids. Some iron may also remain as the difficultly soluble oxide, coloring the residue brown.

PROCEDURE 6

Precipitation of the Zirconium Group

The mixture of the solution and residue from P–5 is heated to boiling and made alkaline with NH_4OH. On heating, a precipitate sometimes forms before the addition of the ammonia. Make barely acid with HCl, then add 1 drop of conc. HCl for each 2 ml. of the solution. A white flocculent precipitate indicates the **zirconium group** (Zr, Ti, Sb, Bi), and any one or all may be present. *Complete solution of all the precipitate shows that all are absent.* Treat the solution by P–8.

If a precipitate remains undissolved, filter, treat the precipitate by P–7 and the filtrate by P–8.

The solution is not boiled after making alkaline, because aluminum hydroxide becomes quite insoluble on long boiling and may give a false indication of the Zr group.

The iron precipitate from P–5 may color the precipitate brown or obscure it entirely. On boiling, the SbOCl may be in part changed to the oxide, Sb_2O_4, which is practically insoluble in acids.

Palladium, rhodium and possibly some of the other platinum metals may be partially precipitated if they are fairly concentrated.

A very small amount of Zr and Ti may remain in the filtrate and reappear in the iron group, and the Sb and Bi that remain in the solution will be precipitated with the H_2S group.

CHEMICAL ANALYSIS OF MINERALS

Procedure 7
Zirconium and Titanium

The precipitate from P–6 is washed from the filter paper, evaporated to dryness and treated with conc. H_2SO_4. Heat till only a drop or two of the acid remains, cool, dilute with water to about 10 ml., filter, add 3 ml. of 3% H_2O_2 and a little sodium phosphate (Na_2HPO_4). A white precipitate indicates **zirconium.** *If no precipitate forms, Zr is absent.* If a precipitate forms and further identification is desired, filter and subject the precipitate to the Zr tests given below.

Titanium gives a reddish-yellow to deep amber color with H_2O_2. *If the solution or filtrate is colorless, Ti is absent.* This color reaction should be sufficient evidence of the presence of Ti. If it is desired to precipitate the titanium, the filtrate from the precipitation of the Zr is treated with 1 ml. of dry sodium sulfite (Na_2SO_3). A white precipitate indicates titanium. *If no precipitate or only a faint cloud forms, Ti is absent.* If a precipitate was formed and further confirmation is desired, filter and submit the precipitate to the tests for Ti given below.

Test the filtrate from the precipitation of Zr and Ti for iron; then the filtrate and any residue from the first part of the procedure are treated together by P–8. A precipitate indicates **antimony, bismuth** and possibly **palladium, rhodium, or any of the platinum metals.** *No precipitate indicates that all are absent.* If a precipitate forms, filter, reject the filtrate and treat the dried precipitate with the fluxes as directed in P–10.

The phosphates of Zr and Ti are very difficultly soluble; if further tests are to be made, they are rendered soluble in acids by boiling with NaOH and filtering. The PO_4 is removed in the filtrate.

There are no simple tests for palladium, rhodium, or the platinum metals. However, they may be recovered as metal by cupellation. See Fire Assay for gold and silver, Chapter VI.

The hydroxides of Zr and Ti, when precipitated in the cold, are readily soluble in dilute acids but when precipitated from boiling solutions, they are very difficultly soluble.

Zirconium and titanium are the only elements precipitated from strong acid solutions by Na_2HPO_4.

ADDITIONAL TESTS

Zirconium, Zr. Zirconium oxide (ZrO_2) is infusible.

Dissolve a portion of the zirconium precipitate in HCl and a little water. Place a drop of this solution and two drops of quinalizarine on the spot plate and mix, then add one drop of 20% NaOH. Zirconium gives a blue color or precipitate quite distinct from the blue-violet of the blank which should be

162

run at the same time. Ti, Sb, and Bi do not give this color reaction or precipitate.

Fuse some of the powdered mineral or precipitate with soda on the Pt foil or make several beads. Dissolve in HCl. Moisten a piece of turmeric paper with this solution or the one above, and allow to dry. If Zr is present, the paper will be turned orange or reddish-brown. (Difference from thorium.) Borates and titanium give the same test and their absence must be determined. They should not be present in the precipitate.

Zirconium gives no reactions with the beads.

Titanium, Ti. Titanium minerals are almost insoluble in acids.

Boil a little of the finely pulverized mineral with conc. HCl; filter, place the filtrate in a porcelain dish, add a little conc. HCl and metallic zinc and boil for a few minutes. If titanium is present a blue-violet color will develop. With small amounts the color may appear as a blue ring around the dish. W, Cb, V, Mo, Ru and U also give color reactions.

Fuse the pulverized mineral with soda on the Pt foil or make several beads. Dissolve this fusion or the residue, or several of the beads, in the least amount of HCl and heat the solution with metallic zinc or tin. The solution should be fairly concentrated. If Ti is present, the liquid will become blue-violet or blue after a time, and subsequently a blue precipitate which turns white, will form.

Fuse some of the precipitate or powdered mineral with $KHSO_4$, dissolve in water and add hydrogen peroxide (H_2O_2). If titanium is present, the solution will become reddish-yellow to deep amber. Chromates, vanadates, molybdates and ceric salts also give color reactions with H_2O_2.

The NaF bead containing Ti fluoresces a light green and the LiF bead is dark green under the short wave ultra-violet light.

With borax in the O.F., Ti gives a bead that is pale yellow while hot and colorless when cold; in the R.F. it is grayish while hot and brownish-violet when cold, becoming enamel blue on flaming.

With S.Ph., in the O.F., the bead is pale yellow while hot and colorless when cold; in the R.F. the bead is yellow while hot and delicate violet when cold.

If tin is added to the borax or S.Ph. bead containing Ti which has been treated in the reducing flame, the violet color appears more quickly. If iron is added the bead becomes brownish-red.

Bismuth, Bi. The tests for this element will be found under P–10.

Antimony, Sb. The tests for this element will be found under P–12.

PROCEDURE 8

Precipitation of the Hydrogen Sulfide Groups

The filtrate from P–6 or, if the oxalic and zirconium groups are not to be tested for, from P–1, should be only weakly acid. The correct acidity is obtained by adding NH_4OH dropwise till the precipitate formed barely dissolves, or by testing for neutrality with litmus paper, then adding 1 drop of conc. HCl for each 2 ml. of the solution, i.e., for 20 ml. of solution (after it has been made neutral) add 10 drops of conc. HCl. This gives an approximately 0.3N HCl solution.

Heat to nearly boiling and pass in H_2S for several minutes. Filter and test the filtrate with H_2S. A precipitate indicates the **copper group** (Cu, Pb, Cd, Bi, Pd, Rh, Os, Re, Po) and/or the **tin group** (Sn, Hg(ic), As, Sb, Mo, Se, Te, Pt, Ir, Ge, Ru) and any one or all may be present. *If no precipitate forms, all are absent.* Treat the solution by P–13.

If a precipitate forms, filter, treat the precipitate by P–9 and the filtrate by P–13.

It is best to heat the filtrate to nearly boiling and again pass in hydrogen sulfide to make sure that the precipitation is complete (with the exception of molybdenum). It is almost impossible to get complete precipitation of molybdenum under these conditions; if the solution has turned blue and a brown precipitate was obtained on the second and subsequent additions of H_2S, **molybdenum is indicated. Vanadium** gives a blue solution but no precipitate. *If Mo is indicated, do not attempt to completely precipitate it.* See P–21 for further treatment of molybdenum and vanadium.

The formation of a white precipitate on diluting or reducing the acidity of the solution shows the presence of considerable antimony and/or bismuth. The precipitate, which consists of SbOCl and/or BiOCl, need not be filtered off, as these substances are converted to sulfide by the hydrogen sulfide.

Care must be taken in the above procedure, as sulfur is easily thrown down as a white precipitate and the analyst is apt to consider this a precipitate of the group.

If the precipitation of gold was not complete in P–3, or Pd and Rh in P–6, it will appear in this group.

If the acidity is too low, indium may be partially precipitated and may be found in both the tin and copper groups.

The treatment in P–6 may tend to form amines with the platinum metals, which may prevent their complete precipitation by the hydrogen sulfide.

Procedure 9

Separation of the Copper and Tin Groups

Transfer the precipitate from P–8 to a beaker or casserole, add 5 ml. of the Na_2S reagent and warm gently for about 3 minutes with constant agitation. Add 5 ml. of water, mix and filter. A residue indicates the **copper group** (Cu, Pb, Bi, Cd, Pd, Rh, Os, Re, Po) and any one or all may be present. *No residue shows that all are absent.* Treat the solution by P–11.

If a further separation of the common elements is desired, treat the residue with a mixture of 1 part conc. HNO_3 and 4 parts water and boil for 2 or 3 minutes while stirring. Filter, treat the filtrate with 1 ml. of conc. H_2SO_4, evaporate to strong fuming, cool and dilute with water. Lead is precipitated as white, $PbSO_4$. Filter and make the filtrate strongly alkaline with NH_4OH. Bismuth is precipitated as white, $Bi(OH)_3$. Filter. A blue filtrate indicates copper. Treat the filtrate by P–8. Copper and cadmium are reprecipitated as sulfides. Filter and reject the filtrate. Treat the precipitate with a mixture of 1 part conc. HCl and 3 parts water and heat slowly to boiling while stirring. CdS is dissolved, leaving the CuS as a black residue. Filter and make the filtrate alkaline with Na_2CO_3. Cadmium is precipitated as white, basic carbonate. This may be greenish-blue from a small amount of copper.

Treat the residue by P–10 and the filtrate from the treatment with the Na_2S reagent by P–11.

As Au, Pt and Ir sulfides are not readily soluble in the Na_2S reagent, a portion may remain with the copper group.

There are no simple tests for the various platinum metals; for further identification the student is referred to texts on advanced qualitative analysis.

PROCEDURE 10

Copper Group Tests

Mix 1 volume of the dried residue from P–9 with 3 volumes of the fluxes and treat with the O.F. on the plaster tablet. The various members of the group react as follows:

IODIDE FLUX

Color of Coat	Remarks
Lead, Pb. Chrome-yellow coat, darker while hot, often covering the entire tablet.	A drop of $(NH_4)_2S_x$ applied to the film yields a black spot, often surrounded by a reddish cloud.
Bismuth, Bi. Chocolate-brown coat with underlying crimson and yellowish on the outer edge.	Subjected to NH_4OH fumes, the brown coating changes to orange-yellow then cherry-red.
Copper, Cu. Very slight lemon-yellow coat.	$(NH_4)_2S_x$ gives a light brown ring and darkens the coat around it.
Cadmium, Cd. Orange-yellow coat near the assay.	$(NH_4)_2S_x$ gives a slight yellowish gray spot with a lemon-yellow border.

BROMIDE FLUX

Color of coat	Remarks
Lead, Pb. Forms a small, quite volatile canary-yellow film.	$(NH_4)_2S_x$ placed beyond the point where the film is visible gives a black spot surrounded by a reddish cloud.
Bismuth, Bi. Near the assay, a brownish-black to red coat. Farther away the coat is canary-yellow and at a distance a brown border develops.	A drop of $(NH_4)_2S_x$ forms a black spot surrounded by a brownish haze. NH_4OH has no effect.
Copper, Cu. Gives a brownish to yellow coat near the assay with a slight purplish band far away.	The assay is greenish and the flame is colored blue. $(NH_4)_2S_x$ gives a brown ring.
Cadmium, Cd. Gives a lemon-yellow coat near the assay.	$(NH_4)_2S_x$ gives a slight grayish spot.

CHROMATE FLUX

Color of Coat	Remarks
Lead, Pb. The coat is black near the assay and brown far away. Traces of white may show in some places.	$(NH_4)_2S_x$ gives a black spot and reddish cloud where no coat was visible before.
Bismuth, Bi. The coat is dark brown near the assay and light brown far away.	$(NH_4)_2S_x$ forms a deeper brown spot.
Cadmium, Cd. Gives a coat near the assay, red while hot and lemon-yellow when cold.	$(NH_4)_2S_x$ gives a light yellow spot.
Copper, Cu. None.	

REACTIONS ON CHARCOAL

Per se	With the fluxes
Lead, Pb. In either flame, lead compounds (except the phosphates which require a flux) are reduced to metallic lead and yield, near the assay, a dark yellow coat which becomes sulfur-yellow when cold and has a bluish-white border. Touched with the R.F., the coating disappears, tinging the flame azure-blue.	**Iodide flux.** The coat is greenish-yellow, darker while hot, brown near the assay; the flame is colored azure-blue. **Bromide flux.** The coat is whitish-gray, volatile and some distance from the assay. Touched with the R.F., the coating disappears, tinging the flame azure-blue. **Chromate flux.** The coat is yellowish-white and volatile. It is not very prominent and is formed at some distance from the assay. Treated with the R.F., it disappears, tinging the flame azure-blue.
Bismuth, Bi. The coat of Bi_2O_3 is dark orange-yellow while hot and lemon-yellow when cold. It is greenish-white far away. Volatile in both flames. In both the O.F. and R.F. a brittle, metallic button is formed and the flame is colored a pale greenish-white.	**Iodide flux.** The coat is chocolate-brown with underlying scarlet. NH_4OH fumes change it to orange-yellow. **Bromide flux.** The coat is white near the assay and greenish far away. **Chromate flux.** Gives a slight whitish coat near the assay.

REACTIONS ON CHARCOAL (*Continued*)

Per se	With the fluxes
Cadmium, Cd. The coating of CdO is black to reddish-brown near the assay and yellowish-green far away. Thin coats show peacock colors. The coat is volatile in both flames.	**Iodide flux.** Gives a slight whitish to greenish coat. **Bromide flux.** The coat is gray and some distance from the assay. **Chromate flux.** The coat is near the assay, reddish while hot and canary-yellow to greenish-yellow when cold.
Copper, Cu. In the R.F. the Cu minerals are reduced to globules of red, malleable metal and the flame is colored emeral-green or azure-blue.	**Iodide flux.** Slight grayish-white coating. **Bromide flux.** Very slight gray coat. The flame is colored a brilliant blue. **Chromate flux.** None.

ADDITIONAL TESTS

Lead, Pb. The lead reactions have been set forth under P–2.

Bismuth, Bi. Strong acid solutions of Bi hydrolyze on the addition of water, similar to Sb, but the precipitate is more soluble than those of antimony.

On heating a Bi compound in the upper reducing flame of a Bunsen burner, the bismuth is reduced to metal which volatilizes and is reoxidized in the uppermost part of the flame. If a porcelain dish filled with water is held over this, a barely visible deposit of Bi_2O_3 is formed. Moisten a piece of asbestos in alcoholic iodine, start burning and hold under the deposit on the dish. A small amount of hydriodic acid is formed which will turn the oxide into the scarlet $H(BiI_4)$. By blowing the fumes from the ammonia bottle over this it is changed to the orange ammonia salt $[NH_4(BiI_4)]$. If the coat is moistened with $SnCl_2$, black metallic bismuth is formed.

If Bi is dissolved in S.Ph. by the O.F. and is then treated on coal with tin in the R.F., a bead is obtained that is colorless while hot but blackish-gray and opaque when cold.

Bismuth in the sodium and lithium fluoride beads causes them to fluoresce under ultra-violet light. The Na bead is blue-white and the Li bead is orange.

The per se reactions of bismuth and lead on coal are quite similar, but the reactions with the fluxes serve to distinguish them.

Dimethylglyoxime added to a hot solution of $BiCl_3$ or $Bi(NO_3)_3$ and made strongly alkaline with NH_4OH gives a yellow precipitate. If the sulfate is used the precipitate is white.

Copper, Cu. With borax and S.Ph. in the O.F., the bead is green while hot and blue to greenish-blue when cold. By repeated slow reduction and oxidation, the bead becomes ruby-red. In the R.F. the bead is greenish to colorless while hot and opaque and brownish when cold. Also by saturating the S.Ph. bead with a substance containing copper, adding NaCl and treating in the O.F., an azure-blue flame is obtained.

NH_4OH added to the solution of a Cu mineral will form a deep blue color. If a precipitate is formed by the NH_4OH, it should be filtered out to determine accurately the color of the liquid.

A slightly acid solution of a Cu mineral will deposit a red copper coating on bright iron, such as a nail or knife blade.

Traces of Cu may be detected as follows: Treat the substance in a borax bead in the O.F.; add a trace of tin or a tin compound and heat until the tin is completely dissolved, then treat the bead lightly in the R.F. and remove quickly. If Cu is present the bead is colorless while hot but ruby-red when cold. If reduced too far it will remain colorless, but by carefully treating in the O.F. the color returns.

Copper may be separated from iron by placing metallic zinc in the acidified solution. Cu is precipitated but Fe remains in solution.

Place a drop of the solution to be tested or a small amount of the precipitate from P-9 on the spot plate and add a drop or two of 1% KCN solution. If the precipitate is used, stir for a few minutes, then place a drop of this on filter paper, add a drop of phosphomolybdic acid and a drop of dilute HCl. Copper gives a blue color. Nitric acid should be absent.

Potassium ferrocyanide [$K_4Fe(CN)_6$] precipitates from acid or neutral solutions of a cupric salt, reddish-brown cupric ferrocyanide. NaOH changes it to black (difference from uranium) and it is soluble in NH_4OH, to a blue color (difference from molybdenum). The only other metals giving similar colored precipitates are molybdenum and uranium.

Cadmium, Cd. H_2S added to an acid solution of a cadmium mineral yields a yellow to orange or almost brown precipitate of cadmium sulfide (CdS).

On smoked plaster, with iodide flux, a white coating is obtained that is changed to orange by ammonium sulfide.

With borax and S.Ph., in the O.F., the bead is clear yellow while hot and colorless when cold, but can be flamed milk-white.

Zinc, lead and bismuth are interfering elements; to confirm Cd, treat with the O.F. to remove As, collect the coat from the charcoal, mix with charcoal dust and heat gently in the C.T. Cadmium will yield either a reddish-brown ring or metallic mirror.

If cadmium oxide is treated in the upper reducing flame of a Bunsen burner, it is reduced to metal which volatilizes and is reoxidized in the upper flame and will give a brown deposit on a glazed porcelain dish filled with water if held over it. If this coat is moistened with silver nitrate solution, a black deposit of metallic silver is obtained. This test may be applied to the residue from P–9 by first roasting to convert it from the sulfide to the oxide.

Palladium, Pd. To test for Pd in a mineral, dissolve in aqua regia, evaporate to a small volume, dilute with water and filter. Test the clear filtrate.

Palladium(ous) is precipitated by dimethylglyoxime, giving a yellow precipitate soluble in NH_4OH and KCN solution but only slightly soluble in 50% alcohol and dilute acids. Gold and platinum interfere as they are reduced to metals, but the other platinum metals do not. However, Pd may be separated from Pt by this method in 0.8–0.9N HCl (1 ml. of conc. HCl to 14 ml. of water) as the Pd is precipitated and the Pt stays in solution.

Palladium sulfide is black. It is soluble in boiling HCl and aqua regia.

In the presence of HCl, $SnCl_2$ forms a red then brown and finally green solution; but if no acid is present a partial reduction to metal occurs and the solution turns green. The precipitate is soluble in HCl, giving an intense green solution. KI added to this forms a black precipitate, which is soluble in excess KI to a red solution.

All Pd compounds yield the metal on ignition. This is soluble in HNO_3 and aqua regia.

An alcoholic solution of iodine dropped on metallic palladium will turn black.

Rhodium, Rh. All Rh compounds are reduced to metal on charcoal with soda. The ignited metal is almost insoluble in aqua regia but may be brought into solution by long fusion with $KHSO_4$ and treatment with water, yielding a yellow solution which turns red on the addition of HCl.

To test a mineral for Rh, mix the powdered mineral with 4 volumes of $KHSO_4$, heat for some time at a dull red heat in a porcelain crucible, cool, add 4 ml. of aqua regia, heat to boiling, allow to cool and filter. The addition of KOH and C_2H_5OH to this filtrate will cause the Rh to be precipitated as the brownish, black rhodium hydroxide $[Rh(OH)_3]$.

From a solution of potassium rhodium sulfate (from $KHSO_4$ fusion) KOH precipitates the yellow $Rh(OH)_3 \cdot H_2O$.

Osmium, Os. An Os containing mineral will give off characteristic, acrid, poisonous vapors if heated with soda on charcoal before the blowpipe.

Compact osmium is insoluble in all acids, but in the finely divided state it is difficultly soluble in HNO_3 and more soluble in aqua regia.

Osmium forms volatile salts and is apt to be lost in the regular process of solution of the mineral and analytical procedures.

To test a mineral for Os, treat 1 part of the finely ground mineral with 4 parts by volume of Na_2O_2 and bring to quiet fusion in an iron crucible. Cool and dissolve in water. This puts the Os into solution as sodium osmate (Na_2OsO_4). Add a little alcohol (C_2H_5OH), make acid with HCl and heat to boiling. The alcohol changes the color of the solution and retards the loss of Os by keeping in the reduced state. Ammonium hydroxide added to this solution precipitates reddish, brown osmium hydroxide [$Os(OH)_4$] which is soluble in HCl.

Stannous chloride gives a brown to black precipitate which is soluble in HCl, giving a brown solution.

Metallic zinc precipitates metallic osmium from acid solutions.

Osmium tetroxide (OsO_4) volatilizes at 100°C. and has a characteristic chlorine-like odor. It is very poisonous and attacks the mucous membranes. Great care should be exercised in handling even minute amounts.

Rhenium, Re and **Polonium,** Po. There are no simple tests for these elements.

PROCEDURE 11

Reprecipitation of the Tin Group

To the filtrate from P–9 add HCl in slight excess. A black or orange-yellow precipitate indicates the **tin group** [Sn, Hg(ic), As, Sb, Mo, Te, Se, Pt, Ir, Ge, Ru] and any one or all may be present. *If no precipitate forms, or it is nearly white, all are absent.* Reject the solution.

If a precipitate was formed, filter, treat the precipitate by P–12 and reject the filtrate.

A further separation of the common elements of this group may be made by treating the precipitate with 1 ml. of conc. HCl and heating almost to boiling, adding seven or eight drops of water and filtering. Sb and Sn are dissolved, leaving the mercury and arsenic as a residue with the sulfur. Treat this residue with 5 ml. of saturated ammonium carbonate solution, warm and filter. The arsenic is dissolved, leaving the mercury as a residue with the sulfur. Make the filtrate acid with HCl. Arsenic is precipitated. The filtrate from the first treatment is diluted to 5–6 ml. with water and treated with H_2S. Antimony and tin are reprecipitated as sulfides.

Metallic iron added to a slightly acid HCl solution of antimony and tin will cause the antimony to be deposited in the metallic state. The tin remains in solution.

When the Na_2S reagent itself is acidified, a considerable pale yellow or grayish-white precipitate of sulfur results in consequence of the decomposition of the Na_2S_2 in the reagent. This may make it doubtful whether a small quantity of the elements of the tin group are present. In case of doubt this sulfur may be removed by allowing the precipitate and filter paper to dry, then pouring a small amount of carbon disulfide (CS_2) through it.

The Au, Pt and Ir sulfides are insoluble in acids and may be separated from the other members of the tin group by boiling in a mixture of 10 ml. of conc. HNO_3 and 70 ml. of water (approximately 2N) and filtering.

If the precipitation of gold was not complete in P–3 it will also be found in this group.

There are no simple tests for the various platinum metals; for further identification the analyst is referred to texts on advanced qualitative analysis.

Hydrazine hydrochloride ($N_2H_4 \cdot 2HCl$) precipitates Se and Te from boiling acid or alkaline solutions.

SO_2 or Na_2SO_3 added to a solution not too strongly acid with HCl, causes the precipitation of Se and Te on boiling.

Se and Te may be separated from the other members of the group by treating the precipitate with conc. HCl, evaporating to dryness, taking up with water and HCl, adding SO_2 or Na_2SO_3 to the not too strongly acid solution and boiling. Antimony is precipitated to a small extent.

PROCEDURE 12

Tin Group Tests

Mix 1 volume of the dried precipitate from P–11 with 3 volumes of flux and treat on the plaster tablet. The various members of this group give the following reactions:

IODIDE FLUX	
Color of Coat	Remarks
Mercury, Hg. If heated gently, a bright scarlet, very volatile coat with yellow fringes is formed.	If heated quickly the coat is pale yellow or greenish-yellow and black.
Arsenic, As. Lemon-yellow to orange-yellow coat which disappears if subjected to ammonia fumes.	A drop of $(NH_4)_2S_x$ on the coat forms a yellow ring that is *completely dissolved* by a drop of ammonia.

IODIDE FLUX — (*Continued*)

Color of Coat	Remarks
Antimony, Sb. Orange to peach-red coat that disappears when subjected to ammonia fumes.	A drop of $(NH_4)_2S_x$ on the coat forms an orange-red ring that is *not dissolved* by a drop of NH_4OH.
Selenium, Se. Gives a reddish-brown to scarlet coat. Reddish fumes are given off.	The flame is indigo-blue. $(NH_4)_2S_x$ dissolves the coat and forms a ring of deeper color.
Tellurium, Te. Gives a purplish-brown to black coat. The flame is colored pale green.	$(NH_4)_2S$ dissolves the coat. $(NH_4)_2S_x$ has no effect. A drop of conc. H_2SO_4 added to the coat and gently heated, yields an evanescent pink color.
Molybdenum, Mo. A slight volatile yellowish coat is formed.	$(NH_4)_2S_x$ forms a slight brown ring. The R.F. *does not turn the coat blue.*
Tin, Sn. The coat is canary-yellow and brownish near the assay.	The coat is obtained by treatment of the sulfide.

BROMIDE FLUX

Color of Coat	Remarks
Mercury, Hg. Only a faint yellow, very volatile coat.	A drop of $(NH_4)_2S_x$ gives a black spot.
Arsenic, As. Gives only a faint yellow coat, very volatile.	A drop of $(NH_4)_2S_x$ forms a ring of slightly darker color. NH_4OH *dissolves* both the ring and coat.
Antimony, Sb. Forms a faint yellow coat far away with reddish-orange near the assay.	$(NH_4)_2S_x$ forms an orange ring and develops the coat around it to orange-yellow. The coat and ring are *not dissolved* by NH_4OH.
Selenium, Se. Gives a brownish-red to yellow coat covering most of the tablet. Reddish fumes are given off.	The flame is colored indigo-blue. $(NH_4)_2S$ and $(NH_4)_2S_x$ dissolve the coat and form a ring of deeper color.

BROMIDE FLUX — (*Continued*)

Color of Coat	Remarks
Tellurium, Te. Gives a coat covering most of the tablet; dark gray to black near the assay, grading into reddish-brown through canary-yellow with brown far away. The flame is colored pale green.	$(NH_4)_2S$ dissolves the coat. $(NH_4)_2S_x$ applied to the lighter portions forms a ring of darker color. H_2SO_4 added to the coat and warmed yields an evanescent pink color.
Molybdenum, Mo. Gives a bluish-green coat with traces of blue and yellow on the edges and sometimes brown near the assay.	A drop of $(NH_4)_2S_x$ gives a brown spot. The R.F. *does not turn the coat blue* but makes it a deeper brown.
Tin, Sn. The treatment of the sulfide yields only a slight darkening of the tablet around the assay.	No sublimate is formed. Very unsatisfactory.

CHROMATE FLUX

Color of Coat	Remarks
Mercury, HG. Shiny black near the assay, with a small brownish-yellow band next and gray far away. The coat is volatile.	A drop of $(NH_4)_2S_x$ gives a ring of darker color.
Arsenic, As. Orange-yellow near the assay and lemon-yellow far away.	$(NH_4)_2S_x$ forms an orange-yellow ring.
Antimony, Sb. Dark brown near the assay, grading into orange-yellow far away.	$(NH_4)_2S_x$ does not form a ring.
Selenium, Se. Cherry-red to crimson, very similar to that from the treatment per se.	$(NH_4)_2S_x$ dissolves the coat and forms a ring of deeper color.
Tellurium, Te. Brown to black, volatile, very similar to that from the per se treatment.	
Molybdenum, Mo. Nothing.	
Tin, Sn. None.	

REACTIONS ON CHARCOALS

Per se	With the Fluxes
Mercury, Hg. Some mercury compounds volatilize without decomposition but most of them are re-reduced and decomposed and yield a grayish-white coat that is very volatile. It consists of metallic mercury and will collect into globules if rubbed.	**Iodide flux.** Yields only a faint yellow coat. **Bromide flux.** A slight yellowish-white, very volatile coat is developed at a considerable distance from the assay. **Chromate flux.** Gives a very slight, extremely volatile gray coat.
Arsenic, As. A white, very volatile coating of As_2O_3 is formed. This is sometimes tinted with brown to yellow from volatilized sulfides. The coating consists of octahedral crystals of As_2O_3 and deposits mostly at a distance from the assay. Often the garlic odor of Arsine gas, AsH_3, is present.	**Iodide flux.** Gives a volatile coat that is white near the assay with a canary-yellow border and a slight yellow coat beyond. **Bromide flux.** Gives a slight white, volatile coat with a faint yellow border. **Chromate flux.** Gives a very volatile, slight white coat with a faintly yellow tinge. It is far from the assay.
Antimony, Sb. Dense white coat of Sb_2O_4 near the assay, bluish far away. The coat is less volatile than that from As. Fumes continue after the flaming is stopped. The flame is colored pale yellowish-green.	**Iodide flux.** Gives a white coat near the assay with yellow far away. **Bromide flux.** The coat is white. **Chromate flux.** Gives a slight whitish coat with traces of brown near the assay.
Molybdenum, Mo. Very near the assay copper-red MoO_2 is deposited. Beyond this but still near the assay is deposited a coating of MoO_3 that is pale yellow while hot and white when cold, bluish far away. It is sometimes crystalline. Touched with the R.F., it *becomes azure-blue* and volatilizes. Volatile in the O.F. The flame is colored yellowish-green.	**Iodide flux.** A white coat near the assay. Touched with the R.F., it is volatilized but *does not turn blue.* **Bromide flux.** A very volatile, yellowish-green coat is first deposited far from the assay, then on longer flaming a white one near the assay. Treated with the R.F., it volatilizes but *does not turn blue.* **Chromate flux.** Nothing.

175

REACTIONS ON CHARCOAL — (*Continued*)

Per se	With the Fluxes
Selenium, Se. Steel gray, very volatile coat near the assay. At some distance white SeO_2 tinged red with metallic Se and beyond a red border of metallic selenium is deposited. Red fumes are given off and the characteristic rotten horseradish odor is produced. The flame is colored blue by the coating.	**Iodide flux.** Small white coat near the assay with a yellowish-green border and traces of reddish-brown. Yellowish fumes are given off. Characteristic odor. **Bromide flux.** Small white coat and yellowish fumes with a characteristic odor. **Chromate flux.** Mixed red and yellow fumes with a characteristic odor given off. The coating is very slight, white near the assay, yellowish beyond and traces of red far away.
Tellurium, Te. Dense white, volatile coat of TeO_2 near the assay. Far away a gray to brownish-black coat of metallic Te. Treated with the R.F., the coat colors the flame green, and volatilizes. The coat somewhat resembles that from antimony.	**Iodide flux.** A white to gray coat. The flame is colored pale green. **Bromide flux.** White near the assay with brownish-black far away. The flame is colored pale green. **Chromate flux.** White near the assay with brownish-black far away. The flame is colored pale green.
Tin, Sn. The coat of SnO_2 is near the assay and is faint yellow and luminous while hot and white when cold. If moistened with $Co(NO_3)_2$ solution and heated strongly, the coat becomes bluish-green. Not volatile in the O.F. The addition of sulfur and soda increases the amount of the coat. In the R.F. a slight coat is formed.	The reactions with the fluxes are obtained by treatment of the sulfide. **Iodide flux.** White coat with patches and streaks of yellow through it. **Bromide flux.** White coat. **Chromate flux.** White coat.

ADDITIONAL TESTS

Mercury, Hg. The reactions of Hg have already been listed under P–2.

Arsenic, As. If an arsenic mineral is mixed with soda and flamed on coal, a strong garlic odor (arsine, AsH_3) is given off and a very volatile white coat will be deposited at an appreciable distance from the assay. The flame is colored azure-blue.

In the O.T., if heated gently, arsenic compounds will deposit a white or colorless crystalline sublimate of arsenious oxide (As_2O_3) at a considerable distance above the mineral. If heated too strongly, the red or yellow sulfide may be deposited. These sublimates are volatile. This serves to distinguish As from Sb which forms a white sublimate of Sb_2O_4 that is nonvolatile.

In the C.T. the sublimate may be the white oxide, the red or yellow sulfide or the black metallic mirror. If, however, a piece of charcoal is placed above the mineral in the tube, the oxide will be reduced and give a mirror also. The mirror is soluble in sodium hypochlorite (NaOCl) solution.

If an oxygen compound of As is held in the upper reducing part of the Bunsen flame, it is reduced to metal. If a glazed porcelain dish filled with water is held directly over the sample, vapors of metallic arsenic will collect, forming a brownish-black coat which is soluble in sodium hypochlorite (NaOCl). If the volatilized metallic arsenic is not collected immediately it will be oxidized in the upper oxidizing zone of the flame, burning with a blue light, and will deposit on the dish of water as white arsenious oxide (As_2O_3). If this is moistened with $AgNO_3$ and held over the ammonia bottle, yellow Ag_3AsO_3 is formed, which disappears on treatment with more NH_4OH vapors.

From neutral arsenic solutions $AgNO_3$ precipitates the yellow arsenite or reddish-brown arsenate, soluble in dilute acids, NH_4OH and ammonium salts.

Antimony, Sb. In the O.T., a dense, white, nonvolatile, amorphous sublimate of Sb_2O_4 is formed. The arsenic sublimate which may be mistaken for it is volatile. If antimony sulfide is too strongly heated it may yield red spots.

In the C.T., the oxide will yield a white fusible sublimate of needle-like crystals. The sulfide gives a sublimate that is black while hot and red when cold.

The S.Ph. bead, with Sb dissolved in it in the O.F., when treated on charcoal with tin in the R.F., will become gray or black.

With soda on coal Sb gives a dense white coating near the assay and a gray, brittle button is formed.

On dilution of a strong acid solution containing Sb, hydrolysis results with the precipitation of the basic salt.

The trioxide (Sb_2O_3) is soluble in conc. acids but the tetroxide (Sb_2O_4) is almost insoluble in conc. acids.

If metallic zinc and platinum are placed in contact in an HCl solution of Sb, metallic antimony is deposited as a black stain on the platinum. On removal of the zinc, the stain will persist (tin will disappear). Zinc will finally reduce the Sb to stibine gas (SbH_3). Treat the precipitate from P–11 with a few drops of a mixture of equal amounts of conc. HCl and water. This dissolves the Sb and Sn as $SbCl_3$ and $SnCl_4$. Place a few drops of this solution on a watch glass, add a piece of metallic zinc, then place a piece of metallic platinum on this in contact with the zinc. Antimony is precipitated on the Pt as dark glittering plates and tin is deposited on the zinc in a spongy form.

Place a drop of the HCl solution of the precipitate on filter paper that has been impregnated with phosphomolybdic acid and hold over steam. Sb gives a blue coloration.

Oxygen compounds of Sb are reduced in the upper reducing part of the Bunsen flame to metal which volatilizes and is reoxidized in the upper oxidizing zone to Sb_2O_3 which will deposit on a glazed porcelain dish filled with water. If this white, almost invisible deposit is moistened with $AgNO_3$ solution and treated with ammonia fumes, it becomes black, due to the separation of metallic Ag.

Tin, Sn. Metallic tin is insoluble in HNO_3 but soluble in HCl.

Cassiterite, SnO_2. Place a fragment of the mineral in contact with metallic zinc and treat with HCl. If the mineral is cassiterite, it will become coated with a thin white layer of metallic tin. Cassiterite is insoluble in all acids.

Treat the precipitate or powdered mineral with a little conc. HCl in an evaporating dish and boil. Cool, dilute to 3–4 times its volume with water, add a little zinc and allow to react for a few minutes. Make a saturated solution of **cacothelin** by adding a little more of the powder than will dissolve. Place a drop or two of the cacothelin solution on a piece of filter paper and allow to become *almost dry,* then place a drop or two of the sample solution in the center of the cacothelin spot. A red to lavendar coloration, according to the amount present, indicates tin, in the *absence* of vanadium, antimony, molybdates and tungstates, which give a similar reaction.

Stir the solution being tested with a test tube containing water, then hold the test tube over the non-luminous flame. If tin is present a blue flame will be seen to play over the surface of the test tube.

Most tin compounds reduce to white, metallic globules by treatment with the R.F. on coal.

The oxide and soda without the addition of charcoal usually forms an infusible mass that reduces with difficulty.

With CuO in a borax bead, a faint blue color should be obtained. If this is treated with a tin compound and flamed until the tin is in solution, then for a moment with the R.F., it becomes reddish-brown or ruby-red. This is a very sensitive test. Compare similar test for copper, using tin.

See under antimony, above, for the tin reaction with zinc and platinum.

Potassium iodide gives yellow crystals of SnI_2 or SnI_4 at the junction of a tin solution and conc. sulfuric acid.

If a bead of metal is obtained on coal and this oxidizes rapidly with sprouting and cannot be fused, it is a good indication of tin.

If zinc is present, the sample should be mixed with soda, borax and charcoal and treated on charcoal with the R.F. Under these conditions the Zn is volatilized and the Sn remains in the fused mass, from which it may be removed by crushing and dissolving in water.

Impregnate a piece of filter paper with phosphomolybdic acid, hold over the ammonia bottle, then allow to dry. The ammonium phosphomolybdate paper thus formed will keep well if stored in a dark, well stoppered bottle. The tin sulfide precipitate from P–11 is soluble in conc. HCl. Dissolve a portion of the precipitate from P–11 in conc. HCl, add a piece of metallic zinc and allow to react for a short time to convert the Sn to the stannous form, then place a drop of this solution on the ammonium phosphomolybdate paper. A blue color indicates tin.

Place another drop or two of the solution on the spot plate, add a drop of 1% $FeCl_3$ solution and allow to stand for a few minutes. Add a crystal of tartaric acid and when dissolved add a drop of dimethylglyoxime and make alkaline with NH_4OH. A red coloration according to the amount of tin present, is formed.

Molybdenum, Mo. Treat some of the precipitate from P–11 with conc. HNO_3 in a porcelain dish and evaporate to dryness but do not ignite. Moisten again with conc. HNO_3 and again evaporate to dryness. A deep blue color indicates Mo. If a drop of water is added a blue solution results.

Place a small amount of the finely powdered mineral in a porcelain dish, add a little conc. HCl then metallic zinc and boil for a few minutes. If molybdenum (as molybdate) is present the solution will become blue, then green then brown. With small amounts the color will appear as a ring around the dish. W, Ti, Cb, V, Ru and U also give color reactions with this test.

Potassium ferrocyanide added to a solution containing Mo gives a reddish-brown precipitate which is soluble in NH_4OH, to a yellow solution (difference from copper). Compare this test with Cu and U.

The borax bead in the O.F. is yellow while hot and colorless when cold; in the R.F. it is brown to black and opaque both hot and cold.

The S.Ph. bead in the O.F. is yellowish-green while hot and pale yellow to colorless when cold. The bead crushed between damp, unglazed paper, will become red, brown, purple and blue, according to the amount present. In the R.F. the bead is dirty green while hot and fine emerald-green when cold.

Treat several S.Ph. beads with the mineral in the O.F. and dissolve in dilute HCl. Heat and add metallic tin, zinc or copper. If Mo is present, the solution will turn blue, green, then brown. If the beads have been treated in the R.F. the solution will become brown only.

To test for molybdates, place a small amount of the powdered mineral in a test tube along with a scrap of paper; add a few drops of water and an equal amount of conc. H_2SO_4 and heat until acid fumes are obtained. Cool and add slowly a few drops of water. Molybdenum is indicated by the formation of a deep blue solution.

Fusion of the molybdenum mineral or precipitate from P–11 with 4 volumes of Na_2CO_3 and extraction with water (no acid) gives a solution of sodium molybdate. Tungsten also goes into solution as sodium tungstate.

Place a drop of this solution on filter paper which has been moistened with HCl to prevent the interference of tungsten, and add a drop of KSCN reagent. A red spot of $Fe(SCN)_3$ may be formed if iron is present, but on the addition of a drop of $SnCl_2$ or $Na_2S_2O_3$ it will disappear and the red spot due to molybdenum $[K_3(Mo[SCN]_6)]$ will appear.

Place a pinch of the powdered mineral or the precipitate from P–11 in a porcelain dish, add conc. H_2SO_4 and heat to fumes. Cool and breathe on the residue. If Mo is present, it will turn blue. The color disappears on heating but returns on cooling. It is destroyed by water.

If a solution containing Mo is evaporated to dryness carefully so as not to overheat and the residue treated with conc. NH_4OH then H_2O_2, a pink or red color is formed. On evaporating to dryness again and treating the residue with HNO_3 or H_2SO_4, yellow permolybdic acid $(HMoO_4)$ is formed.

Stannous chloride or sodium thiosulfate added to a slightly acid solution of a molybdate produces a blue color and precipitate which turns green, then brown.

Selenium, Se. In the C.T. Se compounds give a dark red sublimate and a decaying horseradish odor.

Selenium minerals, fused with Na_2CO_3 on coal in the R.F., if moistened with water and placed on a silver coin, will blacken it similar to sulfur and tellurium.

Stannous choride precipitates red metallic selenium even in the presence of considerabe H_2SO_4.

Fuse the precipitate from P–11 with Na_2CO_3 and dissolve in water and a little HCl. Place a drop of this solution on filter paper that has previously been treated with a drop of KI solution and a drop of HCl. If a brown to black color develops, add a drop of $Na_2S_2O_3$ which will destroy it and leave the red-brown color of the selenium.

If a Se compound is heated on an asbestos thread in the upper reducing flame of the Bunsen burner, it will be reduced to the red metal which will deposit on a test tube of water held over it. If this is immersed in a larger tube containing conc. H_2SO_4 and warmed, the selenium will go into solution, giving a green color. On dilution with water the red metallic Se is reprecipitated.

Red metallic selenium is precipitated by metallic zinc in acid solutions and the zinc becomes coated with Se and looks as if coated with copper. On warming the red Se is changed to brown or gray to black.

Tellurium, Te. A Te mineral fused with soda on coal in the R.F. will discolor silver similar to sulfur and selenium.

In the O.T. a gray sublimate is formed that is fused to clear drops if gently heated.

Treat a mixture of the powdered mineral, with soda and a little charcoal in the C.T. When cool add water. If Te is present the solution will become a reddish-violet that will gradually disappear and a gray precipitate will form if a drop is transferred to a porcelain plate.

The mineral added to hot conc. H_2SO_4 will develop a fine red-violet coloration if tellurium is present. Place a little of the finely pulverized mineral in a porcelain dish, add 5 ml. of conc. H_2SO_4 and heat carefully. Tellurium gives a violet color. If heated further or diluted the color will disappear.

By heating a telluride in the upper reducing part of the flame of a Bunsen burner, metallic Te is formed which volatilizes and can be collected as a black film on a test tube of water held over it. If this tube is immersed in a larger tube containing conc. H_2SO_4, a carmine-red colored solution will result. On dilution with water, black metallic Te is precipitated.

Fuse the precipitate from P–11 with Na_2CO_3 and extract with water. On a spot plate, place a drop of $SnCl_2$, a drop of 20% NaOH and a drop of this solution. A black or gray precipitate or color is developed by tellurium according to the amount present. Selenium does not interfere with this test.

Metallic zinc precipitates gray to black metallic Te from acid solutions.

Platinum, Pt. Platinum, like gold, is usually identified by its physical properties. There are extremely few Pt compounds in nature and all of these, when heated with soda on coal, yield the gray, spongy metal which assumes a metallic luster when rubbed with a pestle in an agate mortar. It is insoluble in all acids, but is soluble in aqua regia. Platinum sulfide is soluble in aqua regia.

Digest the finely ground mineral or bits of metal in aqua regia, evaporate almost to dryness, add a little conc. HCl, again evaporate almost to dryness and dilute with water. This puts platinum, palladium and possibly some iridium and rhodium into solution as chlorides. Treat the solution by P-8.

Potassium iodide added to a solution of the H_2S precipitate gives a pink to red coloration if Pt is present and a black precipitate if Pd and/or Ru is present.

KCl, added to a slightly acid, concentrated solution of Pt will give a yellow precipitate of K_2PtCl_6, slightly soluble in H_2O, insoluble in 75% alcohol.

Oxalic acid does not precipitate platinum but does precipitate gold.

Iridium, Ir. Compact or strongly ignited iridium is almost completely insoluble in all acids including aqua regia. However, in the finely divided state it is quite readily soluble in aqua regia.

Fusion with soda on charcoal yields a gray, brittle button which is insoluble in aqua regia. Fusion with $KHSO_4$ does not attack metallic Ir, but fusion with Na_2O_2 converts it to a form which is partially soluble in water to give a pale yellow solution and is completely soluble in HCl to give a dark blue solution, which changes to a dark reddish, black solution.

NH_4Cl, added to this solution, gives a dark, red precipitate, which is difficultly soluble in water.

On testing a solution of Ir with NaOH, the color changes from red to green and, on warning, is further changed to reddish, then azure blue.

Germanium, Ge. Heat the precipitate or mineral on charcoal, per se, with the O.F. Germanium is volatile and forms a white coat near the assay, which, after prolonged treatment, moves further away, may turn lemon-yellow and greenish or brownish, and contains small fused globules.

Germanium forms volatile salts and is apt to be lost by volatilization in the process of solution and analysis. GeCl distills at 86°C.

Germanium in a mineral may be put into solution by fusing 1 volume of the finely ground sample with 3–4 volumes of a mixture of equal parts of sodium carbonate and sulfur, extracting the fusion with water and filtering. Ge passes into the filtrate.

Germanium sulfide is appreciably soluble in water and dissolves readily in alkali hydroxides. To test the precipitate for Ge, dissolve it in the minimum amount of NaOH and nearly neutralize with HCl. To test for Ge in a mineral, dissolve in HCl and nearly neutralize with NaOH.

Place a drop of the slightly alkaline solution of the precipitate or slightly acid solution of the mineral, on filter paper, add a drop of ammonium molybdate solution, a drop of benzidine reagent and hold over the ammonia bottle. The development of a blue coloration, according to the amount present, indicates germanium. As Sn, Fe, Se, As, P and SiO_2 will also give this color reaction, their absence must be determined.

Blowpipe reactions of Germanium

Per se on coal: bluish white coating near the assay. White, fused droplets.
I flux on coal: coating is white and assay is brown.
Br flux on coal: white ring around assay, not much of a coating.
Cr flux on coal: white coating.
Per se on plaster: nothing.
I flux on plaster: very slight lemon-yellow film.
Br flux on plaster: trace of yellow and brown films.
Cr flux on plaster: nothing.

Ruthenium, Ru. Metallic ruthenium is insoluble in all acids including aqua regia.

To put Ru into solution, fuse 1 volume of the precipitate or finely divided sample with 4 volumes of Na_2O_2 to quiet fusion in an iron crucible and dissolve the melt in cold water. This gives an orange solution of Ru as sodium ruthenate (Na_2RuO_4) from which nitric acid precipitates the Ru as the hydroxide which is soluble in HCl.

Boiling the solution of Na_2RuO_4 causes the immediate formation of a voluminous, black, colloidal precipitate. This is a sensitive reaction.

If a ruthenium solution is made slightly alkaline with Na_2CO_3 and boiled with KNO_2, cooled and a little $(NH_4)_2S$ added, a carmine-red color, which turns brown, is obtained.

Metallic Zn turns a ruthenium solution first blue, then decolorizes it with the precipitation of gray, metallic ruthenium.

Hydrogen sulfide in acid solution causes no precipitation at first, but after a time the solution becomes azure-blue and brown Ru_2S_3 is precipitated. This is characteristic, but also somewhat similar to the reaction of molybdenum.

If a few drops of a ruthenium chloride solution are added to a solution of sodium thiosulfate and made alkaline with ammonia, and the mixture boiled, a permanent reddish-purple color is produced. Unless very dilute, the color by transmitted light is black.

PROCEDURE 13

Test for Phosphate Radical

The filtrate from P–8 is boiled until all the H_2S has been removed (test with lead acetate paper), allowed to cool and is tested for the phosphate radical.

To test for **phosphate** (PO_4), place a drop of the solution on filter paper, add a drop of ammonium molybdate and a drop of benzidine and hold over the ammonia bottle until most of the mineral acid is neutralized. *A blue color indicates the PO_4 radical.*

The following test may also be used. Add 1 ml. of the solution to a mixture of 1 ml. of ammonium molybdate reagent and 1 ml. of conc. HNO_3. *Not vice versa.* Warm slightly and allow to stand. *A yellow precipitate indicates the phosphate radical* (PO_4).

Vanadium, V, is not completely precipitated by any of the group reagents. In P–14, if V is present in the vanadyl form, it will be partially precipitated. If, however, Fe, Al, U or Ba are present in sufficient quantities, the precipitation of V will be complete. The addition of an excess of ferric chloride will cause all of the V to be thrown down. The treatment in P–15 dissolves the vanadium and it will be reprecipitated with the Al group if sufficient Al or U are present, otherwise it will remain in the filtrate and may be precipitated as directed in P–21.

PROCEDURE 14

Precipitation of Iron and Aluminum Groups

To the H_2S free filtrate from P–8, add NH_4OH to alkalinity and heat to boiling. *No precipitate shows the absence of Fe, Cr, Al, Be, U, Ga and In.* Add $(NH_4)_2S$ in slight excess and heat to nearly boiling. A precipitate indicates the **iron group** (Fe, Mn, Co, Ni, In) or the **aluminum group** (Al, Zn, Cr, Be, U, V, Ga), and if a positive test for PO_4 was obtained, or if V is present, possibly all or a part of the **calcium group** (Ca, Ba, Sr, Mg) as phosphates or vanadates, and any one or all may be present. *If no precipitate forms, all are absent.* Treat the solution by P–19.

If a *negative test* for PO_4 was obtained or *if vanadium is absent* the Ca group *will not be precipitated.*

If PO_4 *is absent,* filter, treat the precipitate by P–15 and the filtrate by P–19.

If PO_4 *is present,* filter, treat the precipitate by P–21 and the filtrate by P–22.

The only member of the calcium group that is precipitated by vanadium is barium, and tests must be made to determine its presence or absence in the precipitate.

Nickel may form a colloidal solution of a dark brown color. If this occurs, make slightly acid with acetic acid, and boil. This coagulates the hydrosol so that it can be filtered.

PROCEDURE 15

Separation of Iron and Aluminum Groups

Transfer the precipitate from P–14 to a beaker and dissolve in a little water and 1 ml. of conc. HCl. Stir, then boil for 1 or 2 minutes, add a pinch of potassium chlorate ($KClO_3$) and boil again for 1 or 2 minutes. Filter, and to the filtrate add NaOH until alkaline; cool and add slowly to the cold solution 1 ml. of dry sodium peroxide (Na_2O_2) stirring constantly. Boil for 1 or 2 minutes and filter. If a portion of the precipitate remains undissolved the **iron group** (Fe, Mn, Co, Ni, In) is indicated and any member or all may be present. *If none or only a slight trace of the precipitate remains undissolved, all are absent.* Treat the solution by P–17.

If a residue remains undissolved, filter, treat the residue by P–16 and the filtrate by P–17.

It is sometimes desirable to separate iron from the other members of the group. This can be done by dissolving the residue in a little water and HCl, adding 1 ml. of solid ammonium chloride (NH_4Cl), making strongly alkaline with NH_4OH and filtering. Iron and indium are precipitated but Co, Mn, and Ni remain in solution and may be precipitated as oxides from the filtrate by adding H_2O_2 or Na_2O_2 and boiling. An excess of Na_2O_2 should be avoided. Mn and Co give brown to black and Ni may give apple-green or black precipitates from the H_2O_2 treatment.

Treat the precipitates by P–16.

Nickel sulfide tends to form dark brown colloidal solutions. In this case much of the nickel passes through the filter paper into the filtrate coloring it brown. By making this filtrate faintly acid with acetic acid and boiling, the hydrosol is coagulated and on refiltering the NiS is retained on the filter paper.

If the precipitation of Tl, Th, Sc, the R.E. groups, Zr and Ti was not complete in the previous operations, they will appear with the iron group.

Indium is a very rare element and it is improbable that tests for it will be obtained on the small sample used in this procedure.

Thallium is usually in the trivalent state and unless it has been converted to the monovalent condition it is not precipitated in P–1 but comes down in the iron group.

PROCEDURE 16

Iron Group Tests

Dry the precipitate from P–15 and treat small amounts in the borax and S.Ph. beads. The tests for the various members of this group are as follows:

WITH BORAX

	Oxidizing Flame		Reducing Flame	
	Hot	Cold	Hot	Cold
Iron, Fe	Yellow to red.	Yellow.	Bottle-green.	Little lighter.
Manganese, Mn	Amethystine.	Reddens.*	Colorless.	Colorless.
Cobalt, Co	Blue.	Blue.	Blue.	Blue.
Nickel, Ni	Violet.	Pale-reddish-brown.	Opaque-gray.	Opaque-gray.

* Care must be taken that too much Mn is not used or the bead will be black, and opaque.

WITH SALT OF PHOSPHORUS

	Oxidizing Flame		Reducing Flame	
	Hot	Cold	Hot	Cold
Iron, Fe	Yellow.	Colorless.	Pale yellowish-green.	Colorless.
Manganese, Mn	Grayish-violet.	Violet.	Colorless.	Colorless.
Cobalt, Co	Blue.	Blue.	Blue.	Blue.
Nickel, Ni	Reddish to brownish-red.	Yellowish to reddish-yellow.	Reddish to brownish-red.	Yellow to reddish-yellow.

ADDITIONAL TESTS

Iron, Fe. Dissolve a part of the residue from P–15 in a small amount of water and HCl. Place a drop of this solution on filter paper or the spot plate and add a drop of potassium ferrocyanide [$K_4Fe(CN)_6$]. Ferric iron is indicated by the formation of the brilliant Prussian blue color. Ferrous iron and potassium ferricyanide $[K_3Fe(CN)_6]$ gives the deep Turnballs's blue.

Dissolve another part of the precipitate from P–15 in a little water and HNO_3. Place a drop of this solution on filter paper or the spot plate and add a drop of ammonium or potassium thiocyanate (NH_4SCN or $KSCN$). A red color indicates ferric iron. Co, Ni, Cr and Cu reduce the sensitivity of this reaction.

The ferrocyanide and thiocyanate tests fail in the presence of phosphates, fluorides, borates, oxalates, citrates and tartrates.

Ferrous Iron. Place a drop of the freshly prepared HCl solution of the mineral on filter paper or the spot plate. If paper is used, the solution must contain tartaric acid; if the spot plate is used, a small crystal of tartaric acid is next added, then a drop of KCN solution followed by a drop of dimethylglyoxime and made alkaline with NH_4OH. An intense red color indicates ferrous iron. The color fades due to the oxidation of the iron to the ferric state. Ni and Co in large amounts interfere with the test.

Many iron compounds become magnetic if heated with soda on coal in the R.F. Cobalt and nickel compounds give a similar test but they can easily be differentiated by the bead tests.

With bromide flux, iron gives a blackish coat around the assay with a brownish band far away. $(NH_4)_2S$ vapors turn the coat green and develop spots where no coat was seen before.

Manganese, Mn. If the mineral or residue from P–15 is fused with soda and a little KNO_3 on platinum, and Mn is present, the fusion will be bluish-green. This is a very delicate test. This should have been in evidence if the mineral was put into solution by fusion at the beginning of the operation.

If this green melt is dissolved in a little water and made acid with HCl or acetic acid, the green solution rapidly changes to reddish violet with the formation of a brownish precipitate on standing.

Some manganese minerals, treated with HCl and heated, give off chlorine, a very pungent and irritating gas. The black ores give a greenish black solution.

NH_4OH does not precipitate Mn from solutions containing ammonia salts. Boiling the solution with H_2O_2 or Na_2O_2 precipitates the Mn as oxide. This is used to separate it from Fe, Al and all other elements forming hydroxides that are insoluble in an excess of NH_4OH. An excess of Na_2O_2 should be avoided.

Cobalt, Co. If the bead tests have been made on the precipitate of the group, they will have given a very excellent indication of the presence or absence of this element.

If bead tests are made on the mineral, and sulfur and arsenic are present, it should first be thoroughly roasted on charcoal.

In the presence of HCl, cobaltous compounds give a blue to green solution.

NH_4OH precipitates the hydrous oxide, soluble in excess. Boiling the solution with H_2O_2 or Na_2O_2 precipitates Co as the black oxide. This may be used

186

to separate it from Fe, Al and all other elements forming hydroxides insoluble in an excess of NH_4OH. An excess of Na_2O_2 should be avoided.

Dissolve a part of the precipitate from P–15 in a little water and HCl and add NH_4OH till the solution is only faintly acid. Place a drop on the spot plate and add a drop of saturated ammonium thiocyanate (NH_4SCN). If a red color develops (due to iron) add two or three drops of saturated ammonium acetate and two or three drops of 50% tartaric acid. This dissolves the red of the iron and allows the blue of the cobalt to appear.

Place a drop of the cobalt solution on the spot plate and add two or three drops of acetone, then a crystal of NH_4SCN. Cobalt gives a blue color which becomes pink on the addition of water.

Place a crystal of NH_4SCN on filter paper and moisten with an HCl solution of the precipitate or mineral. Treat with NH_4OH until the spot is decolorized. Chromium may leave a green spot. Dry the paper over the flame almost to carbonization. A bluish-green color (not the same as before heating) becomes apparent if cobalt is present.

Dimethylglyoxime gives no precipitate with an ammoniacal solution of cobalt but a wine-red color is obtained if ammonium sulfide is also present.

To a drop of an HCl solution of the residue or mineral on the spot plate, add two or three drops of 3% H_2O_2 and then a crystal of potassium bicarbonate ($KHCO_3$). Cobalt gives a green color on the crystal.

Treat a portion of the precipitate or powdered mineral with four volumes of soda on charcoal or platinum in the O.F. and dissolve the fusion in the minimum amount of conc. HNO_3. Place a drop or two of this solution on filter paper, add a drop or two of conc. HCl and dry carefully over the flame. The paper will be colored greenish if Ni and bluish if Co is present (with very small amounts it remains colorless). The spot, moistened with 20% NaOH solution and subjected to bromine fumes will become black if Ni and/or Co are present.

Nickel, Ni. Dissolve the mineral or residue from P–15 in HCl, make slightly alkaline with NH_4OH, add a drop or two of dimethylglyoxime, and boil. If nickel is present, a scarlet, crystalline precipitate will be formed. In the *presence of much iron,* as is usually the case in treating the precipitate from P–15, dissolve a part of the residue in water and HCl, leaving it quite strongly acid. Add a little solid NH_4Cl, make strongly alkaline with NH_4OH, filter and test the filtrate as above. Nickel remains in solution.

NH_4OH precipitates the apple-green basic salt, soluble in excess, giving a blue solution that is paler than that obtained from copper, but if sufficient ammonia salts are present, NH_4OH produces no precipitate [similar to Co, Mg, Fe(ous), and Mn(ous)]; NaOH and KOH, however, cause apple-green hydroxide to be thrown down from this solution. Under these conditions cobalt is not precipitated.

The NH_4OH solution, boiled with H_2O_2 or Na_2O_2, precipitates the Ni as the oxide. This may be used to separate nickel from Fe, Al and all other elements forming hydroxides insoluble in an excess of NH_4OH. An excess of Na_2O_2 should be avoided.

Indium, In. Indium may be separated from other members of the iron group by dissolving the precipitate in water and the minimum amount of HCl, adding NH_4OH until the solution is only faintly acid and passing in H_2S. Indium is precipitated as yellow In_2S_3. If the acidity is too high, the indium will not be precipitated. The precipitate (sulfide) formed by ammonium sulfide is white.

While indium is not precipitated with the hydrogen sulfide groups and remains with the iron group in the separation of the ammonium sulfide groups when in fair amounts, some is carried down by the members of the H_2S groups and small amounts may thus be lost. Because of this, if indium is suspected, it is best to dissolve a fresh sample in the regular way, then add conc. HCl and evaporate nearly to dryness; again add conc. HCl, evaporate to near dryness to drive off the HNO_3, dissolve in water, nearly neutralize with NH_4OH, add metallic zinc, and digest or allow to stand until no further precipitation occurs. After the zinc has used all of the free acid, it will cause the precipitation of the indium along with Pb, Cu, etc. (see Reactions with Metallic Zinc in Acid Solutions). The Fe, Al, etc. will remain in solution. When the reaction is completed, filter, wash the precipitate from the filter paper into an evaporating dish, dissolve in HNO_3, treat with about $\frac{1}{2}$ ml of conc. H_2SO_4 and evaporate to strong fuming. Dilute with water and filter off the $PbSO_4$. To the filtrate, add 1 ml of dry NH_4Cl, make alkaline with NH_4OH, boil and filter. Cu, Cd, Mn, Co, etc., remain in solution while the indium is precipitated. If the precipitate is brown, some of the iron has been carried down with the other metals; to free the In from them the precipitate is redissolved in the minimum amount of HCl and again precipitated with metallic zinc. This precipitate is washed from the filter paper, dissolved in water and a little HCl, then NH_4OH is added until the solution is only faintly acid and H_2S passed in. Indium gives a yellow precipitate of In_2S_3.

Per se on plaster: indium gives a slight coating that is orange-yellow while hot and lemon-yellow when cold, near the assay. The assay is lemon-yellow.

Iodide flux on plaster: small dark ring near assay. Light yellow coating at some distance from the assay.

Bromide flux on plaster: small brownish coating near the assay and a slight yellow one far away. The assay is brown.

Chromate flux on plaster: slight yellowish and brownish coat near assay.

Per se on charcoal: indium gives a coating that is orange-yellow while hot and whitish yellow when cold, near the assay with a bluish black, somewhat iridescent ring beyond.

Iodide flux on coal: the coating is white near the assay with a darker ring beyond and bluish far away.

Bromide flux on coal: shiny black near the assay with bluish white next, followed by a darker area and light bluish white far away.

Chromate flux on coal: slight yellowish and brownish coating near the assay.

Indium salts color the flame a peculiar bluish-violet.

NH_4OH and caustic alkalies precipitate white, gelatinous $In(OH)_3$ resembling $Al(OH)_3$ in behavior and appearance, soluble in excess of $NaOH$ and KOH, but the solution becomes turbid on standing, and boiling with NH_4Cl precipitates all of the indium as hydroxide.

The quinalizarine spot test for indium is made as follows: Separate the iron and indium from the other members of the group, then dissolve this in a small amount of water and acetic acid. Add NH_4OH until the solution is almost neutral. Place a drop of this solution in a small casserole and treat with $Na_2S_2O_3$ until no more violet color forms. A crystal of Na_2SO_3 and 5–6 drops of 5% KCN are then added and the mixture warmed until the precipitate is dissolved. The solution should be neutral or slightly acid with acetic acid. A drop of this solution is placed on paper that has been impregnated with the alcoholic quinalizarine and dried. This is then held over the ammonia bottle for a few minutes and then immersed in a saturated solution of boric acid. This decomposes the violet ammonium quinalizarinate and permits the red or violet indium lake to be seen against the red or yellow colored paper. This test is positive in the presence of 400 to 500 times as much iron as indium, but it is better to precipitate the In as sulfide first, then to use this test for confirmation.

PROCEDURE 17

Precipitation of Aluminum Group

Make the filtrate from P–15 acid with HCl, then barely alkaline with NH_4OH; add ½ ml. of solid ammonium chloride (NH_4Cl) and heat to nearly boiling. A precipitate indicates Al, Be, U, Ga and possibly some V. Filter, add 1 ml. of solid Na_2CO_3 and boil until there is no odor of ammonia. Zinc is precipitated as white basic carbonate. Filter, make the filtrate acid with HCl, pass in H_2S for a few minutes, then make alkaline with NH_4OH and pass in H_2S again for several minutes. Chromium is precipitated as the grayish-green hydroxide [$Cr(OH)_3$], and zinc, if not precipitated as indicated above, is thrown down as the white sulfide (ZnS). Filter. If vanadium is present, the filtrate will be yellowish-red to brilliant violet-red. The addition of acids to this solution precipitates black V_2O_4 or V_2O_5. The filtrate from this may be blue and still contain appreciable amounts of vanadium.

If further separation of the Al, Be, U and Ga precipitate is desired, dissolve in a little water and HCl (not over 10 ml.), make barely alkaline with NH_4OH, add 1 ml. of solid ammonium carbonate [$(NH_4)_2CO_3$], and heat to nearly boiling. This solution will show a yellowish green fluorescence under ultra-violet

189

light if uranium is present. Aluminum is precipitated. Filter, boil to a low volume to drive off the ammonium carbonate, make acid with HCl and boil for a minute or two, then make strongly alkaline with NaOH, and boil until there is no odor of ammonia. Uranium is precipitated. Filter; make the filtrate acid with HCl, then strongly alkaline with NH_4OH and heat to nearly boiling. Beryllium and some vanadium are precipitated. Filter; add HCl until the solution is barely alkaline. Gallium is precipitated.

The precipitates are treated by P–18. Reject the final filtrate.

These separations are not sharp and each precipitate may contain small quantities of the other elements. Gallium usually occurs in very small amounts and it is improbable that tests will be obtained on the small sample used in this scheme.

PROCEDURE 18
Aluminum Group Tests

Dry the precipitates from P–17 and treat small amounts in the borax and S.Ph. beads. The tests for the various members of the group are as follows:

	WITH BORAX			
	Oxidizing Flame		Reducing Flame	
	Hot	Cold	Hot	Cold
Chromium, Cr	Yellow to red.	Yellowish-green.	Emerald-green.	Emerald-green.
Uranium, U	Yellow to orange.	Yellow.	Pale-green.	Pale green to colorless.
Vanadium, V	Colorless to yellow.	Yellowish-green to colorless.	Dirty green.	Fine green.
Aluminum, Al	None.			
Zinc, Zn	None.			
Beryllium, Be	None.			
Gallium, Ga	None.			

WITH SALT OF PHOSPHORUS

	Oxidizing Flame		Reducing Flame	
,	Hot	Cold	Hot	Cold
Chromium, Cr	Dirty green.	Fine emerald-green.	Dirty green.	Fine emerald-green.
Uranium, U	Yellow.	Colorless.	Pale dirty green.	Fine green.
Vanadium, V	Dark yellow.	Light yellow.	Dirty green.	Fine green.
Aluminum, Al	None.			
Zinc, Zn	None.			
Beryllium, Be	None.			
Gallium, Ga	None.			

ADDITIONAL TESTS

Aluminum, Al. Dissolve some of the mineral or precipitate from P–17 in HCl and add NH_4OH in excess. A white, flocculent precipitate indicates Al. Beryllium and zinc also give white precipitates, but Zn is soluble in ammonium chloride and Be is soluble in ammonium carbonate. Chromium forms a bluish-green precipitate that is partially soluble.

Moisten a small amount of the dried precipitate from P–17 on plaster with cobalt solution, avoiding an excess, as on heating it leaves black cobalt oxide which may obscure the test. Heat strongly in the O.F. A fine blue color indicates aluminum.

Zinc, Zn. To a small portion of the dried precipitate from P–17 add soda and borax and treat with the O.F. on coal. The presence of Zn will be indicated by the formation of a coating that is yellow while hot and white or grayish when cold. The coat if moistened with cobalt solution and treated with a strong O.F., gives a bright green color on cooling. Avoid an excess of the cobalt solution as it leaves a black oxide which may partially obscure the green of the test.

Dissolve a small portion of the precipitate from P–17 in HCl and add NH_4OH and $(NH_4)_2S$. If Zn is present, a white precipitate will form.

Some of the Zn minerals, when treated with a strong R.F., give a characteristic vivid pale bluish-green light which appears as streaks in the outer parts of the flame.

Some zinc silicates, when treated with cobalt solution in the O.F., give a blue color similar to aluminum.

Chromium, Cr. Fuse some of the precipitate from P–17 with soda and KNO_3 on platinum. This yields yellow alkali chromates. If this is dissolved

191

in water then acidified with acetic acid and $AgNO_3$ added, reddish-brown silver chromate (Ag_2CrO_4) is precipitated. This is a very sensitive test for minute amounts of Cr.

Mix some of the dry precipitate from P–17 with soda and treat on coal. If Cr is present, a green slag will result, which after long heating changes to infusible chromic oxide.

Green chromic acid is converted to blue perchromic acids by H_2O_2.

If a *cold alkaline* solution of a chromate is treated with neutral H_2O_2, the solution is colored red, which gradually changes, with evolution of oxygen, back to the original yellow of the chromate.

If a *cold neutral* solution of a dichromate is treated with H_2O_2, it is colored violet, which gradually changes, with evolution of oxygen, back to the original color of the dichromate.

If a chromate is treated with H_2O_2 in the *presence of dilute H_2SO_4 or HCl,* intensely blue H_7CrO_{10} is formed, which shortly changes to green with the evolution of oxygen.

Dissolve a portion of the precipitate from P–17 in the minimum amount of HCl and water. Place a drop of this solution and a drop of fairly strong sodium peroxide in water, and then a drop of benzidine solution on filter paper. Chromium (chromates) is indicated by a blue ring.

Beryllium, Be. There are no simple blowpipe or chemical tests for this element.

Dissolve a small amount of the precipitate from P–17 in HCl and evaporate nearly to dryness. Add a small amount of water and KOH in the amount necessary to dissolve the precipitate that forms at first, but not a great excess. The solution is diluted to 10 times its volume, filtered and boiled. If beryllium is present, a white precipitate of $Be(OH)_2$ separates out. If this is treated on coal with cobalt solution it should give a gray or lavender mass.

Dissolve a portion of the precipitate from P–17 (Al, Be, U, Ga) in the minimum amount of water and HCl. Place a drop or two of this solution on the spot plate, add a drop of quinalizarine and make slightly alkaline with NaOH. A blue color or precipitate indicates beryllium. If too strongly alkaline the precipitate is soluble. The violet of the blank (which should be run at the same time) is quite different from the blue of the beryllium. Aluminum and zinc give a violet color or precipitate almost identical with the color of the blank; uranium gives a dirty yellowish precipitate; vanadium gives a light purple to violet color that is lighter than the blank and chromium gives a purplish-blue color or precipitate that is similar to beryllium; if the first portion of the precipitate of the group is used, Cr is not present.

$Be(OH)_2$ is soluble in an excess of $(NH_4)_2CO_3$; [$Al(OH)_3$ is not] but it is reprecipitated on boiling; it is insoluble in an excess of NH_4OH; [$Al(OH)_3$ is partially soluble]; it is soluble in an excess of NaOH or KOH; [$Fe(OH)_3$ and uranium are not].

192

If the precipitate from P–17 or some of the powdered mineral is fused with Na_2CO_3 and extracted with water (no acid), beryllium remains in the residue as oxide, but aluminum passes into solution. Treatment of the undissolved residue with HCl will put the beryllium into solution.

Uranium, U. Fuse the powdered mineral with three volumes of soda. Dissolve the melt in HCl, neutralize with NH_4OH, add solid ammonium carbonate, shake and allow to stand for some time. Uranium is precipitated but is soluble in excess of ammonium carbonate and by filtering may be separated from Fe, Al and the other elements that are precipitated by this reagent. Filter, boil to a low volume, make acid with HCl, and boil to drive off the CO_2; add NaOH in excess, and boil. Uranium is thrown down as a yellow precipitate and may be confirmed by the bead tests.

The solution of the Al group which separates it from the Fe group, will show a yellowish green fluorescent ring at the top of the liquid under the ultra-violet light if uranium is present.

The sodium fluoride and lithium fluoride beads are brilliantly fluorescent under ultra-violet light if uranium is present. This is a sensitive test.

Treat the pulverized mineral or precipitate from P–17 with H_2SO_4 and evaporate nearly to dryness, dilute with water, filter, and to the filtrate add metallic zinc. If uranium is present the solution will change color from yellow to green; when all the acid is used, a yellow precipitate will form on the residual zinc. Large amounts of iron and vanadium interfere with the test. W, Cb, Ti, V, Mo and Ru also give color reactions.

From solutions of uranium minerals, ammonium, potassium and sodium hydroxides produce a yellow precipitate.

Dissolve some of the precipitate from P–17 in acetic acid and nearly neutralize with NH_4OH. Place a drop of this solution on filter paper or the spot plate and add a drop of potassium ferrocyanide $[K_4Fe(CN)_6]$. Uranium gives a dark brown color which is turned yellow by NaOH. This is a very sensitive test. Molybdenum and copper are the only other elements giving a brown precipitate with potassium ferrocyanide and they should not be present.

Metallic zinc in contact with a uranium mineral in HCl solution will form a yellow deposit on the residual zinc when the acid is used up.

Vanadium, V. In the C.T. with $KHSO_4$, vanadates give a yellow mass.

Dissolved in H_2SO_4 and reduced with zinc, if a vanadate is present, the solution becomes successively yellow, green, greenish-blue, bluish-green, bluish-violet, and lavender.

Place a little of the finely ground mineral in a porcelain dish, add a little conc. HCl then metallic zinc and boil for a few minutes. If vanadium is present the solution will become blue, green, then bluish-violet. W, Ti, Cb, Mo, U and Ru also give color reactions.

If H_2O_2 is added to a cold acid solution of a vanadate, a deep yellow to red tint is acquired, which changes to blue on heating. Ether does not extract the color but remains colorless (distinction from chromium). The color is not affected by H_3PO_4 (distinction from iron), or HF (distinction from titanium).

Vanadium minerals give a red to yellow solution with strong acids.

Treat the precipitate or powdered mineral with conc. HCl and heat. Cool and dilute with water to 3 or 4 times its volume, add a little metallic zinc and after allowing to react for some time, add a drop or two of freshly made saturated water solution of cacothelin. Vanadium gives a violet to red color according to the amount present. Molybdates, tungstates, tin and antimony give a similar reaction.

Fuse the powdered mineral with four parts of soda and two parts of potassium nitrate (KNO_3) on the platinum foil. Digest the fusion with warm water. Filter and acidify with acetic acid, and add a little lead acetate. Lead vanadate is thrown down as a pale yellow precipitate. Filter, wash, and confirm by the bead tests.

If an ammoniacal solution of vanadium is treated with H_2S, a violet-red color is obtained. This is a very sensitive test in the *absence of molybdenum,* which gives a similar color reaction.

Vanadium may be tested for in the alkaline solution before filtering off the Al group precipitate. Place a drop of the alkaline solution and a drop or two of conc. HCl in a small crucible and evaporate nearly to dryness. Pour the residual solution upon filter paper, add a drop of 1% $FeCl_3$ solution and three drops of dimethylglyoxime and make alkaline with NH_4OH. Vanadium gives a cherry-red to brown color. By dipping the paper into ammonia solution, the brown ferric hydroxide washes off, leaving the paper colored by the iron dimethylglyoxime.

Gallium, Ga. $Ga(OH)_3$ is white, resembling $Al(OH)_3$, and is quite soluble in NH_4OH, which is increased by ammonia salts. $Al(OH)_3$ is insoluble in the presence of ammonia salts. $Ga(OH)_3$ is readily soluble in $(NH_4)_2CO_3$ solution; $Al(OH)_3$ is not soluble.

Gallium can be separated from aluminum by precipitation with potassium ferrocyanide from weak HCl solution, as white or bluish-white gallium ferrocyanide.

Gallium usually occurs in extremely small amounts and it is improbable that tests will be obtained on the small sample used in this scheme.

Procedure 19

Precipitation of the Calcium Group

The filtrate from P–14 is concentrated to a small volume, filtered and allowed to cool. To this is added one volume of strong ammonium carbonate solution and one volume of 95% alcohol and allowed to stand for a half hour, with frequent shaking. A precipitate indicates the **calcium group** (Ca, Ba, Sr, Mg) and any one or all may be present. *If no precipitate forms, all are absent.* Treat the solution by P–22.

If a precipitate is formed, filter; treat the precipitate by P–20 and the filtrate by P–22.

PROCEDURE 20

Calcium Group Tests

Moisten a portion of the precipitate from P–19 with HCl, then take a piece on a clean platinum loop (cleaned by repeated dipping in conc. HCl and flaming until no further flame coloration is obtained) and hold in the nonluminous zone of the O.F. The flame colorations produced by the various members of the group are as follows:

	FLAME COLORS	
	With Naked Eye	With Merwin Screen
Calcium, Ca	Yellowish to orange-red.	Through 1. Flash of greenish-yellow. Through 2. Invisible. Through 3. Flash of crimson.
Barium, Ba.	Yellowish-green.	Through 1. Bright green. Through 2. Faint green. Through 3. Faint green.
Strontium, Sr.	Crimson-red.	Through 1. Invisible. Through 2. Invisible. Through 3. Crimson.
Magnesium, Mg.	None.	None.

ADDITIONAL TESTS

Calcium, Ca. The flame colorations should be sufficient identification for this element.

Calcium oxalate (CaC_2O_4) is virtually insoluble in hot acetic acid.

Calcium sulfate ($CaSO_4$) is quite soluble in water and HCl.

Dissolve a portion of the precipitate from P–19 in a little water and HCl, make alkaline with NH_4OH then acid with acetic acid. Place a drop of this solution, a few drops of a saturated solution of potassium ferrocyanide [$K_4Fe(CN)_6$] and a drop of alcohol on a watch glass and mix. A white, crystalline precipitate indicates Ca. Strontium gives no precipitate, barium is precipitated only from concentrated solutions, and magnesium precipitates only from alkaline solutions.

Barium, Ba. Barium oxalate (BaC_2O_4) is completely soluble in hot acetic acid.

Barium sulfate ($BaSO_4$) is insoluble in water and HCl.

Dissolve a small part of the precipitate from P–19 in acetic acid and add K_2CrO_4 or $K_2Cr_2O_7$. A yellow precipitate indicates barium. Ca, Sr, and Mg do not give this reaction, except from concentrated solutions.

Dissolve a small part of the precipitate from P–19 in conc. HCl and add a drop of H_2SO_4. A white precipitate that is insoluble in acids indicates barium.

Strontium, Sr. The flame colorations should be sufficient indication for this element.

Strontium oxalate (SrC_2O_4) is somewhat soluble in hot acetic acid.

Strontium sulfate ($SrSO_4$) is much less soluble in water and HCl than $CaSO_4$.

Magnesium, Mg. The oxalate and sulfate are completely soluble in hot acetic acid or a mixture of water and HCl.

Dissolve a portion of the precipitate from P–19 in dilute HCl. Place a drop of this solution and two drops of quinalizarine on the spot plate and mix thoroughly, then add one drop of 20% NaOH solution. Magnesium gives a blue precipitate or color. A blank should be run at the same time. The difference between the blue-violet of the blank and the blue of the Mg is intensified by standing, as the color of the blank gradually fades, while the blue of the Mg is stable. The other members of the group do not interfere if the NaOH concentration is sufficient. If there is any doubt, add a drop or two more NaOH. Much calcium may give a violet precipitate the same color as the blank.

Dissolve the remainder of the precipitate from P–19 in a small volume of dilute HCl, make strongly alkaline with NH_4OH, add ammonium oxalate $[(NH_4)_2C_2O_4]$ and allow to stand for some time in the cold. This precipitates the Ca, Ba and Sr as oxalates. Filter, and to the filtrate add sodium phosphate (Na_2HPO_4) and allow to stand. A white precipitate indicates Mg. Place some of this precipitate on charcoal, moisten with cobalt solution, and heat strongly. Magnesium should give a pink or flesh color. An excess of the cobalt solution should be avoided, as it leaves a black oxide which may obscure the test.

Procedure 21

If the PO_4 radical was found in the test in P–13, the precipitate from P–14 will contain the **iron and aluminum groups and a part or all of the calcium group.** In the regular wet methods these are separated, but as this calls for quite elaborate procedure and equipment, and as the tests used in this scheme for the various members of the groups interfere with each other very little, this separation is omitted in this system of analysis.

If PO_4 *is present,* test the precipitate from P–14 by the tests for the iron, aluminum and calcium groups, as outlined in P–16, P–18 and P–20.

If the solution is blue, or if further precipitation of molybdenum and vanadium is desired, or if no test for either was obtained and one wishes to make certain that these elements (especially vanadium) are not being overlooked, the filtrate from P–19 is made acid with HCl, boiled to expel the CO_2, cooled, made strongly alkaline with NH_4OH and H_2S passed in to complete saturation or until a bright red color is obtained. The color may be yellowish if Mo and V are present in very small amounts. On acidifying this, the Mo is thrown down as brown MoS_3 and the V is precipitated as black V_2S_4 or V_2S_5. Even this treatment may not give quantitative removal of Mo and V and detectable amounts may still remain in the filtrate, coloring it blue.

The vanadium precipitate is soluble in $(NH_4)_2CO_3$ and may be used to separate it from the MoS_3, which is only slightly soluble.

The filtrate is treated by P–22.

PROCEDURE 22

The filtrate from P–19, P–21 or, if PO_4 was present, from P–14, contains the **sodium group** (Na, K, Li, Cs, Rb). *If the mineral was put into solution by fusion with soda or potassium bisulfate, this must be taken into consideration, as Na and K from this will be present.* If this is the case, the presence of the sodium group may be determined by taking *a new sample of the finely ground mineral,* mixing with one part of ammonium chloride (NH_4Cl) and eight parts of precipitated calcium carbonate ($CaCO_3$), heating on charcoal or in platinum (not silica or porcelain, as these are attacked), grinding and leaching with water (no acid). This puts the alkali metals in solution as chlorides, along with a little calcium. The calcium is removed by P–19, is filtered, and the filtrate treated as below.

Evaporate in a silica or porcelain dish to dryness, slowly, to prevent spattering; ignite below redness until no more white fumes are given off, keeping the dish in continual motion and making sure that all parts of the dish have been heated to remove all ammonia and volatile salts. The residue left in the dish is the **sodium group** (Na, K, Li, Cs, Rb) and any one or all may be present. *If no residue remains, all are absent.*

Treat the residue by P–23.

PROCEDURE 23

SODIUM GROUP TESTS

Moisten the residue from P–22 with HCl, then take a small piece in a clean platinum loop (cleaned by repeated dipping in conc. HCl and flaming until no further coloration of the flame is obtained) and hold in the non-luminous part of the O.F. The coloration produced by the various members of the group are as follows:

FLAME COLORATION

	With Naked Eye	With Merwin Screen
Sodium, Na	Intensely yellow.	Through 1. Invisible. Through 2. Invisible. Through 3. Invisible.
Potassium, K	Pale violet.	Through 1. Blue-violet. Through 2. Deep red-violet. Through 3. Red-violet.
Lithium, Li	Carmine.	Through 1. Invisible. Through 2. Invisible. Through 3. Crimson.

If much sodium is present, it is likely to mask the colors of the others so that they can not be seen with the naked eye. Lithium, however, usually shows through the sodium.

Caesium, Cs and Rubidium, Rb give flame tests almost identical with potassium and a spectroscope must be used to identify them.

ADDITIONAL TESTS

There are no simple chemical tests for the separation and identification of the alkali metals.

Caesium, Cs. Add a small amount of water to the precipitate, so that not all of the salt is dissolved, thus giving a saturated solution, and add HNO_3 until it is neutral or only faintly acid. To a drop of this solution on a spot plate add a drop of potassium ferricyanide-lead acetate reagent. A yellow to orange precipitate after a few minutes indicates caesium.

Place another drop of the solution and a drop of potassium-bismuth iodide on filter paper. An orange to yellow stain indicates caesium. A blank should be run at the same time.

PROCEDURE 24

Tests for Anions

In addition to the indications obtained by the Reactions with $KHSO_4$ in the Closed Tube (page 69), further tests for the acid radicals and elements may be carried out as follows:

Boron as **Borate.** Warm some of the finely ground mineral with HCl and water; moisten a piece of turmeric paper with this solution and dry carefully (on a test tube of boiling water). A reddish-brown color that becomes blue to black on moistening with NH_4OH indicates boron.

Mix a small amount of the powdered mineral with three parts of boric acid flux and water to a paste. With a clean Pt loop, test this in the tip of the non-luminous flame. If boron is present, the flame will have a momentary green color. With this test lithium gives a carmine red.

Most boron minerals give a yellowish-green flame if moistened with H_2SO_4, also if mixed with H_2SO_4 and NH_4F.

Alcohol, added to an H_2SO_4 solution of a borate, will burn with a green flame.

Carbon, C as **Carbonate.** All carbonates effervesce with strong HCl, most of them in the cold. Add conc. (HNO_3 should be used with lead compounds) to the powdered mineral in the C.T. Carbon (CO_2) is indicated by effervescence. Place a glowing splinter in the tube. If CO_2 is present, it will be extinguished at once. Pour the gas, which is heavier than air, into another tube containing a solution of $Ca(OH)_2$ or $Ba(OH)_2$, close with the thumb, and shake. If CO_2 is present, a white precipitate will be formed.

The addition of a carbonate to a clear S.Ph. bead will cause effervescence during fusion.

Most carbonates are decomposed, by treatment before the blowpipe, into the oxide of the metal and CO_2. The noble metals yield the metal instead of the oxide.

As **Hydrocarbon.** If the specimen gives the odor of a burning substance when ignited, it is probably organic and is one of the hydrocarbons. Heated in the C.T., hydrocarbons usually deposit a ring of oily substance in the upper part of the tube.

On the plaster tablet, carbonaceous material forms a brownish-black non-volatile coat.

Fluorine, F as **Fluoride.** Mix the powdered mineral with four volumes of sodium meta-phosphate ($NaPO_3$) and heat in the C.T. Fluorine is indicated by the etching of the glass and the deposition of a ring of SiO_2 that can not be removed by washing.

In a lead dish (porcelain or glass coated with paraffin will serve) add conc. H_2SO_4 to the mineral. Hold a watch glass over this in the fumes. The evolution of hydrofluoric acid (HF) and the etching of the glass, indicate fluorine.

Fluorides give a momentary green flame when heated in the O.F. with borax and $KHSO_4$.

Most fluorides are unchanged by ignition, but by heating them with silica in moist air they are more or less completely decomposed.

Hydrogen, H as **H_2O.** Hydrogen as water of crystallization is tested for by heating the substance in the C.T. Care must be used that only the bottom part of the tube is heated to allow the water to condense in the upper, cooler portion.

Some minerals yield acid or alkaline water. To determine this, test with litmus paper.

As **Hydrocarbon.** Hydrogen and carbon occur together in the hydrocarbons; if carbon as hydrocarbon is indicated above, hydrogen is also present.

Nitrogen, N as Nitrate. Boil some of the finely ground mineral with water (no acid), cool and add twice its volume of conc. H_2SO_4. After cooling, pour a concentrated solution of ferrous sulfate ($FeSO_4$) carefully on top of the mixture. A dark ring at the juncture of the two liquids indicates nitrogen as nitrate.

Heat the mineral in the C.T. with $KHSO_4$. Red-brown acrid vapors (NO_2 and N_2O_5) indicate the NO_3 radical. Moisten a piece of filter paper in $FeSO_4$ solution and hold in the vapors. If the fumes are due to nitrates, the paper will be turned brown.

Mix a small amount of the powdered sample with copper filings in a test tube, add conc H_2SO_4 and heat. Nitrogen as nitrate is indicated by the evolution of red-orange vapors with a pungent odor.

Nitrates deflagrate very violently if fused on charcoal.

As **Ammonia.** Mix the powdered mineral with an equal amount of slaked lime [$Ca(OH)_2$] and make into a paste with water (moistening the mineral with strong NaOH will give the same result), and heat in the C.T. If NH_3 is present, it will be evolved as a gas and can be detected by its odor and will turn red litmus paper blue. Ammonia turns turmeric paper brownish.

Oxygen, O. Oxygen is usually not tested for independently, as only a few of the minerals have an excess which will be liberated on heating. The usual test is in conjunction with the oxy-acids. If none of the acid elements are found in the mineral and it is not a metal, it is usually considered as being an oxide.

A few of the higher oxides, such as manganese dioxide (MnO_2), if heated in the C.T., yield oxygen. If a glowing splinter is held in this it will burst into flame and burn brightly.

Fuse the finely ground mineral with four volumes of soda, crush the fuse mass, boil with water (no acid), filter, divide the filtrate into three parts and treat as below.

PART 1

Acidify with HCl, boil, filter and test small portions as follows:

Sulfur as Sulfate. Add a drop of $BaCl_2$ solution. A white precipitate that is insoluble in acids indicates the sulfate radical (SO_4).

Some sulfates are insoluble in acids and must be put into solution by fusion with soda on charcoal. Barite is such a mineral. The sulfate is reduced to sulfide.

As **Sulfide.** If lead acetate is added to the acidified solution *before boiling* it will turn black if sulfide is present.

See also soda bead tests, P–24.

Most sulfides on roasting, yield SO_2.

Some sulfides yield a sublimate of sulfur when heated in the C.T. This is red while hot and yellow when cold.

Silicon, Si as **Silica,** SiO_2. Evaporate a portion to dryness, treat with conc. HCl and again evaporate to dryness, add HCl and water. A white insoluble residue indicates silica.

Fuse some of the mineral with an equal volume of soda on charcoal in the O.F. Silica (SiO_2) will dissolve with effervescence to a colorless bead (unless colored by one of the metals); additional soda will cause the bead to become opaque.

Borax with silica gives a clear bead.

Treat a speck of the mineral in the S.Ph. bead. The silicates will remain as a skeleton of about the same shape as the original particle and will float around in the bead.

If S.Ph. is added to a clear borax bead that is nearly saturated with silica, it will become opaque.

The procedure for putting the mineral into solution in preparation for analysis describes methods of removing silica.

SiO_2 treated with HF forms volatile SiF_4. Many silicates, if treated with conc. H_2SO_4 and HF and heated, will decompose with the evolution of SiF_4, leaving a silica-free residue. This is often used for the removal of silica in preparation for analysis.

PART 2

Acidify with HNO_3, boil, filter and test small portions as follows:

Arsenic, As, as **Arsenate.** Arsenates give the same test with ammonium molybdate as phosphates. See below.

Chlorine, Cl as **Chloride.** Add a drop of $AgNO_3$. A white precipitate which dissolves in NH_4OH and is reprecipitated on again making acid with HNO_3, indicates chloride.

Mix the powdered mineral with four volumes of $KHSO_4$ and a little manganese dioxide (MnO_2) and heat in the C.T. Cl is indicated by acrid yellowish-green vapors.

Saturate an S.Ph. bead with CuO, add a speck of the mineral and heat in the O.F. Cl gives an azure-blue flame with a little green.

Bromine, Br, as **Bromine.** To another portion add a drop of $AgNO_3$. A yellow precipitate which dissolves with difficulty in NH_4OH, indicates Br as bromide *in the absence of iodine.*

Saturate an S.Ph. bead with CuO, add a small amount of the mineral and treat in the O.F. Br is indicated by an azure-blue or emerald-green flame.

Fuse the mineral with soda, pulverize, mix with manganese dioxide (MnO_2), add a few drops of conc. H_2SO_4 and heat in the C.T. Br. is indicated by the evolution of choking red-brown vapors.

Iodine, I, as **Iodide.** To a third portion add a drop of starch solution and a few drops of chlorine water. A blue color indicates iodine.

Add a speck of the mineral to an S.Ph. bead saturated with CuO and treat in the O.F. Iodine will give an emerald-green flame.

Phosphorus, P as **Phosphate.** To a fourth portion, add a few drops of conc. HNO_3 and ammonium molybdate solution. Warm and let stand for a few minutes. A yellow precipitate indicates phosphate.

Most phosphates give a bluish-green flame if moistened with H_2SO_4.

Fuse the mineral with a small piece of metallic magnesium or sodium in the C.T. and moisten with water. If P is present, phosphine (PH_3), recognizable by its disagreeable odor, is evolved.

The same test may be made by mixing the powdered mineral with an equal amount of soda, placing it in the C.T. as a cover over metallic magnesium, and heating. All must be dry. On heating, if P is present, there will be a bright incandescence and on crushing the mass and moistening with water, the odor of PH_3 will be detected. This is somewhat like the garlic odor of arsine (AsH_3).

Fuse 1 volume of the powdered mineral with 4 volumes of soda on charcoal or platinum, dissolve the fusion in the minimum amount of water, filter, neutralize the filtrate with acetic acid and add a crystal or silver nitrate. The formation of a yellow layer around the crystal indicates the presence of PO_4 radical.

See P–13 for other tests.

PART 3

Acidify with acetic acid, boil, filter and treat small portions as follows:

Chromium, Cr, as **Chromates.** Add a drop of lead acetate solution. A yellow precipitate indicates the chromate (CrO_4) or dichromate (Cr_2O_7) radical.

See P–18 for other tests.

Carbon, C as **Oxalate,** C_2O_4. To another portion add a few drops of calcium chloride ($CaCl_2$) solution. A white precipitate which, when mixed with manganese dioxide (MnO_2) and conc. H_2SO_4 and warmed, gives off CO_2, indicates the oxalate radical (C_2O_4).

All oxalates are decomposed on ignition, with slight carbonization.

ABBREVIATIONS

A, adamantine

B.B., before the blowpipe
Blk., black
Blksh., blackish
Blu., blue
Blush., bluish
Brt., bright
Brwn., brown
Brwnsh., brownish

c.c., cubic centimeter (almost the same as a milliliter)
Coal, charcoal
Conc., concentrated
Conch., conchoidal
C.T., closed tube (a glass tube closed at one end)

D., dull
Dcpd., decomposed
Diff., difficult
Dil., dilute
Dist., distinct in cleavage on at least one plane
Drk., dark in color

E., earthy in luster or eminent in cleavage

F., fusibility
Fus., fusible

G., greasy in luster
Gelat., gelatinous or gelatinizes
Grn., green
Grnsh., greenish
Gra., gray
Grash., grayish

H., hexagonal or hardness

I., isometric
Imperf., imperfect
Indist., indistinct
Inf., infusible
Ins., insoluble

Lt., light in color

M., metallic or monoclinic
Mic., micaceous
Micro., microscopic
ml., milliliter (1/1000 part of a liter, approximately 1 cubic centimeter)
mm., millimeter (there are 25.4 mm. in an inch)

N., normal (a normal solution contains 1 gram molecular weight of a substance divided by its hydrogen equivalent in 1 liter of solution; i.e., 36.47 grams of HCl, 49.04 grams of H_2SO_4, 32.68 grams of H_3PO_4)

O., orthorhombic
O.F., oxidizing flame
O.T., open tube (a glass tube open at both ends in which a substance is heated, allowing air to pass through, causing oxidation to take place)

P., pearly
P-1, P-2, etc., Procedure No. 1, Procedure No. 2, etc.
Perf., perfect cleavage on at least one face
Per se, alone, by itself
Plaster, plaster of Paris
Pris., prismatic
Pt. sol., partly soluble or soluble with difficulty
Pt. vol., partly volatile

ABBREVIATIONS—*Cont.*

R., rhombohedral or resinous in luster
Rd., red
Rdsh., reddish
Rdns., reddens
R.E., rare earths
R.F., reducing flame

S., silky in luster
Sa., subadamantine
Slt sol., slightly soluble
Slvr., silver
Sm., submetallic
Soda, sodium carbonate or bicarbonate
Sol., soluble
S.Ph., salt of phosphorus (microcosmic salt) $HNaMH_4PO_4 \cdot 4H_2O$
Sr., subresinous
Stl., steel

Sub., sublimate
Subconch., subconchoidal
Sv., subvitreous

T., tetragonal
Tr., triclinic

V., vitreous
Vol., volatile

W., waxy in luster
Wht., white
Whtsh., whitish

Ylw., yellow
Ylwsh., yellowish

CHAPTER VIII

Mineral Identification Tables

GROUP 1
Specific Gravity 23.00-7.00

H	SP. GR	F	HCL	COLOR	STREAK	LUSTER	CLEAV-AGE	FRACTURE
1 7+	20.0	......	Ins	Silver white	....	....	....	Irregular
2 6.5-7	7.3-7.0	Easy	Pt sol	Silver, tin wht, tarnish ylw, brwn	....	M	Perf	Brittle
3 6-7	21.0-17.6	Inf	Ins	Tin white	Gray	M	Perf	....
4 6-7	21.0-17.6	Inf	Ins	Steel gray	Gray	M	Perf	....
5 6-7	10.58	2	Ins	Tin white	Black	M	Indist	Conch ......
6 6-7	22.84-22.65	Inf	Ins	Silver white, yellow tinge	Gray on fracture	....	Indist	Hackly
7 6-7	11.2	Inf	Ins	Grayish yellow	....	Bright	....	
8 6.5	9.7	Inf	Ins	Blk, gray, brwnsh	Gray, grnsh gray	Sm	Poor	Uneven to subconch
9 6-6.5	8.0-5.15	Inf	Ins	Iron blk, gray, brwnsh blk	Red to blk	Sr, Sm	Dist	Uneven to subconch
10 6-6.5	7.3-7.0	Inf	Ins	Blk to steel gray	....	Sm		Uneven to subconch
11 6-6.5	7.95-7.85	Inf	Pt sol	Black	Blksh to cinnamon brwn	Sa, Sm	None	Uneven to subconch
12 6-6.5	7.95-7.85	Inf	Pt sol	Black	Blksh to cinnamon brwn	Sa, Sm	None	Uneven to subconch
13 6	7.9-7.6	......	....	Brown	Yellow with grnsh tint	R to A	Perf	....
14 5.5-6	7.1±	2	Ins	Tin white, red tinge	Grysh black	M	Prismatic	Uneven
15 5.5-6	7.65-7.2	Inf	Slowly sol	Tin white, flesh colored	....	....	Good	Brittle
16 5-6	7.29-6.58	Fus	Ins	Ylwsh, brwn, grn, blk	Straw, ylw, cinnamon brwn	G, Sm	Indist	Small conch
17 5-6	10.63-8.0	Inf	Sol in HNO₃	Grysh, grnsh, brwnsh, blk	Grysh, olive green	Sm, G, P, D	....	Conch to uneven
18 5.5	8.63-8.23	1.5-2	Sol in HNO₃	Copper red to violet	Rdsh brwn	M	None	Conch to uneven
19 5.5	7.9	.....	....	Reddish white	Brwnsh blk	M	Poor	....
20 5.5	9.44-9.4	2	Sol	Iron blk to brwn	Chestnut brwn	M, A	None	Small conch
21 5.5	7.53-5.68	4	Ins	Rdsh to grnsh ylw, ylw	Ylw to brwnsh	R to A	Perf	Subconch
22 5.5	7.53-5.68	4	Ins	Rdsh to grnsh ylw, ylw	Ylw to brwnsh	R to A	Perf	Subconch
23 5-5.5	7.78-7.66	2	Ins	Copper red, black tarnish	Pale brwnsh black	M	None	Uneven
24 5-5.5	7.5-7.2	4	Dcpd	Grysh to brwnsh blk, brwnsh red	Blk, brwn, gray	Sm, M, A, R	Perf	Uneven
25 5-5.5	7.5-7.2	2.5-3	Sol in H₂SO₄	Grysh to brwnsh blk, brwnsh red	Nearly black	Sm, M, A, R	Perf	Uneven
26 5-5.5	7.48-7.0	2	....	Silver white	Grayish blk	M	Basal	Uneven
27 5	8.44-8.03	......	Ins	Black	Black	Sm	None	Subconch
28 5	8.22-7.8	Inf	Sol	Silver to grysh white	....	M	None	Flexible
29 5	8.04-7.83	2	Pt sol	Rdsh to silver white	Blksh gray	M	None	Uneven
30 5	7.73-7.02	......	....	Tin-white	....	M	Perf	....

GROUP 1
Specific Gravity 23.00-7.00

INDEX OF REF.	NAME	COMPOSITION	REMARKS
....	AUROSMIRIDIUM	Au,Os,Ir	Brittle. A solid solution of Au and Os in cubic Ir. Insoluble in aqua regia.
....	SCHREIBERSITE	$(Fe,Ni)_3P$	B.B., a strongly magnetic globule. Strongly magnetic.
....	**IRIDOSMINE**	**Ir,Os**	**Slightly malleable to nearly brittle. Per cent of Ir is greater than that of Os.**
....	SISERSKITE	Os,Ir	Like iridosmine but % of Os is greater than that of Ir.
....	**SPERRYLITE**	**PtAs₂**	**Brittle. Heated in the O.T., it gives a sublimate of As₂O₃.**
....	PLATINIRIDIUM	Ir,Pt	Somewhat malleable. Unattacked by acids. Very rare.
....	TANTALUM	Ta	Minute cubic crystals and fine grains.
2.25	THORIANITE	ThO_2	Brittle. Radioactive. Uranium is usually present. Soluble in HNO_3 and H_2SO_4 with evolution of Helium gas.
2.25-2.45	**COLUMBITE-TANTALITE**	**$(Fe,Mn)(Cb,Ta)_2O_6$**	**Brittle. Partially decomposed by boiling H_2SO_4.**
....	IXIOLITE	$(Fe,Mn)(Cb,Ta)_2O_6$	Probably identical with Tapiolite.
2.27Li	TAPIOLITE	$FeTa_2O_6$	Gives only a faint reaction for manganese.
2.26Li	MOSSITE	$Fe(Cb,Ta)_2O_6$	Gives only a faint Mn reaction. Differs from Tapiolite in containing more columbium.
2.38±	THOREAULITE	$SnTa_2O_7$	
....	RAMMELS-BERGITE	$NiAs_2$	In C.T., gives a sublimate of metallic arsenic.
....	COHENITE	$(Fe,Ni)_3C$	Strongly magnetic. Becomes light bronze to golden yellow on exposure.
....	MONIMOLITE	$3(Pb,Fe,Ca)O·Sb_2O_5$	B.B. on coal, gives a malleable lead colored globule.
....	**URANINITE**	**UO_2 or U_3O_8,PbO, etc.**	**Brittle. The borax bead is yellow in the O.F.; becoming green in the R.F.**
....	BREITHAUPTITE	NiSb	Brittle. On coal, fuses, gives antimony fumes and coats the coal white.
....	TMISKAMITE	Ni_4As_2	Reacts for arsenic and nickel.
.3±	PLATTNERITE	PbO_2	Brittle. Fibrous. B.B. on coal, gives a lead button.
.404	STIBIOTANTALITE	$Sb(Ta,Cb)O_4$	Only slightly attacked by boiling H_2SO_4.
.419	STIBIO-COLUMBITE	$Sb(Cb,Ta)O_4$	Only slightly attacked by H_2SO_4.
....	**NICCOLITE**	**NiAs**	**Brittle. In C.T., gives a small white sublimate of As₂O₃.**
.22	**HUEBNERITE**	**MnWO₄**	**With soda and niter on Pt foil, gives greenish blue Mn reaction.**
.36Li	**WOLFRAMITE**	**$(Fe,Mn)WO_4$**	**Brittle. B.B., gives manganese reactions.**
....	**LOELLINGITE**	**FeAs₂**	**In C.T., gives a sublimate of metallic arsenic.**
....	BISMUTO-TANTALITE	$Bi(Ta,Cb)O_4$	Insoluble in acids including HF
....	NICKEL-IRON	Ni,Fe	Malleable.
....	MAUCHERITE	$Ni_{11}As_8$	Brittle. Gives tests for nickel and arsenic.
....	PARARAMMELS-BERGITE	$NiAs_2$	

GROUP 1
Specific Gravity 23.00-7.00°

	H	SP. GR.	F	HCL	COLOR	STREAK	LUSTER.	CLEAV-AGE	FRACTURE
31	4.5-5	7.45-6.95	2.5	....	Tin-white	Grysh blk	M	Dist	Uneven to conch
32	4-5	9.5	....		Steel-gray	....	M	Fair	Conch
33	4-5	8.81	1.5	....	Silver-white	....	M	....	Uneven
34	4-5	7.26	Inf	Sol	Orange-red	Orange	A	Perf	....
35	4-5	9.5±	....	Ins	Silver-white, steel-gray	....	M	None	Uneven
36	4-5	9.22-8.64	....		Grysh grn, grnsh, ylw, bright ylw	Grysh to ylw	Sa, D, E	....	Uneven to earthy
37	4-4.5	19-14	Inf	Ins	Steel-gray	Gray, shiny	M	None	Hackly
38	4-4.5	11.9	Inf	Sol in HNO$_3$	Steel-gray	Gray, shiny	M	None	Hackly
39	4	7.87-7.3	Inf	Sol	Steel-gray to iron-black	....	M	Perf	Hackly
40	4	8.38	2	Ins	Steel-gray, silver-white	....	M	None	Subconch
41	3.5-4	9.81-9.67	1.5	Dcpd by HNO$_3$	Silver white	Silver-white	M	Dist	Uneven
42	3.5-4	7.1-6.5	1.5-2	Sol in HNO$_3$	Grn, ylw, brwn, various shades	Wht to ylwsh	R	Traces	Subconch to uneven
43	3.5-4	7.02	1.5	Sol	Smoky to yellow-brown	Yellow	R to A	Perf	....
44	3.5	16.11-13.48	....	Ins	Silver white	Same	M	Doubtful	Brittle
45	3.5	7.5-7.0	1	Sol in HNO$_3$	Ylw, brwn, orange, white	White	R	Imperf	Uneven
46	3.5	7.37-7.33	....		Pale ylw to grnsh	....	....	....	....
47	3.5	7.1	2	Sol in HNO$_3$	Wht to brnsh ylw	....	R		
48	3.5	7.29	Easy	Sol	Yellow	....	E	Scaly	....
49	3.5	7.98	....	Sol	Yellow to orange	....	....	Good	....
50	3.5	7.5	Easy	....	Ylw to brwnsh	....	....	....	....
51	3.5	13.71-13.48	Pt vol	Sol in HNO$_3$	Silver-white	....	Bright M	Dist	Conch
52	3.5	7.54	1	Sol in HNO$_3$	Deep purple	....	M	....	Irregular
53	3-3.5	7.01	....	....	Lead-gray	Black	M	Good	Conch to uneven
54	3-3.5	7.51	1	Sol in HNO$_3$	Pale bronze	Grysh to blk	....	....	Conch to uneven
55	3-3.5	14.1-13.7	Part vol	Ins	Silver white	Same	M	....	Conch to uneven
56	3-3.5	7.9-7.2	2	Ins	Tin-white to steel-gray	....	M	....	Uneven
57	2.5-3.5	7.04	1	Sol	Lead-gray to tin-white	Black	M	Good	Flexible
58	3	8.15	1.5	....	Tin white, yellow tinge	....	M	Perf	Subconch
59	3	7.6	1	Sol	Honey-yellow	....	....	Perf	....
60	3	7.29	....		....	....	M	Good	....

GROUP 1
Specific Gravity 23.00-7.00°

INDEX OF. REF.	NAME	COMPOSITION	REMARKS
....	SAFFLORITE	$(Co,Fe)As_2$	Brittle. In C.T., gives a sublimate of metallic arsenic.
....	COOPERITE	PtS	Minute crystal grains.
....	HORSFORDITE	Cu_5Sb	Brittle. Reacts for antimony and copper.
2.11	CURITE	$2PbO \cdot 5UO_3 \cdot 4H_2O$?	B.B, it blackens. Treated with conc HCl, it yields Cl gas.
....	STIBIO-PALLADINITE	Pd_3Sb	
2.42±	BISMITE	Bi_2O_3	
....	**PLATINUM**	**Pt**	**Malleable and ductile. Usually in grains and scales. Soluble in aqua regia.**
....	PALLADIUM	Pd	Ductile and malleable. Usually in grains; sometimes in divergent fibers.
....	**IRON**	**Fe**	**Malleable. Strongly magnetic. Very rare.**
....	ALGODONITE	Cu_6As	In O.T., gives a sublimate of As_2O_3. Sol in HNO_3.
....	DYSCRASITE	Ag_3Sb	Sectile. B.B. on coal a globule of silver and a white coating. The HNO_3 solution leaves a white residue.
2.05	**PYROMORPHITE**	**$3Pb_3(PO_4)_2 \cdot PbCl_2$**	**Brittle. In C.T., gives a sublimate of $PbCl_2$. Colors the flame green.**
2.35Li	NADORITE	$PbO \cdot Sb_2O_3 \cdot PbCl_2$	In C.T., decrepitates and gives a sublimate of $PbCl_2$.
....	POTARITE	Pd_3Hg_2	Spurts on heating, losing Hg. HNO_3 sol in brown. Occurs as grains and nuggets.
2.135	**MIMETITE**	**$3Pb_3(AsO_4)_2 \cdot PbCl_2$**	**Brittle. In O.T., gives a sublimate of $PbCl_2$. Colors flame bluish green.**
....	RUSSELLITE	$(Bi_2,W)O_3$	Fine grained, compact masses.
2.17	GEOGIADESITE	$3PbCl_2 \cdot 3PbO \cdot As_2O_3$	B.B. on coal, a yellow sublimate. In C.T., decrepitates.
....	BOKSPUTITE	$6PbO \cdot Bi_2O_3 \cdot 3CO_2$	Occurs as fine-grained, crystalline masses.
.19	KLEINITE	$Hg,NH_4,Cl,SO_4 \cdot etc.$	Reacts for mercury.
....	CHILLAGITE	$3PbWO_4 \cdot PbMoO_4$	
....	MOSCHELLANDS-BERGITE	Ag_2Hg_3	Brittle. On coal, Hg volatilizes leaving a globule of Ag.
....	RICKARDITE	Cu_4Te_3	Brittle. On heating, the Te volatilizes leaving a globule of Cu.
....	LINDSTROMITE	$PbCuBi_3S_6$	Striated, prismatic crystals.
....	EMPRESSITE	$AgTe$	Brittle. B.B., gives a globule of metallic silver.
....	**AMALGAM**	**Hg_xAg_y**	**B.B., the Hg volatilizes leaving metallic Ag. Amalgam containing gold is yellowish. Moschellandsbergite is amalgam with definite proportions of Ag and Hg.**
....	DOMEYKITE	Cu_3As	In O.T., gives a white sublimate of As_2O_3. Sol in HNO_3.
....	GALENOBISMU-TITE	$PbBi_2S_4$	B.B., gives bismuth and lead coatings.
....	**ALTAITE**	**PbTe**	**Secatile. In O.T., gives a white sublimate.**
35Li	LORETTOITE	$6PbO \cdot PbCl_2$	The hot HCl solution deposits white crystals on cooling.
....	GOONGARRITE	$Pb_4Bi_2S_7$	Fibrous to platy.

GROUP 1
Specific Gravity 23.00-7.00°

	H	SP. GR.	F	HCL	COLOR	STREAK	LUSTER	CLEAV-AGE	FRACTURE	S
61	3	7.65	Vol	Ins	Grayish black	Black	M	....	Uneven to subconch	
62	3	8.2-8.1	Inf	Sol	Black, lustrous	....	....	Fair	....	
63	3	8.44-8.43	......	....	Bronze	Blk, shining	M	Perf	Lemellar	
64	2.75-3	7.0-6.7	2	Dcpd	Orange, ylw, grn, gray, brwn, red	White	R to A	Very smooth	Subconch	
65	2.75-3	7.1-6.66	1.5	Dcpd	Ruby, brwnsh, ylw straw	White or ylwsh	R	....	Uneven to conch	
66	2.5-3	19.3-15.2	2.5-3	Ins	Yellow	Yellow	M	None	Hackly	
67	2.5-3	7.1-6.7	Easy	Sol in HNO₃	Lead gray	Black	M	Perf	Brittle	
68	2.5-3	11.1-10.1	2	Ins	Silver white	Same	M	None	Hackly	
69	2.5-3	9.02-8.7	1.5	Dcpd by HNO₃	Steel gray to iron black	....	M	Fair	Subconch	
70	2.5-3	7.8	2	Sol in HNO₃	Bluish lead-gray	Darker	M	Cubic	Granular	
71	2.5-3	8.13-7.87	2	Dcpd by HNO₃	Grn, ylwsh, gray, brwn, red	Uncolored	R, Sm	Imperf	Conch to uneven	
72	2.5-3	8.95	3	Ins	Reddish brown	Metallic, shiny	M	None	Hackly	
73	2.5-3	9.26-9.22	1	Ins	Brass ylw to silver white	Ylwsh to grnsh gray	M	None	Subconch to uneven	
74	2.5-3	7.2-7.0	1	Sol in HNO₃	Ylwsh, white, red, or blue	White	P to A	Perf	Uneven to conch	
75	2.5-3	7.14-6.89	1.5	Sol in HNO₃	Bright ylw to grn	....	V to G	Nearly perf	....	
76	2.5-3	7.21	1	Sol in HNO₃	Yellowish	....	A	Imperf	Uneven	
77	2-3	7.14-6.97	......	....	Steel-gray	Same, darker	M	Good	Brittle	
78	2-3	8.33	Vol	Dcpd	Yellow, bronze	Grnsh to canary ylw	R to A	None	Uneven	
79	2-3	7.70	......	Sol	Red-brown	Ylwsh red	Sm	Good	....	
80	2-3	8.725	Vol	Sol	Grnsh sulfur-ylw	Lemon-ylw	A	Perf	....	
81	2-3	8.45-8.24	1	....	Lead to steel gray	....	M	Indist	Even	
82	2-3	8.28	......	Sol	Ylw to brwn	....		Perf		
83	2-3	7.2-7.0	......	....	Steel-gray	Black	M	Good	....	
84	2-3	7.27	......	....	Gray to blk, olive grn	....	....	Dist	....	
85	2-3	7.95	......	....	Sulfur-yellow			Perf		
86	2-3	7.98	......	....	Like graphite	Blk, shining	M, D	Good	....	
87	2-3	8.62	......	Ins	Silver wht to brass yellow	....	M	Perf	Subconch to uneven	
88	2.5	8.47-8.3	Vol	....	Blksh, lead, steel to gray	Nearly blk	M	None	Uneven to conch	
89	2.5	8.04	1	Sol in HNO₃	Iron blk to gray	....	M	None	Subconch to uneven	
90	2.5	8.0-7.0	2	....	Iron-black	Iron-black	M	Perf	....	

GROUP 1
Specific Gravity 23.00-7.00°

INDEX OF REF.	NAME	COMPOSITION	REMARKS
....	**METACINNABAR**	HgS	Brittle. In C.T., with soda, gives a sublimate of metallic Hg.
.49Li	CADMIUM OXIDE	CdO	Transparent. Red to orange in transmitted light.
....	PARKERITE	Ni_2S_3	
.4	**WULFENITE**	$PbMoO_4$	Brittle. With S.Ph. in O.F., gives a yellowish green glass; darker in R.F.
.354	**VANADINITE**	$3Pb_3(VO_4)_2 \cdot PbCl_2$	Brittle. Fused with $KHSO_4$, gives a yellow mass that reddens on cooling, finally becoming yellow.
....	**GOLD**	Au	Very ductile and malleable. B.B., a yellow globule. Insoluble in ordinary acids. Native gold is never pure.
....	PENROSEITE	$(Ni,Cu,Pb)Se_2$	In C.T., gives a sublimate of red metallic selenium.
....	Silver	Ag	Ductile and malleable. Soluble in HNO_3, from which HCl gives a white, curdy precipitate, which darkens on exposure to sunlight.
....	**PETZITE**	Ag_3AuTe_2	Sectile to brittle. B.B. on coal gives a metallic globule.
....	**CLAUSTHALITE**	PbSe	In O.T., gives fumes of selenium and a red sublimate.
269	STOLZITE	$PbWO_4$	B.B., decrepitates and fuses to a crystalline, lustrous pearl.
....	**COPPER**	Cu	Ductile and malleable. In HNO_3, gives off red fumes. Native Cu often contains enough Fe to make it soluble in HCl.
....	**CALAVERITE**	$AuTe_2$	Brittle. On heating, leaves a button of gold. Colors the flame green.
27	MENDIPITE	$2PbO \cdot PbCl_2$	In C.T., decrepitates and becomes more yellow.
32Li	ECDEMITE	$Pb_4As_2O_7 \cdot 2PbCl_2$	B.B., gives a yellow globule and white sublimate.
15	MATLOCKITE	PbF,Cl	B.B., fuses to metallic lead, giving off acid vapors.
....	WEIBULLITE	$PbBi_2(S,Se)_4$	Flexible. Doubtful.
49Li	EGLESTONITE	$Hg_2O \cdot 2HgCl$	In C.T., decrepitates, becomes orange-red, gives dense white fumes.
....	**HAEMATOPHANITE**	$Pb(Cl,OH)_2 \cdot 4PbO \cdot 2Fe_2O_3$?	Transparent in very thin flakes.
64	TERLINGUAITE	Hg_2OCl	Mercury reactions. Similar to Eglestonite.
....	**HESSITE**	Ag_2Te	Sectile. B.B., gives a globule of Ag and reacts for Te.
10	TRIGONITE	$6PbO \cdot 2MnO \cdot 3As_2O_3 \cdot H_2O$	Gives reactions for manganese, lead and arsenic.
....	LILLIANITE	$Pb_3Bi_2S_6$	B.B., on coal, gives lead and bismuth coatings.
295	FINNEMANITE	$9PbO \cdot 3As_2O_3 \cdot PbCl_2$	Crystalline crusts in crevices in hematite.
74	SAHLINITE	$12PbO \cdot As_2O_5 \cdot 2PbCl_2$	
....	PLATYNITE	$PbBi_2(Se,S)_3$	
....	**KRENNERITE**	$AuTe_2$	Brittle. On heating, leaves a globule of metallic gold.
....	**TIEMANNITE**	HgSe	Brittle. In C.T., decrepitates, giving a black sublimate.
....	**COLORADOITE**	HgTe	Brittle and friable. B.B., fuses, gives metallic Hg and a sublimate of Te.
....	NAUMANNITE	Ag_2Se	Sectile and malleable. B.B. with soda and borax, gives a bead of metal.

MINERAL IDENTIFICATION TABLES

GROUP 1
Specific Gravity 23.00-7.00°

	H	SP. GR.	F	HCL	COLOR	STREAK	LUSTER	CLEAVAGE	FRACTURE
91	2.5	9.2-8.9	1	Sol	Scarlet, brwnsh, yellowish	Orange-ylw	G to D	....	....
92	2.5	7.4	Inf	Ins	Dark lead-gray	Same	....	Fair	Sectile
93	2.5 ,	7.8-7.6	2	Sol in HNO₃	Silver-white, lead-gray	Shining	M	None	Sectile
94	2.5	7.36	Easy	Sol	Grysh, creamy wht	....	P, G, S	Good	....
95	2.5	7.59-7.57	2	Sol in HNO₃	**Lead-gray**	**Same**	**M**	**Cubic**	**Uneven or flat conch**
96	2.5	7.586	......	....	Iron-black	....	M	None	Hackly
97	2.5	**11.23**	**Vol**	**Sol**	**Deep red**	**Ylw-brwn**	**V to A**	**Perf**	**Sectile**
98	2-2.5	7.08-7.06	1	Dcpd by HNO₃	Blksh red-gray, tarnish brwn, ylw	Grnsh blk	M	Doubtful	Uneven
99	2-2.5	**9.83-9.7**	**1**	Sol in HNO₃	**Silver-wht, rdsh hue**	**Same**	**M**	**Perf**	**Sectile**
100	2-2.5	**8.09**	**Vol**	**Ins**	**Red, brwn, gray**	**Scarlet**	**A to M**	**Perf**	**Subconch to uneven**
101	2-2.5	**7.4-7.2**	**1.5**	....	**Blksh lead-gray**	**Same, shining**	**M**	**Poor**	**Subconch**
102	2-2.5	7.3-7.2	1.5	....	Iron-black	Same, shining	M	Indist	Uneven
103	2-2.5	7.12	......	Sol in HNO₃	Lead-gray	Black	M	Good	....
104	2	9.3-7.83	2	Sol	Ylw with some rdsh	Same, lighter	D to G	Traces	Flexible
105	2	7.31	1	Sol	Wht, grysh, bluish	Iron-gray	M	None	Hackly
106	2	8.18	......	....	Grysh blk, gray	....	M	Perf	Flexible
107	2	9.14 ⌉	2	Sol	Red	....	G to D	Fair	....
108	2	7.2-6.9	1	Sol	White	White	M	Perf	Uneven
109	2	8.08	......	....	Gray	....	M	Dist	Flexible
110	1.5-2.5	8.44-8.38	Fus	....	Tin-wht, steel-gray	....	M	Perf	Flexible
111	1.5-2	**8.161**	**1**	**Dcpd by HNO₃**	**Ylwsh, gray, silvery**	**Same**	**M**	**Perf**	**Uneven**
112	1.5-2	**7.5-7.1**	**1.5**	....	**Pale steel-gray**	**Same**	**M**	**Perf**	**Flexible**
113	1.5-2	15.46	1	Ins	Pinkish silver-wht, tarnish red to blk	....	M	Dist	Sectile
114	1.5-2	7.96-7.66	Vol	....	Pale lead-gray	Same	....	Perf	Flexible
115	1.5	**11.37**	**1**	**Insol**	**Gray**	**Same**	**M**	**None**	**Malleable**
116	1-1.5	**7.46-7.36**	**1.5**	**Insol**	**Blksh lead-gray**	**Same**	**M**	**Perf**	**Flexible**
117	1-1.5	7.35	Easy	Sol in HNO₃	Rdsh wht, brwn tinge	Dark gray ⌡	M	Good	Flexible
118	Soft	8.8?	......	....	Grysh grn, grn, ylwsh grn	....	W to D	....	....
119	Liquid	13.596	Vol	Insol	Tin-white	....	M		

MINERAL IDENTIFICATION TABLES

GROUP 1
Specific Gravity 23.00-7.00

INDEX OF REF.	NAME	COMPOSITION	REMARKS
2.42	MINIUM	Pb_3O_4	In C.T., gives off oxygen.
....	TUNGSTENITE	WS_2	Soils the fingers. Earthy or foliated in minute scales.
....	EUCAIRITE	CuAgSe	B.B. on coal, gives fumes of Se, leaving a bead of metal.
....	BISMOCLITE	BiOCl	In C.T., yields acid water and a white sublimate.
....	**GALENA**	**PbS**	**B.B., emits SO_2 fumes; gives a coat that is yellow near the assay and bluish white at a distance.**
....	AGUILARITE	Ag_4SeS	Sectile. In O.T., heated slowly, yields metallic silver and a red sublimate
2.5	**MONTROYDITE**	**HgO**	**Flexible. Volatilizes completely in C.T., giving metallic mercury.**
....	AIKINITE	$PbCuBiS_3$	Decomposed by HNO_3 with separation of sulfur and lead sulfate.
....	**BISMUTH**	**Bi**	**On Coal, volatilizes, giving a coat that is orange-yellow while hot and lemon-yellow when cold.**
2.876	**CINNABAR**	**HgS**	**Sectile. In C.T., gives a black sublimate; on coal entirely volatile.**
....	**ARGENTITE**	**Ag_2S**	**Sectile. On coal, intumesces; yields SO_2 and a globule of silver.**
....	ACANTHITE	Ag_2S	Sectile. On coal, intumesces; yields SO_2 and a globule of silver.
....	WITTITE	$Pb_5Bi_6(S,Se)_{14}$	Dissolved in HNO_3 and diluted with water, gives a white precipitate.
.61Li	MASSICOT	PbO	Fuses to a yellow glass and reduces to metallic lead. The HCl sol precipitates $PbCl_2$ on cooling.
....	TIN	Sn	Ductile and malleable. Found in the placers of New South Wales.
....	JOSEITE	$Bi_3Te(Se,S)$	In O.T., gives off SO_2 then white fumes of tellurium oxide.
.665	LITHARGE	PbO	Slowly soluble in alkalies. The HCl sol precipitates $PbCl_2$ on cooling.
....	ZINC	Zn	Rather brittle. Existence in nature rather doubtful.
....	GRUENLINGITE	Bi_4TeS_3	Bismuth reactions.
....	WEHRLITE	Bi,Ag,Te,S	On coal, fuses, volatilizes, tinges the R.F. bluish green, coats the coal white then orange.
....	**SYLVANITE**	**$(Au,Ag)Te_2$**	**Brittle. On coal, gives a metallic globule and a white sublimate.**
....	**TETRADYMITE**	**Bi_2Te_2S**	**Volatilizes; coats coal white then orange; tinges R.F. bluish green.**
....	MALDONITE	Au_2Bi	Malleable. Soluble in aqua regia. On coal, a Bi coating and Au button.
....	TELLURO-BISMUTHITE	Bi_2Te_3	Somewhat sectile. In O.T., a white sublimate of TeO_2.
.5	**LEAD**	**Pb**	**Soluble in HNO_3. Very rare in nature.**
....	**NAGYAGITE**	**$Pb_5Au(Te,Sb)_4S_{5-8}$**	**On coal, gives two coats, one white and volatile and the other yellow and less volatile. Soluble in HNO_3 with a residue of gold.**
....	MELONITE	$NiTe_2$	In O.T., melts to colorless drops. On coal, burns and leaves a greenish gray residue.
.42+	SILLENITE	Bi_2O_3	A secondary product associated with Bismutite.
....	MERCURY	Hg	Completely volatile. Soluble in HNO_3

GROUP 1
Specific Gravity 23.00-7.00

	H	SP. GR.	F	HCL	COLOR	STREAK	LUSTER	CLEAV- AGE	FRACTURE	
120	?	7.1	Fus	Sol in HNO$_3$	Steel-gray	....	M	....	Granular, fibrous	
121	?	10.0	......	....	Steel-gray	....	M	....	.... ••••	
122	?	8.7	......	....	Brown	....			....	
123	?	15.47	Pt vol	Ins	White to ylwsh	....	M	....	Conch	
124	?	7.00	......	....	Tin-white	....			....	

214

URANINITE   GOLD in Quartz   Placer GOLD   Native SILVER   SILVER in CALCITE

AMALGAM (Gold. Silver)   ALTAITE on Quartz   Native COPPER   CALAVERITE (bright)   SYLVANITE

TIEMANNITE   CINNABAR   Placer CASSITERITE   COLUMBITE   TANTALITE

IRON METEORITE (polished)   WULFENITE   VANADINITE   GALENA   ARGENTITE

NICCOLITE   HUEBNERITE and Quartz   WOLFRAMITE and Quartz   LÖLLINGITE   BREITHAUPTITE NICCOLITE

MIMETITE   SMALTITE   ARSENOPYRITE   NAGYAGITE and Quartz   JOSEPHINITE

PLATE 19

MINERAL IDENTIFICATION TABLES

GROUP 1
Specific Gravity 23.00-7.00

INDEX OF REF.	NAME	COMPOSITION	REMARKS
....	BADENITE	$(Co,Ni,Fe)_2(As,Bi)_3$	B.B. on coal, gives fumes and a magnetic globule.
....	BRAGGITE	$(Pt,Pd,Ni)S$	Rounded grains and prisms.
....	PALLADINITE	PdO	An ochrous coating found on palladium gold from Brazil.
....	GOLD AMALGAM	Au_2Hg_3?	B.B., looses mercury leaving a globule of gold.
....	SELENOCOSALITE	$Pb_2Bi_2(S,Se)_5$	

GROUP 2
Specific Gravity 6.99-6.00

	H	SP. GR.	F	HCL	COLOR	STREAK	LUSTER	CLEAVAGE	FRACTURE
1	7.5	6.99-6.00	Inf	Ins	Dark iron-gray	Dark gray	Bright M	Perf	Subconch
2	6-7	6.99	Inf	Pt sol	Brwn, blk, red, gray, wht, ylw.	Wht, grnsh, brwnsh	A	Imperf	Uneven to subconch
3	6-7	7.03-6.6	Inf	Pt sol	Iron-blk, grysh, brwnsh	Red to black	Sm	Dist	Uneven to subconch
4	6.5	6.02-5.4	6	Ins	Colorless, ylw, brwn, blk	Wht to brwnsh wht	G to V	Nearly perf	Subconch to uneven
5	6-6.5	8.0-5.15	Inf	Ins	Iron-blk, gray, brwnsh blk	Red to blk	Sr, Sm	Dist	Uneven to subconch
6	6	6.26±	Inf	Ins	Black	....	....	Poor	....
7	6	6.72	......	....	Silver-white, steel-gray	....	M	None	Uneven
8	5.5-6	6.9-6.1	2.5	Sol in HNO$_3$	Tin-white to silver-gray	Grayish blk	Bright M	Dist	Conch to uneven
9	5.5-6	6.9-6.1	2.5	Sol in HNO$_3$	Tin-white to silver-gray	Grayish blk	Bright M	Dist	Conch to uneven
10	5.5-6	6.9-6.1	2.5	Sol in HNO$_3$	Tin-wht, steel-gry	Grysh blk	M	Dist	Conch to uneven
11	5.5-6	6.9-6.1	2.5	Sol in HNO$_3$	Tin-white, steel-gray	Grysh blk	M	Dist	Conch to uneven
12	5.5-6	6.22-5.92	2	Dcpd by HNO$_3$	Silver-white to steel-gray	Drk grysh blk	M	Dist	Uneven
13	5-6	7.29-6.58	Fus	Ins	Ylw, brwn, grn, blk	Straw, ylw, cinnamon brwn	G, Sm	Indist	Small conch
14	5-6	6.4-6.2	......	Pt sol	Black	Dark brown	W	....	Conch
15	5.5	6.898	Inf	Pt sol	Drk pistachio green	Brwnsh blk	V	....	....
16	5.5	6.46-6.38	Inf	Ins	Pale ylw to brwn, red	Pale ylwsh to brwnsh	V, R	Dist	Subconch to uneven
17	5.5	6.33	2-3	Dcpd by HNO$_3$	Rdsh wht, gray, grysh wht	Grysh blk	M	Perf	Uneven
18	5-5.5	6.69-6.61	1.5	Dcpd by HNO$_3$	Tin-wht to steel-gray	Grysh blk	M	Perf	Uneven
19	5	6.16-5.92	2-3	Dcpd by HNO$_3$	Grnsh to rdsh, tin-white	Black	M	Perf	Uneven
20	5	6.19	2.5	Sol	Drk rdsh brwn	....	V, Sm, D	Dist	Uneven
21	5	6.07	......	Sol	Nearly blk	Red	....	Good	....
22	4.5-5	6.37	2	Dcpd by HNO$_3$	Silver to tin-white	Black	M	....	Uneven
23	4.5-5	6.13	Inf	Ins	Wax-ylw, rdsh ylw	....	R	Perf	....
24	4.5-5	6.1-5.9	5	Dcpd	Brwn, gray, wht, ylw, grn, red	White	V to A	Dist	Uneven
25	4.5-5	7.45-6.95	2.5	....	Tin-white	Grysh blk	M	Dist	Uneven to conch
26	4.5-5	6.05-5.95	2	Dcpd by HNO$_3$	Silver-wht to steel-gray	Black	M	....	Uneven
27	4.5	6.6	2	Sol in HNO$_3$	Steel gray	Nearly blk	M	Perf	Uneven

MINERAL IDENTIFICATION TABLES

GROUP 2
Specific Gravity 6.99-6.00

INDEX OF REF.	NAME	COMPOSITION	REMARKS
....	LAURITE	RuS_2	B.B., gives sulfur fumes, then usually fumes of osmium. Insoluble in aqua regia and unattacked by fusion with $KHSO_4$
2.00±	**CASSITERITE**	SnO_2	**Brittle. Placed in contact with metallic zinc in HCl, it is coated with a layer of metallic tin.**
2.25	MANGANO-TANTALITE	$MnO·(Ta,Cb)_2O_5$	Tantalite rich in manganese. B.B. with soda and niter, gives the greenish blue manganese reaction.
2.19	BADDELEYITE	ZrO_2	Brittle. B.B., glows, turns white and is nearly infusible.
2.25-2.45	**COLUMBITE-TANTALITE**	$(Fe,Mn)(Cb,Ta)_2O_6$	**Brittle. Partially decomposed by boiling H_2SO_4**
2.40Li	FERRO-COLUMBITE	$FeCb_2O_6$	Columbite rich in iron.
....	GUDMUNDITE	$FeSbS$	Brittle.
....	SKUTTERUDITE	$(Co,Ni)As_2$	Brittle. In C.T., gives a sublimate of metallic arsenic.
....	NICKEL-SKUTTERUDITE	$(Ni,Co)As_3$	Brittle. In C.T., gives a sublimate of metallic arsenic.
....	**SMALTITE**	$(Co,Ni)As_{3-x}$	In C.T., gives a sublimate of metallic arsenic.
....	**CHLOANTHITE**	$(Ni,Co)As_{3-x}$	In C.T., gives a sublimate of metallic arsenic.
....	**ARSENOPYRITE**	$FeAsS$	**Brittle. In C.T., gives first a red then black lustrous sublimate.**
....	MONIMOLITE	$3(Pb,Fe,Ca)O·Sb_2O_5$	On coal, gives a malleable lead colored bead.
....	ISHIKAWAITE	$(U,Fe,Y,etc.)(Cb,TaO_4)$	
2.37Li	BUNSENITE	NiO	Occurs with native bismuth and cobalt arsenates.
4.93	**MICROLITE**	$(Na,Ca)_2Ta_2O_6$ (O,OH,F)	**Brittle. With S.Ph., after long heating, gives a pale bluish green bead.**
....	**COBALTITE**	$(Co,Fe)AsS$	**Brittle. In O.T., gives SO_2 fumes and a crystalline sublimate of As_2O_3.**
....	ULLMANNITE	$(Ni,Co,Fe)(Sb,As,Bi)S$	Brittle. B.B., on coal, gives a globule of metal; boils and emits Sb fumes and coats coal.
....	GLAUCODOT	$(Co,Fe)AsS$	Brittle. In O.T., gives SO_2 fumes and a sublimate of As_2O_3.
2.20	KENTROLITE	$2PbO·Mn_2O_3·3SiO_2$	On Coal, gives a Pb coating and with soda a globule of metallic lead.
....	PLUMBOFERRITE	$PbFe_4O_7$	The HCl solution yields Cl and a residue of $PbCl_2$.
....	WOLFACHITE	$Ni(As,Sb)S$	In C.T., heated slowly, gives a narrow yellowish red and broad yellow zones.
4.613	FLUOCERITE	$(Ce,La,Y)F_3$	In C.T., yields water that etches the glass.
4.918	**SCHEELITE**	$CaWO_4$	**Brittle. B.B., gives a transparent bead which later becomes opaque. Blue under ultra-violet light.**
....	SAFFLORITE	$(Co,Fe)As_2$	Brittle. In C.T., gives a sublimate of metallic arsenic.
....	CORYNITE	$Ni(As,Sb)S$	Like Walfachite. Between Ullmannite and Gersdorffite.
....	ALLOCLASITE	$Co(As,Bi)S$	Close to Glaucodot

217

GROUP 2
Specific Gravity 6.99-6.00

	H	SP. GR.	F	HCL	COLOR	STREAK	LUSTER	CLEAV-AGE	FRACTURE
28	4.5	6.04	5-6	Sol	Purplish to pitch black	Brwnsh blk	Brilliant M, A	None	Flat conch
29	4.5	6.1	2	....	Gray, brwn, ylw	Uncolored, ylwsh gray	R to A	Imperf	Uneven
30	4.5	6.49	3	Sol in HNO₃	Colorless or wht	....	A	Perf	....
31	4-4.5	6.9-6.86	1.5	Sol	Grn, wht, gray, ylw	Grnsh gray to colorless	V	....	....
32	4-4.5	6.39	......	....	Orange to dark brown	Ylwsh brwn	W	None	Conch
33	4	6.4	......	....	Black	Black	V, Sa	Perf	....
34	4	6.4	......	....	Brwnsh black	Brown	D, Sm	Indist	....
35	4	6.25	2	Sol	Rdsh brwn	Yellow	V to A	Perf	Subconch
36	4	6.4	1.5	....	Sulfur-yellow	....	A	Indist	....
37	3.5-4	7.1-6.5	1.5	Sol in HNO₃	Grn, ylw, brwn, various shades	Wht to ylwsh	R	Traces	Subconch to uneven
38	3.5-4	6.14	3	Sol	Various shades of red, blksh	Brwnsh red, shining	A, Sm, E	Interrupted	Uneven to conch
39	3-4	6.2-5.8	1	....	Tin-white or reddish gray	Gray	M	Perf	....
40	3-4	6.1	1.5	Sol in HNO₃	Siskin to olive green	....	....	None	....
41	3-4	6.046	Inf	Sol	Red, golden, brwn	....	A	Perf	....
42	3.5	6.5-5.8	Inf	Sol	Blk scales, steel to iron-gray	....	M	Perf	Uneven to conch
43	3.5	6.2-5.9	1.5	Sol in HNO₃	Red, brwn, blk	Orange, brwnsh, red, ylwsh, gray	G	None	Uneven to conch
44	3.5	6.13-6.09	2	Sol	Emerald-green	....	V	....	....
45	3.5	6.84	1.5	Sol	Colorless	....	P	Perf	....
46	3.5	6.34	......	Sol	Gray, tarnishing ylw to rdsh	Dull lead-gray	M	Fair	....
47	3-3.5	6.72-6.61	1	Sol in conc	Tin-white	Gray	M	Perf	Uneven
48	3-3.5	6.57-6.46	1.5	Sol in HNO₃	Colorless, blue, wht, gray, grn, blk	Uncolored	V, R, A, P	Dist	Conch
49	2.5-5	6.4-3.9	......	....	Ylw, orange, rdsh, brown to blk	Ylw, brwnsh, olive grn	G, W, V, D	....	Conch to uneven
50	3-3.5	6.24	1	Sol in HNO₃	Colorless	....	A	Dist	....
51	2.5-3.5	6.98-6.25	1.5	Ins	Bluish gray	Gray, shining	M	Dist	Sectile
52	3	6.72-6.11	2.5	Dcpd	Gray, white	....	P	Dist	Uneven
53	3	6.0	......	....	Blue-black	Black	M	....	....
54	3	6.43-6.33	1	Dcpd by HNO₃	Lead-gray	Black	M	Perf	Conch
55	3	6.17-6.13	1	Sol in HNO₃	Black	Black	M	None	Conch to irregular

SCHEELITE   CUPRITE   BADDELEYITE   BUNSENITE (green)   BISMUTITE

TENORITE CHRYSOCOLLA   DESCLOIZITE VANADINITE   ALLEMONTITE and Quartz   CERUSSITE   ANGLESITE GALENA

CLAUSTHALITE and Quartz   CHLOANTHITE   GERSDORFFITE   PHOSGENITE   STROMEYERITE CHALCOPYRITE

CROCOITE   BOULANGERITE   STEPHANITE   BISMUTHINITE CASSITERITE   CALOMEL

BERZELIANITE and Calcite   FERGUSONITE   SAMARSKITE   TEALLITE   MICROLITE in LEPIDOLITE

ZINCITE FRANKLINITE CALAMINE   CHALCOCITE   PYRARGYRITE   PROUSTITE   CERARGYRITE

PLATE 20

GROUP 2
Specific Gravity 6.99-6.00

INDEX OF REF.	NAME	COMPOSITION	REMARKS
....	PARA-MELACONITE	CuO	On coal in R.F., yields metallic copper.
?.05	EULYTITE	$2Bi_2O_3 \cdot 3SiO_2$	On coal, fuses and froths, staining it yellowish brown; may be tinged green.
.961	ALAMOSITE	$PbSiO_3$	Gives lead reactions.
?.26±	BISMUTITE	$Bi_2O_3 \cdot CO_2 \cdot nH_2O$	Occurs as a powder. The HCl solution is deep yellow.
?.098	CLARKEITE	$(Ca,Pb,K_2,Na_2)O \cdot UO_3, nH_2O$	An alteration product of Uraninite.
?.40Li	FERBERITE	$FeWO_4$	
....	REINITE	$FeWO_4$	
?.50Li	PUCHERITE	$BiVO_4$	The HCl solution is deep red and yields chlorine; if diluted it becomes green.
.15	ATELESTITE	$3Bi_2O_3 \cdot As_2O_5 \cdot 2H_2O$	
.05	**PYROMORPHITE**	$3Pb_3(PO_4)_2 \cdot PbCl_2$	**Brittle. In C.T., gives a sublimate of $PbCl_2$. Colors flame green.**
.489	**CUPRITE**	Cu_2O	**Brittle. On coal, fuses and reduces to metallic copper. Soluble in NH_4OH and $NaOH$.**
....	**ALLEMONTITE**	$AsSb$	**Fuses to a globule; takes fire and burns, leaving a coating of Sb_2O_3 on the coal.**
?.31Li	CUPRO-DESCLOIZITE	$2PbO \cdot 2CuO \cdot V_2O_5 \cdot H_2O$	
.92	FOURMARIERITE	$PbO \cdot 4UO_3 \cdot 5H_2O?$	An alteration product of Uraninite. B.B., blackens but does not fuse.
....	**TENORITE**	CuO	**Brittle. Gives copper reactions.**
.27	DESCLOIZITE	$(Pb,Zn)_2(OH)VO_4$	With S.Ph. in R.F., the bead is chrome-green; in R.F., orange-yellow.
.92	TSUMEBITE	$4PbO \cdot 2CuO \cdot P_2O_5 \cdot nH_2O$	Gives Pb reactions; Cu flame; phosphorous tests.
.09	HYDROCERUSSITE	$2PbCO_3 \cdot Pb(OH)_2$	Yields a lead button on charcoal.
....	BENJAMINITE	$Pb(Cu,Ag)Bi_2S_4$	In C.T., a sublimate of sulfur.
....	ANTIMONY	Sb	Brittle. Gives dense white fumes and continues to fume after flame is removed. HCl sol diluted yields a white precipitation.
.076	**CERUSSITE**	$PbCO_3$	**Brittle. In C.T., turns yellow, then dark red, then yellow again on cooling. Soluble in HNO_3 with effervescence.**
.762	GUMMITE	$UO_3, Pb, Th, R.E., etc. H_2O$	Brittle.
.116	LAURIONITE	$PbCl_2 \cdot Pb(OH)_2$	Fuses to yellowish, opaque beads.
....	GUANAJUATITE	Bi_2Se_3	B.B. on coal, fuses; colors flame blue; gives strong selenium odor. Soluble in aqua regia on slow heating.
.033	BARYSILITE	$2PbO \cdot 2SiO_2$	Decrepitates and fuses to a clear brown bead.
....	WEISSITE	Cu_5Te_3	
....	JORDANITE	$Pb_{14}As_7S_{24}$	Brittle. In C.T., gives a sublimate of S and As_2S_3.
....	PEARCEITE	$(Ag,Cu)_{16}As_2S_{11}$	Brittle. On coal with soda, gives a metallic globule. Reacts for S and As.

GROUP 2
Specific Gravity 6.99-6.00

	H	SP. GR.	F	HCL	COLOR	STREAK	LUSTER	CLEAVAGE	FRACTURE
56	3	6.19	......	....	Pale apple-green	....	V, D	....	....
57	2.75-3	7.1-6.66	1.5	Dcpd	Red, brwnsh, ylw, straw	Wht or ylwsh	R	....	Uneven to conch
58	2.75-3	7.0-6.7	2	Dcpd	Orange, ylw grn, gray, brwn, red	White	R to A	Very smooth	Subconch
59	2.75-3	6.39-6.3	1.5	Sol in HNO$_3$	Colorless, wht, tinged	Uncolored	A, R, V	Dist	Conch
60	2.75-3	6.3-6.0	Fus	Sol in HNO$_3$	Wht, gray, ylw	White	A	Dist	Sectile
61	2.5-3	7.1-6.7	Easy	Sol in HNO$_3$	Lead-gray	Black	M	Perf	Brittle
62	2.5-3	6.4	1.5	Sol in HNO$_3$	Bluish green	Greenish wht	R	Perf	Uneven
63	2.5-3	6.78-6.55	1	Pt sol	Lead to steel-gray	Black	M	....	Uneven
64	2.5-3	6.334	1	Sol	Blksh lead to steel-gray	Black	....	Prismatic	Granular, fibrous
65	2.5-3	6.3-6.2	1.5	Sol in HNO$_3$	Dark steel-gray	Same	M	None	Subconch to conch
66	2.5-3	6.1-5.8	2?	Sol in H$_2$SO$_4$	Grn to brwnsh blk	Grnsh, brwnsh	A to R	....	Uneven
67	2.5-3	6.04	1	Sol in HNO$_3$	Steel-gray	....	M	None	Uneven to subconch
68	2.5-3	6.1-5.9	1.5	....	Hyacinth-red	Orange-ylw	A to V	Rather dist	Conch to uneven
69	2.5-3	6.4-5.96	1	Sol	Bluish lead-gray	Brwnsh gray, brwn	M	Good	Flexible
70	2.5-3	7.14-6.89	1.5	Sol in HNO$_3$	Bright ylw to green	....	V to G	Nearly perf	....
71	2.5-3	6.9	1	Ins	Lead-gray	....	M	....	Brittle
72	2-3	6.36	Inf	....	Orange-yellow, brick-red	Yellow	G	Perf	....
73	2-3	6.92	1-1.5	....	Lead-gray	....	M	Good	Foliated
74	2-3	7.14-6.97	......	......	Steel-gray	Same, darker	M	Good	Brittle
75	2-3	6.96	......	......	Lead-gray	Black	M	Good	....
76	2-3	6.2-6.0]	1	Dcpd by HNO$_3$	Blk, in splinters cherry-red	Black	M	Imperf	Uneven
77	2-3	6.0-5.8	1	Sol in NH$_4$OH	Yellow-green	....	R to A	None	Uneven
78	2.5	6.974	1	Sol in HNO$_3$	Blksh gray, iron-black	Black	M	Cubic	Uneven
79	2.5	6.3-6.1	2	....	Black with bluish tinge	Grysh black	M	None	Uneven to subconch
80	2.5	6.39-6.09	1-1.5	Pt sol	Lead-gray	Black	M	Indist	Uneven
81	2.5	6.46-6.1	1	Slowly sol	Steel-gray, tarnish brass or iridescent	Black	M	Dist	Uneven
82	2.5	6.5-6.3	1	Sol	Lead to bluish gray	Same	M	Dist	Uneven
83	2.5	6.9	1	Sol in HNO$_3$	Iron-blk to gray	Light gray	M	None	Uneven
84	2.5	6.15-5.82	1	....	Gray to black	Black	M	Perf	....

MINERAL IDENTIFICATION TABLES

GROUP 2
Specific Gravity 6.99-6.00

INDEX OF REF.	NAME	COMPOSITION	REMARKS
2.06	DUFTITE	$2PbO \cdot 2CuO \cdot As_2O_5 \cdot H_2O$	Olivenite group with Pb replacing about $\frac{1}{2}$ the Cu.
2.354	VANADINITE	$3Pb_3(VO_4)_2 \cdot PbCl_2$	Brittle. Fused with $KHSO_4$, gives a yellow mass which reddens on cooling, finally becoming yellow.
2.40Li	WULFENITE	$PbMoO_4$	Brittle. S.Ph. in O.F., gives a yellowish brown bead which is dark green in R.F.
.882	ANGLESITE	$PbSO_4$	Brittle. With sodium carbonate gives metallic lead.
.114	PHOSGENITE	$PbCO_3 \cdot PbCl_2$	Melts to a globule which on cooling, becomes white and crystalline. Dissolves with effervescence in HNO_3.
....	PENROSEITE	$(Ni,Cu,Pb)Se_2$	In C.T., gives a sublimate of red, metallic selenium.
.866	CALEDONITE	$(Pb,Cu)_2(OH)_2SO_4$	Dissolved in HNO_3, leaves a residue of $PbSO_4$.
....	COSALITE	$Pb_2Bi_2S_5$	Soluble in HNO_3 with separation of $PbSO_4$.
....	KOBELLITE	$Pb_2(Bi,Sb)_2S_5$	On charcoal, gives a yellow coat near the assay and a white one beyond.
....	STROMEYERITE	$CuAgS$	In C.T., fuses but gives no sublimate.
.22	VAUQUELINITE	$2(Pb,Cu)CrO_4 \cdot (Cu,Pb)_3P_2O_8$	Fuses to a gray submetallic globule also small globules of metal.
....	DIAPHORITE	$Pb_2Ag_2Sb_3S_8$	Brittle. In O.T., gives SO_2 and a sublimate of Sb and Pb oxides.
.37Li	CROCOITE	$PbCrO_4$	Sectile. With S.Ph., gives an emerald-green bead in both flames.
....	BOULANGERITE	$Pb_5Sb_4S_{11}$	Brittle. On charcoal, almost entirely volatile; gives a dark yellow sublimate near the assay with white edges.
.32Li	ECDEMITE	$Pb_4As_2O_7 \cdot 2PbCl_2$	B.B., gives a yellow globule and white sublimate.
....	CROOKESITE	$(Cu,Tl,Ag)_2Se$	Fuses to a greenish black enamel. Soluble in HNO_3.
.985	URANO-SPHAERITE	$Bi_2O_3 \cdot 2UO_3 \cdot 3H_2O$	B.B., decrepitates and falls to pieces to a mass of crystalline needles.
....	CHIVIATITE	$Pb_3Bi_8S_{15}$	On charcoal, gives a coat that is yellow near the assay and white far away.
....	WEIBULLITE	$PbBi_2(Se,S)_4$	Flexible. Doubtful.
....	GLADITE	$PbCuBi_5S_9$	
74±	POLYBASITE	$(Ag,Cu)_{16}Sb_2S_{11}$	In O.T., fuses, giving sulfurous and antimonial fumes.
253	BROMYRITE	$AgBr$	On charcoal, emits pungent Br odors and yields a globule of silver.
....	POLYARGYRITE	$Ag_{24}Sb_2S_{15}$	Malleable and ductile. Fuses to a black globule, giving Sb fumes and a brittle globule of Ag and Sb.
....	CANFIELDITE	Ag_8SnS_6	Brittle. On charcoal, gives a white or grayish sublimate near the assay, tinged yellow on the edges.
....	REZBANYITE	$Pb_3Cu_2Bi_{10}S_{19}$	Reacts for bismuth, copper and lead.
....	KLOPROTHITE	$Cu_6Bi_4S_9$	Brittle. On charcoal with sodium carbonate, yields a dark yellow sublimate and silver-white bead of metal.
....	GEOCRONITE	$Pb_5(Sb,As)_2S_8$	Almost entirely volatile in O.F.; yields a dark yellow sublimate near the assay with white edges.
....	MATILDITE	$AgBiS_2$	Brittle. On charcoal, a globule of metal and bismuth coating.
....	SEMSEYITE	$Pb_9Sb_8S_{21}$	Brittle.

GROUP 2
Specific Gravity 6.99-6.00

	H	SP. GR.	F	HCL	COLOR	STREAK	LUSTER	CLEAVAGE	FRACTURE
85	2.5	6.06-6.03	......	......	Black	Black	Bright	Perf	......
86	2.5	6.14	......	......	Silver-gray	Lead-gray	....	......	......
87	2.5	6.24	......	......	Gray-black to lead-gray	Black to light brown		Dist	......
88	2.5	6.44-6.26	1.5	Dcpd by HNO$_3$	Wht, ylw, grn, gray	Uncolored	P, R, A	Perf	Conch
89	**2.5**	6.24-6.2	1	....	Dark lead-gray	Black	M	None	Brittle
90	2.5	6.37-6.35	1	Dcpd by HNO$_3$	Blksh lead-gray	Blk, shining	M	Perf	Conch
91	2.5	6.3-6.1	2	....	Steel-gray, rdsh tint, blk to bluish	Grysh blk	M	None	Uneven to flat conch
92	2.5	6.41	Easy	Sol in HNO$_3$	Sky-blue		....	Perf	......
93	2.5	6.76	Easy	Sol in HNO$_3$	Dull olive green		R, A	Perf	......
94	2.5	6.84	Inf	Sol	Pitch-black	Drk brwn-gray	M to A	Perf	Flexible
95	2.5	6.03	1	Sol	Steel-gray, silver-white	Rdsh brwn	M	Perf	Fibrous
96	2-2.5	6.5-6.4	1.5	Sol	Ylwsh to grysh white				
97	2-2.5	6.4-6.3	2	Dcpd by H$_2$SO$_4$	Grnsh wht, pale ylw or gray	White	P, A, R	Perf	Flexible
98	2-2.5	6.23-6.04	1	....	Steel to lead-gray, silver-wht	Same	M	Imperf	Subconch to uneven
99	2-2.5	6.3-6.1	1	Ins˙	Tin-white	Gray	M	Perf	Brittle
100	2-2.5	6.3-6.2	1	Sol in HNO$_3$	Honey to straw-yellow	Straw-ylw	A	Dist	Brittle
101	**2-2.5**	**6.27-6.22**	**1**	**Sol in HNO$_3$**	**Iron-black**	**Same**	**M**	**Imperf**	**Uneven to subconch**
102	2	6.38	1	Dcpd by HNO$_3$	Grayish to tin-white		M	Perf	Uneven to subconch
103	**2**	**6.81-6.75**	**1**	**Sol in HNO$_3$**	**Lead-gray, tin-wht, ylwsh tarnish**	**Same**	**M**	**Perf**	**Flexible**
104	2	7.2-6.9	1	Sol	White	White	M	Perf	Uneven
105	2	6.737	1	....	Lead-gray to blk		M	None	Uneven
106	2	6.88-6.78	1	Sol	Light lead-gray	Gray	M	Indist	Brittle
107	2?	6.57-6.05	......	....	Whitish gray				
108	**2**	**6.71**	**1.5**	**Ins**	**Silver-white**	**Shining**	**M**	**None**	......
109	**1-2**	**6.48**	**Vol**	**Ins**	**Wht, grayish, ylwsh, brwn**	**Pale ylw to white**	**A**	**Dist**	**Conch**
110	1.5	6.36	......	Sol	Blksh gray	Black	M	Perf	Flexible
111	?	6.05	......	....	White			Basal	
112	?	6.26	......	Sol	Chocolate-brown		E		
113	?	6.69	......	....	Deep red			Perf	
114	?	6.27-5.92	......	Ins	Colorless with creamy surface				

GROUP 2
Specific Gravity 6.99-6.00

INDEX OF REF.	NAME	COMPOSITION	REMARKS
....	BLOCKITE	$(Co,Ni)Se_2$	Differs from Penroseite in containing more Se and less Pb.
....	COCINERITE	Cu_4AgS	
....	FALKMANITE	$Pb_6Sb_2S_6$	
2.00	LEADHILLITE	$PbSO_4 \cdot 2PbCO_3 \cdot Pb(OH)_2$	Sectile. Fuses and turns yellow but becomes white on cooling.
....	GRATONITE	$Pb_9As_4S_{15}$	Decrepitates violently B.B.
....	MENEGHINITE	$Pb_{13}Sb_7S_{23}$	Brittle. Treated with HNO_3, it decomposes, leaving a residue of Sb oxides and $PbSO_4$.
....	ARGYRODITE	Ag_8GeS_6	Brittle. In C.T., a sublimate of S and at high temperatures a slight deposit of GeS which fuses to yellow drops.
1.98	DIABOLEITE	$2Pb(OH)_2 \cdot CuCl_2$	
2.24	CHLOROXIPHITE	$2PbO \cdot Pb(OH)_2 \cdot CuCl_2$	
2.30±	QUENSELITE	$PbMnO_2(OH)$	Soluble in dilute acids, including acetic, with evolution of Cl.
....	OWYHEEITE	$Pb_5Ag_2Sb_6S_{15}$	Brittle. Acicular needles or massive with indistinct fibrous structure.
1.91	DAUBREEITE	$2Bi_2O_3 \cdot BiCl_4 \cdot 3H_2O$	In C.T., gives acid water; becomes grayish and on longer heating turns yellow.
1.99	LANARKITE	$PbO \cdot PbSO_4$	
....	FREIESLEBENITE	$Pb_3Ag_5Sb_5S_{12}$	Rather brittle. On charcoal, gives a coat that is yellow near the assay and white far away.
....	TELLURIUM	Te	On charcoal, almost completely volatile, tinging the flame green, giving a white coating. Hot conc H_2SO_4 gives a carmine-red color.
2.36Li	SCHWARTZEMBERGITE	$Pb(I,Cl)_2PbO$	B.B., gives violet vapors of iodine.
....	**STEPHANITE**	Ag_5SbS_4	**Brittle. In O.T., fuses and gives sulfur and antimony fumes.**
....	EMPLECTITE	$CuBiS_2$	Brittle. On charcoal, fuses with frothing and spitting coating the charcoal with bismuth oxide.
....	**BISMUTHINITE**	Bi_2S_3	**Sectile. On charcoal, fuses with spirting, giving a coat of yellow bismuth oxide.**
....	ZINC	Zn	Rather brittle. Existence in nature rather doubtful.
....	SCHIRMERITE	$PbAg_4Bi_4S_9$	Brittle. Occurs massive and finely granular.
....	ALASKAITE	$Pb(Ag,Cu)_2Bi_4S_8$?	In C.T., melts but does not form a sublimate. Soluble in hot HCl with the formation of a white precipitate.
....	SELENOKOBELLITE	$Pb_2(Bi,Sb)_2(S,Se)_5$?	
....	**BERZELIANITE**	Cu_2Se	**Malleable. In C.T., gives a red sublimate of metallic selenium and a white one of selenium oxide. Soluble in HNO_3.**
1.973	**CALOMEL**	Hg_2Cl_2	**Sectile. In C.T., volatilizes without fusion and condenses in the colder part of the tube.**
....	TEALLITE	$PbSnS_2$	Malleable. In C.T., does not melt but affords a sublimate of sulfur.
2.146	PARALAURIONITE	$PbCl_2 \cdot PbO \cdot H_2O$	
1.86	PARSONSITE	$2PbO \cdot UO_3 \cdot P_2O_5 \cdot H_2O$	In C.T., yields water.
....	BERESOWITE	$6PbO \cdot 3CrO_3 \cdot CO_2$	
2.06	SIMPSONITE	$Al_2Ta_2O_8$	Interior of the rough, cream-colored crystal is colorless. Tabular.

GROUP 3
Specific Gravity 5.99–5.00

	H	SP. GR.	F	HCL	COLOR	STREAK	LUSTER	CLEAV-AGE	FRACTURE
1	8-9?	5.39?	Inf	....	Golden-yellow	....			
2	6.5	5.73	2-2.5	Dcpd by HNO₃	Blk to blksh gray	Grnsh gray	M to G	Good	....
3	6.5	6.02-5.4	6	Insol	Colorless, ylw, brwn, blk	White to brwnsh wht	G to V	Perf	Subconch to uneven
4	6.5	5.41	6	Ins	Honey-yellow	....		Dist	....
5	6.5	5.04	......	....	Pitch-black	Brwnsh gray	Sm	None	Subconch
6	6.5	5.36	......	....	Iron-gray	....		......	Uneven
7	6-6.5	5.11	......	....	Dark brown				
8	6-6.5	8.0-5.15	Inf	Ins	Iron-blk, gray, brwnsh blk	Red to blk	Sr, Sm	Dist	Uneven to subconch
9	6-6.5	5.08-5.04	Inf	Sol	Steel to iron-gray	Blk, bluish black	M	Perf	Uneven
10	6-6.5	5.02-4.82	2.5-3	Ins	Pale brass-ylw	Grnsh, brwnsh, brwnsh blk	M	Indist	Conch to uneven
11	6-6.5	5.079	Inf	Pt sol	Tarry black	Black		......	....
12	6	5.52	......	Slowly sol	Gray-black	Dark brown	M	Perf	....
13	6	5.18-4.85	Inf	Sol	Black	Dark brown	Sm, shining	Indist	Uneven
14	6+	5.30	Inf	Ins	Black	Brwnsh blk	Sm	None	Conch
15	6±	5.0	......	....	Light yellow				......
16	5.5-6.5	5.22-5.07	Inf	Sol	Iron-black	Rdsh brwn to black	M, D	Indist	Conch to uneven
17	5.5-6.5	5.8-5.6	Inf	Dcpd by H₂SO₄	Gray, ylw, brwn, fresh break blk	Ylw brwn, brwn, grnsh gray	D, V, Sm	Traces	Subconch
18	5.5-6.5	5.18-5.17	5-5.5	Sol	Iron-black	Black	M, Sm	Indist	Subconch to uneven
19	5.5-6.5	5.8-5.6	Inf	Dcpd by H₂SO₄	Gray, ylw, brwn, fresh break blk	Brwn, ylw brwn, grnsh gray	D, V, Sm	Traces	Subconch
20	5.5-6.5	5.9-4.9	Inf	Dcpd	Blk, grn or brwnsh tint	Ylw, grayish, rdsh brwn	Sm, G, V	None	Subconch to conch
21	5.5-6.5	5.9-4.9	Inf	Dcpd	Blk, grn or brwnsh tint	Ylwsh, grysh, rdsh brwn	Sm, G, V	None	Subconch to uneven
22	5.5-6	6.22-5.92	2	Dcpd by HNO₃	Silver-white to steel-gray	Drk grysh blk	M	Dist	Uneven
23	5.5-6	5.03	6	Ins	Ylw to resin-brown	....	G	......	....
24	5-6	5.69±	4.5-5	Pt sol	Velvet-black	Drk rdsh brwn	V to R	Indist	Conch
25	5-6	5.26	Inf	Sol	Steel-gray	Cherry-red to brown	M, Sm, D	None	Conch to uneven
26	5-6	5.05-4.84	Inf	Ins	Brwn, blk, ylw, various shades	Rdsh ylw	Sm, R, W	Traces	Conch
27	5-6	5.24-5.14	Inf	Ins	Blk, brwn, ylw, various shades	Blk to brwn	Sm, R, W	Traces	Conch
28	5.5	5.4-5.0	Inf	Pt sol	Emerald-green, black in mass	Brown	V	Fair	Fibrous break

GROUP 3
Specific Gravity 5.99-5.00

INDEX OF REF.	NAME	COMPOSITION	REMARKS
....	OSBORNITE	TiN	Reported in a meteorite from India.
2.17	MELANOTEKITE	$2PbO \cdot Fe_2O_3 \cdot 2SiO_2$	Fuses with intumescence to a black bead.
2.19	BADDELEYITE	ZrO_2	Glows brightly when heated, turns white and is nearly infusible.
2.09	SCHNEEBERGITE	$4(Ca,Fe)O \cdot 2Sb_2O_4$	
....	TODDITE	Columbite with U replacing some Mn-Fe	Possibly a mixture of columbite and Euxenite.
....	EICHBERGITE	$(Cu,Fe)(Bi,Sb)_2S_5$	
....	MAUZELIITE	(Ti,Sb) of Pb and Ca	
2.25-2.45	COLUMBITE-TANTALITE	$(Fe, Mn)(Cb,Ta)_2O_6$	Brittle. Partially decomposed by boiling H_2SO_4
....	PYROLUSITE (crystals)	MnO_2	Brittle. Treated with HCl, yields acrid fumes of chlorine.
....	PYRITE	FeS_2	Brittle. In C.T., gives off sulfur and leaves a magnetic residue.
....	ISHKULITE	$FeFe_2O_4 \cdot FeCrO_4 \cdot MgFe_2O_4$	Magnetic.
....	MAGNETO-PLUMBITE	(Pb,Mn^2,Mn^3) $(Fe^3,Mn^3,Ti)_6O_{10}$	Strongly magnetic.
2.34±	HETAEROLITE	$ZnMn_2O_4$	Brittle. Dissolved in HCl, it yields chlorine.
2.50Li	SENAITE	$(Fe,Mn,Pb)TiO_2$	Decomposed by boiling H_2SO_4.
....	SILESITE	Sn,SiO_2	Probably a mixture of wood tin and silica.
2.36±	FRANKLINITE	$ZnFe_2O_4$	With sodium carbonate on charcoal, gives a zinc coating.
2.077±	FORMANITE	(U,Zr,Th,Ca) $(Ta,Cb,Ti)O_4$	Brittle. Decomposed by fusion with $KHSO_4$.
2.42Na	MAGNETITE	$FeFe_2O_4$	Brittle. Strongly magnetic. In O.T., looses its influence on the magnet.
2.07±	FERGUSONITE	(Y,Er,Ce,Fe) $(Ta,Cb,Ti)O_4$	Brittle. Decomposed by fusion with $KHSO_4$.
2.24±	EUXENITE	(Y,Ca,Ce,U,Th) $(Cb,Ta,Ti)_2O_6$	Glows on heating. Decomposed by boiling H_2SO_4.
2.248	POLYCRASE	(Y,Ca,Ce,U,Th) $(Ti,Cb,Ta)_2O_6$	B.B. in forceps, swells up and changes color to a light grayish brown. Decomposed by boiling H_2SO_4.
....	ARSENOPYRITE	FeAsS	Brittle. In C.T., gives first a red then black, lustrous sublimate.
1.83	ATOPITE	$2CaO \cdot Sb_2O_5$	On charcoal in R.F., sublimes in part. May be Romeite.
2.2±	SAMARSKITE	$(Y,Er,Ce,U,Ca,Fe,Pb,$ $Th)(Cb,Ta,Ti,Sn)_2O_6$	Brittle. B.B., gives a momentary bright light.
3.22Li	HEMATITE	Fe_2O_3	Brittle. Sometimes distinct parting or pseudo cleavage. On charcoal in R.F., becomes magnetic.
2.142	PRIORITE	(Y,Er,Ca,Fe,Th) $(Ti,Cb)_2O_6$	Brittle. Powder partly decomposed by boiling HCl or H_2SO_4.
2.26±	ESCHYNITE	(Ce,Ca,Fe,Th) $(Ti,Cb)_2O_6$	Brittle. B.B. in forceps, swells up and changes color from black to rusty brown.
2.16	MANGANOSITE	MnO	B.B., it blackens.

GROUP 3
Specific Gravity 5.99–5.00

	H	SP. GR.	F	HCL	COLOR	STREAK	LUSTER	CLEAV-AGE	FRACTURE
29	5.5	5.99-5.35	2	Dcpd by HNO₃	Silver-white, steel-gray	Grysh wht	M	Perf	Uneven
30	5.5	5.88-5.75	......	....	Ylwsh to grnsh brwn, grnsh blk	....	....	....	Irregular
31	5.5	5.98	4	Ins	Grn, ylw, brwn, red	Ylw to brwn	R to A	Perf	Subconch
32	5.5	5.41	Easy	Sol	Black	Black	M	Imperf	Brittle
33	5.5	5.87	......	....	Dark red-gray	....			Conch
34	5.5	5.0?	......	Pt sol	Yellowish red	....	R		....
35	5.5	5.44	Inf	Pt sol	Black	....	D	None	Subconch
36	5-5.5	5.9-5.5	Inf	Ins	Black, brown	Gray	Sm, V, G	Indist	Small conch
37	5-5.5	5.3-4.9	Inf	Pt sol	Red, brown, ylwsh brwn	....	R	Perf	Conch to uneven
38	5	6.16-5.92	2-3	Dcpd by HNO₃	Grysh to rdsh, tin-white	Black	M	Perf	Uneven
39	5	5.49	......	....	Black	....	Brilliant		....
40	5	5.16	Inf	Pt sol	Blk, brwnsh blk	Brwn	M, Sm, D	Parting	Subconch to uneven
41	5	5.8-5.2	Inf	....	Blk, to iron-blk	Grysh blk, brwnsh, grn tint	M	None	Granular
42	5	5.00	......	....	Orange ylw to ylw brwn	....			....
43	4.5-5	5.2-4.4	Inf	Gelat	Orange to brwnsh ylw, blksh, gray	Lt orange to drk brown	V, R, G	Perf	Conch
44	4.5-5	5.4-5.2	Inf	Gelat	Orange, brwn, blk, grn	Lt orange to drk brwn	V, R, G	Prismatic	Conch
45	4.5-5	6.1-5.9	5	Dcpd	Wht, ylw, brwn, grn, gray, rdsh	White	V to A	Dist	Uneven
46	4.5-5	5.5-5.2	......	....	Dark gray to blk	Brwnsh blk	D to Sm	....	....
47	4.5-5	5.04	......	....	Black-brown	Brown	V	....	Uneven
48	4.5-5	5.58-5.07	5-6	Ins	Ylw to ylwsh and rdsh white	....	P to E	....	....
49	4.5-5	6.05-5.95	2	Dcpd by HNO₃	Silver-wht to steel-gray	Black	M	....	Uneven
50	4-5.5	5.0-3.7	6	Pt sol	Grnsh brwn	....	W, V, Sm		Conch
51	4-5	5.49	1	Dcpd by HNO₃	Gray-black	Black	M	None	Granular
52	4.5	5.96	......	Gelat	Ochre-yellow	....	....	Perf	....
53	4-5	5.09-4.08	Inf	Sol	Ylw, wht, sometimes rdsh wht	Wht to ylwsh wht	G to P	....	Fibrous or powder

GROUP 3
Specific Gravity 5.99-5.00

INDEX OF REF.	NAME	COMPOSITION	REMARKS
. . . .	**GERSDORFFITE**	NiAsS	**Brittle. In O.T., gives SO_2 fumes and a crystalline sublimate of As_2O_3. In C.T., a yellowish brown sublimate of As_2S_3.**
1.97	DJALMAITE	(U,Ca,Pb,Bi,Fe) (Ta,Cb,Ti,Zr)$_3O_9$· nH_2O	Transparent in thin splinters with a yellowish brown color.
2.419	STIBIO-COLUMBITE	$SbCbO_4$	Brittle. Only slightly attacked by boiling H_2SO_4.
. . . .	DELAFOSSITE	$CuFeO_2$	Becomes magnetic on heating. Not soluble in HNO_3.
2.15-2.2	ESCHWEGITE	$10TiO_3·5Y_2O_3·2Ta_2O_5·$ $4Cb_2O_5·7H_2O$	Dark red thru thin splinters.
1.72	BUSZITE	Nd,Er,Eu,Pr,etc, SiO_2	Splinters are yellow.
1.77	MACHINTOSHITE	SiO_2 of U, Th,Ce,etc, H_2O	
2.15±	YTTROTANTALITE	(Fe,Y,U,Ca,etc) $(Cb,Ta,Zr,Sn)O_4$	In C.T., yields water and turns yellow.
1.788	**MONAZITE**	**(Ce,La,Di)PO_4**	**B.B., turns gray when treated with H_2SO_4; flame bluish green.**
. . . .	GLAUCODOT	(Co,Fe)AsS	Brittle. In O.T., gives SO_2 fumes and a sublimate of As_2O_3.
. . . .	YTTRO-COLUMBITE	More columbium than yttrotantalite	
2.3?	TREVORITE	$NiFe_2O_4$	Strongly magnetic.
2.3	HJELMITE	Y,Fe,U,Sn,Mn,Ca,Cb, Ta,etc	In C.T., decrepitates and yields water.
1.915	HUEGELITE	Hydrous vanadate of lead and zinc	
1.72	**THORITE**	**$ThSiO_4$**	**In C.T., usually yields water and changes color.**
1.69	ORANGITE	$ThSiO_4·nH_2O$	Altered thorite.
1.918	**SCHEELITE**	**$CaWO_4$**	**Brittle. With borax, gives a transparent glass which later becomes opaque and crystalline. Blue under ultra-violet light.**
. . . .	CORONADITE	$MnPbMn_6O_{14}$	Botryoidal crusts with fibrous structure.
. . . .	NOHLITE	(Ca,Mg,Fe,Y,etc,U)$_2$ $(Cb,Zr,Fe)_3O_{10}$	Brittle.
1.7±	**STIBICONITE**	**$Sb_3O_6(OH)$**	**In C.T., gives water but does not fuse. On coal decrepitates.**
. . . .	CORYNITE	Ni(As,Sb)S	Like walfachite. Between ullmannite and gersdorffite. May be a mixture.
1.925	BETAFITE	(U,Ca)(Cb,Ta,Ti)$_3O_9$ nH_2O	Brittle. B.B., gives a black slag.
. . . .	BERTHONITE	$Pb_2Cu_7Sb_5S_{13}$	Brittle. Treated with HNO_3, yields sulfur and a precipitate of lead sulfate.
1.91	KASOLITE	$3PbO·3UO_3·3SiO_2·$ $4H_2O$	
1.8±	**CERVANTITE**	**Sb_2O_4?**	**Reduces easily to metal on charcoal.**

MINERAL IDENTIFICATION TABLES
GROUP 3
Specific Gravity 5.99-5.00

	H	SP. GR.	F	HCL	COLOR	STREAK	LUSTER	CLEAV-AGE	FRACTURE	S
54	4.5	5.35	2-3	Sol in HNO$_3$	Grysh to blksh green	Siskin to apple grn	R	....	Subconch to uneven	M
55	4.5	5.29	Inf	Sol	Steel-gray	....	D, Sm	....		
56	4.5	5.43-4.5	Inf	Ins	Black on fresh break	Drk grnsh brown	....	....	Conch	T
57	3-4.5	5.1-4.6	1	....	Gray to iron-black	Red, gray, brown, blk	M	None	Subconch to uneven	I
58	4	5.68-5.64	Inf	Sol	Orange-ylw, deep red	Orange-ylw	Sa	Perf	Conch	H
59	4	5.03-4.99	6	Sol	Iron-black	Blk, brwnsh	M	Perf	....	M
60	4	5.7	1	Sol in HNO$_3$	Wht to ylwsh wht	....	R	Good	....	E
61	4	5.0-4.6	3-4	....	Gray, wht, brwn, ylwsh	Wht to gray or ylwsh	R, D, E	....		
62	4	5.02	4	Sol	Clove brwn	Light brwn	....	Perf	....	T
63	4	5.03-4.91	3	Sol	Dark grn to blk	Green	....	Perf	....	T
64	3.5-4	5.0-4.6	1.5-3	....	Lt bronze-ylw	Lt bronze-brown	M	None	Conch	I
65	3-4	5.0-4.9	1	Dcpd by HNO$_3$	Lead to iron-gray	....	M	Perf	Subconch	C
66	3-4	6.2-5.8	1	....	Tin-wht to rdsh gray	Gray	M	Perf	....	
67	3.5	6.4-5.8	Inf	Sol	Steel or iron-gray to black	....	M	Perf	Uneven to conch	
68	3.5	5.76	1.5	....	Wax-yellow	....	A	Dist	....	T
69	3.5	5.78-5.63	Vol	....	Tin-white	Tin-white	M	Perf	Uneven	
70	3.5	6.2-5.9	1.5	Sol in HNO$_3$	Red, brwn, blk	Brwnsh red, ylwsh gray	G	None	Uneven to conch	C
71	3.5	5.38	......	......	Deep red	....	....	None	....	C
72	3.5	5.33-5.27	1	Insol	Gray-black	Light red, ylwsh tone	Sm, M	Good	Uneven to conch	C
73	3-3.5	5.75	1.5	Sol	Cochineal to hyacinth red	Brick-red	R to A	Perf	....	C
74	3-3.5	5.7-5.3	1.5-2	....	Brass to bronze ylw, tarnished	Grnsh blk	M	Perf	Uneven	
75	3-3.5	5.37-5.33	1	Sol	Drk steel-gray	Black	M	None	Conch	
76	3-3.5	5.35-5.25	1	Sol	Steel-gray	Steel-gray	M	Indist	Uneven	
77	3-3.5	5.0-4.9	Inf	Sol	Various shades of yellow	Orange-yellow to brick-red	A to R	Dist	Conch	
78	2.5-5	6.4-3.9	......	......	Ylw, orange, rdsh, brwn to blk	Ylw, brwnsh, olive grn	G, W, V, D	....	Conch to uneven	
79	3	5.94	1	......	Bluish gray	Same	M	....	Uneven	
80	3	5.74	3?	Sol in HNO$_3$	Colorless to gray	....	R to V	Dist	Uneven	
81	3	5.54-5.44	......	......	Dark lead-gray to black	Chocolate brwn, purplish blk	M	Poor	Conch	

GROUP 3
Specific Gravity 5.99-5.00

INDEX OF REF.	NAME	COMPOSITION	REMARKS
1.97	BAYLDONITE	$4(Pb,Cu)O \cdot As_2O_5 \cdot 2H_2O$	B.B., gives off water and becomes black.
....	CESAROLITE	$PbMn_3O_7 \cdot H_2O$	Treated with HCl it yields chlorine.
2.3	BRANNERITE	$(U,Ca,Fe,Y,Th)_3 \cdot Ti_5O_{16}$	Altered mineral is brownish yellow. Decomposed by hot conc H_2SO_4.
2.72Li	TETRAHEDRITE-TENNANTITE	$(Cu,Fe,Zn,Ag)_{12} \cdot (Sb,As)_4S_{13}$	Decomposed by HNO_3 with separation of sulfur.
2.013	ZINCITE	ZnO	Brittle. In C.T., blackens but on cooling returns to its original color.
....	CREDNERITE	$CuMn_2O_4$	Insoluble in HNO_3. Dissolved in HCl, yields chlorine.
1.948	HEGYPHANE	$9PbO \cdot 9(Ca,Ba)O$ $6P_2O_5 \cdot 2PbCl_2$	
1.86±	BINDHEIMITE	$2PbO \cdot Sb_2O_5 \cdot H_2O$	On charcoal, reduces to metallic Sb and Pb.
1.905	YEATMANITE	$(Mn,Zn)_{16}Sb_2Si_4O_{29}$	
1.78	VANDEN-BRANDITE	$CuO \cdot UO_3 \cdot 2H_2O$	B.B., fuses to a black mass which becomes crystalline on cooling.
....	PENTLANDITE	$(Fe,Ni)_9S_8$	Brittle. Nonmagnetic. In O.T., gives sulfurous fumes.
....	CHALCOSTIBITE	$CuSbS_2$	Brittle. In C.T., gives a sublimate that is dark red on cooling.
....	ALLEMONTITE	$AsSb$	B.B. on charcoal, fuses to a globule, takes fire and gives a white coating of arsenic and antimony oxides.
....	TENORITE	CuO	Brittle. Reduces to metallic copper.
2.00±	WALPURGITE	$5Bi_2O_3 \cdot 3UO_3 \cdot 2As_2O_5 \cdot 12H_2O$	
....	ARSENIC	As	Brittle. B.B., volatilizes without fusing coating the charcoal white.
2.27	DESCLOIZITE	$(Pb,Zn)_2OH \cdot VO_4$	S.Ph bead is chrome-green in R.F.; orange-yellow in O.F.
2.36	PYROBELONITE	$4(Mn,Pb)O \cdot V_2O_5 \cdot H_2O$	
2.72	VRBAITE	$Tl(As,Sb)_3S_5$	Brittle. Splinters are translucent red.
2.38	PHENI-COCHROITE	$3PbO \cdot 2CrO_3$	On charcoal, gives a dark mass which is crystalline when cold.
....	MILLERITE	NiS	Brittle. On charcoal, fuses to a magnetic globule.
....	ANDORITE	$PbAgSb_3S_6$	Brittle. In C.T., decrepitates and melts.
....	ZINKENITE	$Pb_6Sb_{14}S_{27}$	Dissolved in hot HCl, gives H_2S and $PbCl_2$ settles out on cooling.
2.43Li	GREENOCKITE	CdS	Brittle. In C.T., the mineral is carmen-red while hot, becoming yellow on cooling.
....	GUMMITE	$UO_3,Pb,Th,R.E.,etc,$ H_2O	Brittle.
....	GUITERMANITE	$Pb_{10}As_6S_{19}$	Brittle. Possibly a mixture.
1.91	GANOMALITE	$3PbO \cdot 2(Ca,Mn)O \cdot 3SiO_2$	Fuses to a clear glass which in R.F., is colored black.
....	SELIGMANNITE	$PbCuAsS_3$	Brittle.

GROUP 3
Specific Gravity 5.99-5.00

	H	SP. GR.	F	HCL	COLOR	STREAK	LUSTER	CLEAV-AGE	FRACTURE
82	3	5.56-5.5	2	Sol in HNO₃	Steel to lead-gray	Rdsh brwn	M	Perf	Conch
83	3	**5.08-5.06**	2	**Sol in HNO₃**	**Red to brwn, iridescent**	**Pale gray to black**	**M**	**Traces**	**Conch to uneven**
84	3	5.41-5.33	......	....	Lead-gray, often iridescent tarnish	Chocolate brown	....	Perf	Conch
85	3	5.12-5.08	1	Sol in HNO₃	Dark lead-gray	Chocolate brown	M	Fair	Conch
86	3	5.18-4.79	1	....	Iron-black	Black	M	....	Conch to uneven
87	3	5.3	....						
88	3	5.43	2	....	White	....	G	Imperf	....
89	3	5.+	......	....	Rdsh violet, slate-gray	....	M	Perf	Granular
90	3	5.33	......	....	Lead to steel-gray	Chocolate brown	M	Perf	Conch
91	3	5.7	......	....	Ylwsh green, brown tinge	....			
92	3	5.9	......	....	White	....	G	Good	....
93	3	5.88	......	Sol in HNO₃	Colorless	....		Dist	....
94	3	5.62	Easy	Sol in HNO₃	Dark cherry-red, violet tinge	Black	M	None	Uneven to subconch
95	2.5-3	5.92-5.88	1	Dcpd by HNO₃	Grayish black	Same	M	Perf	Flexible
96	2.5-3	6.1-5.8	2?	Sol in H₂SO₄	Grn to blk, brown	Grnsh to brwnsh	A to R	....	Uneven
97	2.5-3	**6.1-5.9**	1.5	....	**Hyacinth-red**	**Orange-ylw**	**A to V**	**Dist**	**Conch to uneven**
98	2.5-3	**5.86-5.8**	1	**Dcpd by HNO₃**	**Steel, blksh lead-gray, iron-blk**	**Same**	**Brilliant M**	**Imperf**	**Uneven to sunconch**
99	2.5-3	5.73	......	....	Iron-black	Black	M	Good	Uneven
100	2.5-3	**5.8-5.5**	2-2.5	**Sol in HNO₃**	**Blksh lead-gray**	**Same**	**M**	**Indist**	**Conch**
101	2.5-3	5.76	1.5	Sol	White, gray, rose	White	A to P	Perf	Brittle
102	2.5-3	**6.4-5.96**	1	**Sol**	**Bluish lead-gray**	**Brnsh gray, brwn**	**M**	**Good**	**Flexible**
103	2.5-3	5.546	Easy	Sol in HNO₃	Blue to black	....	....	Good	Conch
104	2-3	**6.0-5.8**	1	**Sol in NH₄OH**	**Yellow, green**	....	**R to A**	**None**	**Uneven**
105	2-3	5.2	......	....	Amber to brwnsh yellow	Yellow	A to G	Perf	....
106	2-3	5.68-5.4	1	Sol in HNO₃	Red, brwn, orange, yellow	Orange-ylw	A	Dist	Subconch
107	2.5	5.49-5.43	1	Slowly sol	Blksh lead-gray	Black	M	Circular	Slightly malleable
108	2.5	**5.72-5.48**	1	**Dcpd by HNO₃**	**Grayish black**	**Grysh blk**	**M**	**Good**	**Uneven to conch**
109	2.5	**5.87-5.77**	1	**Dcpd by HNO₃**	**Deep red**	**Purplish red**	**A**	**Dist**	**Conch to uneven**

EUXENITE   XENOTIME TOURMALINE   PYRRHOTITE   STANNITE   PENTLANDITE PYRRHOTITE

BARITE   PYROLUSITE   LIVINGSTONITE   STIBNITE   TENNANTITE GERMANITE PYRITE

BRAUNITE   BROOKITE   PLEONASTE   COVELLITE   FERRI MOLYBDITE

CORUNDUM   SPINEL   EMBOLITE (greenish)   ALMANDITE   SPESSARTITE

RUTILE   TEPHROITE ZINCITE   ALLANITE   ILVAITE CHALCOPYRITE   TURGITE

WILLEMITE ZINCITE   PEROVSKITE (brown xtls)   BLOMSTRANDINE   LIMONITE   LIMONITE

PLATE 21

GROUP 3
Specific Gravity 5.99-5.00

INDEX OF REF.	NAME	COMPOSITION	REMARKS
2.72±	DUFRENOYSITE	$Pb_2As_2S_5$	Brittle. In O.T., an odor of SO_2; in upper portion a sublimate of S and in the lower portion one of As_2O_3.
....	**BORNITE**	Cu_5FeS_4	**Brittle. On charcoal in R.F., fuses to a brittle magnetic globule.**
....	RATHITE	$Pb_{13}As_{18}S_{40}$	
....	SARTORITE	$PbAs_2S_4$	Brittle. In C.T., gives a sublimate of S and As_2S_3.
....	STYLOTYPITE	$(Cu,Ag,Fe)_3SbS_3$	On charcoal, a steel-gray, magnetic globule and fumes of Sb.
....	LIVEINGITE	$Pb_5As_8S_{17}$	
1.945	NASONITE	$5PbO·4CaO·PbCl_2·$ $6SiO_2$	In C.T., gives a sublimate of white lead chloride.
....	KLOCKMANNITE	$CuSe$	
....	BAUMHAUERITE	$Pb_4As_6S_{13}$	
....	ARSENOBISMITE	$2Bi_2O_3·As_2O_5·2H_2O$	
1.95	LARSENITE	$PbO·ZnO·SiO_2$	
2.102	FIEDLERITE	$PbO·2PbCl_2·H_2O$	
....	UMANGITE	Cu_3Se_2	
....	FRANCKEITE	$Pb_5Sn_3Sb_2S_{14}$	On charcoal, a yellow coat near the assay and white one far away.
2.22	VAUQUELINITE	$2(Pb,Cu)CrO_4·$ $(Cu,Pb)(PO_4)_2$	Fuses to a gray metallic bead and small globule of metal
2.37Li	**CROCOITE**	$PbCrO_4$	**Sectile. S.Ph, gives an emerald-green bead in both flames.**
....	**BOURNONITE**	$PbCuSbS_3$	**Brittle. In C.T., decrepitates and gives a dark red sublimate. The HNO_3 solution is blue.**
....	HETERO-MORPHITE	$Pb_7Sb_8S_{19}$	Brittle. Striated and rounded, also massive.
....	**CHALCOCITE**	Cu_2S	**Rather brittle. On charcoal, boils and spirts.**
2.35	VALENTINITE	Sb_2O_3	In C.T., fuses and partially sublimes.
....	**BOULANGERITE**	$Pb_5Sb_4S_{11}$	**Brittle. On charcoal, almost entirely volatile giving a dark yellow sublimate with white edges.**
....	DIGENITE	$Cu_{2-x}S$	Brittle. On charcoal, melts with spurting.
2.253	**BROMYRITE**	$AgBr$	**On charcoal, yields pungent bromine odors and gives a globule of silver.**
1.82	BECQUERELITE	$2UO_3·3H_2O$	An alteration product of Uraninite.
3.0	XANTHOCONITE	Ag_2AsS_3	Brittle. In C.T., heated gently, becomes dark red; regains color on cooling.
....	CYLINDRITE	$Pb_3Sn_4Sb_2S_{14}$	Treated with hot HNO_3, it yields sulfur and tin and antimony oxides.
....	**JAMESONITE**	$Pb_4FeSb_6S_{14}$	**Brittle. On charcoal, gives a coat that is dark yellow near the assay and has white edges.**
3.084Li	**PYRARGYRITE**	Ag_3SbS_3	**Brittle. In C.T., fuses and gives a reddish sublimate.**

GROUP 3
Specific Gravity 5.99-5.00

	H	SP. GR.	F	HCL	COLOR	STREAK	LUSTER	CLEAV-AGE	FRACTURE	S T
110	2.5	5.598	1	Ins	Brass-yellow, gray-white	Iron-gray	....	Perf	....	.
111	2.5	5.4	......	....	Light gray	....	M	....	....	C
112	2.5	5.62-5.6	.....	....	Iron-black	Black	M	Perf	Sectile	T
113	2.5	5.82?	Inf	Ins	Golden, ylw-grn	....	R, P	Perf	....	C
114	2.5	5.45-5.3	1 5	Sol in HNO₃	Deep sky-blue	Pale blue	V to A	Perf	Conch	M
115	2.5	5.51	1	....	Steel-black	Dark red	M	....	Conch	M
116	2.5	5.6-5.53	1	Dcpd	Blksh lead-gray	Same	M	Good	Conch to uneven	M
117	2.5	5.08	1	Sol in HNO₃	Indigo-blue	....	....	Perf	....	T
118	2.5	6.15-5.82	1	....	Gray to black	Black	M	Perf	Brittle	M
119	2.5	5.0-4.85	1	Ins	Indigo-blue	....	P	Perf	....	T
120	2.5	5.59	1.5?	....	Oil-brown, etc.	Orange-yellow	A	....	Subconch	I
121	2.5	5.5	2	....	Bright crimson, yellow, orange	Pale yellow	A	....	....	F
122	2.5	5.23	1	Ins	Lead-gray, bluish, bronzy	Rdsh gray	M	None	Uneven	
123	2.5	5.94	.....	....	Colorless	....	V, A	Good	....	M
124	2.5	5.3-5.2	1	Dcpd by HNO₃	Iron-black, steel-gray	Cherry-red	M, A	Imperf	Subconch to uneven	
125	2-2.5	5.64-5.55	1	Dcpd by HNO₃	Scarlet-vermilion	Vermilion	A	Dist	Conch to uneven	
126	2.2-5	5.0-4.4	Inf	Sol	Iron-black to dark gray, bluish	Blk, bluish, submetallic	M	Perf	Uneven	T
127	2-2.5	5.53	1	Sol in HNO₃	Cochineal-red	Cherry-red	M, A	Perf	Flexible	I
128	2-2.5	5.5	1.5	Sol	Colorless or grayish white	White	R, Sa	Traces	Uneven	
129	2	5.92-5.88	Vol	Sol	Honey or straw-yellow, white	....	Sa	Perf	Flexible	C
130	2	5.0-4.06	1	Ins	Blackish gray	Red	M, A	Perf	Flexible	
131	2	5.94	1	Dcpd by HNO₃	Hyacinth-red	Orange-yellow	A	Perf	Conch	X
132	2	5.64	1	....	Yellow	Same, darker	A	Dodeca hedral	....	
133	2	5.5-5.3	.....	....	Lead-gray	Black	M	Perf	....	
134	2	5.25-4.67	1	Sol in HNO₃	Sky-blue	Sky-blue	....	....	....	
135	2	5.43	.....	....	Dark gray	Gray-black	M	....	Uneven	
136	2	5.01-3.8	Inf	Ins	Black	Black	M	Good	Uneven	
137	1-1.5	5.55	1	Ins	Colorless, grnsh, grysh, white	....	R to A	None	Conch	
138	1-1.5	5.81-5.31	1	Ins	Grns to ylws, colorless	....	R to A	None	Uneven	
139	1-1.5	5.7-5.6	1	Ins	Ylwsh, grnsh, brwnsh	Yellow	R to A	Perf	....	

GROUP 3
Specific Gravity 5.99–5.00

INDEX OF REF.	NAME	COMPOSITION	REMARKS
....	MUTHMANNITE	$(Ag,Au)Te$	Mostly soluble in HNO_3. B.B., similar to Sylvanite.
....	DURFELDTITE	$Pb(Ag,Cu,Fe)MnSb_2$ S_6	Probably a mixture.
....	ARAMAYOITE	$Ag(Sb,Bi)S_2$	Blood-red in splinters.
2.24	TUNGSTITE	$WO_3 \cdot H_2O$	Soluble in alkalies.
1.838	LINARITE	$PbO \cdot CuO \cdot SO_3 \cdot H_2O$	In C.T., yields water and loses its color.
....	SAMSONITE	$Ag_4MnSb_2S_6$	Brittle. Splinters are deep red to brown. On charcoal in R.F., an Ag button and black crust which reacts for Mn.
....	**PLAGIONITE**	$Pb_5Sb_8S_{17}$	**Brittle. Decrepitates. In hot HCl, it yields H_2S and $PbCl_2$ settles out on cooling.**
2.05	BOLEITE	$9PbCl_2 \cdot 8CuO \cdot 3AgCl \cdot 9H_2O$	
	SEMSEYITE	$Pb_9Sb_8S_{21}$	
2.03	PSEUDOBOLEITE	$5PbCl_2 \cdot 4CuO \cdot 6H_2O$	Soluble in HNO_3. Probably identical with Boleite.
2.346	MARSHITE	Cu_2I_3	Brittle.
2.16	BELLITE	$PbO \cdot Cr_2O_3 \cdot As_2O_3 \cdot$, etc	B.B., yields a globule of lead and an arsenic coating.
	FULOPPITE	$Pb_3Sb_8S_{15}$	Brittle. B.B., on charcoal, gives a yellow and white sublimate. In O.T., melts and yields SO_2 and a sublimate of Sb_2S_3.
1.91	SCHULTENITE	$PbO \cdot As_2O_5 \cdot H_2O$	
2.72Li	MIARGYRITE	$AgSbS_2$	Brittle. In C.T., decrepitates and gives a sublimate of antimony oxysulfide.
2.979Li	**PROUSTITE**	Ag_3AsS_2	**Brittle. On charcoal, fuses and emits fumes of S and Sb, leaving a button of silver.**
....	**PYROLUSITE** (massive)	MnO_2	**Brittle. Treated with HCl, it yields acrid fumes of chlorine.**
3.71Li	LORANDITE	$TlAsS_2$	Colors flame green. Volatilizes completely, giving As fumes.
2.087	SENARMONTITE	Sb_2O_3	Brittle. In C.T., fuses and partially sublimes.
2.18Li	TELLURITE	TeO_2	In O.F., fuses to brown drops and sublimes.
3.0	LIVINGSTONITE	$HgSb_4S_7$	With sodium carbonate in C.T., yields a sublimate of metallic Hg.
....	PYROSTILPNITE	Ag_3SbS_3	In C.T., gives a reddish sublimate of Sb_2S_3.
2.2	MIERSITE	$4AgI \cdot CuI$	Soluble in NH_4OH.
....	ARSENOLAMPRITE	As	Massive with fibrous, foliated structure.
2.05	PERCYLITE	$PbO \cdot CuCl_2 \cdot H_2O$	In C.T., yields water and colorless fumes.
....	RAMDOHRITE	$Pb_3Ag_2Sb_6S_{13}$	Brittle.
.91	DAUBREELITE	Cr_2FeS_4	Brittle. In R.F., looses luster and becomes magnetic. Soluble in HNO_3 with liberation of sulfur.
.061	**CERARGYRITE**	**AgCl**	**Soluble in NH_4OH.**
.15±	**EMBOLITE**	**AgCl·AgBr**	**Soluble in NH_4OH.**
.21	**IODYRITE**	**AgI**	**Soluble in NH_4OH.**

GROUP 3
Specific Gravity 5.99-5.00

	H	SP. GR.	F	HCL	COLOR	STREAK	LUSTER	CLEAV-AGE	FRACTURE	S T
140	1	5.83-5.24	1	Ins	Wht, ylw, grnsh	White	A, S, P	Perf	....	C
141	1	**5.71**	1	**Ins**	**Colorless, ylw, etc**	....	**R**	**Indist**	....	I
142	Soft	5.85-5.8	......	....	Steel-gray	Black	M	Perf	Flexible	T
143	?	5.24	Easy	....	Black	....	....	....	....	.
144	?	6.27-5.92	......	Ins	Colorless with creamy surface	....	....	....	....	E
145	?	5.484	......	....	Yellow-gold	....	....	....	....	I

GROUP 3
Specific Gravity 5.99-5.00

INDEX OF REF.	NAME	COMPOSITION	REMARKS
2.217	COTUNNITE	$PbCl_2$	Soluble in hot water.
2.2	**IODOBROMITE**	**Ag(Cl,Br,I)**	**On charcoal, gives a globule of silver and pungent odors of Br.**
. . . .	LENGENBACHITE	$Pb_6(Ag,Cu)_2As_4S_{13}$	Somewhat malleable. Leaves a mark on paper.
. . . .	KHLOPINITE	$(Y,U,Th)_3 \cdot (Cb,Ta,Fe,Ti)_7O_{20}$	Contains helium.
2.06	SIMPSONITE	$Al_2Ta_2O_8$	Interior of rough, tabular, cream colored crystals is colorless.
. . . .	SEYRIGITE	$Ca(W,Mo)O_4$	

GROUP 4
Specific Gravity 4.99-4.50

	H	SP. GR.	F	HCL	COLOR	STREAK	LUSTER	CLEAVAGE	FRACTURE
1	7.5-8	4.62-4.03	Inf	Ins	Grn, ylw, brwn, blk	Grayish	V to D	Indist	Conch to uneven
2	7.5	4.86-4.2	Inf	Ins	Colorless, ylw, gray, grn, brwn, red	Uncolored	A	Imperf	Conch
3	6.5-7	4.5-4.0	Inf	Gelat	Blk, brwn, grn	Grnsh gray	V to G	None	Conch to splintery
4	6-7	4.52	Inf	Gelat	Drk grn or red.	....	....	....	Conch
5	6.5	4.92	Inf	Pt sol	Iron-black	Drk rdsh brown	M	None	Conch
6	6.5	4.85-4.77	Inf	Ins	Black	Drk brwn	Sm, M	Traces	Conch
7	6.5	4.74-4.48	......	....	Jet black	Grysh brwn	Sm	None	Conch to irregular
8	6.5	4.91	Inf	....	Shiny black	Pale ylw	V	None	Conch
9	6.5	4.97	......	....	Honey ylw, brwn	....	V to A	None	....
10	6-6.5	4.887	2.5-3	Ins	Pale brass ylw, fresh break wht.	Grnsh to brwnsh blk	M	Dist	Uneven
11	6-6.5	5.02-4.82	2.5-3	Ins	Pale brass ylw	Grnsh, brwnsh, brwnsh blk	M	Indist	Conch to uneven
12	6-6.5	4.83-4.72	Inf	Sol	Drk brwnsh blk to steel-gray	Same	Sm	Perf	Subconch to uneven
13	6-6.5	4.65-4.56	Inf	Pt sol	Iron-black	Black	M, Sm	....	....
14	6-6.5	4.945	4	Pt sol	Black	Black	M, Sm	Traces	Irregular
15	5.5-6.5	5.9-4.9	Ins	Dcpd	Black, grn or brwnsh tint	Ylw, grayish, rdsh, brwn	Sm, V, G	None	Subconch to uneven
16	5.5-6.5	5.9-5.4	Inf	Dcpd	Black, green or brownish tint	Ylw, grayish, rdsh brwn	Sm, V, G	None	Subconch to uneven
17	6	4.76	Inf	Sol	Deep black	Brwnsh blk	M		....
18	6	5.18-4.85	Inf	Sol	Black	Dark brown	Sm, shining	Indist	Uneven
19	6	4.95	......	....	Silver to grysh blk, blk	Black	M, shining	Dist	Brittle
20	6	4.8-4.39	6	Pt sol	Drk brown to blk	Ochre ylw to rdsh brwn	M, A, G	Dist	Uneven to subconch
21	5.5-6	4.7±	......	....	Black	....	R	....	Subconch
22	5.5-6	4.80	Inf	Sol in H₂SO₄	Black, dull brwn coating	....	R	....	Uneven to conch
23	5.5-6	4.62	......	....	Steel-gray		M	Good	Conch to uneven
24	5-6	4.54	Inf	Sol	Deep blood-red	Orange-ylw, grnsh tinge	M, Sm	Perf	Conch to subconch
25	5-6	4.76-4.68	Inf	Pt sol	Iron-black	Black to red	M to Sm	None	Conch
26	5-6	4.72-4.70	6	Sol	Iron black to steel-gray	Brwnsh blk to black	Sm, D	....	....
27	5-6	4.6?	Inf	Sol	Dark brwnsh to brwnsh black	Dark brown	Sm	Good	....

GROUP 4
Specific Gravity 4.99-4.50

INDEX OF REF.	NAME	COMPOSITION	REMARKS
1.79	**GAHNITE**	$ZnAl_2O_4$	**Brittle. Gives a coating of ZnO with soda and borax on charcoal. Slowly soluble in conc H_2SO_4.**
1.926	**ZIRCON**	$ZrSiO_4$	**Some varieties change color on heating.**
1.78±	**GADOLINITE**	$2BeO \cdot FeO \cdot 2Y_2O_3 \cdot 2SiO_2$	**B.B., gives a temporary bright light, swell and cracks open.**
1.725	ROWLANDITE	$2Y_2O_3 \cdot 3SiO_2$	Pale green in splinters.
2.36Li	LANGBANITE	$Mn_2O_3 \cdot SiO_2 \cdot Fe_2O_3 \cdot Sb_2O_3$	With niter and soda, gives a deep green mass.
2.22	POLYMIGNITE	(Ca,Fe,Y,etc,Zr,Th) $(Cb,Ti,Ta)O$	Reddish brown in thin sections. Fine powder partially decomposed by conc H_2SO_4.
2.095	CALCIO-SAMARSKITE	(Ca,Y,etc,U,Th) $(Cb,Ta,Fe,Ti,Sn)_5O_{15}$	
2.19	LYNDOCHITE	$(Ce,La,Di)_2O_3 \cdot (Y,Er)_2O_3 \cdot CaO \cdot H_2O \cdot$ etc	A thorium, calcium Euxenite, low in uranium.
2.21	WESLIENITE	$Na_2O \cdot FeO \cdot 3CaO \cdot 2Sb_2O_5$	
....	**MARCASITE**	FeS_2	**Brittle. In C.T., gives a sublimate of sulfur and leaves a magnetic residue.**
....	**PYRITE**	FeS_2	**Brittle. In C.T., gives off sulfur and leaves a magnetic residue.**
....	**BRAUNITE**	$(Mn,Si)_2O_3$	**Brittle. Treated with HCl, it yields chlorine and leaves a gelatinous residue of silica.**
2.43Li	MAGNESIO-FERRITE	$MgFe_2O_4$	Strongly magnetic.
....	BIXBYITE	$(Mn,Fe)_2O_3$	Dissolved in HCl, gives acrid chlorine vapors.
2.24±	**EUXENITE**	(Y,Ca,Ce,U,Th) $(Cb,Ta,Ti)_2O_6$	**Glows on heating. Decomposed by boiling H_2SO_4**
2.248	POLYCRASE	(Y,Ca,Ce,U,Th) $(Ti,Cb,Ta)_2O_3$	Decomposed by boiling H_2SO_4. B.B., in forceps, swells and changes color to light grayish brown.
2.3±	JACOBSITE	$MnFe_2O_4$	Magnetic. Treated with HCl, it yields a small amount of chlorine.
2.34±	HETAEROLITE	$ZnMn_2O_3$	Brittle. Dissolved in HCl, it yields chlorine.
....	HOLLANDITE	$MnBaMn_6O_{14}$	
2.39Li	PSEUDO-BROOKITE	$FeTiO_5$	Partially decomposed by boiling H_2SO_4.
....	DELORENZITE	$(Y,U,Fe)(Ti,Sn,?)_3O_8$	Brittle. Radioactive.
2.13±	YTTROCRASITE	$(Y,Th,U,Ca)_2 \cdot (Ti,Fe,W)_4O_{11}$	B.B., assumes a dark gray color and cracks open to a slight extent. Radio active.
....	BRAVOITE	$(Ni,Fe)S_2$	Brittle.
2.481	PYROPHANITE	$MnTiO_3$	Red in fine splinters.
....	**ILMENITE**	$FeTiO_3$	**B.B., gives titanium tests.**
....	**PSILOMELANE**	$BaMnMn_8O_{16}(OH)_4$	With HCl, yields pungent odors of chlorine.
2.26	HYDRO-HETAEROLITE	$Zn_2Mn_4O_8 \cdot H_2O$	An alteration product of Hetaerolite.

GROUP 4
Specific Gravity 4.99-4.50

	H	SP. GR.	F	HCL	COLOR	STREAK	LUSTER	CLEAV-AGE	FRACTURE
28	5-6	5.05-4.85	Inf	Ins	Brwn, blk, ylw, various shades	Rdsh ylw	Sm, R, W	Traces	Conch
29	5.5	4.91-4.86	Inf	Gelat	Clove-brown, cherry-red, gray	Grayish white	A to R	....	Splintery
30	5.5	4.74	......	Ins	Black	Ylw to gray	....	....	Conch
31	5.5	4.8-4.5	6	Ins	Iron to brownish black	Brown	M	None	Uneven
32	5.5	4.95	3	Ins	Yellow to brown	Light ylwsh brown	V to R	Perf	....
33	5.5	4.75	6	Ins	Black	....	R	....	Conch
34	5.5	4.5	......	Ins	Black, red in splinters	....	M	Perf	....
35	5.5	4.85-4.83	Inf	Sol	Brownish black	Chestnut brwn	Sm	Perf	Uneven
36	5-5.5	5.3-4.9	Inf	Pt sol	Red, brown, yellowish brown	....	R	Perf	Conch to uneven
37	5-5.5	4.57	Inf	Sol	Olive grn to drab orange, yellow	....	V to G	None	Conch to splintery
38	5-5.5	4.55-4.51	4	Gelat	Velvet black	Dark brown	V		....
39	4.5-5.5	4.8-4.5	1.5-2	Ins	Steel-gray with faint rdsh hue	Blksh gray	M	Imperf	Subconch to uneven
40	4.5-5.5	4.8-4.5	1.5-2	Ins	Pale steel-gray	Blksh gray	M	Imperf	Subconch to uneven
41	4.5-5.5	4.8-4.5	1.5-2	Ins	Light steel to gray	Blksh gray	M	Imperf	Subconch to uneven
42	4.5-5.5	4.8-4.5	1.5-2	Ins	Pale steel-gray	Blksh gray	M	Imperf	Subconch to uneven
43	4.5-5.5	4.8-4.5	1.5-2	Ins	Violet-gray	Blksh gray	M	Imperf	Subconch to uneven
44	5	4.53-4.51	Inf	Ins	Pitch blk to dark brwn	....	R	....	Conch
45	5	4.6-4.16	Inf	Ins	Black	Grnsh gray	Sm	....	Conch
46	4.5-5	4.8-4.4	Inf	Gelat	Orange to brwnsh ylw, blk to brwn	Light orange to dark brwn	V, G, R	Dist	Conch]
47	4.5-5	4.62	......	....	Dark brown	Rdsh brown	A	Dist	....
48	4.5-5	5.0-3.7	6	Pt sol	Greenish brown	....	W, V, Sm	....	Conch
49	4-5	4.56-4.45	Inf	Ins	Brwn, red, wht, ylw	Pale brwn, ylwsh, rdsh	R to V	Perf	Uneven, splintery
50	4-5	4.9-4.51	Inf	Ins	Blk, ylwsh, brwn	....	R	....	Subconch
51	4-5	5.09-4.08	Inf	Sol	Ylw, wht, sometimes rdsh wht	Wht to ylwsh white	G to P	....	Fibrous or powder
52	4-5	4.9-4.0	2	Sol in HNO₃	Ylwsh, gray brwnsh, grnsh	Uncolored	R	....	....
53	4.5	5.43-4.5	Inf	Ins	Black on fresh break	Dark grnsh brwn		....	Conch

GROUP 4
Specific Gravity 4.99-4.50

INDEX OF REF.	NAME	COMPOSITION	REMARKS
2.142	PRIORITE	(Y,Er,Ca,Fe,Th) (Ti,Cb)$_2$O$_6$	Brittle. The fine powder is partially decomposed by boiling H$_2$SO$_4$.
4.818	CERITE	Hydrated cerium group silicate	B.B., not dissolved by soda but gives a dark slaggy mass.
....	SCHETELIGITE	(Ca,Y,Sb,Mn)$_2$ (Ti,Ta,Cb)$_2$(O,OH)$_7$	Insoluble in all acids except HF.
2.08	**CHROMITE**	FeCr$_2$O$_4$	**Brittle. Decomposed by fusion with KHSO$_4$. Insoluble in acids.**
2.2	LEWISITE	5CaO·2TiO$_2$·3Sb$_2$O$_3$	
2.19	ZIRKELITE	(Ca,Fe,Th,U)$_2$· (Ti,Zr)$_2$O$_5$?	Brittle. Non-magnetic.
.95	CATOPTRITE	14(Mn,Fe,Ca)O· 2(Al,Fe)$_2$O$_3$·2SiO$_2$· Sb$_2$O$_5$	
2.46Li	**HAUSMANNITE**	MnMn$_2$O$_4$	**Brittle. Treated with HCl, it yields acrid vapors of chlorine.**
.788	**MONAZITE**	(Ce,La,Di)PO$_4$	**B.B., turns gray when heated with H$_2$SO$_4$; flame is bluish green.**
.758	YTTRIALITE	Y$_2$O$_3$·ThO$_2$,etc,SiO$_2$	B.B., decrepitates violently and falls to a powder.
.88±	TSCHEFFKINITE	Ce,Th,Ti,SiO$_2$,etc	Glows, then intumesces, becomes brown and fuses to a black glass.
....	CARROLLITE	Co$_2$CuS$_4$	Soluble in HNO$_3$. On charcoal, gives SO$_2$ fumes and fuses to a magnetic globule.
....	**LINNAEITE**	Co$_3$S$_4$	**On charcoal, gives SO$_2$ and fuses to a magnetic globule. Decompose d by H$_2$SO$_4$.**
....	POLYDYMITE	Ni$_3$S$_4$	In C.T., decr epitates, gives a sublimate of S and fuses to a dark green mass. Like linnaeite.
....	SEIGENITE	(Co,Ni)$_3$S$_4$	Decomposed by HNO$_3$ with separation of S. Like linnaeite.
....	VIOLARITE	Ni$_2$FeS$_4$	Like linnaeite.
.45Li	DERBYLITE	FeO·Sb$_2$O$_5$ plus 5FeO·TiO$_2$	With S.Ph., the bead is yellow while hot and violet when cold.
....	LORANSKITE	(Y,Ce,Ca,Zr,?) (Ta,Zr,?)O$_4$	Brittle. Incompletely decomposed by acids and fusion with alkalies.
....	**THORITE**	ThSiO$_4$	**B.B., looses color on heating but regains it on cooling.**
.04	GAMAJARITE	Ba(Fe,Mn)$_2$V$_4$O$_{15}$ (OH)$_2$	
.925	BETAFITE	(U,Ca)(Cb,Ta,Ti)$_3$O$_9$· nH$_2$O	Brittle. B.B., gives a black slag.
.721	**XENOTIME**	YPO$_4$	**When moistened with H$_2$SO$_4$, it colors the flame green.**
.98	HATCHETTOLITE	Pyrochlore containing uranium	Brittle.
.8±	**CERVANTITE**	Sb$_2$O$_4$?	**On charcoal, reduces easily to metal.**
.654	PLUMBOGUMMITE	PbO·2Al$_2$O$_3$·P$_2$O$_5$· 9H$_2$O	B.B. in forceps, swells and colors the flame azure blue.
3	BRANNERITE	(U,Ca,Fe,Y,Th)$_3$· Ti$_5$O$_{16}$	Decomposed by hot conc H$_2$SO$_4$.

GROUP 4
Specific Gravity 4.99-4.50

	H	SP. GR.	F	HCL	COLOR	STREAK	LUSTER	CLEAV-AHE	FRACTURE	S T
54	4.5	4.86	......	....	Grn, grnsh blk, brwnsh red	Light grn, ylwsh grn	V	None	Subconch	T
55	4.5	4.94	......	Sol	Lt grn to olive	....				M
56	4.5	4.69	......	....	Red, ylw, grnsh		V			.
57	4.5	4.65	......	....	Colorless with grnsh cast		V to G	Perf		F
58	4.5	4.83	......	....	Greenish yellow	....				F
59	4.5	4.5	1.5-2	Pt sol	Colorless	....	V	None		C
60	4.5	4.83	......	....	Greenish yellow					T
61	4-4.5	4.93	Inf	Pt sol	Wax to ylw, rdsh brwn	Lt ylwsh gray	V to G			F
62	3.5-4.5	4.65-4.58	2.5-3.5	Sol	**Bronze ylw to copper-red**	**Dark grysh black**	M	None	Uneven to subconch	M
63	4	5.03-4.99	6	Sol	Iron-black	Blk, brwnsh	M	Perf		M
64	4	4.9-4.88	......	Sol	Light green				Conch	T
65	4	5.0-4.6	3-4	....	Gray, wht, brwn, ylwsh	Wht to gray or ylwsh	R, D, E			
66	4	4.64-3.36	Fus	Pt sol	Ylw brwn, brwn, brwnsh blk		G		Irregular to conch	C
67	4	4.82-4.75	2.5-3	Sol	Tomback brown	Black				
68	4	4.5-4.3	1.5	Dcpd by HNO$_3$	**Steel-gray to iron-black**	**Blackish**	M	Indist	Uneven	
69	4	5.03-4.91	3	Sol	Drk grn to blk	Green		Perf		r
70	4	4.80	......	....	Clove-brown					r
71	4	4.77	Inf	Sol in HNO$_3$	Bluish green	....		Perf		.
72	4	4.59	1.5	Sol	Lt wine-ylw to colorless	....		Good		
73	4	4.59-4.46	6	Sol in HNO$_3$	Deep rdsh gray	Gray to blk	M	None	Brittle	r
74	3-4.5	5.1-4.6	......	....	**Gray to iron-blk**	**Red, gray, brwn, blk**	M	None	Subconch to uneven	
75	3.5-4	5.0-4.6	1.5-2	....	**Light bronze-ylw**	**Lt bronze-brown**	M	None	Conch	
76	3.5	4.57-4.47	1-1.5	....	**Gray, tinted copper-red**	**Black**			Uneven	
77	3.5	4.53	4.5	Dcpd	Pale grnsh ylw	....	R	None	Uneven	
78	3.5	4.5	......	Sol in HNO$_3$	Steel-gray	Black	M	....	Uneven	
79	3-4	5.0-4.9	1	Dcpd by HNO$_3$	Lead to iron-gray	....	M	Perf	Subconch	
80	3-4	4.72	5	....	Colorless to pale green	....	P to V	Perf	....	
81	3-4	4.5-4.43	......	....	Bronze	Black	M	None	Uneven to hackly	
82	2.5-5	6.4-3.9	......	....	Ylw, orange, rdsh, brwn, blk	Ylw, brwnsh, olive green	G, W, V, D	....	Conch to uneven	.
83	3-4	4.63	Inf	Gelat	Greenish yellow	....				.
84	3-3.5	4.9±	1.5	Sol in HNO$_3$	Blk to steel-gray	Black	M to Sm	Fair	Brittle	

GROUP 4
Specific Gravity 4.99-4.50

INDEX OF REF.	NAME	COMPOSITION	REMARKS
....	MACKAYITE	$Fe_2(TeO)_3 \cdot xH_2O$	
1.852	TOERNEBOHMITE	$(Ce \cdot La,Di,Al)_2O_3 \cdot 4SiO_2 \cdot H_2O$	
....	LESSINGITE	$H_2Ca_2Ce_4Si_3O_{15}$	Occurs as rolled pebbles.
4.671	HINSDALITE	$2PbO \cdot 3Fe_2O_3 \cdot 2SO_3 \cdot P_2O_5 \cdot 6H_2O$	
....	OBERITE	La,Ce,Yt,Er?	In grains. From inner Mongolia.
4.754	CARACOLITE	$Na_2O \cdot Pb(OH)Cl \cdot SO_3$	Fuses to a brown glass, giving a soda flame with a blue spot near the assay.
....	BEIYINITE	La,Ce,Yt,Er	
4.717	BASTNAESITE	$(Ce,La \cdot Di)F \cdot CO_2$	Treated with strong H_2SO_4, it yields CO_2 and HF.
....	**PYRRHOTITE**	Fe_xS_y	**Magnetic. Brittle. Treated with HCl, it yields H_2S. B.B., a magnetic globule.**
....	CREDNERITE	$CuMn_2O_4$	Insoluble in HNO_3. Dissolved in HCl, it yields chlorine.
4.9	BELLINGERITE	$3Cu(IO_3)_2 \cdot 2H_2O$	Brittle. Slightly soluble in hot water.
4.88±	BIMDHEIMITE	$2PbO \cdot Sb_2O_5 \cdot H_2O$	On charcoal, reduces to a globule of metallic lead and antimony.
2.13	AMPANGABEITE	$(Y,Er,U,Ca,Th)_2 \cdot (Cb,Ta,Fe,Ti)_7O_{16}$	Radio active. HCl solution is golden yellow.
....	TROILITE	FeS	Near pyrrhotite. Treated with HCl, it yields H_2S.
....	**STANNITE**	Cu_2FeSnS_4	**Treated with HNO_3, gives a blue solution and a precipitate of S and SnO.**
4.78	VANDEN-BRANDITE	$CuO \cdot UO_3 \cdot 2H_2O$	B.B., fuses to a black mass which becomes crystalline on cooling.
....	YEATMANITE	$(Mn,Zn)_6Sb_2Si_4O_{29}$	
2.07	SALESITE	$CuIO_3(OH)$	In C.T., snaps to splinters and gives copious fumes of iodine which condense on the sides of the tube.
4.84	LAUTARITE	$CaO \cdot I_2O_5$	Sparingly soluble in water.
....	GERMANITE	$(Cu,Ge)(S,As)$	Decrepitates on heating.
4.72Li	**TETRAHEDRITE-TENNANTITE**	$(Cu,Fe,Zn,Ag)_{12}(Sb,As)_4S_{13}$	**Decomposed by HNO_3 with separation of sulfur.**
....	**PENTLANDITE**	$(Fe,Ni)_9S_8$	**Brittle. No magnetic. In O.T., gives sulfurous fumes.**
....	**FAMATINITE**	$Cu_3(Sb,As)S_4$	**Brittle. On charcoal, gives fumes of Sb and a black, brittle, metallic globule.**
4.974	POWELLITE	$CaMoO_4$	Yellow phosphorescence. Molybdenum reactions.
....	EPIGENITE	$(Cu,Fe)_5AsS_6$?	On charcoal, a magnetic slag with copper globules.
....	CHALCOSTIBITE	$CuSbS_2$	Brittle. In C.T., gives a sublimate that is dark red on cooling.
4.815	MOLYBDO-PHYLLITE	$(Pb,Mg)SiO_4 \cdot H_2O$	B.B., with soda, gives a metallic bead.
....	COLUSITE	$Cu_3(As,Sn,V,Fe,Te)S_4$	In brittle granules.
....	GUMMITE	$UO_3,Pb,Th R.E.,etc, H_2O$	Brittle.
4.68	SODDYITE	$5UO_3 \cdot 2SiO_2 \cdot 6H_2O$?	In C.T., blackens and looses water and oxygen.
....	LAUTITE	$CuAsS$	Decrepitates violently. In C.T., yields a sublimate of As.

GROUP 4
Specific Gravity 4.99-4.50

	H	SP. GR.	F	HCL	COLOR	STREAK	LUSTER	CLEAV-AGE	FRACTURE	
85	3-3.5	5.0-4.9	Inf	Sol	Various shades of yellow	Orange-ylw to to brick-red	A to R	Dist	Conch	
86	3	5.18-4.79	1	....	Iron-black	Black	M	....	Conch to uneven	
87	3	4.59-4.45	......	Sol	Yellow		E	....	Friable	
88	3	4.89	......	....	Iron to grnsh black					
89	3	4.6±	......	Sol						
90	3	4.7	......	....	Iron-gray to blk	Black				
91	3	4.5-4.4	1	Ins	Grayish to iron-black	Grayish blk	M	Perf	Uneven	
92	2.5-3.5	4.6-4.3	3	Ins	Wht, tinted red, blue, grn, brwn	White	V to R	Perf	Uneven	
93	2.5	5.0-4.85	1	Ins	Indigo-blue		P	Perf		
94	2.5	4.8	1	Ins	Indigo-blue			Good		
95	2-3	4.8	......		Black					
96	2-3	4.8	......	....	Sulfur to citron-yellow	Yellow	A	Perf		
97	2-3	4.5-4.3	1	Sol	Steel-gray, tin-white	Black	....	....	Conch	
98	2-3	4.64	Easy	Sol	Drk steel-gray to brown	Dark brwnsh gray	M	Indist	Brittle	
99	2-2.5	5.0-4.4	Inf	Sol	Iron-blk to dark gray, brwnsh	Blk to bluish blk, submet	M	Perf	Uneven	
100	2	5.0-4.06	1	Ins	Blksh gray	Red	M, A	Perf	Flexible	
101	2	4.65-4.61	1	Sol	Lead-gray	Lead-gray	M	Perf	Subconch	
102	2	4.8	Vol	....	Gray	Red	M	Good	Flexible	
103	2	5.25-4.67	1	Sol in HNO₃	Sky-blue	Sky-blue	....	....	....	
104	2	4.6	Inf	Ins	Green, yellowish		V	Imperf		
105	2	5.01-3.8	Inf	Ins	Black	Black	M	Good	Uneven	
106	1.5-2	4.76-4.6	2.5	Ins	Indigo-blue or darker	Lead-gray to black	Sm, R	Perf	Flexible	
107	1.5-2	4.6	......	....	Scarlet-vermilion to deep cherry-red	Same	A	Good	Conch	
108	1.5-2	4.88	......	....	Lt red, changing to orange	Vermilion	A	Perf	Conch	
109	1.5-2	4.7	......	....	Scarlet-vermilion	Same	A	Good	Conch	
110	1.5	4.5	......	....	Sulfur-yellow					
111	1-1.5	4.73-4.62	Inf	Dcpd by HNO₃	Lead-gray	Bluish to grnsh	M	Perf	Flexible	
112	1-1.5	4.68	1	Sol	Cherry-red	Brwnsh red	A to Sm	Perf	Flexible	
113	?	4.87	......	....	Orange-yellow					
114	?	4.9	......	Sol	Yellow		....	Perf		
115	?	4.5	......	....	Black	Greenish gray	....	....		

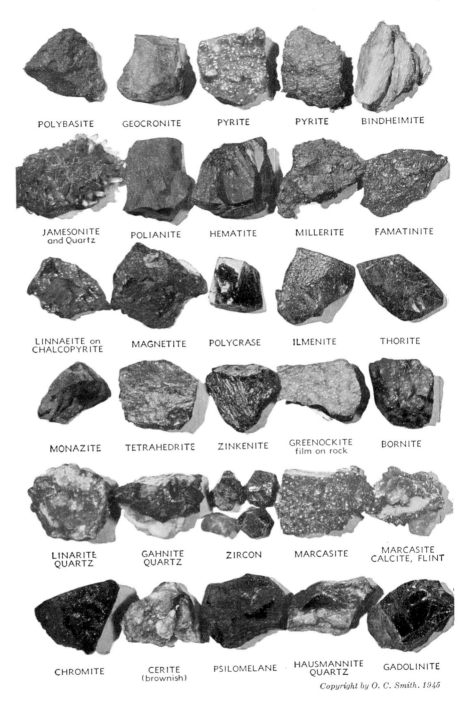

POLYBASITE	GEOCRONITE	PYRITE	PYRITE	BINDHEIMITE
JAMESONITE and Quartz	POLIANITE	HEMATITE	MILLERITE	FAMATINITE
LINNAEITE on CHALCOPYRITE	MAGNETITE	POLYCRASE	ILMENITE	THORITE
MONAZITE	TETRAHEDRITE	ZINKENITE	GREENOCKITE film on rock	BORNITE
LINARITE QUARTZ	GAHNITE QUARTZ	ZIRCON	MARCASITE	MARCASITE CALCITE, FLINT
CHROMITE	CERITE (brownish)	PSILOMELANE	HAUSMANNITE QUARTZ	GADOLINITE

PLATE 22

GROUP 4
Specific Gravity 4.99-4.50

INDEX OF REF.	NAME	COMPOSITION	REMARKS
2.43Li	**GREENOCKITE**	**CdS**	**Brittle. In C.T., the mineral is carmen-red while hot becoming yellow on cooling.**
....	STYLOTYPITE	$(Cu,Ag,Fe)_3 \cdot SbS_3$	On charcoal, gives a steel-gray, magnetic globule and fumes of antimony.
4.55	HOCHSCHILDITE	$5SnO_2 \cdot 2PbO \cdot Fe_2O_3 \cdot SiO_2 \cdot 10H_2O$	
....	MACKENSITE	$Fe_2O_3 \cdot SiO_2 \cdot 2H_2O$	
4.74±	PILBARITE	$UO_2 \cdot ThO_2 \cdot PbO \cdot 2SiO_2 \cdot 4H_2O$	
....	RAMSDELLITE	MnO_2	
....	**ENARGITE**	$Cu_3(As,Sb)S_4$	**Brittle. In C.T., gives a sublimate of sulfur and on stronger heating also one of arsenic sulfide.**
.637	**BARITE**	**$BaSO_4$**	**With soda on charcoal, gives the sulfide test on a silver coin.**
2.03	PSEUDOBOLEITE	$5PbCl_2 \cdot 4CuO \cdot 6H_2O$	Soluble in HNO_3. Probably identical with boleite.
2.041	CUMENGEITE	$4PbCl_2 \cdot 4CuO \cdot 5H_2O$	Soluble in HNO_3.
....	LUBECKITE	$8CuO \cdot Co_2O_3 \cdot 2Mn_2O_3 \cdot 8H_2O$	Colloidal. In small spheres. Probably a mixture.
.714	SCHOEPITE	$4UO_3 \cdot 9H_2O?$	An alteration product of uraninite.
....	WITTICHENITE	Cu_3BiS_3	B.B., throws out sparks. Dissolved in HCl, it yields H_2S.
....	BERTHIERITE	$FeSb_2S_4$	B.B., a weakly magnetic globule. Treated with HCl, yields H_2S.
....	**PYROLUSITE** (massive)	**MnO_2**	**Brittle. Treated with HCl, it yields acrid fumes of chlorine.**
.0	LIVINGSTONITE	$HgSb_4S_7$	With soda in C.T., yields a sublimate of metallic mercury.
.046	**STIBNITE**	**Sb_2S_3**	**Flexible. Sectile. Treated with KOH, it yields a characteristic yellow coating.**
....	SELENIUM	Se	B.B., gives a brown smoke and rotten horseradish odor.
.05	PERCYLITE	$PbO \cdot CuCl_2 \cdot H_2O$	In C.T., yields water and colorless fumes.
.95	HYDRO-TUNGSTITE	$H_2WO_4 \cdot H_2O$	
.91	DAUBREELITE	Cr_2FeS_4	Brittle. B.B., in R.F., looses luster and becomes magnetic. Soluble in HNO_3 with liberation of sulfur.
.45Na	**COVELLITE**	**CuS**	**B.B., burns with a blue flame and fuses to a globule. In C.T., yields sulfur.**
.176	HUTCHINSONITE	$(Pb,Tl)_2(Cu,Ag) As_5S_{10}$	Brittle. Red in splinters.
.27	SMITHITE	$AgAsS_2$	Brittle. Red in splinters.
.6Li	TRECHMANNITE	$Ag_2As_2S_4$	Brittle. Transparent to translucent.
....	FERRI-MOLYBDITE	$Fe_2O_3 \cdot 3MoO_3 \cdot 8H_2O$	An oxidation product of molybdenite.
....	**MOLYBDENITE**	**MoS_2**	**Sectile. Feels greasy. In O.T., gives a pale yellow sublimate of MoO_3. Looks like graphite.**
.72	KERMESITE	Sb_2S_2O	Sectile. In C.T., fuses and gives a white sublimate which becomes black to dark red on stronger heating.
....	ENALITE	$(Th,U)O_2 \cdot nSiO_2 \cdot 2H_2O$	
.763	DEWINDTITE	$3PbO \cdot 5UO_3 \cdot 2P_2O_5 \cdot 12H_2O$	Radio active.
.774	CALCIO-GADOLINITE	Gadolinite rich in calcium	Weakly radio active.

GROUP 5
Specific Gravity 4.49-4.00

H	SP. GR.	F	HCL	COLOR	STREAK	LUSTER	CLEAVAGE	FRACTURE
1 9	4.1-4.0	Inf	Ins	Blue, red, ylw, gray, brwn, wht	Uncolored	A to V	None	Uneven to conch
2 8	4.1-3.5	Inf	Ins	Red, blue, grn, ylw, brwn, blk	White	V	Imperf	Conch to uneven
3 8	4.29	......	Ins	Colorless to wine yellow	....	....	Dist	....
4 8	4.08	Inf	Ins	Ylwsh to grnsh brwn	White	V	None	Conch
5 7.5-8	4.62-4.03	Inf	Ins	Grn, ylw, brwn, gray, blk	Grayish	V to D	Indist	Conch to uneven
6 7.5	4.1	......	....	Drk grn to brwn	....	....	....	....
7 7.5	4.86-4.2	Inf	Ins	Colorless, ylw, gray, grn, red, brwn	Uncolored	A	Imperf	Conch
8 7.5	4.4	......	....	Gray	....	....	....	....
9 7.5	4.23	Inf	Ins	Black	Red-brown	V	Imperf	Conch
10 7.5	4.09	......		Grnsh gray, brwn, grn	....			
11 7	4.2-3.9	3	Ins	Red, brown	White	V to R	Good	Subconch to uneven
12 7	4.03	Inf	Ins	Colorless	....	G	Good	
13 6.5-7.5	4.3-4.0	3.5	Ins	Hyacinth, tinged violet to brwnsh	White	V to R	Good	Subconch to uneven
14 6.5-7.5	4.3-3.15	3-6	Ins	Red, brwn, ylw, wht, grn	White	V to R	Varies	Subconch to uneven
15 6.5-7	4.5-4.0	Inf	Gelat	Blk, brwn, grn	Grnsh gray	V to G	None	Conch to splintery
16 6.5-7	4.0	3	....	Ylwsh, rdsh	....	G	....	Subconch
17 6-7	4.03	3	Ins	Brownish red			Basal	....
18 6.5	4.17-3.9	3	Gelat	Gray, ylw, blk, red, whtsh, brwn, grn	....	G	Dist	Subconch to uneven
19 6.5	4.14-4.0	4	Gelat	Ylw, brwnsh, blk	....	M to R	Dist	Imperf conch
20 6.5	4.22	......		Flesh-red	....		None	Uneven to splintery
21 6.5	4.3	4	Gelat	....			Dist	....
22 6.5	4.74-4.48	......	....	Jet black	Graysh brwn	Sm	None	Conch to irregular
23 6-6.5	4.41	4-5	Sol	Grnsh brwn	....	V to G	None	Conch
24 6-6.5	4.25-4.21	Inf	Ins	Brwn, red, ylw, blk, blue, violet	Pale brwn to ylwsh	M to A	Dist	Subconch to uneven
25 6	4.8-4.39	6	Pt sol	Drk brwn to blk	Ochre-ylw to rdsh brwn	M, A, G	Dist	Uneven to subconch
26 6	4.35	......	....	Dark rdsh brwn	....		Imperf	Brittle

GROUP 5
Specific Gravity 4.49-4.00

INDEX OF REF.	NAME	COMPOSITION	REMARKS
4.768	**CORUNDUM**	Al_2O_3	Sometimes perfect parting giving a pseudo-cleavage. B.B., gives a blue color with cobalt nitrate.
4.72±	**SPINEL**	$MgAl_2O_4$	Brittle. B.B., the color changes but returns on cooling.
4.772	SWEDENBORGITE	$Na_2O \cdot 2Al_2O_3 \cdot Sb_2O_5$	
4.05±	PICOTITE	$(Mg,Fe)O \cdot (Al,Cr)_2O_3$	A chrome spinel.
4.79	**GAHNITE**	$ZnAl_2O_4$	Brittle. Gives a coating of ZnO when treated with soda and borax on charcoal. Slowly soluble in conc H_2SO_4.
....	OYAMALITE	A variety of Zircon with P_2O_5	In radial aggregates.
4.926	**ZIRCON**	$ZrSiO_4$	The colored varieties change color on heating.
....	HAGATALITE	$ZrSiO_4$ plus Rare Earths	A variety of zircon.
4.923	GALAXITE	$MnAl_2O_4$	Spinel group.
4.818	NAEGITE	$SiO_2 \cdot ZrO_2 \cdot UO_3 \cdot ThO_2 \cdot (Cb,Ta,Y)_2O_3$	Radio active. A rare earth zircon.
4.801	**ALMANDITE**	$3FeO \cdot Al_2O_3 \cdot 3SiO_2$	One of the precious garnets.
4.696	BARYLITE	$4BaO \cdot Al_2O_3 \cdot 7SiO_2$	
4.811	**SPESSARTITE**	$3MnO \cdot Al_2O_3 \cdot 3SiO_2$	One of the garnet family.
4.8±	**GARNET**	$3(Ca,Mg,Fe,Mn)O \cdot (Al,Fe,Mn,Cr,Ti)_2O_3 \cdot 3SiO_2$	Most varieties fuse easily to a black or light brown glass.
4.78±	**GADOLINITE**	$2BeO \cdot FeO \cdot 2Y_2O_3 \cdot 2SiO_2$	B.B., gives a momentary bright light; swell and cracks open.
4.8±	PARTSCHINITE	$3(Mn,Fe)O \cdot Al_2O_3 \cdot 3SiO_2$	May be spessartite.
4.81	HANCOCKITE	$4(Pb,Ca,Sr)O \cdot 3(Al,Fe,Mn)_2O_3 \cdot 6SiO_2 \cdot H_2O$	With soda on charcoal, gives a lead oxide coating.
4.838	KNEBELITE	$2(Fe,Mn)O \cdot SiO_2$	
4.877	**FAYALITE**	$FeO \cdot SiO_2$	Fuses to a black globule.
4.738	THALENITE	$2Y_2O_3 \cdot 4SiO_2 \cdot H_2O$	
4.836	MANGAN-FAYALITE	$2(Mn,Fe)O \cdot SiO_2$	
4.095	CALCIO-SAMARSKITE	$(Ca,Y,etc,U,Th)_3 \cdot (Cb,Ta,Fe,Ti,Sn)_5 O_{15}$	
4.76	CAPPELENITE	B,SiO_2 of Y,Ba,Ce,La,Th,etc	B.B., swells and fuses to a white enamel
4.6	**RUTILE**	TiO_2	Brittle. With S.Ph. in R.F., gives a violet colored bead.
4.39Li	PSEUDOBROOKITE	Fe_2TiO_5	Partially decomposed by boiling H_2SO_4.
4.75	ABUKUMALITE	$Ca,Y_2(Si,P)_2O_8$	Isomorphous with britholite with Y in place of Ce.

GROUP 5
Specific Gravity 4.49-4.00

	H	SP. GR.	F	HCL	COLOR	STREAK	LUSTER	CLEAVAGE	FRACTURE
27	6	4.25-4.17	......	Gelat	Black, red in splinters	....	......	Dist	....
28	6	4.0	3-4	Gelat	Red-brown			Dist	
29	5.5-6	4.12-4.0	3.5-6	Gelat	Red, brwn, gray	Pale gray	V to G	Dist	Subconch
30	5.5-6	4.03	......	....	Ylwsh brwn to blk	Gray	V to R	....	Conch
31	5.5-6	4.2	Inf	Dcpd	Sulfur, lemon or wine-ylw	....	P to V	Perf	Conch
32	5.5-6	4.23	......	....	Ylwsh grn	....		....	Fibrous
33	5.5-6	4.08-3.95	6	Gelat	Ylw, grn to blk	Ylw to rdsh gray	V to G	Dist	....
34	5.5-6	4.5-3.5	2.5	Gelat	Brwn, blk, grn, gray, ylw	Gray, grnsh, or brwnsh	V, Sm, R, P	Traces	Uneven to subconch
35	5.5-6	4.05-3.99	2.5	Gelat	Iron-blk to dark grysh blk	Blk inclining to grn or brwn	Sm	Good	Uneven
36	5.5-6	4.2-4.08	Inf	Ins	Brwn, ylw, rdsh brwn, blk	Uncolored, grysh ylwsh	M, A, Sm	Indist	Subconch to uneven
37	5-6	4.05	Inf	Pt sol	Brwnsh blk	Blk to brwnsh red	M to Sm	Perf	Conch to uneven
38	5-6	4.13	Inf	Dcpd	Deep brwn to blk	Light brwn	G to V	None	Conch
39	5-6	4.29	Inf	Sol	Nut-brown	....	V to G	None	Conch
40	5-6	4.16	......	....	Brownish red	....		Good	....
41	5.5	4.25	......	Pt sol	Steel-gray	Brown	Sm, M	....	Subconch
42	5.5	4.3-4.1	Inf	Ins	Black	Brown	M	None	Uneven
43	5.5	4.25-4.15	......	Gelat	Dark brown	Ylwsh gray	R	Indist	....
44	5.5	4.18-3.89	3.5-5	Gelat	Wht, grn, ylw, brwn red	Uncolored	V, R	Easy	Conch to uneven
45	5.5	4.05-3.97	Inf	Ins	Blk, brwn, ylw	Colorless, grayish	A to M	Imperf	Uneven to subconch
46	5.5	4.446	......	....	Brown	....	G to V	....	Uneven
47	5.5	4.25-4.05	......	....	Black	Gray to brwnsh blk	....	....	Conch
48	5.5	4.02	......	....	Pink, grayish pink	....	......	None	....
49	5-5.5	4.3-3.3	6	Sol	Ylw, red, brwn, blk	Brwnsh to ochre-ylw	A, D, S	Perf	Uneven
50	5-5.5	4.45-4.33	Inf	Pt sol	Dark red, blksh brwn, brwn	Light to ylw brwn	V to R	Indist	Subconch uneven
51	5-5.5	4.13	......	....	Lt to drk brwn	Lt brwn to ylwsh brwn	R	....	Uneven to conch
52	5	4.02-3.9	4.5	Sol	Grnsh to blk, tinged violet	Dark	S	....	....
53	5	4.21	Easy	Sol	Black	Brwnsh blk	M		Granular
54	5	4.09-4.07	3	Sol	Ylw to rdsh	Wht to orange-ylw	R	None	Subconch
55	5	4.07-3.94	2	....	Lt to drk orange-red	Cream-ylw	V	Dist	Uneven

MOLYBDENITE   GOETHITE   LUDWIGITE   VONSENITE   SMITHSONITE

SMITHSONITE   CERVANTITE   CONICHALCITE (green)   MANGANITE   AMPANGABEITE

CHALCOPYRITE   SPHALERITE   SHATTUCKITE   PIEDMONTITE   DIASPORE

FORSTERITE   ALABANDITE   MALACHITE   WITHERITE   ENARGITE

OLIVENITE on Quartz   CARNOTITE   STAUROLITE   SCHORLOMITE   CHRYSOBERYL

PYROPE   GROSSULARITE   ANDRADITE   CYANITE   RHODONITE

PLATE 23

GROUP 5
Specific Gravity 4.49-4.00

INDEX OF REF.	NAME	COMPOSITION	REMARKS
....	PICROILMENITE	$(Mg,Fe)TiO_3$	Between geikielite and ilmenite.
1.727	PICROTEPHROITE	$2(Mn,Mg)O \cdot SiO_2$	
1.807	**TEPHROITE**	$2MnO \cdot SiO_2$	**The streak darkens on exposure, to brown or black.**
....	PISEKITE	Cb,Ta,Ti of U, Rare Earths, Th and Sn	
....	NORDEN- SKIOELDINE	$CaO \cdot SnO_2 \cdot B_2O_3$	Colors flame green. Strong double refraction.
....	STASZICITE	$(Ca,Cu,Zn)_5(AsO_4)_2 \cdot (OH)_4$	An alteration product of tennantite.
1.786	ROEPPERITE	$2(Fe,Mn,Zn)O \cdot SiO_2$	On charcoal with soda, gives a ZnO coating.
1.73±	**ALLANITE** (orthite)	$4(Ca,Fe)O \cdot 3(Al,Ce, Fe,Di)_2O_3 \cdot 6SiO_2 \cdot H_2O$	**Most varieties gives much water in C.T.**
....	**ILVAITE**	$CaO \cdot 4FeO \cdot Fe_2O_3 \cdot 4SiO_2 \cdot H_2O$	**B.B., fuses to a black magnetic bead**
2.586	**BROOKITE**	TiO_2	**Brittle. With S.Ph. in R.F., it gives a violet colored bead.**
2.31	GEIKIELITE	$MgTiO_3$	Titanium reactions.
1.73±	MELANOCERITE	Ce,Di,La,Y,B,Th,Ta, Zr,Si,F,etc	B.B., becomes lighter in color and swells without fusing.
1.74±	CARYOCERITE	Ce,Di,Y,La,Th,Zr, SiO_2,F,B,etc	B.B., becomes lighter in color and swells.
1.81	ARSENOKLASITE	$5MnO \cdot As_2O_5 \cdot 2H_2O$	
2.62±	ARIZONITE	$Fe_2Ti_3O_9$	Brittle. Decomposed by hot H_2SO_4.
....	MAGNESIO- CHROMITE	$MgCr_2O_4$	Brittle.
1.757±	TRITOMITE	Ce,Di,La,Y,Th,Zr, SiO_2,B,F,etc	With HCl, it yields chlorine.
1.691	**WILLEMITE**	Zn_2SiO_4	**Glows in ultra violet light.**
2.34	**PEROVSKITE**	$CaTiO_3$	**Brittle. Decomposed by hot conc H_2SO_4.**
1.775	BRITHOLITE	SiO_2 and P_2O_5 of Ce metals and Ca	
....	UHLIGITE	$Ca_3(Ti,Al,Zr)_9O_{20}$	May be a variety of perovskite.
1.78	ALLEGHANYITE	$5MnO \cdot 2SiO_2$	
2.393	**GOETHITE**	$HFeO_2$	**Brittle. Moistened with H_2SO_4, some varieties impart a bluish green color to the flame.**
2.00	**PYROCHLORE**	$Na,Ca,Cb_2O_6 \cdot F$	**Brittle. When tested it glows momentarily as though it had taken fire.**
....	MARIGNACITE	Variety of pyrochlore	
1.85±	LUDWIGITE	$Mg_3Fe^2Fe^3B_2O_{10}$	Heated in air it becomes red. Cuts easily.
....	VONSENITE	$3(Fe,Mg)O \cdot B_2O_3 \cdot FeO \cdot Fe_2O_3$	Brittle. B.B., yields a black, magnetic mass and green boron flame.
1.748±	BERZELIITE	$3(Ca,Mn,Mg)O \cdot 2(AsO_4)$	Reacts for arsenic and manganese.
1.673	DURANGITE	$NaF,AlAsO_4$	In C.T., blackens but regains color on cooling. Decomposed by H_2SO_4.

GROUP 5
Specific Gravity 4.49-4.00

	H	SP. GR.	F	HCL	COLOR	STREAK	LUSTER	CLEAV-AGE	FRACTURE
56	5	4.45-4.3	Inf	Sol	Wht, blue, grn, brwn	White	V to P	Perf	Uneven to conch
57	5	4.15	Inf	Sol	Yellow			Cubic	Conch
58	5	4.1	......	Sol	Peacock to grnsh blue				
59	5	4.2±	......	....	Black	Brown			
60	5	4.12	......	....	Apple-green		W, R		
61	5	4.19	......	Dcpd	White		P	Perf	
62	5?	4.41	Inf	Dcpd by H_2SO_4	Brwnsh ylw	Grnsh ylw	A	None	Uneven
63	5	4.6-4.16	Inf	Ins	Black	Grnsh gray	Sm	....	Conch
64	5	4.13-4.05	Inf	Sol	Ruby-red to rdsh brwn	Dull orange	Sm	Perf	Brittle
65	4.5-5	4.4-4.0	2-2.5	Sol	Drk emeral-grn	Lighter grn	A to V	Perf	Conch to uneven
66	4.5-5	4.4-3.4	2-2.5	Sol	Green	Pale green	V		
67	4.5-5	4.8-4.4	Inf	Gelat	Orange to brwnsh ylw, blk to brwn	Lt orange to dark brown	V, G, R	Dist	Conch
68	4.5-5	4.414	Inf	....	Dark red-brown	Ylw-brown	R to V	....	Subconch
69	4.5-5	4.04	2-2.5 '	Sol in HNO_3	Emerald-green	Paler green	D, R	Traces	
70	4-5.5	5.0-3.7	6	Pt sol	Grnsh brwn		W, V, Sm	....	Conch
71	4-5.5	4.3-2.7	Inf	Sol	Brwn to nearly blk, ylw	Ylwsh brwn to rdsh	S, Sm, E	....	Conch to uneven
72	4-5	4.56-4.45	Inf	Ins	Brwn, red, ylw, wht	Pale brwn, ylwsh, rdsh	R to V	Perf	Uneven to splintery
73	4-5	5.09-4.08	Inf	Sol	Ylw, wht, sometimes rdsh wht	Wht to ylwsh wht	G to P	....	Fibrous or powder
74	4-5	4.9-4.0	2	Sol in HNO_3	Ylwsh gray, brwnsh, grnsh	Uncolored	R		
75	4-5	4.47-4.13	Inf	Sol	Black, steel-gray	Black	D, M	Good	Uneven to conch
76	4-5	4.19-4.17	4	Sol	Rose to flesh-red, rdsh ylw	Lt rose-red	G	Dist	
77	4.5	4.17-4.16	Easy	....	Green				Conch
78	4.5	4.12	2.5-3	Sol	Green	Green			Splintery
79	4.5	4.26	Easy	Sol	Green			Perf	
80	4.5	4.36	Inf	Sol	Brwnsh yellow	Ylwsh white	V, R, P	Perf	Small conch
81	4.5	4.31	Inf	Sol	Pale wax-ylw		V to A	Dist	Uneven
82	4.5	1.33	3	Sol	Malachite to ylwsh green				
83	4.5	4.07	......	....	Light green to sky-blue				
84	4-4.5	4.21	......	....	Red-orange				

MINERAL IDENTIFICATION TABLES

GROUP 5
Specific Gravity 4.49-4.00

INDEX OF REF.	NAME	COMPOSITION	REMARKS
4.849	**SMITHSONITE**	$ZnCO_3$	**In C.T., gives off CO_2.**
4.812	BECKELITE	$2(Ce,La,Di)_2O_3 \cdot 3(CaO \cdot 3SiO_2)$	S.Ph. bead is pale ylw-green in the O.F. and does not change in the R.F.
4.81	CORNETITE	$6CuO \cdot P_2O_5 \cdot 3H_2O$	
4.3	KNOPITE	$(Ca,Y,Fe,Ce)O \cdot TiO_2$	Near perovskite but containing cerium.
4.702	ARANDISITE	$5SnO \cdot 3SiO_2 \cdot 4H_2O$	Probably a mixture. Decomposed by H_2SO_4.
4.616	SANBORNITE	$BaO \cdot 2SiO_2$	With HCl, it swells and opens to shreds.
4.24	METALOPARITE	Si,Ti,Cb,Ta,Th,etc	Brittle. B.B., turns brownish black.
....	LORANSKITE	$(Y,Ce,Ca,Zr,?)(Ta,Zr,?)O_4$	Brittle. Incompletely decomposed by acids and fusion with alkalies.
4.2Na	LEPIDOCROCITE	$FeO \cdot (OH)$	
4.762	DIHYDRITE	$2Cu(OH)_2 \cdot Cu_3(PO_4)_2$	In C.T., yields water and turns black.
4.762	PSEUDO-MALACHITE	$Cu_3(PO_4)_2 \cdot 3Cu(OH)_2$	In C.T., yields water and turns black.
....	**THORITE**	$ThSiO_4$	**B.B., looses color on heating but regains it on cooling.**
4.71	URANOTHORITE	$ThO_2 \cdot SiO_2 \cdot UO_3 \cdot CaO \cdot$ etc	
4.86	ERINITE	$Cu_3(AsO_4)_2 \cdot 2Cu(OH)_2$	B.B., on charcoal emits arsenical odors.
4.925	BETAFITE	$(U,Ca)(Cb,Ta,Ti)_2O_9 \cdot nH_2O$	Brittle. B.B., gives a black slag.
4.06±	**LIMONITE**	$HFeO_2 \cdot nH_2O$	**Usually in stalactitic, botryoidal or mammilary form.**
4.721	**XENOTIME**	YPO_4	**When moistened with H_2SO_4, it colors the flame green.**
4.8±	**CERVANTITE**	$Sb_2O_4?$	**On charcoal, reduces easily to metal.**
4.654	PLUMGOGUMMITE	$PbO \cdot 2Al_2O_3 \cdot P_2O_5 \cdot 9H_2O$	B.B. in forceps, swells and colors the flame azure-blue.
....	STAINERITE	$CoO(OH)$	Nonmagnetic. HCl solution is green and yields chlorine.
4.807	SARKINITE	$Mn_3(AsO_4)_2 \cdot Mn(OH)_2$	With soda on charcoal, gives a brownish mass and arsenical odors.
4.81	CORNWALLITE	$Cu_3(AsO_4)_2 \cdot 2Cu(OH)_2 \cdot H_2O$	On charcoal, gives arsenical fumes and a bead of copper enveloped in a brittle crust.
4.778	**CONICHALCITE**	$8(Cu,Ca)As_2O_3 \cdot 3H_2O$	**In forceps, colors the flame green then light blue near the assay.**
4.00	LINDGRENITE	$2CuMoO_4 \cdot Cu(OH)_2$	In C.T., darkens, decrepitates and forms a brownish sublimate.
4.676±	PARISITE	$2(Ce,La,Di,Th)OF \cdot CaO \cdot 3CO_3$	In C.T., gives off CO_2 and becomes lighter in color.
4.764	CORDYLITE	Fluo-carbonate of Ce metals and Ba	Moistened with HCl, it colors the flame green.
4.831	HIGGINSITE	$2CuO \cdot 2CaO \cdot As_2O_5 \cdot H_2O$	
4.83	ROSASITE	$CuO \cdot 3CuCO_3 \cdot 5ZnCO_3$	
....	SODA-BERZELIITE	$(Na_2,Ca)(Mn,Mg)_2 \cdot (As,V)_3O_{12}$	

GROUP 5
Specific Gravity 4.49-4.00

	H	SP. GR.	F	HCL	COLOR	STREAK	LUSTER	CLEAVAGE	FRACTURE	S
85	3.5-4.5	4.3-4.0	3.5	Sol	Grn, blk, brwn	Grnsh ylw to yellow	V, Sa, R	Easy	....	M
86	4	4.34-4.32	Inf	Sol	Steel-gray to black	Rdsh brwn to nearly blk	Sm	Perf	Uneven	M
87	4	4.5-4.3	1.5	Dcpd by HNO$_3$	Steel-gray to iron-black	Blackish	M	Indist	Uneven	T
88	4	4.59-4.46	6	Sol in HNO$_3$	Deep rdsh gray	Gray to blk	M	None	Brittle	I
89	4	4.13-4.02	Inf	Sol	Rose-red	Peach-bloom red	V	....		F
90	4	4.13	......	....	White	....	....	Dist	Fibrous	T
91	4	4.64-3.36	Fus	Pt sol	Ylw brwn, brwn, brwnsh blk	....	G	....	Irregular to conch	C
92	4	4.15	6	Sol	Dark chocolate to chestnut-brown	Lighter brown	V to G	None	Conch to uneven	O
93	4	4.2±	Inf	Sol	Olive, ylw, brwn, black	Grnsh to grysh blk	V, Sa, R	Easy	....	R
94	4	4.15-4.12	2	Sol	Colorless, ylw, brwn, red, grn	....	V	Good	....	T
95	4	4.23	2	Sol	Black	Brown	....	Poor	....	T
96	4	4.07	......	....	Reddish brown	....	....	Indist	....	O
97	3.5-4	4.3-4.1	2	Sol in HNO$_3$	Brass-yellow, iridescent	Grnsh blk	M	Fair	Uneven	T
98	3.5-4	4.1-3.9	5	Sol	Ylw, brwn, blk, red, wht	Lt brwn to ylw, wht	R to A	Perf	Conch	I
99	3.5-4	4.0±	3	Sol	Iron-blk, brwnsh tarnish	Green	Sm	Perf	Uneven	I
100	3.5-4	4.03-3.9	2	Sol	Bright green	Lighter	A, V, S, E	Perf	Sunconch to uneven	N
101	3-4	4.35-4.28	2	Sol	Wht, ylwsh, grysh	White	V to R	Dist	Uneven	O
102	3-4	4.5-4.43	......	....	Bronze	Black	M	None	Uneven to hackly	I
103	3-4	4.08	2-2.5	Sol	Verdigris to emerald-green	Verdigris green	V	Dist	Uneven	M
104	3-4	4.2	......	Dcpd	Dark brown	....	....	Basal	....	H
105	2.5-5	6.4-3.9	......	....	Ylw, orange, rdsh, brwn to blk	Ylw, brwnsh, olive grn	G, W, V, D	....	Conch to uneven	.
106	3.5	4.35-4.34	3	Sol	Ylw, violet, red, grn, colorless	White	V	Dist	Uneven	O
107	3.5	4.04-3.98	Inf	Dcpd	Blk to brwn	Red-brwn	Sm	....	Conch	M
108	3.5	4.01-3.94	Inf	Sol	Brwn, pinkish, ylwsh wht	....	G	....	Uneven	
109	3.5	4.18-4.03	2	....	Bronze to brass-yellow	Rdsh bronze to black	....	None	Conch	O
110	3.5	4.3	......	....	Red to brown	....	....	Good	....	T
111	3.5	4.0	......	....	Bronze-yellow	Black	M	Perf	....	I
112	3-3.5	4.25	2.5	Sol in HNO$_3$	Brwn to ylwsh brwn	Ylwsh wht	G	Good	Splintery	O
113	2.5-3.5	4.6-4.3	3	Ins	Wht tinted red, blue, ylw, brwn	White	V to R	Perf	Uneven	O
114	3	4.0	......	....	Silver-white	....	....	None	Brittle	

GROUP 5
Specific Gravity 4.49-4.00

INDEX OF REF.	NAME	COMPOSITION	REMARKS
1.96	BEUDANTITE	P_2O_5, As_2O_5, SO_3, of Pb and Fe	Yields water.
2.25Li	**MANGANITE**	$MnO(OH)$	**Brittle. In C.T., yields water. Treated with HCl, it yields chlorine.**
....	**STANNITE**	Cu_2FeSnS_4	**Treated with HNO_3, gives a blue solution and a deposit of S and tin oxide.**
....	GERMANITE	$(Cu,Ge)(S,As)$	Decrepitates on heating.
1.855	SPHAERO-COBALTITE	$CoCO_3$	In C.T., becomes black.
1.755	BRICKERITE	$4ZnO \cdot 3CaO \cdot 2As_2O_5$	Probably identical with austinite.
2.13	AMPANGABEITE	$(Y,Er,U,Ca,Th)_2 (Cb,Ta,Fe,Ti)_7O_{18}$	Radio active. HCl solution is dark golden-yellow.
1.788	RETZIAN	Basic As_2O_3 of Mn,Ca and Rare Earths	On Charcoal with soda, gives As fumes.
1.93	CORKITE	$2PbO \cdot 3Fe_2O_3 \cdot P_2O_5 \cdot 2SO_3 \cdot 6H_2O$	In C.T., yields water.
1.765	TARBUTTITE	$Zn_3P_2O_5 \cdot Zn(OH)_2$	In C.T., decrepitates and gives a small amount of water.
2.01	ARMANGITE	$3MnO \cdot As_2O_5$	
1.77	HOLDENITE	$8MnO \cdot 4ZnO \cdot As_2O_5 \cdot 5H_2O$	
....	**CHALCOPYRITE**	$CuFeS_2$	**Brittle. In C.T., decrepitates and gives a sublimate of sulfur.**
2.34Li	**SPHALERITE**	ZnS	**In O.T., gives SO_2 and generally changes color.**
2.7Li	**ALABANDITE**	MnS	**Brittle. Treated with HCl, it evolves H_2S.**
1.875	**MALACHITE**	$CuCO_3 \cdot Cu(OH)_2$	**In C.T., blackens and yields water.**
1.676	**WITHERITE**	$BaCO_3$	**Colors flame yellowish green.**
....	COLUSITE	$Cu_3(As,Sn,V,Fe,Te)S_4$	In brittle granules.
1.84	TAGILITE	$4CuO \cdot P_2O_5 \cdot 3H_2O$	In C.T., yields water and turns black.
1.96	DIXENITE	$5MnO \cdot SiO_2 \cdot As_2O_3 \cdot H_2O$	Red in transmitted light.
....	GUMMITE	$UO_3, Pb, Th, R.E.,$ etc, H_2O	Brittle.
1.744	ADAMITE	$4ZnO \cdot As_2O_5 \cdot H_2O$	In C.T., decrepitates feebly, yields a little water and becomes white.
1.769	KALKOWSKITE	$Fe_2Ti_3O_?$?	In thin plates with a fibrous structure.
1.654	RHABDOPHANITE	$(La,Di,Y)PO_4 \cdot H_2O$	Bead test is rose-red in both flames.
....	CUBANITE	$CuFe_2S_3$	Magnetic. On charcoal, gives SO_2 and fuses to a magnetic globule.
....	SCHAFARZIKITE	$nFeO \cdot P_2O_5$	
....	SULVANITE	Cu_3VS_4	In C.T., a sublimate of sulfur.
1.78	CARYINITE	$(Pb,Mn,Ca,Mg)_3 (AsO_4)_2$	
1.637	**BARITE**	$BaSO_4$	**With soda on charcoal, gives the sulfide test on a silver coin.**
....	NIGGLIITE	$PtTe_3$?	

GROUP 5
Specific Gravity 4.49-4.00

	H	SP. GR.	F	HCL	COLOR	STREAK	LUSTER	CLEAV-AGE	FRACTURE
115	3	4.5-4.4	1	Ins	Grayish to iron-gray	Grayish blk	M	Perf	Uneven
116	3	4.4-4.1	2-2.5	Sol in HNO$_3$	Various shades of grn, brwn, ylw	Olive grn to brwn	A to V	Traces	Conch to uneven
117	3	4.1	......	....	Bluish green	....			
118	3	4.3-4.0	......	....	Colorless	....	V, Sv	....	....
119	3	4.59-4.45	......	Sol	Yellow	....	E		Friable
120	3	4.19	......	....	Grass-green	Grnsh wht to gray	V to G	None	Uneven
121	3	4.06	Inf	....	Yellow	....	R	....	
122	3	4.28	Fus	Sol	Black	Black	Sm	....	
123	2.5-3	4.36-4.19	2-2.5	Sol in HNO$_3$	Green	Bluish green	P, V, R	Perf	....
124	2-3	4.3-4.1	......		Black	....		....	
125	2-3	4.5-4.3	1	Sol	Steel-gray, tin-white	Black	....	....	Conch
126	2.5	4.1-3.9	6	Sol	Bluish to iron-black	Chocolate brown	M	Perf	Flexible
127	2.5	4.15	1	Sol	Colorless to wht	....	P, V	Perf	Fibrous
128	2.5	4.1	2-3	Sol in HNO$_3$	Carmine to tile-red	Reddish ylw	V, P	Good	....
129	**2-2.5**	**5.0-4.4**	**Inf**	**Sol**	**Iron-blk to dark gray, bluish**	**Blk to bluish blk**	**M**	**Perf**	**Uneven**
130	2	5.0-4.06	1	Ins	Blksh gray	Red	M, A	Perf	Flexible
131	2	5.0-3.8	Inf	Ins	Black	Black	M	Good	Uneven
132	1-1.5	4.21-4.1	1.5	Ins	Brown, velvet tarnish	Black	M	Perf	Flexible
133	1-1.5	4.21	1.5	Ins	Brown to black	Black	M	Perf	....
134	**Soft**	**4.1$\pm$**	**2.5**	**Sol**	**Yellow**	....		**Perf**	
135	Soft	4.3-3.7	Easy	....	Yellow			Perf	
136	Soft	4.36	......	Sol	Canary-yellow	....		....	
137	?	4.33	......	....	White				
138	?	4.45-4.31	......		Black				
139	?	4.13	......		Orange-yellow to orange-red				
140	?	4.23	......		Red				
141	?	4.01	......		Canary-yellow	....		Fair	....
142	?	4.13	......		Yellow	....			
143	?	4.31	......			....			
144	?	4.42			White		G	Indist	
145	?	4.0	......		Yellow			Perf	....

GROUP 5
Specific Gravity 4.49-4.00

INDEX OF REF.	NAME	COMPOSITION	REMARKS
....	**ENARGITE**	$Cu_3(As,Sb)S_4$	**Brittle. In C.T., gives a sublimate of sulfur and on stronger heating also one of arsenic sulfide.**
1.788	**OLIVENITE**	$Cu_3(AsO_4)_2 \cdot Cu(OH)_2$	**In C.T., gives water. Colors flame green.**
....	CUPROZINCITE	$(Cu,Zn)CO_3 \cdot (Cu,Zn)(OH)_2$	Botryoidal or earthy. Zinc bearing malachite.
1.826	MALACON	$ZrO_2 \cdot SiO_2 \cdot nH_2O$	
4.55	HOCHSCHILDITE	$5SnO_2 \cdot 2PbO \cdot Fe_2O_3 \cdot SiO_2 \cdot 10H_2O$	
4.774	BARTHITE	$3ZnO \cdot CuO \cdot As_2O_5 \cdot 2H_2O$	
4.665	AUERLITE	Silico-phosphate of Th,etc	Becomes brown on ignition, yellow on cooling.
....	HULSITE	$10(Mg,Fe)O \cdot 2Fe_2O_3 \cdot SnO_2 \cdot 3B_2O_3 \cdot 2H_2O$	Yields water in C.T. Reacts for boron.
4.87	CLINOCLASITE	$Cu_3(AsO_4)_2 \cdot 3Cu(OH)_2$	In C.T., yields water. Colors the flame green.
....	MELNIKOVITE	FeS_2	Unstable mineral formed between layers of pyrite.
....	WITTICHENITE	Cu_3BiS_3	B.B., throws out sparks. Treated with HCl, it yields H_2S.
2.72Li	CHALCOPHANITE	$(Zn,Mn,Fe)Mn_2O_5 \cdot 2H_2O$	In C.T., yields water and oxygen, exfoliates and becomes golden. HCl treatment yields chlorine.
4.92	CLAUDETITE	As_2O_3	Flexible. Sublimes in C.T. condensing above in minute octahedrons.
2.05	CARMINITE	$Pb_2(AsO_4)_2 \cdot 10FeAsO_4$	On charcoal, a steel-gray globule giving arsenical odors.
....	**PYROLUSITE** (massive)	MnO_2	**Brittle. Treated with HCl, it yields chlorine.**
3.0	LIVINGSTONITE	$HgSb_4S_7$	With soda in C.T., yields a sublimate of metallic mercury.
4.91	DAUBREELITE	Cr_2FeS_4	Brittle. B.B., in R.F., looses luster and becomes magnetic. Soluble in HNO_3 with liberation of sulfur.
....	STERNBERGITE	$AgFe_2S_3$	On charcoal, gives off SO_2 and fuses to a magnetic globule.
....	FRIESEITE	$AgFe_5S_8$	Very close to sternbergite.
4.91±	**CARNOTITE**	$K_2O \cdot 2UO_3 \cdot V_2O_5 \cdot 8 \pm H_2O$	**Uranium and vanadium tests. Radio active.**
4.9±	TYUYAMUNITE	$CaO \cdot 2UO_3 \cdot V_2O_5 \cdot 8 \pm H_2O$	
4.85	BEAVERITE	$Fe_2O_3 \cdot CuO \cdot PbO \cdot 2SO_3 \cdot 4H_2O$	
4.669	ZINKOSITE	$ZnSO_4$	
....	MAITLANDITE	$2(Pb,Ca)O \cdot 3ThO_2 \cdot 4UO_3 \cdot 8SiO_2 \cdot 23H_2O$	
2.16±	PYRRHITE	Near Pyrochlore	From Azores and Lacher Sea.
....	BRANDAOSITE	$4(Fe,Mn)O \cdot (Al,Fe)_9O_3 \cdot 4SiO_2$	
4.709	LEGRANDITE	$28ZnO \cdot 9As_2O_5 \cdot 25H_2O$	
....	NICOLAYITE	$2(Pb,Ca)O \cdot 3ThO_2 \cdot 4UO_3 \cdot 8SiO_2 \cdot 21H_2O$	Possibly an alteration product of mackintoshite.
....	CARDYLITE	$BaF_2 \cdot Ce_2O_3 \cdot CO_2$	
4.769	CALCIUM LARSENITE	$(Pb,Ca)O \cdot ZnO \cdot SiO_2$	Crysolite group.
1.736	RENARDITE	$PbO \cdot 4UO_3 \cdot P_2O_5 \cdot 9H_2O$	

GROUP 5
Specific Gravity 4.49-4.00

	H	SP. GR.	F	HCL	COLOR	STREAK	LUSTER	CLEAV-AGE	FRACTURE	S T
146	?	4.12	......	....	Colorless	....	Sa	Good	....	
147	?	4.08-8.97	......	....	Black	....	....	....	....	.
148	?	4.1	......	....	Brown	....	....	....	....	

GROUP 5
Specific Gravity 4.49-4.00

INDEX OF REF.	NAME	COMPOSITION	REMARKS
5..........	AUSTINITE	$CaZn(OH)AsO_4$	Occurs in septer-like or bladed crystals.
7..........	PAREDRITE	$TiO_2 \cdot H_2O$	Rutile plus water. Occurs a pebbles and compact masses.
8..........	TALASSKITE	$20FeO \cdot 2Fe_2O_3 \cdot 13SiO_2$	A variety of fayalite.

GROUP 6
Specific Gravity 3.99-3.66

	H	SP. GR.	F	HCL	COLOR	STREAK	LUSTER	CLEAV-AGE	FRACTURE	SYTH
1	8.5	3.85-3.65	Inf	Ins	Grn, ylw, red	Uncolored	V	Dist	Uneven to conch	O
2	8	4.1-3.5	Inf	Ins	Red, brwn, blk, ylw, blue, grn	White	V	Imperf	Conch	I
3	7.5-8	3.95-3.91	Inf	Ins	Black	Grayish to leek-green	V	Imperf	Conch	I
4	7.5	3.8±	Inf	Ins	Black	....		None	....	I
5	7.5	3.77	Inf	Ins	Black to cobalt blue	Light blue	V	....	Subconch	O
6	7-7.5	3.75-3.65	Inf	Ins	Ylw, rdsh, brwn, brwnsh blk	Uncolored to grayish	Sv, R	Dist	Subconch	O
7	7-7.5	3.88-3.81	3-4	Gelat	Black, sometimes tarnished blue	Grayish blk	V	....	Conch	I
8	7	4.2-3.9	3	Ins	Red, brown	White	V to R	Good	Subconch to uneven	
9	7	3.7	4	Gelat	Black	White	V to R	None	Conch to uneven	I
10	7	3.84	Inf	Ins	Dark red, etc	White	V to R	None	Conch to uneven	I
11	6.5-7.5	4.3-3.15	3-6	Ins	Red, brwn, blk, wht, grn, ylw	White	V to R	Varies	Subconch to uneven	I
12	6.5-7.5	3.75-3.7	3.5-4	Ins	Red to black	White	V to R	None	Subconch to uneven	I
13	6.5-7.5	3.66-3.55	3	Ins	Wht, grn, ylw, brwn	White	V to R	None	Subconch to uneven	I
14	6-7.5	3.9-3.8	3.5	Gelat	Ylw, brwn, blk, grn	White	V to R	None	Subconch to uneven	I
15	6.5	4.17-3.9	3	Gelat	Gray, whtsh, brwn, blk, grn, ylw, red	....	G	Dist	Subconch to uneven	O
16	6.5	3.91	4	Gelat	Ylw, ylwsh grn, blk	....	V to R	Good	Uneven	O
17	6.5	3.77-3.52	4-4.5	Dcpd	Brwnsh blk	Grysh brwn to dirty ylw	V to R	Dist	....	M
18	6.5	3.81±	Inf	Ins	Black	Gray	M, A	Imperf	Conch	H
19	5-7.5	3.67-3.56	Inf	Ins	Colorless, blue, blk, grn, gray, wht	Uncolored	V to P	Perf	....	T
20	6	3.88	5	Sol	Black	Brwnsh gray	M	Perf	Brittle	C
21	6	3.71-3.67	......	Pt sol	Colorless to pale wine-yellow	....	High	Fair	Conch	
22	6	3.85	......	....	Dark green	....		Perf	....	C
23	6	3.72	......	....	Brown to black	....		Perf	....	T
24	6	3.89	2.5	Ins	Honey-yellow, light brown	....		....	....	C
25	6	3.7	4	Gelat	Black	Grysh black	A	....	Conch	I
26	5.5-6.5	3.68-3.4	2.5-3.5	Pt sol	Red, pink, brwnsh	White	V	Perf	Conch to uneven	T

256

GROUP 6
Specific Gravity 3.99-3.66

	INDEX OF REF.	NAME	COMPOSITION	REMARKS
1	1.748	CHRYSOBERYL	$BeAl_2O_4$	Brittle. B.B., with cobalt solution, gives a blue color. Decomposed by fusion with $KHSO_4$.
2	1.72±	SPINEL	$MgAl_2O_4$	Brittle. B.B., the color changes but returns on cooling.
3	1.8±	HERCYNITE	$FeAl_2O_4$	The heated powder becomes brick-red.
4	1.77±	PLEONASTE	$(Mg.Fe)O \cdot Al_2O_3$	Iron, maganesium spinel.
5	1.74	LUSAKITE	$4(Fe,Co,Ni,Mg)O \cdot 9(Fe,Al)_2O_3 \cdot 8SiO_2 \cdot H_2O$	Cobalt bearing staurolite. Not affected by HF.
6	1.741	STAUROLITE	$HFeAl_5Si_2O_{13}$	Slightly soluble in H_2SO_4. Reacts for Fe and sometimes for Mn.
7	1.98	SCHORLOMITE	$3CaO \cdot (Fe,Ti)_2O_3 \cdot 3(Si,Ti)_2O_3$	The HCl solution boiled with metallic tin, becomes violet.
8	1.801	ALMANDITE	$3FeO \cdot Al_2O_3 \cdot 3SiO_2$	One of the precious garnets.
9	1.94	MELANITE	$3CaO \cdot (Fe,Ti)_2O_3 \cdot 3(Si,Ti)O_2$	One of the common garnets.
0	1.76	RHODOLITE	$3(Fe,Mg)O \cdot Al_2O_3 \cdot 3SiO_2$	One of the garnet family.
1	1.8±	GARNET	$3(Ca,Fe,Mn,Mg)O \cdot (Al,Fe,Cr,Ti)_2O_3 \cdot 3SiO_2$	Most varieties fuse easily to a black or light brown glass.
2	1.742	PYROPE	$3MgO \cdot Al_2O_3 \cdot 3SiO_2$	A precious garnet.
3	1.735	GROSSULARITE	$3CaO \cdot Al_2O_3 \cdot 3SiO_2$	A precious garnet.
4	1.865	ANDRADITE	$3CaO \cdot Fe_2O_3 \cdot 3SiO_2$	A common garnet.
5	1.838	KNEBELITE	$2(Mn,Fe)O \cdot SiO_2$	Fe and Mn reactions.
6	1.792	HORTONOLITE	$(Fe,Mg)_2SiO_4$	Fe and Mn reactions.
7	1.935	KEILHAUITE	$15CaO \cdot 14TiO_2 \cdot (Al,Fe,Y)_2O_3 \cdot 16SiO_2(Si,Ti)O_2$	With S.Ph., the bead has Fe colors and an SiO_2 skeleton. In R.F., the bead is violet.
8	1.853	HOEGBOMITE	$Mg(Al,Fe,Ti)_4O_7$	Brittle. Transparent in thin splinters.
9	1.72	CYANITE	$Al_2O_3 \cdot SiO_2$	With cobalt solution, gives a blue color on ignition.
0	2.05	PINAKIOLITE	$2MgO \cdot MnO \cdot Mn_2O_3 \cdot B_2O_3$	With $KHSO_4$ and CaF_2, it colors the flame intensely green.
	....	STIEPELMANNITE	$YPO_4 \cdot AlPO_4 \cdot 2Al(OH)_3$	
2	1.675	IRON ANTHOPHYLLITE	$7(Fe,Mg)O \cdot 8SiO_2 \cdot H_2O$	One of the amphibole group.
3	1.752	SOBRALITE	$(Mn,Fe,Mg,Ca)O \cdot SiO_2$	
4	1.767	JOAQUINITE	$3Na_2O \cdot 6BaO \cdot 5TiO_2 \cdot 16SiO_2$	
5	2.01	IVAARITE	Near Schorlomite	Ti tests.
6	1.724	RHODONITE	$MnSiO_3$	Manganese reactions.

GROUP 6
Specific Gravity 3.99-3.66

	H	SP. GR.	F	HCL	COLOR	STREAK	LUSTER	CLEAV-AGE	FRACTURE	SYTE
27	5.5-6	4.5-3.5	2.5	Gelat	Brwn, blk, grn, gray, ylw	Gray, grayish or brwnsh	V, Sm, R, P	Traces	Uneven to subconch	M
28	5.5-6	3.8	3	Ins	Amber, ylw, brwn, rdsh, dark grn	....	V to R	Dist	....	T
29	5.5-6	3.85	3	Sol	Lt purplish red, rose, colorless	....	V	Indist	....	M
30	5.5-6	4.08-3.95	6	Gelat	Ylw, grn to blk	Ylw, rdsh gray	V to G	Dist	....	O
31	5.5-6	4.05-3.99	2.5	Gelat	Iron-blk to dark grayish black	Blk inclining to grn or brwn	Sm	Good	Uneven	O
32	5.5-6	3.9	Inf	Ins	Brwn, blue, blk	Uncolored or yellowish	A to M	Perf	Subconch	T
33	5.5	4.18-3.99	3.5-5	Gelat	Wht, grn, ylw, red, brwn	Uncolored	V, R	Easy	Conch to uneven	R
34	5.5	4.05-3.97	Inf	Ins	Blk, brwn, ylw	Colorless, grayish	A to M	Imperf	Uneven to subconch	N
35	5.5	3.85-3.75	3	Ins	Black	Rdsh brwn	V	Dist	Uneven	T
36	5.5	3.92	1	Ins	Reddish brown	....	V to S	Perf	....	O
37	5.5	3.7-3.35	2-3	Sol	Nut brwn to brwnsh red	....	......	......	......	M
38	5.5	3.77	......	......	Drk grysh brwn inclining to red	Ash gray	G	None	Splintery, subconch	I
39	5.5	3.91	......	Sol	Black	....	R	......	....	N
40	5-5.5	3.81	3?	Ins	Colorless, wht, pearly, gray	....	V to G	Good	....	C
41	5-5.5	4.3-3.3	6	Sol	Ylw, red, brwn, blk	Brwnsh to ochre-ylw	A, D, S	Perf	Uneven	C
42	5-5.5	3.67	2.5-3	Sol	Colorless, white	....	V	Good	....	T
43	5	4.07-3.94	2	....	Lt to drk orange red	Cream-ylw	V	Dist	Uneven	N
44	5	3.66	......	....	Yellow to brown	....	......	......	......	I
45	5	3.76-3.71	2-3	Sol	Gray, ylwsh gray	....	R to G	None	Conch to uneven	N
46	5	3.67	......	....	Reddish yellow	Pale yellow	D	....	....	.
47	5	3.8-3.5	5	Sol	Colorless to grn	....	G, V	None	....	F
48	5	4.02-3.9	4.5	Sol	Grnsh to black tinged violet	Dark colored	S	....	....	C
49	4.5-5	3.91	2-3	Gelat	Pink to pale rdsh brown	....	V	Perf	....	M
50	4.5-5	3.76-3.72	......	....	Bluish black	....	......	......	....	.
51	4.5-5	4.4-3.4	2-2.5	Sol	Green	Pale green	V	......	....	.
52	4-5	3.8-3.44	1.5	Sol	Pale salmon-brwn to black	Ylwsh gray or brwnsh	R to A	Perf	Small conch	N
53	4-5.5	5.0-3.7	6	Pt sol	Greenish brown	Ylwsh gray or brwnsh	W, V, Sm	....	Conch	I

GROUP 6
Specific Gravity 3.99–3.66

INDEX OF REF.	NAME	COMPOSITION	REMARKS
1.72±	ALLANITE (orthite)	$4(Ca,Fe)O\cdot 3(Al,Ce,Fe,Di)_2O_3\cdot 6SiO_2\cdot H_2O$	**Most varieties give much water in the C.T.**
1.75	PYROXMANGITE	$(Mn,Fe)O\cdot SiO_2$	Manganese reactions
1.771	LEUCO-PHOENICITE	$7(Mn,Zn,Ca)O\cdot 3SiO_2\cdot H_2O$	Treated with HCl, yields gelatinous silica.
1.786	ROEPPERITE	$2(Fe,Mn,Zn)O\cdot SiO_2$	On charcoal with soda, gives a ZnO coating.
....	ILVAITE	$CaO\cdot 4FeO\cdot Fe_2O_3\cdot SiO_2\cdot H_2O$	**Fuses to a black, magnetic globule.**
2.554	ANATASE	TiO_2	**Brittle. S.Ph. in R.F., gives a violet colored bead. Decomposed by fusion with $KHSO_4$.**
1.691	WILLEMITE	Zn_2SiO_4	**Glows in ultra-violet light.**
2.34	PEROVSKITE	$CaTiO_3$	**Brittle. Decomposed by hot conc H_2SO_4. S.Ph. in O.F. gives a bead that is pale yellow while hot and colorless when cold.**
1.8	AENIGMATITE	Titano-Silicate of columbium and iron	**B.B., fuses to a brownish black glass.**
1.774	TARAMELLITE	$4BaO\cdot FeO\cdot 2Fe_2O_3\cdot 10SiO_2$	Fibrous. In bundles and radiating aggregates.
1.65	HELLANDITE	$3(Al,Fe,Mn,Ce)_2O_3\cdot 2CaO\cdot 4SiO_2\cdot 3H_2O$	
1.87±	CHALCO-LAMPRITE	$Na_4(Ca,F)_2Cb_2SiO_9$	Brittle. May be pyrochlore.
1.76	NAGATELITE	$4(Ca,Fe,etc)O\cdot 3(Al,Fe,etc)_2O_3\cdot 6SiO_2\cdot P_2O_5\cdot 2H_2O$	Epidote group, related to allanite.
1.903	HYALOTEKITE	$9(Ca,Ba,Pb)O\cdot B_2O_3\cdot 12SiO_2\cdot H_2O$	With soda on charcoal, gives a PbO coating and metallic lead.
2.393	GOETHITE	$HFeO_2$	**Brittle. Moistened with H_2SO_4, some varieties impart a bluish green color to the flame.**
1.711	BRANDTITE	$Ca_2Mn(AsO_4)_2\cdot 2H_2O$	On charcoal, gives arsenical odors.
1.673	DURANGITE	$NaF\cdot AlAsO_4$	In C.T., blackens but regains color on cooling. Decomposed by H_2SO_4.
....	HYDROROMEITE	$2\text{-}3CaO\cdot 2Sb_2O_5\cdot 6\text{-}8H_2O$	
1.721	ADELITE	$2CaO\cdot 2MgO\cdot As_2O_5\cdot H_2O$	With soda on charcoal yields arsenical odors.
....	STIBIANITE	$Sb_2O_5\cdot H_2O$	An alteration product of stibnite.
1.68±	SVABITE	$9CaO\cdot 3(As_2O_5\cdot P_2O_5)\ Ca(F,OH)_2$	
1.85±	LUDWIGITE	$Mg_3Fe^2Fe^3B_2O_{10}$	Heated in air it becomes red. Cuts easily.
1.742	HODGKINSO-NITE	$2ZnO\cdot MnO\cdot 2SiO_2\cdot H_2O$	In C.T., decrepitates and yields water.
1.713	REPOSSITE	$3(Fe,Mn,Ca)O\cdot P_2O_5$	Salmon-pink on fresh fracture, darkens to brown on exposure.
1.763	PSEUDO-MALACHITE	$Cu_2(PO_4)_2\cdot 3Cu(OH)_2$	In C.T., yields water and turns black.
1.673±	TRIPLITE	$(Fe,Mn)FPO_4$ with Ca and Mg	Moistened with H_2SO_4, it colors the flame green.
1.925	BETAFITE	$(U,Ca)(Cb,Ta,Ti)_3O_9\cdot nH_2O$	Brittle. B.B., gives a black slag.

GROUP 6
Specific Gravity 3.99-3.66

	H	SP. GR.	F	HCL	COLOR	STREAK	LUSTER	CLEAV-AGE	FRACTURE	SYS TE
54	4-5.5	4.3-2.7	Inf	Sol	Brown to nearly black, yellow	Ylwsh brwn to rdsh	S, Sm, E	....	Conch to uneven	..
55	4-5.5	3.7	1.5	Sol	Yellow to reddish brown	Nearly wht	V, G, A	Perf	Subconch	M
56	4.5	3.9	Inf	Sol	Wax-ylw, ash-gray, hair-brown	....	G, V, A	None	Conch to splintery	R
57	4.5	3.95	Inf	Sol	Yellow, orange, brown, green	....	V to G	....	Splintery	O
58	4.5	3.84	5-6	Sol	Brownish red	Brwnsh gray	V to G	Dist	Uneven, splintery	M
59	4-4.5	3.87	2-3	Sol	Grnsh brwn	....	V to G	Poor	....	O
60	4-4.5	3.8-3.7	Inf	Dcpd	Ylwsh red, brwnsh	....	V to G	Fair	....	M
61	4-4.5	3.78	......	....	Gray	....	....	....	....	M
62	4-4.5	3.76-3.61	......	....	Amber-ylw, dark brown to black	....	A	....	Subconch to uneven	I
63	4-4.5	3.72	6	Sol	Colorless, white, cream, pink	....	V	Poor	Uneven	O
64	3.5-4.5	3.93	2.5	Sol	Dark green to yellowish green	Ylwsh grn	V	....	Subconch	..
65	4	3.8-3.6	2-2.5	Sol in HNO3	Dark olive green	Olive grn	R	Poor	Subconch to uneven	O
66	4	3.846	......	....	Black	....	....	....	....	..
67	4	3.598	......	Sol	Yellow to brownish yellow	Dull ylw	R	....	Uneven to conch	..
68	4	3.82	......	....	Brownish yellow	....	....	....	....	..
69	4	3.66-3.64	5-6	Sol	Colorless, white, gray, grn, ylw	White	V to R	Perf	Subconch to uneven	M
70	4	3.7	......	....	Brick-red	Same	....	Good	....	O
71	4	4.64-3.36	Fus	Pt sol	Ylw-brwn, brwn, brwnsh blk	....	G	....	Irregular to conch	O
72	3.5-4	3.98	6	Sol	Brwnsh to blk	Brown	R	Easy	Conch to uneven	H
73	3.5-4	4.1-3.9	5	Sol	Ylw, brwn, red, blk, wht	Brwn to lt ylw or wht	R to A	Perf	Conch	I
74	3.5-4	3.91	3.5	Sol	Emerald to blksh grn	Paler green	V	Perf	Uneven	O
75	3.5-4	4.0±	3	Sol	Iron-black, brown tarnish	Green	Sm	Perf	Uneven	I
76	3.5-4	4.03-3.9	2	Sol	Bright green	Lighter grn	A, V, S, E	Perf	Subconch to uneven	N
77	3.5-4	3.88-3.83	4.5-5	Sol	Gray, ylw, brwn, colorless	White	V to P	Perf	Subconch to uneven	R
78	3.5-4	3.83-3.77	3	Sol	Azure-blue	Lighter	V to A	Fair	Conch	N
79	3.5-4	3.71-3.68	5-6	Sol	Colorless, green, yellow, brown	White	V to R	Good	Uneven	C
80	3.5-4	3.69	......	....	Reddish brown	Brown	D, G	....	Conch	
81	3-4	3.79	2	Ins	Emerald-green, whitish	Lighter	....	....		
82	3-4	3.8	......	....	Ylwsh, grn, blk	....	....	....	Conch to uneven	..

GROUP 6
Specific Gravity 3.99-3.66

INDEX OF REF.	NAME	COMPOSITION	REMARKS
2.06±	LIMONITE	$HFeO_2 \cdot nH_2O$	Usually in stalactitic, botryoidal or mammilary form.
1.726	TRIPLOIDITE	$(Mn,Fe)_2 \cdot (OH)_2(PO_4)_2$	In C.T., gives off water; turns black and becomes magnetic.
....	SYNCHISITE	$CeF \cdot CaC_2O_6$	Glows brilliantly when ignited.
1.7	ANCYLITE	$2Ce_2O_3 \cdot 3SrO \cdot 7CO_2 \cdot 5H_2O$	Moistened with HCl, it gives an intense red flame.
1.799	ALLACTITE	$7MnO \cdot As_2O_5 \cdot 4H_2O$	B.B., looses water and becomes black.
1.801	FLINKITE	$MnAsO_4 \cdot 2Mn(OH)_2$	
2.03±	VOLTZITE	Zn_5S_4O	Treated with HCl, it gives off H_2S.
....	METAJARLITE	$NaSr_3Al_3F_{16}$	
1.89±	ELLSWORTHITE	$CaO \cdot Cb_2O_5 \cdot 2H_2O$	Brittle. Contains U and Ti oxides also.
1.671	BROMLITE	$(Ca,Ba)CO_3$	B.B., colors flame yellowish green.
1.88	CHENEVIXITE	$Cu_2Fe(AsO_4)_2 \cdot 3H_2O$	On charcoal, gives As fumes and a black, magnetic scoria with copper grains.
1.745	LIBETHENITE	$Cu_3(PO_4)_2 \cdot Cu(OH)_2$	In C.T., yields water and turns black. On charcoal with soda, gives metallic copper.
....	TRANSVAALITE	$Co,AsO?$	
....	STIBIOFERRITE	SbO,Fe,H_2O,Si,etc	Brittle. An alteration product of stibnite.
....	CALCIOANCYLITE	$5[(Ce,Y)_2O_3 \cdot 3CO_2]$ $7[(Sr,Ca,Ba)O \cdot CO_2]$ $10H_2O$	
1.684	BARYTOCALCITE	$BaCO_3 \cdot CaCO_3$	Colors flame yellowish green.
....	HYDROGOETHITE	$3Fe_2O_2 \cdot 4H_2O$	Probably lepidocrocite.
2.13	AMPANGABEITE	$(Y,Er,U,Ca,Th)_2 \cdot (Cb,Ta,Fe,Ti)_7O_{18}$	Radio active. HCl solution is dark golden-yellow.
2.356Na	WURTZITE	ZnS	In O.T., gives SO_2 and generally changes color.
2.34Li	SPHALERITE	ZnS	In O.T., gives SO_2 and generally changes color.
1.771	BROCHANTITE	$CuSO_4 \cdot 3Cu(OH)_2$	In C.T., yields H_2O and at higher temperatures H_2SO_4. Becomes black.
2.71Li	ALABANDITE	MnS	Brittle. Treated with HCl, it yields H_2S.
1.875	MALACHITE	$CuCO_3 \cdot Cu(OH)_2$	In C.T., blackens and yields water.
1.785	SIDERITE	$FeCO_3$	In C.T., decrepitates, gives off CO_2, blackens and becomes magnetic.
1.758	AZURITE	$2CuCO_3 \cdot Cu(OH)_2$	In C.T., blackens and yields water.
1.667	STRONTIANITE	$SrCO_3$	Swells and throws out minute sprouts when heated.
....	POECHITE	$H_{16}Fe_8Mn_2Si_3O_{29}$	
1.745	MIXITE	$2Cu_3(AsO_4)_2 \cdot BiAsO_4 \cdot 4Cu(OH)_2 \cdot 7H_2O$	Treated with HCl, the mineral becomes covered with a white powder.
....	PARTZITE	SbO,Cu,Ag,etc	An alteration product of antimony sulfide ores.

GROUP 6
Specific Gravity 3.99-3.66

H	SP. GR.	F	HCL	COLOR	STREAK	LUSTER	CLEAV-AGE	FRACTURE	SYS-TEM
83 3-4	3.93	......	....	Colorless, brwnsh	....	....	....	....	M
84 3-4	3.7	1	....	Dark golden-ylw	....	V	Imperf	Conch	M
85 2.5-5	6.4-3.9	......	....	Ylw, orange, rdsh, brwn to blk	Ylw, brwnsh, olive grn	G, W, V, D	....	Conch to uneven	..
86 3.5	4.01-3.94	Inf	Sol	Brwn, pinkish, ylwsh wht	....	G	....	Uneven	..
87 3.5	4.04-3.98	Inf	Dcpd	Black to brown	Red-brown	Sm	....	Conch	M
88 3.5	3.68-3.5	1.5-3	....	Yellow-green	Grn to brwnsh yellow	P	Good	....	M
89 3.5	3.75	......	Sol	Yellowish green	....	....	Good	....	H
9. 3.3-5	3.97-3.95	3	Ins	White, colorless, slightly colored	White	V to P	Dist	Uneven	O
91 3.3-5	3.77-3.75	3-4	Sol	Various shades of green	Apple-green	A to V	Perf	Conch	O
92 3	3.74	......	....	Bright green	Green	V	Good	Conch	R
93 3	3.9	......	....	Light green	....	Brilliant	Perf	....	O
94 3	3.96	......	Sol	Grass-green	....	....	Perf	....	O
95 3	3.72	......	....	Brownish red	....	....	Traces	....	H
96 3	3.72-3.43	......	....	Bluish to violet black	Dark brown	....	....	....	..
97 2.5-3	3.99	Fus	....	Colorless to transparent	....	P	Perf	....	Tr
98 2.5-3	3.76	1.5	Sol	Blue	....	V	....	....	M
99 2.5	4.1-3.9	6	Sol	Bluish to iron-black	Chocolate-brown	M	Perf	Flexible	H
100 2.5	3.8	2	Sol	Blue, bluish gray	Bluish wht	Good	Good	Brittle	O
101 2.5	3.75	......	....	Deep black	Submetallic	....	....	....	..
102 2-3	3.9-3.81	Inf	Gelat	Yellow	....	V	....	....	O
103 2-2.5	3.93	1.5	Sol	Colorless, white, grayish	....	A	Cubic	Conch	I
104 2.2-5	3.8-3.53	Inf	Dcpd	White, gray, ylw	Shining	E, D	Perf	....	M
105 2	5.0-3.8	Inf	Ins	Black	Black	M	Good	Uneven	I
106 2	3.68	3	Sol in HNO₃	Green, ylw, red	....	....	....	....	T
107 1-2	3.88-3.52	2-3	Sol	Blk, ylwsh, brwn	Ylwsh brwn	S	....	....	O
108 1.5	3.88-3.86	Vol	Sol	Wht tinged ylw or red	White, pale yellow	V to S	Fair	Conch	I
109 Soft	3.79	1.5	Sol	Ylw, white, grnsh, reddish	....	E	....	....	..
110 Soft	4.3-3.7	Easy	....	Yellow	....	....	Perf	....	O
111 Soft	3.97-3.75	......	....	Yellow	....	....	....	....	T

OCTAHEDRITE QUARTZ   ELLSWORTHITE   WURTZITE   BROCHANTITE   SIDERITE

AZURITE   STRONTIANITE   CELESTITE   ATACAMITE   URANOPHANE

HYDRO-ZINCITE   TOPAZ   UVAROVITE KAEMMERERITE on CHROMITE   OLIVINE   JADEITE

DUMORTIERITE   DUMORTIERITE   EPIDOTE   CHLORITOID   VESUVIANITE

VESUVIANITE   ACMITE QUARTZ   GRUNERITE   HYPERSTHENE   ZOISITE

CELSIAN   GILLESPITE SANBORNITE   BENITOITE NEPTUNITE NATROLITE   ARFVEDSONITE   BARKEVIKITE QUARTZ

PLATE 24

GROUP 6
Specific Gravity 3.99-3.66

INDEX OF REF.	NAME	COMPOSITION	REMARKS
.432	JARLITE	$NaSr_3Al_3F_{16}$	
.842	DIETZEITE	$Ca(IO_3)_2 \cdot 8CaCrO_4$	Soluble in hot water.
....	GUMMITE	$UO_3,Pb,Th,R.E.,etc, nH_2O$	Brittle.
.654	RHABDOPHANITE	$(La,Di,Y)PO_4 \cdot H_2O$	Bead tests are rose-red in both flames.
.769	KALKOWSKITE	$Fe_2Ti_3O_9$	In thin plates with a fibrous structure.
.05	CALCIO-VOLBORTHITE	Cu,Ca,V_2O_5,etc	
.87	DUSSERTITE	$6CaO \cdot 3Fe_2O_3 \cdot 2As_2O_5 \cdot 9H_2O$	
.624	**CELESTITE**	$SrSO_4$	**Colors the flame red.**
.861	**ATACAMITE**	$CuCl_2 \cdot 3Cu(OH)_2$	**On charcoal the O.F. is azure-blue with green edges and the coal is coated with brown and gray-white coats.**
.846	PARATACAMITE	$CuCl_2 \cdot 3Cu(OH)_2$	
.738	**ANTLERITE**	$3CuO \cdot SO_3 \cdot 2H_2O$	
....	KAMEREZITE	$3CuO \cdot SO_3 \cdot 8H_2O$	In C.T., decrepitates and gives off water the H_2SO_4.
.754	McGOVERNITE	$21(Mn,Mg,Zn)O \cdot 3SiO_2 \cdot \frac{1}{2}As_2O_3 \cdot As_2O_5 \cdot 10H_2O$	
....	WINKLERITE	$Co,Ni,(OH)?$	An alteration product of erythrite.
.773	MARGAROSANITE	$PbO \cdot 2(Ca,Mn)O \cdot 3SiO_2$	Lamellar. Difficultly fusible in O.F.; fuses at 2 in R.F.
.731	CHALCOMENITE	$CuSeO_3 \cdot 2H_2O$	On charcoal, a black slag; Se fumes and a deep blue flame.
72Li	CHALCOPHANITE	$(Zn,Mn,Fe)Mn_2O_5 \cdot 2H_2O$	In C.T., yields water and oxygen; exfoliates and becomes golden-brown. Treated with HCl, it yields chlorine.
782	TEINEITE	$10CuTeO_4 \cdot 3CuSO_4 \cdot 26H_2O$	HCl solution is green. HNO_3 solution is blue, separates TeO_3, then complete solution. C.T., gives H_2. B.B., a black bead.
....	HEUBACHITE	$Co,Ni,Fe,(OH)?$	A secondary product coating barite.
667	URANOPHANE	$CaO \cdot 2UO_3 \cdot 2SiO_2 \cdot 6H_2O$	B.B., turns black and yields water.
93	NANTOKITE	$CuCl_2$	Gives off chlorine when struck with a hammer. Colors the flame azure-blue.
736	**HYDROZINCITE**	$ZnCO_3 \cdot 2Zn(OH)_2$	**In C.T., yields water.**
91	DAUBREELITE	Cr_2FeS_4	Brittle. B.B. in R.F., looses luster and becomes magnetic. Soluble in HNO_3 with liberation of sulfur.
623	META-TORBERNITE	$CuO \cdot UO_3 \cdot P_2O_5 \cdot 8H_2O$	Formed from torbernite by hydration.
898	ARSENIOSIDERITE	$CaO \cdot 4Fe_2O_3 \cdot 3As_2O_5 \cdot 9H_2O$	Red in splinters.
755	ARSENOLITE	As_2O_3	In C.T., sublimes and condenses in the tube above. Slightly soluble in hot water.
09±	MONTANITE	$Bi_2O_3 \cdot FeO \cdot 2H_2O$	Earthy incrustations. In C.T., gives water.
9±	TYUYAMUNITE	$CaO \cdot 2UO_3 \cdot V_2O_5 \cdot 8 \pm H_2O$	
623	URANOPILITE	$CaO \cdot 8UO_3 \cdot 2SO_3 \cdot 25H_2O$	Velvety incrustations; small lath-like crystals.

GROUP 6
Specific Gravity 3.99-3.66

	H	SP. GR.	F	HCL	COLOR	STREAK	LUSTER	CLEAV-AGE	FRACTURE
112	Soft	3.67	Inf	Sol	Black	....	M	Perf	....
113	?	3.7	......	Sol	Yellow	....	....	Perf	....
114	?	4.08-3.97	.....	....	Black	....	....	....	....
115	?	3.79	.....	....	Blue-green	....	....	....	....
116	?	3.09	.....	....	Brown	....	....	....	....

GROUP 6
Specific Gravity 3.99-3.66

INDEX OF REF.	NAME	COMPOSITION	REMARKS
74	TORDORIKITE	Hydrous oxide of Mn, etc	An alteration product of Inesite. Treated with HCl, it yields chlorine.
635	SKLOWDOWSKITE	$MgO \cdot 2UO_3 \cdot 2SiO_2 \cdot 7H_2O$	Radio active.
. . . .	PEREDRITE	$TiO_2 \cdot H_2O$	Rutile plus a small amount of water. In pebbles and compact masses.
782	SHATTUCKITE	$2CuSiO_3 \cdot H_2O$	Compact, granular masses, spherulitic, fibrous.
718	MAGNESIUM-ORTHITE	$7[(Mg,Fe,Ca)O+ (Fe,Al,Ce,Cb,La)_2 O_3], 6SiO_2 \cdot H_2O+F$	

GROUP 7
Specific Gravity 3.65-3.33

H	SP. GR.	F	HCL	COLOR	STREAK	LUSTER	CLEAV-AGE	FRACTURE
1 10	3.53-3.50	Inf	Ins	Colorless, white, various shades	....	A to G	Perf	Conch
2 8.5	3.85-3.65	Inf	Ins	Green, yellow, red	Uncolored	V	Dist	Uneven to conch
3 8	4.1-3.5	Inf	Ins	Red, blue, grn, ylw, brwn, blk	White	V	Imperf	Conch
4 8	3.65-3.4	Inf	Ins	Colorless, ylwsh, grnsh, reddish	Uncolored	V	Perf	Subconch to uneven
5 8	3.41-3.38	5-6	Ins	White	....	V to A	....	
6 7.5	3.5-3.4	Inf	Ins	Pale blue, bluish or grnsh gray	....	V	Indist	Subconch to uneven
7 7.5	3.42	......	....	Greenish gray	....		....	....
8 7.5	3.52-3.41	6	Ins	Emerald green	White	V to R	None	Subconch
9 7-7.5	3.75-3.65	Inf	Ins	Ylw, red, brwn, brwnsh, blk	Uncolored to gray	Sv, R	Dist	Subconch
10 6.5-7.5	4.3-3.15	3-6	Ins	Red, brwn, ylw wht, grn, blk	White	V to R	Varies	Subconch to uneven
11 6.5-7.5	3.66-3.55	3	Ins	White, green, yellow, brown	White	V to R	None	Subconch to uneven
12 7	3.36-3.26	Inf	Ins	Blue, grnsh, rdsh, violet	....	V	Dist	....
13 7	3.5	3	Ins	Colorless	White	V to R	None	Subconch to uneven
14 5-7.5	3.67-3.56	Inf	Ins	Colorless, blk, blue, wht, grn	Uncolored	V to P	Perf	....
15 6.5-7	3.5-3.3	Inf	Ins	Pink to dark red, various shades	....	V to P	Perf	Conch
16 6.5-7	3.37-3.27	5-6	Gelat	Green, brwnsh	Uncolored	V	Dist	Conch
17 6.5-7	3.35-3.33	2.5	Ins	Green, whitish	Uncolored	Sv, P	Perf	Splintery
18 6.5-7	3.42	Inf	Pt sol	Blue	....	V	None	Subconch
19 6-7	3.62-3.58	2-2.5	Ins	Yellow, brown	....	....	Perf	Subconch to uneven
20 6-7	3.5-3.25	3-4	Pt sol	Colorless, grn, red, gray, wht, etc	Uncolored, grayish	V, P, R	Perf	Uneven
21 6-7	3.47	5-6	Sol	Colorless, pink	....	V	Dist	Conch
22 6-7	3.33-3.21	Inf	Gelat	Wht, grnsh, ylwsh, bluish, gray	Uncolored	V	Dist	Subconch to uneven
23 6-7	3.49	......	....	Grayish green	....		....	....
24 6-7	3.57	5-6	Pt sol	Grysh grn, wht or rdsh gray	....	A	Good	Conch to ueven
25 6.5	3.4	3	Pt sol	Black, reddish	Reddish	V	Good	Uneven
26 6.5	3.77-3.52	4-4.5	Dcpd	Brwnsh black	Grysh brwn to dirty ylw	V to R	Dist	....
27 6.5	3.57-3.5?	5-6	....	Gray green	Uncolored, grysh, grnsh	P	Perf	Brittle

GROUP 7
Specific Gravity 3.65–3.33

INDEX OF REF.	NAME	COMPOSITION	REMARKS
.42	DIAMOND	C	Brittle. Hardest mineral.
.748	CHRYSOBERYL	$BeAl_2O_4$	Brittle. Not attacked by acids. Decomposed by fusion with $KHSO_4$. Cobalt solution gives a blue color on heating.
.72±	SPINEL	$MgAl_2O_4$	B.B., the color changes but returns on cooling.
.62	TOPAZ	$Al_2O_3 \cdot (OH,F) \cdot SiO_2$	Reacts for fluorine. With cobalt solution, gives a blue color.
.69	RHODIZITE	$4(H,Na,K,Cs,Rb)_2O \cdot 4BeO \cdot 3Al_2O_3 \cdot 6B_2O_3$	Flame is green, then green below and red above, then all red.
.707	SAPPHIRINE	$(Mg,Fe)_{15}(Al,Fe)_{34}Si_7O_{80}$	B.B., does not dissolve in borax.
....	DUPARCITE	Al and Ca silicate	Radiated, elongated, prysmatic crystals.
838	UVAROVITE	$3CaO \cdot Cr_2O_3 \cdot 3SiO_2$	A chrome garnet.
741	STAUROLITE	$HFeAl_5Si_2O_{13}$	Reacts for Fe and sometimes Mn. Slightly soluble in H_2SO_4. Brittle.
.8±	GARNET	$3(Ca,Fe,Mn,Mg)O \cdot (Al,Fe,Cr,Ti)_2O_3 \cdot 3SiO_2$	Most varieties fuse easily to a black or light brown slag.
735	GROSSULARITE	$3CaO \cdot Al_2O_3 \cdot 3SiO_2$	A precious garnet.
686	DUMORTIERITE	$8Al_2O_3 \cdot B_2O_3 \cdot 6SiO_2 \cdot H_2O$	Usually in fibrous or columnar aggregates.
745	PYRENEITE	$3CaO \cdot Al_2O_3 \cdot 3SiO_2$	One of the garnet family.
72	KYANITE	Al_2SiO_5	With cobalt solution, gives a blue color after ignition.
722	DIASPORE	$HAlO_2$	Brittle. Viewed on different cleavages, different colors are seen.
81	CHRYSOLITE	$2(Mg,Fe)O \cdot SiO_2$	An olivine.
659	JADEITE	$NaAl(SiO_3)_2$	Sometimes white with spots of green.
703	SERENDIBITE	$2CaO \cdot 4MgO \cdot 3Al_2O_3 \cdot B_2O_3 \cdot 4SiO_2$	With CaF_2 and $KHSO_4$, it yields the boron flame.
79	ARDENNITE	$8MnO \cdot 4Al_2O_3 \cdot V_2O_5 \cdot 8SiO_2 \cdot 5H_2O$	B.B., gives a black glass. Reacts for Mn.
742	EPIDOTE	$4CaO \cdot 3(Al,Fe)_2O_3 \cdot 6SiO_2 \cdot H_2O$	In C.T., gives water on strong ignition.
72	TRIMERITE	$3MnO \cdot SiO_2 \cdot BeO \cdot SiO_2$	B.B., forms a black slag.
661	FORSTERITE	Mg_2SiO_4	In C.T., gives traces of water and becomes colorless.
....	BEFANAMITE	$Sc_2Si_2O_7 + Zr$ and Al	
793	THORTVEITITE	$(Sc,Y)_2O_3 \cdot 2SiO_2$	
782	PIEDMONTITE	$3(Al,Mn,Fe)_2O_3 \cdot 4CaO \cdot 6SiO_2 \cdot H_2O$	
935	KEILHAUITE	$15CaO \cdot 15TiO_2 \cdot (Si,Ti)O_2 \cdot (Al,Fe,Y)_2 O_3 \cdot 16SiO_2$	With S.Ph., the bead has Fe colors and an SiO_2 skeleton. In R.F., the bead is violet.
722	CHLORITOID	$(Fe,Mg)O \cdot Al_2O_3 \cdot SiO_2$	B.B., becomes darker color and magnetic. Dcpd by H_2SO_4.

GROUP 7
Specific Gravity 3.65-3.33

H	SP. GR.	F	HCL	COLOR	STREAK	LUSTER	CLEAVAGE	FRACTURE
28 6.5	3.45-3.35	3	Pt sol	Ylw, blue, grn, brwn	White	V to R	Poor	Subconch to uneven
29 6.5	3.45-3.35	3	Pt sol	Ylw, blue, grn, brwn	White	V to R	Poor	Subconch to uneven
30 6.5	3.34-3.27	Inf	Ins	Colorless, blk, ylw, brwn	....	V	Good	....
31 6-6.5	3.55-3.50	2-3.5	Pt sol	Ylw, grn, brwn, blk	Pale grnsh gray	V to R	Perf	Uneven
32 6-6.5	3.37-3.25	3-4	Ins	Ylw, wht, grn, red, brwn	Uncolored	V to P	Perf	Uneven to subconch
33 6-6.5	3.36-3.16	3-4.5	Gelat	Ylw, brwn, grn	Uncolored	V to P	Traces	Uneven to conch
34 6-6.5	3.5	......	....	Flesh-red	....	......	....	....
35 6-6.5	3.37	6	Sol	Colorless	....	V	Perf	....
36 6-6.5	3.65-3.64	3	Ins	Blue, colorless	....	....	Imperf	Conch
37 6-6.5	3.42	Easy	Ins	Colorless or tinged violet, brwn	....	A	Dist	Brittle
38 6-6.5	3.55-3.51	Fus	Pt sol	Colorless, ylw, green	....	V	Good	Brittle
39 6-6.5	3.49	3-4	Gelat	Ylw, brwn	Uncolored, whtsh gray	A	Dist	....
40 6-6.5	3.45-3.44	2.5	Ins	Black	Deep bluish gray	V	Perf	Uneven
41 6-6.5	3.42	3	Ins	Brown	Reddish	V	Perf	Uneven
42 6-6.5	3.5	2	Pt sol	Green, brown	Pale ylwsh gray	V to R	Perf	Uneven
43 6	3.55	3.5	Ins	Brwnsh blk, grn	Pale ylwsh gray	V to R	Perf	Uneven
44 6	3.6	4	Ins	Green, brown	Wht, gray, grayish grn	V to R	Perf	Uneven
45 6	3.43	......	....	Drk brwn to blk	....	....	....	....
46 6	3.4	4	Dcpd	Gray, brown	....	....	Good	....
47 6	3.41	3.5	Gelat	Bluish green	....	....	....	....
48 6	3.65	2.5-3.5	Pt sol	Brown	White	V	Perf	Conch to uneven
49 6	3.63	3	Ins	Brown	White	V to R	None	Subconch to uneven
50 6	3.43	2	Ins	Deep velvet blk	Deep bluish gray	V	Perf	Uneven
51 6	3.42	Inf	Ins	....	....	....	Perf	Uneven
52 6	3.5	Fus	....	Black, brown	....	S	Perf	Fibrous
53 6	3.5	Fus	....	Black, brown	....	S	Perf	Fibrous
54 5.5-6.5	3.68-3.4	2.5-3.5	Pt sol	Red, pink, brwnsh	White	V	Perf	Conch to uneven
55 5.5-6.5	3.385	......	....	Colorless to white	....	....	Perf	Brittle

GROUP 7
Specific Gravity 3.65-3.33

INDEX OF REF.	NAME	COMPOSITION	REMARKS
.716	**VESUVIANITE** (Idocrase)	$12CaO \cdot 3(Al,Fe)_2O_3 \cdot 10SiO_2 \cdot 2H_2O$	**B.B., fuses to a greenish or brownish glass.**
.716	CALIFORNITE	$12CaO \cdot 3(Al,Fe)_2O_3 \cdot 10SiO_2 \cdot 2H_2O$	The gem variety of vesuvianite. Resembles jade.
.676	KORNERUPINE	$MgO \cdot Al_2O_3 \cdot SiO_2$	Bright blue when treated with cobalt solution and heated.
.816	**ACMITE**	$Na_2O \cdot Fe_2O_3 \cdot 4SiO_2$	**B.B., gives a lustrous, black, magnetic globule; colors the flame deep yellow.**
.703	**ZOISITE**	$4CaO \cdot 3Al_2O_3 \cdot 6SiO_2 \cdot H_2O$	**In C.T., gives off water when heated strongly.**
.739	HELVITE	$3(Fe,Mn)O \cdot MnS \cdot 3BeO \cdot 3SiO_2$	Looks very much like garnet. Treated with HCl, it gives off H_2S.
....	BODEN-BENDERITE	Ti, Al, Yt, Mn, SiO_2	Near beckelite.
.589	CELSIAN	$BaO \cdot Al_2O_3 \cdot 2SiO_2$	Barium feldspar.
.757	BENITOITE	$BaO \cdot TiO_2 \cdot 3SiO_2$	Attacked by HF and dissolved in fused Na_2CO_3.
.01	LORENZENITE	$Na_2O \cdot 2(Ti,Zr)O_2 \cdot 2SiO_2$	B.B., fuses to a black globule.
.723	LAVENITE	$Na, Ca, Mn, Fe, Zr, Ta, Ti, Si$	
658	GUARINITE	$CaO \cdot TiO_2 \cdot SiO_2$	B.B., some varieties change color; fuses to a yellow, brown or black slag.
.70	**ARFVEDSONITE**	$4Na_2O \cdot 3CaO \cdot 14FeO \cdot R_2O_3 \cdot 21SiO_2$	**Fuses with intumescence to a black magnetic globule.**
761	MANGANEPIDOTE	$4(Ca,Na_2,Mn)O \cdot 3(Al, Fe)_2O_3 \cdot 6SiO_2 \cdot H_2O$	A member of the Epidote group.
768	DIOPSIDEACMITE	$nNa_2O \cdot Fe_2O_3 \cdot 4SiO_2 \cdot mCaO \cdot (Mg,Fe)O \cdot 2SiO_2$	Gives a magnetic, lustrous globule; colors flame deep yellow.
77	**AEGIRITE**	$Na_2O \cdot (Fe,V)_2O_3 \cdot 4SiO_2 + CaO \cdot MgO \cdot 2SiO_2$	**B.B., fuses to a black magnetic globule.**
708	DIOPSIDE-HEDENBERGITE	$CaO \cdot (Mg,Fe)O \cdot 2SiO_2$	A pyroxene.
....	RAMSAYITE	$MgO \cdot 2SiO_2 \cdot 2TiO_2$	
719	JOHANNSENITE	$MnO \cdot CaO \cdot 2SiO_2$	B.B., fuses to a black globule.
716	GLAUCOCHROITE	$CaMnSiO_4$	Reacts for manganese with borax.
728	IRONRHODONITE	$(Mn,Fe,Mg,Ca)Mn Si_2O_6$	Probably identical with pyroxmangite.
763	HESSONITE	$3CaO \cdot (Al,Fe)_2O_3 \cdot 3SiO_2$	A member of the garnet family.
707	BARKEVIKITE	Between Hornblende and Arfvedsonite	Fuses with intumescence to a black, magnetic globule.
691	PIGEONITE	$(Mg,Fe,Ca)O \cdot SiO_2$	A pyroxene.
684	GRUENERITE	$7(Fe,Mg,Mn)O \cdot 8SiO_2 \cdot H_2O$	One of amphibole group. Between 50-100% $FeSiO_3$.
85	CUMMINGSTO-NITE	$7(Fe,Mn,Mg)O \cdot 8SiO_2 \cdot H_2O$	One of amphibole group. Between 50-70% $MgSiO_3$.
724	**RHODONITE**	$MnSiO_3$	**Manganese reactions.**
38	KAYSERITE	$Al_2O_3 \cdot H_2O$	A micaceous alteration product of corundum.

GROUP 7
Specific Gravity 3.65-3.33

	H	SP. GR.	F	HCL	COLOR	STREAK	LUSTER	CLEAV-AGE	FRACTURE
56	5.5-6	4.2-3.5	2.5	Gelat	Brwn, blk, grn, gray, yellow	Gray, grnsh, brwnsh	Sm, R, V, P	Traces	Uneven to subconch
57	5.5-6	3.44-3.41	3-3.5	Sol	Lt ylw, gray, brwn	Ylwsh wht	V to R	Dist	Conch to splintery
58	5.5-6	3.43	3	Gelat	Red to gray	Same, lighter	V to R	....	Uneven to subconch
59	5.5-6	3.37-3.35	3	Ins	Grn to brwnsh blk	....	V	Perf	Subconch
60	5.5-6	3.49	5-6	Dcpd	Lt ylwsh to drk grayish brwn	Uncolored	....	None	Uneven
61	5.5-6	3.52-3.39	Fus	Sol	Blk, grnsh, gray, violet	Red	R, M	Good	....
62	5-6	3.4-2.9	2-4	Ins	Blk, wht, grn	Uncolored	V to P	Perf	Subconch to uneven
63	5-6	3.43	Easy	Dcpd	Light brown	White	....	Good	Uneven to conch
64	5-6	3.47-3.05	......	Ins	Black	....	V to P	Perf	Subconch to uneven
65	5-6	3.38-3.2	4	Ins	Colorless, grnsh, green, black	....	V	Perf	Uneven to conch
66	5-6	3.6-3.2	4-7	Ins	Usually grn, but varying in color	Wht to grnsh	V to R	Poor	Uneven to conch
67	5-6	3.5-3.4	5	Pt sol	Grnsh, brwn, blk	Gray, brwnsh gray	P	Perf	Uneven
68	5-6	3.58-3.5	2.5	Ins	Green	....	Sm, D	Good	Uneven
69	5-6	3.52	5-6	Pt sol	Brwnsh blk, chestnut brwn	Light brwn	V	Dist	....
70	5.5	3.41	5-6	Sol	Light rose, ylwsh brwn	....	G	Dist	Uneven
71	5.5	3.57-3.55	Inf	Sol	Colorless, gray, ylwsh, drk grn	White	V	Perf	....
72	5.5	3.33	4	Gelat	Colorless, wht, amathystine	....	V	Perf	....
73	5.5	3.7-3.35	2-3	Sol	Nut brwn to brwnsh red	....	....	....	....
74	5.5	3.44	......	....	Brown	....	V	....	....
75	5.5	3.55	2-3	Ins	Colorless	....	V, P	Perf	....
76	5.5	3.4	Easy	Sol	Brown	....	R to V	None	Conch to uneven
77	5.5	3.9-3.3	......	Ins	Lt to drk brwn	....	....	Perf	Uneven
78	5.5	3.36	......	Pt sol	Blue	....	....	....	Fibrous
79	5-5.5	3.56-3.41	3-4	Sol in H_2SO_4	Gray, brwn, ylw, grn, red, blk	Wht, slightly red or grn	A to R	Good	....
80	5-5.5	4.3-3.3	6	Sol	Ylw, red, brwn, blk	Brwnsh to ochre ylw	A, D, S	Perf	Uneven
81	4-5.5	4.8-2.7	Inf	Sol	Brwn to nearly blk, ylw	Ylwsh brwn to rdsh	S, Sm, E	....	Conch to uneven

GROUP 7
Specific Gravity 3.65-3.33

INDEX OF REF.	NAME	COMPOSITION	REMARKS
1.72±	ALLANITE (Orthite)	$4(Fe,Ca)O\cdot 3(Al,Ce,Fe,Di)_2O_3\cdot 6SiO_2\cdot H_2O$	Most varieties give much water in the C.T.
1.716	WOEHLERITE	$(Ca,Na_2)O\cdot Cb_2O_5\cdot ZrO_2\cdot SiO_2$	B.B., fused to a yellow glass.
1.754	DANALITE	$3(Fe,Zn,Mn)O\cdot 3BeO\cdot 3SiO_2\cdot (Fe,Zn)S$	Treated with HCl, gives H_2S.
1.730	BABIBGTONITE	$(Ca,Fe,Mn)O\cdot SiO_2\cdot Fe_2O_3\cdot 3SiO_2$	B.B., fuses to a black magnetic globule.
....	ERIKITE	$(Ce,La,Di)_2O_3\cdot P_2O_5\cdot ThO_2\cdot Na_2O\cdot Al_2O_3\cdot SiO_2\cdot H_2O$	In C.T., looses water and becomes white.
.89	HETEROSITE	$(Fe,Mn)_2O_3\cdot P_2O_5\cdot H_2O$	Fuses to a deep brown, submetallic enamel.
.7	AMPHIBOLE	$RO\cdot(Na_2,K_2,H_2)O\cdot R_2O_3\cdot 2SiO_2$	B.B., tests variously with various members of the group.
.635±	NORDITE	Si,Ti,Cb,Ta,Th,etc	Brittle. B.B., turns brownish black.
.67	HORNBLENDE	As amphibole	One of the amphibole group.
.671	DIOPSIDE	$CaO\cdot MgO\cdot 2SiO_2$	One of the pyroxene group.
.68	PYROXENE	Ca,Mg,Fe,Si,etc	B.B., varies with different members.
.702	HYPERSTHENE	$(Mg,Fe)SiO_3$	B.B., on coal, yields a black magnetic mass.
.74	HEDENBERGITE	$CaO\cdot FeO\cdot 2SiO_2$	Fuses to a black, magnetic globule.
.688	URBANITE	$Na_2O\cdot 2Fe_2O_3\cdot (Ca,Mg)O\cdot 4SiO_2$	Fuses with difficulty to a magnetic slag.
.689	CENOSITE	$CaO\cdot(Y,Er)_2O_3\cdot CO_2\cdot 4SiO_2\cdot 2H_2O$	In C.T., gives water at a low heat.
.736	PERICLASE	MgO	With cobalt solution on long testing, gives a flesh-red pink.
.667	CLINOHEDRITE	$ZnO\cdot CaO\cdot SiO_2\cdot H_2O$	On coal, gives a coating of ZnO.
65	HELLANDITE	$3(Al,Fc,Mn,Ce)_2O_3\cdot 2CaO\cdot 4SiO_2\cdot 3H_2O$	
93	FERSMANNITE	$8(Ca,Na_2)(O,F_2)\cdot 4TiO_2\cdot 3SiO_2$	
.568	EPIDIDYMITE	$HNaBeSi_3O_8$	Fuses easily to a colorless glass; yields water only at high temperatures.
.64±	GRIPHITE	$MnO\cdot P_2O_5\cdot H_2O$ with Fe,Al,Ca,etc	Translucent.
.683	ZINC SCHEFFERITE	$(Mg,Mn,Zn)O\cdot CaO\cdot 2SiO_2$	A pyroxene.
.66	PLANCHEITE	$2CuO\cdot 2SiO_2\cdot H_2O$	
.907	TITANITE (Sphene)	$CaO\cdot TiO_2\cdot SiO_2$	Some varieties change color and fuse to a yellow, brown or black slag.
.393	GOETHITE	$HFeO_2$	Brittle. Moistened with H_2SO_4, some varieties impart a bluish green color to the flame.
.06±	LIMONITE	$HFeO_2\cdot nH_2O$	Usually in stalactitic, botryoidal or mammilary form.

GROUP 7
Specific Gravity 3.65-3.33

	H	SP. GR.	F	HCL	COLOR	STREAK	LUSTER	CLEAV-AGE	FRACTURE
82	5	3.46	2-3	Dcpd	Ylwsh brwn, straw ylw	....	V to G	Dist	....
83	5	3.61	......	....	Dark green	....	....	....	....
84	5	3.8-3.5	5	Sol	Colorless to grn	....	G, V	None	....
85	5	3.38-3.4	2	Gelat	Blk to drk brwn	Grayish	R to V	Indist	Subconch
86	**5**	**3.35-3.28**	**Inf**	**Gelat**	**Emerald green**	**Green**	**V**	**Perf**	**Conch to uneven**
87	5	3.59	Inf	Pt sol	Clear pale yellow	....	G to R	Good	Splintery, subconch
88	5	3.33	4	Sol	Rdsh violet, gets colorless	....		Poor	....
89	5	3.52	......	....	Pinkish wht to wht	....			
90	5	3.4	......	Sol	Yellowish green	....		Poor	....
91	**4.5-5**	**3.56-3.42**	**1.5**	**Sol**	**Ylw, brwn, blk grnsh, gray, blue**	**Uncolored to grysh wht**	**V to R**	**Perf**	**Uneven to subconch**
92	4.5-5	4.4-3.4	2-2.5	Sol	Green	Pale green	V	....	....
93	4.5-5	3.63	......	....	Brwn, red tinge	....			
94	4.5-5	3.8-3.44	1.5	Sol	Pale salmon brwn to blk	Ylwsh gray or brwnsh	R to A	Perf	Small conch
95	4.5-5	3.59	......	....	Grnsh blk	....	....	....	Granular
96	**4.5-5**	**3.56-3.42**	**2-2.5**	**Sol**	**Pale pink, liver brwn, ylw, grn**	**Uncolored to grayish wht**	**V to R**	**Perf**	**Uneven to subconch**
97	4.5-5	3.34	5-6	Dcpd	Red-brown	Colorless	V, W	Perf	....
98	**4.5-5**	**3.5-3.4**	**6**	**Gelat**	**Colorless, white, sometimes tinted**	**White**	**V, P, A**	**Perf**	**Uneven to subconch**
99	4.5-5	3.41	2-2.5	Sol	Deep wine ylw	....	R to A	Perf	Uneven to subconch
100	4-5	3.5-3.45	2-3?	Sol	Brwnsh, blk	....	V to G	....	Uneven to conch
101	4-5	3.58-3.57	2-3	Sol	Rdsh brwn, blk	Ochre ylw	Sm, D	....	....
102	4-5	3.43	1.5-3	Sol	Colorless, ylw, rdsh, brwn	....	Sr, G	Good	Uneven
103	4-5	3.49	......	....	Ylwsh brwn	....	....	Perf	....
104	4-5	3.45-3.36	Inf	Sol	Violet, blue, wht, rdsh brwn	....	V to P	Perf	Uneven
105	4-5	3.63-3.39	Diff	Ins	Brwn, grn, blk	....	....	Perf	....
106	4.5	3.55	Fus	Sol	Ylwsh, brwn, grn	....	V to G	Imperf	Uneven
107	4.5	3.44	......	....	Drk chocolate brwn	Ylwsh gray	V, M, G	None	Subconch, splintery

GROUP 7
Specific Gravity 3.65-3.33

INDEX OF REF.	NAME	COMPOSITION	REMARKS
.668	RINKITE	Na,Ca,Ce,Ti,Si	Fuses to a black, shining glass with continued intumescence.
....	HEADDENITE	P_2O_5 of Na,K,Fe,Mn, Ca	Occurs in nodules.
.68±	SVABITE	$9CaO·3(As_2O_5·P_2O_5)$ $Ca(F·OH)_2$	
.725	HOMOLITE	$2CaO·FeO·B_2O_3·$ $2SiO_2$	Fuses to a black glass.
.654	**DIOPTASE**	**$CuSiO_3.H_2O$**	**In C.T., blackens and yields water.**
.68±	FLORENCITE	$3Al_2O_3·Ce_2O_3·2P_2O_5·$ $6H_2O$	In C.T., gives acid water and slight etching of the tube.
.487	HACKMANITE	$3Na_2O·3Al_2O_3·6SiO_2·$ $2NaCl(S)$	Treated with HCl, gives H_2S and a small amount of flocule nt SiO_2. Changes its color under ultra-violet light.
.66	FERMORITE	$9(Ca,Sr)O·(P,As)_2O_5·$ $Ca(OH,F)_2$	A member of the apatite group.
.645	RINKOLITE	Ti and Si of rare earths, Na, Sr, Ca	Related to rinkite.
.69±	**TRIPHYLITE**	**$Li(Fe,Mn)PO_4$**	**In C.T., turns to a dark color and gives off water.**
.763	PSEUDO-MALACHITE	$Cu_3(PO_4)_2·3Cu(OH)_2$	In C.T., yields water and turns black.
....	MANGANO-SPHERITE	$3FeCO_3·2MnCO_3$	In botryoidal aggregates.
.673±	TRIPLITE	$(Fe,Mn)FPO_4$ with Ca and Mg	Moistened with H_2SO_4, it colors the flame green.
....	DASHKESANITE	Fe,Al,Mg,Ca,K,Na, $SiO_2·H_2O$	
.666	**LITHIOPHYLITE**	**$Li(Fe,Mn)PO_4$**	**Colors flame red with pale bluish green exterior.**
.704	SCHALLERITE	$8MnO·6SiO_2·\frac{1}{2}As_2O_3·$ $4H_2O$	In C.T., gives H_2O and an arsenic coating. B.B., turns black.
.617	**CALAMINE**	**$ZnSiO_3·Zn(OH)_2$**	**In C.T., decrepitates, whitens and gives off water.**
.574	NATROPHILITE	$NaMnPO_4$	B.B., colors the flame intensely yellow.
.87	SYNADELPHITE	$2(Al,Mn)AsO_4·$ $5Mn(OH)_2$	Gives off chlorine when warmed with HCl.
.88	MAZAPILITE	$3CaO·2Fe_2O_3·$ $2As_2O_5·5H_2O$	In C.T., yields water and at red heat the powder becomes brick-red.
.572	FILLOWITE	$(Mn,Fe,Ca,Na_2)_3·$ $(PO_4)_2·H_2O$	In C.T., a little neutral water.
.747	MOLEN-GRAAFFITE	$Na_2O·CaO·Al_2O_3·$ $SiO_2·TiO_2·etc$	
.434	YTTROCERITE	$(Er,Y,Ce)F_3·5CaF_2·$ H_2O	In C.T., gives water.
.39	JEFFERSONITE	$(Mn,Zn,Fe,Mg)O·$ $CaO·2SiO_2$	Pyroxene group. Zinc may be present as an impurity.
.457	YTTROFLUORITE	$(Ca_3,Y_2)F_6$	
....	ENDEIOLITE	$R''·Cb_2O_6(OH)_2$ $R'''·SiO_3$	Probably altered pyrochlore.

MINERAL IDENTIFICATION TABLES

GROUP 7
Specific Gravity 3.65-3.33

	H	SP. GR.	F	HCL	COLOR	STREAK	LUSTER	CLEAV-AGE	FRACTURE
108	4-4.5	3.76-3.61	......	....	Amber, ylw, drk brwn, blk	....	A	....	Subconch to uneven
109	4-4.5	3.40	2-3	Sol	Deep red or purple	Purple or rose	S	Dist	Uneven
110	**3.5-4.5**	**3.6-3.45**	**Inf**	**Sol**	**Pink, ylw, red, brwn**	**Whlte**	**V to P**	**Perf**	**Uneven**
111	4	3.66-3.64	5-6	Sol	Colorless, wht, gray, grn, ylw	White	V to R	Perf	Uneven to subconch
112	4	3.8-3.6	2-2.5	Sol in HNO₃	Drk olive grn	Olive grn	R	Poor	Uneven to subconch
113	4	3.46	3	Sol	Brwnsh blk, rdsh brwn	Brwnsh red	M, A	Imperf	Uneven to subconch
114	4	3.64	......	Sol	Flesh, red, lavender	Straw ylw	S, G	Perf	....
115	4	4.64-3.36	Fus	Pt sol	Ylw brwn, brwn, brwnsh blk	....	G	....	Conch to uneven
116	4	3.45	Easy	Sol	Dark brwn, etc	Light brown	....	Good	....
117	4	3.45	......	....	Bronze to brown	....	Sm	Perf	....
118	4	**3.44**	**3?**	**Ins**	**Blue to black**	....	**V**	**Perf**	....
119	4	3.5	2-3	Pt sol	Wht to lt gray	....		Perf	....
120	3.5-4	3.53	Fus	....	Grnsh blue	Same		....	....
121	3.5-4	3.42-3.33	Inf	Sol	Wht, ylwsh, brwn	Wht, colorless	V to P	Perf	....
122	3.5-4	3.4-3.2	2.5	Sol	Shades of green	Siskin grn	S	Indist	....
123	3.5-4	3.39	2-2.5	Sol in HNO₃	Emerald to leek green	....	V	Traces	Uneven to to conch
124	3.5-4	3.34	2.5-3	Sol	Olive to grass green	....	V to P	Perf	Uneven
125	3.5-4	3.62-3.55	......	....	Ylw to grysh grn	Grysh grn	....	....	Uneven
126	3.5-4	3.42	......	Sol	Ylwsh wht, gray, brwn	Wht, colorless	V to P	Perf	....
127	3.5	3.6-3.5	3	Sol	Rose-red	....	V	Perf	....
128	3.5	3.86-3.5	1.5-3	....	Ylw-grn	Grn to brwnsh ylw	P	Good	....
129	3.5	3.4-3.3	Inf	Sol	Brwn, red	Chocolate brwn	V, G	Perf	Uneven
130	3.5	3.35-3.34	4	Gelat	Black	Drk olive grn	V	Perf	....
131	3.5	3.39	......	....	Black	Black	....	....	Conch
132	3-4	3.44	......	....	Blk, rdsh, brwnsh blk	Dark brwn	D-V	....	Conch
133	3-4	3.38	2.5-3	Sol	Ylw, brwnsh	....		....	....
134	3-4	3.37-3.27	3	Sol	Yellowish	....	V	....	Even
135	3-4	3.36	Inf	Ins	Drk brwn to dull black	Bluish blk	Sm, V, P	Perf	Uneven
136	3-4	3.4	5	Gelat	White	....	V	Good	....

274

GROUP 7
Specific Gravity 3.65-3.33

INDEX OF REF.	NAME	COMPOSITION	REMARKS
1.89±	ELLSWORTHITE	$CaO \cdot Cb_2O_5 \cdot 2H_2O$	Brittle. Contains U and Ti oxides also.
1.86	PURPURITE	$2(Fe,Mn)PO_4 + H_2O$	In C.T., gives off water and becomes brown. Satin-like luster.
1.826	**RHODOCHROSITE**	**$MnCO_3$**	**Dissolves with effervescence in HCl.**
1.684	BARYTOCALCITE	$BaCO_3 \cdot CaCO_3$	Colors flame greenish yellow.
.745	LIBETHENITE	$Cu_3(PO_4)_2 \cdot Cu(OH)_2$	In C.T., yields H_2O and turns black. On coal with soda, gives Cu.
2.69Li	HAUERITE	MnS_2	In C.T., gives a sublimate of sulfur. In O.T., gives SO_2.
.728	SARCOPSIDE	$6(Fe,Mn,Ca) \cdot 2P_2O_5 \cdot (Fe,Mn,Ca)F_2$	
.13	AMPANGABEITE	$(Y,Er,U,Ca,Th)_2 (Cb,Ta,Fe,Ti)_7O_{18}$	Radio active. HCl solution is dark golden yellow
.735	SICKLERITE	$6MnO \cdot Fe_2O_3 \cdot 4P_2O_5 \cdot 3(Li,H)_2O$	Gives lithium flame.
.754	LAMPROPHYLITE	$SiO_2 \cdot Ti,Fe,Mn,Na$	
.687	**RIEBECKITE**	**$Na_2O \cdot Fe_2O_3 \cdot FeO \cdot 5SiO_2 \cdot H_2O$**	**One of the amphiboles.**
.59	CRANDALLITE	$CaO \cdot 2Al_2O_3 \cdot P_2O_5 \cdot 6H_2O$	Fibrous under the microscope.
.658	VEZELEYITE	$7(Cu,Zn) \cdot 8(OH) \cdot (P,As)_2O_5 \cdot 9H_2O$	
.788	MESITITE	$2MgCO_3 \cdot FeCO_3$	B.B., blackens and becomes magnetic.
.84	DUFRENITE	$FePO_4 \cdot Fe(OH)_3$	In C.T., blackens.
.698	EUCHROITE	$Cu_3(AsO_4)_2 \cdot Cu(OH)_2 \cdot 6H_2O$	In C.T., gives water.
.662	DICKINSONITE	$3(Na_2,K_2,Li_2,R'')_3 \cdot (PO_4)_2 \cdot 3H_2O$	B.B., colors flame at first green then greenish yellow.
....	RIVIOTITE	Sb,Ag,Cu,CO_2,etc	
....	PISTOMESITE	$MgCO_3 \cdot FeCO_3$	B.B., blackens and becomes magnetic.
.73	ROSELITE	$(Co,Ca,Mg)_3(AsO_4)_2 \cdot 2H_2O$	At 100° C, it is dark blue and splits up but regains its color on cooling.
.05	CALCIO-VOLBORTHITE	Ca,Cu,V_2O_5,etc.	Tests for vanadium and copper.
.733	HEMATOLITE	$(Al,Mn)AsO_4 \cdot 4Mn(OH)_2$	B.B., becomes first black then brown.
3	CRONSTEDTITE	$4FeO \cdot 2Fe_2O_3 \cdot 3SiO_2 \cdot 4H_2O$	In R.F., gives a magnetic black or gray globule.
....	SCHULZENITE	$CuO \cdot 2CoO \cdot Co_2O_3 \cdot 4H_2O$	Treated with HCl, it yields chlorine.
....	HETEROGENITE	$Co(ous)Co(ic)O$	
.582	CACOXENITE	$2FePO_4 \cdot 2Fe(OH)_3 \cdot 9H_2O$	Occurs in radiating tufts. Colors flame bluish green.
.665	PINNOITE	$MgO \cdot B_2O_3 \cdot 3H_2O$	B.B., fuses to a dense white mass.
.81	WARWICKITE	$6MgO \cdot FeO \cdot 2TiO_2 \cdot 3B_2O_3$	Decomposed by H_2SO_4.
.69	HARDYSTONITE	$2CaO \cdot ZnO \cdot 2SiO_2$	On coal, glows and yields a sublimate of ZnO.

GROUP 7
Specific Gravity 3.65-3.33

	H	SP. GR.	F	HCL	COLOR	STREAK	LUSTER	CLEAV-AGE	FRACTURE
137	3-3.5	3.55	1.5?	....	Olive grn, citron ylw	Ylwsh grn	P to V	Perf	....
138	3-3.5	3.55	......	....	Lt gray-grn	....	....	Dist	....
139	3-3.5	3.43	3	Gelat	White	....	....	....	Fibrous
140	3-3.5	3.37	......	....	White	....	....	Good	....
141	3	3.65-3.5	2?	Sol	Brwnsh to garnet red	Brick-red	V to G	Dist	Uneven
142	3	3.42	2	Sol	Wht tinged ylw	....	S to P	....	....
143	3	3.72-3.43	......	....	Blksh to violet blk	Dark brown	....	....	....
144	3	3.4-3.1	......	....	Gray-black	....	Bronze	....	....
145	**3**	**3.4-3.3**	**2.5-3**	**Dcpd**	**Bronze ylw**	**Golden**	**Sm, P**	**Perf**	**Brittle**
146	3	3.36	2.5	Sol	Blue	Grnsh blue	V	....	....
147	3	3.58	Inf	Dcpd	Colorless	....	V	....	....
148	3	3.33	1	Dcpd	Rose-red	....	....	Basal	....
149	2.5-3	3.99	Fus	....	Colorless to transparent	....	P	Perf	....
150	2.5-3	3.5	3.5	Sol	Blue to grnsh blue	....	V to S	Good	....
151	2.5-3	3.54	......	....	Copper-red	....	Bronze-like	Perf	....
152	2-3	3.45	Fus	Sol	Ylw-grn	....	....	Perf	....
153	2.5	3.48	Easy	Sol	Black	....	....	Perf	....
154	2-2.5	3.6-3.4	3	Sol	Green	Paler	P, Sa	Traces	Brittle
155	**2-2.5**	**3.8-3.53**	**Inf**	**Dcpd**	**Wht, gray, ylw**	**Shining**	**E, D**	**Perf**	....
156	**2**	**3.64-3.54**	**Inf**	**Sol**	**Pale grn to blue**	**Same**	**P**	**Traces**	....
157	2	3.43	2	Sol	Emerald-green	Lighter green	V	Perf	Sectile
158	2	3.53	3?	Sol	Ylw-grn	....	P	Perf	....
159	**1.5-2**	**3.49**	**1**	**Ins**	**Lemon-yellow**	**Paler**	**P, R**	**Perf**	**Flexible**
160	**1.5-2**	**3.56**	**1**	**Ins**	**Red to orange ylw**	**Orange to aurora red**	**R to G**	**Good**	**Small conch**
161	1-2	3.88-3.52	2-3	Sol	Blk, ylwsh, brwn	Ylwsh, brwn	S	....	....
162	Soft	3.58	......	....	Green	....	....	....	....
163	?	3.63	......	Sol	Ylw, brwn	....	....	Good	....
164	?	3.58	......	....	Drk olive grn	....	....	....	Granular

GROUP 7
Specific Gravity 3.65-3.33

INDEX OF REF.	NAME	COMPOSITION	REMARKS
?.01	VOLBORTHITE	$6(Cu,Ca,Ba)O \cdot V_2O_5,15H_2O$	Gives a black bead which in the R.F., is blackish gray.
..69	CHLORO- PHOENICITE	$10(Mn,Zn)O \cdot As_2O_5 \cdot 7H_2O$	Purplish in artificial light.
.64	ROEBLINGITE	$7CaO \cdot 2PbO \cdot 6SiO_2 \cdot 2SO_3 \cdot 5H_2O$	With soda on coal, gives metallic lead and a lead coating.
.672	MAGNESIUM CHLORO- PHOENICITE	$10(Mg,Mn)O \cdot As_2O_5 \cdot 7H_2O$	
.88	HEMAFIBRITE	$6MnO \cdot As_2O_5 \cdot 5H_2O$	In C.T., darkens and yields neutral water.
.709	SUSSEXITE	$H(Mn,Mg,Zn)BO_3$	In C.T., darkens and yields neutral water.
....	WINKLERITE	$Co,Ni(OH)?$	
....	BOODTITE	$5Co_2O_3 \cdot CuO \cdot Fe_2O_3 \cdot 11H_2O$	Occurs as friable masses.
.705	**ASTROPHYLLITE**	**Si, Ti, Al, Fe, Zn, Mn, Mg, Ca, Na, K**	**B.B., swells up and fuses to a black magnetic enamel.**
.724	CONNELLITE	Sulfo-chloride of copper	In C.T., gives abundant acid water.
.734	GAGEITE	$8(Mg,Mn,Zn)O \cdot 2SiO_2 \cdot 2H_2O$	Transparent.
..621	GILLESPITE	$BaO \cdot FeO \cdot 4SiO_2$	
.773	MARGAROSANITE	$PbO \cdot 2(Ca,Mn)O \cdot SiO_2$	Lemellar. Difficultly fusible in O.F.; fuses at 2 in R.F.
....	LANGITE	$CuSO_4 \cdot 3Cu(OH)_2 \cdot H_2O$	B.B., on heating, becomes bright green, olive green, then black.
....	CASWELLITE	$CaO \cdot MgO \cdot Mn_2O_3 \cdot Fe_2O_3 \cdot Al_2O_3 \cdot SiO_2$	An altered mica. Inelastic.
..582	URANOSPINITE	$Ca(UO_3)_2 \cdot (AsO_4)_2 \cdot 8H_2O$	
..96	MELANO- VANADITE	$2CaO \cdot 3V_2O_5 \cdot 2V_2O_4 \cdot nH_2O$	
..592	TORBERNITE	$CuO \cdot 2UO_3 \cdot P_2O_5 \cdot 8H_2O$	In C.T., gives water. Glows under ultra-violet light.
.736	**HYDROZINCITE**	$ZnCO_3 \cdot 2Zn(OH)_2$	**In C.T., yields water.**
.74	**AURICHALCITE**	$2(Zn,Cu)CO_3 \cdot 2(Zn,Cu)(OH)_2$	**In C.T., blackens and yields water.**
.713	GERHARDITE	$Cu(NO_3)_2 \cdot 3Cu(OH)_2$	In C.T., gives nitrous fumes and acid water.
.623	URANOCIRCITE	$Ba(UO_2)_2 \cdot (PO_4)_2 \cdot 8H_2O$	
.81Li	**ORPIMENT**	As_2S_3	**In C.T., gives a dark yellow sublimate. Soluble in caustic alkalies.**
.59Li	**REALGAR**	AsS	**In C.T., a transparent red sublimate. Soluble in caustic alkalies.**
.898	ARSENIO- SIDERITE	$6CaO \cdot 3Fe_2O_3 \cdot 3As_2O_5 \cdot 6H_2O$	Red in splinters.
96	CHAPMANITE	$5FeO \cdot Sb_2O_5 \cdot 5SiO_2 \cdot 2H_2O$	Lath shaped crystals.
.875	PLUMBOJAROSITE	$3Fe_2O_3 \cdot PbO \cdot 4SO_3 \cdot 6H_2O$	
....	VARULITE	$Na_2O \cdot 5(Mn,Fe,Ca)O \cdot 2P_2O_5$	

GROUP 7
Specific Gravity 3.65-3.33

	H	SP. GR.	F	HCL	COLOR	STREAK	LUSTER	CLEAV-AGE	FRACTURE
165	?	3.57	......	....	Red-brown	Chocolate brown	....	....	Conch
166	?	3.39-3.27	......	....	Dark brown	....	....	....	....
167	?	3.33	2-3	Sol	Colorless	....	P, V	....	....
168	?	3.42	......	....	Brown	....	....	....	....
169	?	3.58	......	....	Black to brown	Red-brown	M	Good	....
170	?	3.65	......	....	Yellow, brown	....	Brilliant	Good	....
171	?	3.55	......	....	Black	....	....	....	....
172	?	3.33	......	....	Sky-blue	....	....	....	....
173	?	3.37	......	....	....	....	....	Perf	....
174	?	3.38	......	....	Brown	....	....	....	....
175	?	3.48-3.44	......	....	Blk, bluish tinge	....	....	....	....

HORNBLENDE QUARTZ	HEDENBERGITE	DIOPSIDE	TRIPHYLITE	LITHIOPHILITE
CALAMINE	TITANITE	TITANITE	DIOPTASE QUARTZ	RHODOCHROSITE
RIEBECKITE	ASTROPHYLLITE	AURICHALCITE	ORPIMENT REALGAR	REALGAR
ANDALUSITE	PHENACITE	DANBURITE	AXINITE	SPODUMENE
SILLIMANITE	AUGITE	GLAUCOPHANE (black xtls)	ACTINOLITE	HARMOTOME on Basalt
LAZULITE QUARTZ	ENSTATITE	MONTICELLITE in CALCITE	DATOLITE	SVANBERGITE

PLATE 25

GROUP 7
Specific Gravity 3.65-3.33

INDEX OF REF.	NAME	COMPOSITION	REMARKS
.749	ALLODELPHITE	$5MnO \cdot 2(Mn,Al)_2O_3 \cdot As_2O_3 \cdot SiO_2 \cdot 5H_2O?$	
....	FERRI-SICKLERITE	$12(Mn,Li_2)O \cdot 5Fe_2O_3 \cdot 9P_2O_5$	
.712	PALMIERITE	$3(K,Na)_2O \cdot 4PbO \cdot 7SO_3$	Decomposed by boiling water.
.694	GIRNARITE	Fe,Al,Ca,Mg,Na,SiO_2	A member of the hastingsite group.
....	RHOENITE	$(Ca,Na_2,K_2)_3Mg_4, Fe_2,Fe_3,Al_4(Si, Ti)_6O_{30}$	Like aenigmatite but less alkalies and FeO and more $(Fe,Al)_2O_3$.
.882	ARGENTIO-JAROSITE	$Ag_2O \cdot 3Fe_2O_3 \cdot 4SO_3 \cdot 6H_2O$	Minute micaceous scales.
....	METATRIPLITE	$6MnO \cdot 3Fe_2O_3 \cdot 3P_2O_5 \cdot 2(Mn,Ca)F_2 \cdot 4H_2O$	An alteration product of triplite.
.75±	BUTTGEN-BACHITE	$16CuO \cdot 2CuCl_2 \cdot Cu(NO_3)_2 \cdot 19H_2O$	May be connellite.
....	FERRO-HASTINGSITE	$Ca_2Na(Fe,Mg)_4 \cdot (Al,Fe)_3Si_{16}O_{22}(OH)_2$	Amphioble group. Hastingsite rich in iron.
....	BERYLLIUM-VESUVIANITE	$2(Mg,Mn,Zn)O \cdot 6CaO \cdot 4BeO \cdot Al_2O_3 \cdot 6SiO_2$	In slender crystals.
....	TAMARITE	Na,Fe amphibole	Similar to hastingsite.

GROUP 8
Specific gravity 3.32–3.00

	H	SP. GR.	F	HCL	COLOR	STREAK	LUSTER	CLEAVAGE	FRACTURE
1	10	3.29–3.15	Inf	Ins	Black	....	R to A	None	....
2	9.5	3.1	Inf	Ins	Green to black	....	M	Poor	Conch
3	9	3.07	Inf	Pt sol	Colorless	....	....	Dist	....
4	8-8.5	3.09–3.08	4	Ins	Pale to grnsh blue	....	V to G	Perf	Uneven
5	7.5-8	3.0–2.97	Inf	Ins	Cclorless, rose, ylw, brwn	....	V	Dist	Conch
6	7.5	3.2–3.16	Inf	Ins	Colorless, red, gray, grn, wht	Uncolored	V	Perf	Uneven to subconch
7	7.5	3.0	Inf	Ins	Bluish green	....	V	Good	....
8	7.5	3.1–3.05	5.5	Ins	Colorless, pale blue, grn, wht	Uncolored	V to P	Perf	Conch
9	7.5	3.23	......	....	Green	....	....	Good	....
10	7-7.5	3.2–2.98	Fus	Ins	Blk, brwnsh to bluish blk, red, grn	Uncolored	V to R	Diff	Subconch to uneven
11	7-7.5	3.02–2.97	3.5	Ins	Colorless, wine ylw, whtsh, brwn	White	V to G	Poor	Subconch to uneven
12	7	3.0–2.9	2	Sol	Wht, gray, ylw, grn	White	V to A	Traces	Conch to uneven
13	7	3.36–3.26	Inf	Ins	Blue, rdsh, grnsh, violet	....	V	Dist	....
14	6.5-7.5	4.3–3.15	3-6	Ins	Red, brwn, ylw, wht, grn, blk	White	V to R	Varies	Subconch uneven
15	6.5-7	3.2–3.13	3.5	....	Wht, ylw, grn, violet	White	V	Perf	Subconch to uneven
16	6.5-7	3.5–3.3	Inf	Ins	Pink to dark red, various shades	....	V to P	Perf	Conch
17	6.5-7	3.37–3.27	5-6	Gelat	Green, brwnsh	Uncolored	V	Dist	Conch
18	6.5-7	3.29–3.27	2-3	Ins	Gray, ylw, brwn, pinkish, blue	Uncolored	Glassy	Dist	Conch
19	6-7	3.3	5-6	....	Grnsh blk, blksh gray	Grysh, grnsh	....	Perf	....
20	6-7	3.33–3.21	Inf	Gelat	Wht, grnsh, ylwsh, bluish, gray	Uncolored	V	Dist	Subconch to uneven
21	6-7	3.5–3.25	3-4	Pt sol	Colorless, grn, red, gray, wht, etc.	Uncolored, grayish	V, P, R	Perf	Uneven
22	6-7	3.24–3.23	Inf	Ins	Brwn, grysh, grnsh, whtsh	Uncolored	V, Sa	Perf	Uneven
23	6-7	3.23	Inf	Ins	Colorless, gray	....	....	Perf	....
24	6.5	3.34–3.27	Inf	Ins	Colorless, blk, ylw, brwn	....	V	Good	....
25	6.5	3.312	......	....	Yellow	....	V	Prismatic	....
26	6.5	3.28	Inf	Ins	Colorless, pale yellow	....	V	None	Uneven
27	6.5	3.19	3.5	Ins	Brwn, gray, grn, blk	Wht, gray, grnsh	V to R	Good	Uneven to conch

GROUP 8
Specific Gravity 3.32-3.00

INDEX OF REF.	NAME	COMPOSITION	REMARKS
....	CARBONADO	C	Black diamond.
.654Na	MOISSANITE	SiC	Found in meteorites; not dcpd by acids or aqua regia. Slowly dcpd by fused KOH.
.719	BROMELLITE	BeO	Slowly soluble in HCl and HNO_3, more readily in conc H_2SO_4.
.674	LAWSONITE	$H_4CaAl_2Si_2O_{10}$	Yields water in C.T.
.654	PHENACITE	$2BeO \cdot SiO_2$	B.B. with soda, gives a white enamel.
.639	ANDALUSITE	$Al_2O_3 \cdot SiO_2$	With cobalt solution, gives a blue color after ignition.
.636	GRANDIDIERITE	$2Na_2O \cdot 8(Al,Fe,B)_2O_3 \cdot 4FeO \cdot 5SiO_2$	
.656	EUCLASE	$2BeO \cdot Al_2O_3 \cdot 2SiO_2 \cdot H_2O$	B.B. in forceps, cracks and whitens, throws out points.
.67	LOTRITE	$4SiO_2 \cdot 2(Al,Fe)_2O_3 \cdot 3(Ca,Mg)O \cdot 2H_2O$	
.64±	TOURMALINE	B,Si of Fe,Al,Mg,Cr, Li,K,Na	With $KHSO_4$ and CaF_2, gives a strong reaction for boron.
.633	DANBURITE	$CaO \cdot B_2O_3 \cdot 2SiO_2$	In O.F., colors flame green. Phosphoresces.
667	BORACITE	$6MgO \cdot MgCl_2 \cdot 8B_2O_3$	Fuses with intumescence to a white pearl, colors flame green.
686	DUMORTIERITE	$8Al_2O_3 \cdot B_2O_3 \cdot 6SiO_2 \cdot H_2O$	Usually in fibrous and columnar aggregates.
8±	GARNET	$3(Ca,Fe,Mn,Mg)O \cdot (Al,Fe,Cr,Ti)_2O_3 \cdot 3SiO_2$	Most varieties fuse easily to a black or light brown slag.
666	SPODUMENE	$Li_2O \cdot Al_2O_3 \cdot 4SiO_2$	B.B., becomes white and opaque; swells up; colors flame purplish red.
722	DIASPORE	$HAlO_2$	Brittle. Viewed on different cleavages, different colors are seen.
681	CHRYSOLITE	$2(Mg,Fe)O \cdot SiO_2$	An olivine.
685	AXINITE	$6(Ca,Fe,Mn)O \cdot 2Al_2O_3 \cdot 8SiO_2 \cdot H_2O$	B.B., intumesces and imparts a green color to the flame.
73	OTTRELITE	$(Fe,Mn)O \cdot Al_2O_3 \cdot 2SiO_2 \cdot H_2O$	Yields water in C.T. Decomposed by H_2SO_4.
661	FORSTERITE	$MgSiO_4$	In C.T., gives traces of water and becomes colorless.
742	EPIDOTE	$4CaO \cdot 3(Al,Fe)_2O_3 \cdot 6SiO_2 \cdot H_2O$	In C.T., gives water on strong ignition.
66	SILLIMANITE	Al_2SiO_5	With cobalt solution, gives a blue color after ignition.
342	MULLITE	$3Al_2O_3 \cdot 2SiO_2$	
376	KORNERUPINE	$MgO \cdot Al_2O_3 \cdot SiO_2$	Bright blue when treated with cobalt solution and heated.
329	TIRODITE	Mg,Mn,SiO_2	Amphibole group.
4	JEREMEJEVITE	$Al_2B_2O_6$	B.B. in forceps, loses transparency, becomes white and colors flame green.
704	AUGITE	$CaO \cdot 3(Fe\ Mg)O \cdot Al_2O_3 \cdot 4SiO_3$	An aluminous pyroxene.

GROUP 8
Specific Gravity 3.32-3.00

	H	SP. GR.	F	HCL	COLOR	STREAK	LUSTER	CLEAV-AGE	FRACTURE
28	6.5	3.27	......	....	Green	....	....	Perf	....
29	6.5	3.11	5-6	Sol in H₂SO₄	....	....	....	Perf	....
30	6.5	3.22	......	....	Green	....	....	Good	....
31	6.5	3.13	......	....	Colorless, light yellow	....	....	None	....
32	6.5	3.18	4-5	Gelat	Lt grn, wht, dull	Wht, grayish	R to V	Perf	....
33	6.5	3.05	5-6	Ins	Wht inclining to grysh blue	....	V, P	Dist	Uneven
34	6.5	3.312	......	....	Honey-yellow	....	....	Prismatic	....
35	6.5	3.21	3	Ins	Pale grn, brwn	....	....	Perf	....
36	6-6.5	3.37-3.25	3-4	Ins	Ylw, wht, grn, red, brwn	Uncolored	V to P	Perf	Uneven to subconch
37	6-6.5	3.36-3.16	3-4.5	Gelat	Ylw, brwn, grn	Uncolored	V to P	Traces	Uneven to conch
38	6-6.5	3.2-3.1	Inf	Gelat	Ylw, wht, brwn	....	V to R	Perf	Subconch to uneven
39	6-6.5	3.2-3.1	Inf	Gelat	Ylw, red, grn	....	V	Poor	Subconch
40	6-6.5	3.2-3.1	Inf	Gelat	Ylw to rdsh brwn	....	V	Poor	Subconch
41	6-6.5	3.11-3.04	3-4	Ins	Blue to bluish blk, grayish	Grayish blue	V to P	Perf	Conch to uneven
42	5.5-6.5	3.0	5-6	Pt sol	Pale pink to brwn	....	P to V	Perf	....
43	6	3.09-3.01	2	Sol	Wht, grnsh, brwn, bluish, ylw	Wht	P, V, G	Perf	Uneven to subconch
44	6	3.0	2	....	White	....	......	Perf	....
45	6	3.2-3.0	4	Ins	Green	Uncolored	V, P, S	Perf	Uneven to subconch
46	6	3.03	3	Sol	Rose to flesh red	White	V	Perf	Uneven
47	6	3.14	......	Dcpd	Ylw-brwn, brwn, etc.	....	......	......	....
48	6	3.18	......	....	Colorless	....	V, P	Perf	Conch
49	6	3.04	6	Gelat	Colorless	....	......	Imperf	....
50	6	3.25	Fus	Ins	Gray-brown	....	......	Perf	....
51	6	3.1	Inf	Gelat	Ylw to rdsh brwn	....	......	Poor	....
52	6	3.12-3.04	......	....	Brwn to wht	....	A	....	....
53	6	3.05	Inf	Sol	Colorless, pale yellow	....	....	None	Brittle
54	6	3.3	......	Pt sol	Pale pink	....	V	Perf	Conch to uneven
55	6	3.15	Fus	Gelat	Pale grn to colorless	....	V	Good	....
56	6	3.09	......	....	Wht, gray, grn, brwn	....	....	Perf	....

GROUP 8
Specific Gravity 3.32–3.00

INDEX OF REF.	NAME	COMPOSITION	REMARKS
1.674	DIOPSIDE-JADEITE	$Na_2O \cdot CaO \cdot MgO \cdot Al_2O_3 \cdot SiO_2$	
1.653	KOTOITE	$Mg_3B_2O_6$	Lemellar twinning and parting. From Suan, Korea.
1.671	VIRIDINE	$(Al,Fe \cdot Mn)_2O_3 \cdot SiO_2$	Green variety of andulusite.
1.675	PLAZOLITE	$3CaO \cdot Al_2O_3 \cdot 2(SiO_2,CO_2) \cdot 2H_2O$	
1.691	FUGGERITE	$(Ca,Na_2)(Al,Mg)(Al,Si)_2O_7$	Close to gehlenite.
1.661	LEUCOSPHENITE	$Na_4Ba(TiO_2)(Si_2O_5)_5$	B.B., decrepitates and fuses to a dark glass.
1.639	TIRODITE	$SiO_2 \cdot (Al,Fe)_2O_3 \cdot (Fe,Mn,Mg,Ca,Na_2,K_2,H_2)O$	Basal parting. Differs from dannemorite and richterite in containing more Mg and has higher optical properties.
1.717	**CLINOZOISITE**	$4CaO \cdot 3Al_2O_3 \cdot 6SiO_2 \cdot H_2O$	
1.703	**ZOISITE**	$4CaO \cdot 3Al_2O_3 \cdot 6SiO_2 \cdot H_2O$	**In C.T., gives off water when heated strongly.**
.739	HELVITE	$3(Fe,Mn)O \cdot MnS, 3BeO \cdot 3SiO_2$	Looks very much like garnet. Treated with HCl, gives off H_2S.
.632	**HUMITE**	SiO_2 of Mg and Fe with F	**Treated with $KHSO_4$ in C.T., gives reactions for fluorine.**
.62	**CHONDRODITE**	$4MgO \cdot 2SiO_2 \cdot Mg(F,OH)_2$	**As humite.**
.636	**CLINOHUMITE**	As humite	**As humite.**
.638	**GLAUCOPHANE**	$Na_2O \cdot Al_2O_3 \cdot 4SiO_2 \cdot 2(Mg,Fe)O \cdot 2SiO_2$	
.625	EPHESITE	$(Na,Ca,Li)_2Al_4 \cdot Si_2O_{10}(O,OH,F)_2$	In C.T., yields water.
.623	**AMBLYGONITE**	$LiF \cdot AlPO_4$	**In C.T., yields water; at high temperatures it is acid and corrodes the glass.**
.611	MONTEBRASITE	$Al_2O_3 \cdot P_2O_5 \cdot 2Li(OH,F)$	A variety of amblygonite. Soluble in H_2SO_4.
.627	**ACTINOLITE**	$CaO \cdot 3(Mg,Fe)O \cdot 4SiO_2$	**One of the amphiboles.**
.636	INESITE	$2(Ca,Mn)O \cdot SiO_2 \cdot H_2O$	In C.T., gives off water and turns brown.
.567	NORBERGITE	$3MgO \cdot SiO_2 \cdot H_2O + F$	Member of the humite family.
.613	STOKESITE	$CaO \cdot SnO_2 \cdot 3SiO_2 \cdot 2H_2O$	
.669	VELARDENITE	$2CaO \cdot Al_2O_3 \cdot SiO_2$	A member of the melilite group.
.65	CUMMINGSTONITE	$7(Mg,Fe)O \cdot 8SiO_2 \cdot H_2O$	One of the amphibole group. Between 50–70% $MgSiO_3$.
.67	TITANOHYDROCLINOHUMITE	$8MgO \cdot 4SiO_2$ and $TiO_2 \cdot Mg(OH)_2$	
.625	GEOCEIXITE	$(Ba,Ca,Ce)O \cdot 2Al_2O_3 \cdot P_2O_5 \cdot 5H_2O$	Alunite group.
.67	HIBSCHITE	$CaO \cdot Al_2O_3 \cdot 2SiO_2 \cdot H_2O$	Yields water freely.
.674	BUSTAMITE	$MnO \cdot CaO \cdot 2SiO_2$	A form of rhodonite.
.711	MERWINITE	$MgO \cdot 3CaO \cdot 2SiO_2$	
.619	EDENITE	$8CaO \cdot 2Na_2O \cdot 18MgO \cdot 4Al_2O_3 \cdot 26SiO_2 \cdot H_2O \cdot 3F_2$	One of the amphibole group. Resembles anthophyllite and tremolite.

GROUP 8
Specific Gravity 3.32-3.00

	H	SP. GR.	F	HCL	COLOR	STREAK	LUSTER	CLEAV-AGE	FRACTURE	
57	6	3.16	Fus	Ins	Bluish black	....	....	Perf	....	
58	6	3.04	Fus	....	Brwn, ylw, red	....	....	Perf	....	
59	6	3.15	....	....	Green	....	....	Perf	....	
60	6	3.1	3-4	Ins	Shades of brwn	....	....	Perf	....	
61	5.5-6	3.2-3.1	5-6	Ins	Gray, grn, brwn	Uncolored to brwnsh	V to P	Perf	....	
62	5.5-6	3.27	3?	Gelat	Ylw, brwn	....	V to G	Indist	Brittle	
63	5.5-6	3.07-2.9	5-7	Gelat	Lt grn, wht, brwn	Wht, grysh	R to V	Imperf	Uneven, splintery	
64	**5-6**	**3.4-2.9**	**2-4**	**Ins**	**Blk, wht, grn**	**Uncolored**	**V to P**	**Perf**	**Subconch to uneven**	
65	**5-6**	**3.47-3.05**	......	**Ins**	**Black**	....	**V to P**	**Perf**	**Subconch to uneven**	
66	5-6	3.3	Easy	Sol	Orange, gray	....	V	Perf	Uneven	
67	**5-6**	**3.38-3.2**	**4**	**Ins**	**Colorless, grnsh, grn, blk**	....	**V**	**Perf**	**Uneven to conch**	
68	**5-6**	**3.6-3.2**	**4-7**	**Ins**	**Usually grn, but varying in color**	**Wht to grnsh**	**V to R**	**Poor**	**Uneven to conch**	
69	**5-6**	**3.12-3.06**	**Inf**	**Ins**	**Blue**	**White**	**V**	**Indist**	**Uneven**	
70	5-6	3.08	4	Dcpd	Pale ylw	....	....	None	....	
71	5-6	3.23	2.5	Ins	Black	Cinnamon brwn	V	Dist	Conch	
72	**5.5**	**3.3-3.1**	**6**	**Ins**	**Wht, grn, brwn**	**Uncolored, gray**	**P to V**	**Perf**	**Uneven**	
73	5.5	3.04	Easy	Sol	Grysh wht to wht	....	V to G	Dist	....	
74	5.5	3.23	......	....	Colorless	....	....	Imperf	....	
75	5.5	3.05	......	Sol	Colorless	....	V	....	Small conch	
76	5.5	3.9-3.3	......	Ins	Lt to drk brwn	....	....	Perf	Uneven	
77	5.5	3.09	Inf	....	Colorless	....	....	....	....	
78	5.5	3.05	Fus	Ins	Ylwsh wht	....	P	Good	....	
79	5.5	3.2	......	....	Bluish grn	....	....	Perf	....	
80	**5-5.5**	**3.35-3.03**	**6**	**Sol**	**Wht, colorless, different shades**	**Uncolored**	**V to R**	**Dist**	**Subconch to uneven**	
81	5-5.5	3.1-2.91	2.5	Gelat	Pale pink, red, brown	Uncolored	V	Dist	Subconch, splintery	
82	**5-5.5**	**4.3-3.3**	**6**	**Sol**	**Ylw, red, brwn, blk**	**Brwnsh to ochre ylw**	**A, D, S**	**Perf**	**Uneven**	
83	5-5.5	3.07-2.98	4	Sol	Colorless, red, ylw, wht	Wht	V	Imperf	Uneven to splintery	

GROUP 8
Specific Gravity 3.32-3.00

INDEX OF REF.	NAME	COMPOSITION	REMARKS
.67	CROSSITE	$Na_2O\cdot4(Mg,Fe)O\cdot$ $(Fe,Al)_2O_3\cdot8SiO_2$	An amphibole intermediate between glaucophane and riebeckite.
.629	RICHTERITE	$Ca_2Na_2(Mg,Mn)_{10}Si_{16}$ $O_{44}(OH)_4$	An amphibole.
.631	HASTINGSITE	$Na_2O\cdot3(Al,Fe)_2O_3\cdot$ $30SiO_2\cdot2H_2O$	A group of amphiboles low in SiO_2.
.636	GEDRITE	$(Mg,Fe,Al)_7$ $(Al,Si)_8O_{22}(OH)_2$	See anthophyllite. A variety of amphibole.
.638	ANTHOPHYLLITE	$(Mg,Fe\ O\cdot SiO_2$	One of the amphiboles.
.658	HIORTDAHLITE	$(Na_2,Ca)O\cdot(Zr,Si)O_{\circ}$	B.B., fuses to a yellowish white enamel.
.691	GEHLENITE	$3CaO\cdot Al_2O_3\cdot2SiO_2$	B.B., with borax, fuses slowly to a glass colored by iron.
.7	**AMPHIBOLE**	**$RO\cdot(Na_2K_2,H_2)O\cdot$ $R_2O_3\cdot2SiO_2$**	**B.B., tests variously with different members of the group.**
.67	**HORNBLENDE**	**As Amphibole**	**A common member of the amphibole group.**
.687	ROSENBUSCHITE	$2Na_2O\cdot6CaO\cdot7SiO_2\cdot$ $ZrO_2\cdot2TiO_2$	
.671	**DIOPSIDE**	**$CaO\cdot MgO\cdot2SiO_2$**	**One of the pyroxenes.**
.68	**PYROXENE**	**Ca,Mg,Fe,Si,etc.**	**B.B., varies with different members.**
.634	**LAZULITE**	**$(Fe,Mg)O\cdot Al_2O_3\cdot$ $P_2O_5\cdot H_2O$**	**In C.T., whitens and yields water.**
....	CIRROLITE (KIRROLITE)	$Ca_3(PO_4)_2\cdot AlPO_4\cdot$ $Al(OH)_3$	B.B., fuses to a white enamel.
699	NEPTUNITE	$(Na,K)_2O\cdot(Fe,Mn)O\cdot$ $TiO_2\cdot SiO_2$	Deep red in splinters.
653	**ENSTATITE**	**$(Mg,Fe)O\cdot SiO_2$**	**One of the pyroxenes.**
603	FREMONTITE	$Na_2O\cdot Al_2O_3\cdot P_2O_5\cdot$ H_2O	In C.T., gives water.
67	IRON-AKERMANITE	$2CaO\cdot FeO\cdot2SiO_2$	Melilite group.
68	HARSTIGITE	$6CaO\cdot2MnO\cdot Al_2O_3\cdot$ $6SiO_2\cdot2H_2O$	Treated with HCl, it yields chlorine.
683	ZINC SCHEFFERITE]	$(Mg,Mn,Zn)O\cdot CaO\cdot$ $2SiO_2$	A pyroxene.
554	GROTHINE	SiO_2 of Al,Ca,Fe	B.B., becomes white. Dcpd by H_2SO_4. Small tabular crystals.
652	BITYITE	SiO_2 of Ca,Al with H_2O	
718	PUMPELLYITE	$CaO\cdot3Al_2O_3\cdot7SiO_2\cdot$ $4H_2O$	In minute fibers and narrow plates.
662	**MONTICELLITE**	**$CaO\cdot MgO\cdot SiO_2$**	**Gelatinizes on evaporation with HCl.**
606	EUDIALYTE	$6Na_2O\cdot6(Ca,Fe)O\cdot$ $20(Si,Zr)O_2\cdot NaCl$	Fuses to a light green, opaque glass. In C.T., yields water.
393	**GOETHITE**	**$HFeO_2$**	**Brittle. Moistened with H_2SO_4, some varieties impart a bluish green color to the flame.**
.57	WAGNERITE	$Mg_3(PO_4)_2\cdot MgF_2$	B.B., gives a greenish gray glass; with H_2SO_4, colors the flame bluish green.

GROUP 8
Specific Gravity 3.32-3.00

	H	SP. GR.	F	HCL	COLOR	STREAK	LUSTER	CLEAV-AGE	FRACTURE
84	5-5.5	3.02-3.0	Fus	Ins	Ylw, red, blk	....	V	Dist	Brittle
85	**5-5.5**	**3.0-2.9**	**2**	**Gelat**	**Wht, gray, grn, ylw, red**	**White**	**V**	....	**Conch to uneven**
86	5-5.5	3.13-2.97	......	....	Lt red to brwn	....	V	Perf	Uneven
87	**5**	**3.35-3.28**	**Inf**	**Gelat**	**Emerald green**	**Green**	**V**	**Perf**	**Conch to uneven**
88	5	3.3	6	Pt sol	Ylw, brwn, red	Colorless, rdsh	V to A	Perf	....
89	5	3.26	4	Ins	Ylwsh, wht	....	....	Perf	....
90	5	3.1	2.5	Gelat	Colorless, brwn, red, etc	Uncolored	V	Poor	Subconch, splintery
91	5	3.15-2.97	4-5	Ins	Colorless	....	V	Perf	Conch
92	**5**	**3.1-2.9**	**4**	**Ins**	**Colorless, wht, gray**	**Uncolored**	**V to P**	**Perf**	**Subconch to uneven**
93	5	3.1-2.9	3	....	Wht, ylw, brwn, rdsh	....	V to R	Dist	Conch to uneven
94	5	3.14-3.10	......	....	Colorless	....	V, Sr	None	Subconch to uneven
95	**5**	**3.05**	**Inf**	**Sol**	**Pale, ylwsh wht**	....	**R**	**None**	....
96	5	3.2	......	....	Dark blue	....	....	....	....
97	5	3.2-3.18	3	Sol	Orange, red, violet, nearly colorless	White	V to G	Good	....
98	5	3.01-2.99	Diff	Sol	Ylwsh to grnsh	....	V, Sr	Poor	Subconch
99	5	3.23	5.5	Gelat	Pale rose red, yellow	....	....	Imperf	....
100	5	3.05	......	Sol	Colorless, ylw	....	....	Perf	....
101	**5**	**3.2**	**5**	**Sol**	**Colorless, grn, blue, ylw, red, etc**	**White**	**V**	**Imperf**	**Conch to uneven**
102	5	3.28	4-5?	Sol	Gray with tinge of violet	....	R, V	Perf	....
103	5	3.18	......	....	Wine to honey ylw, colorless	....	A to V	Fair	Brittle
104	**5**	**3.2**	**5**	**Sol**	**Colorless, grn, blue, ylw, red, etc**	**White**	**V**	**Imperf**	**Conch to uneven**
105	5	3.32	Fus	Sol	Brown	....	....	....	Conch
106	5	3.05	2	Sol	Colorless, ylw, grysh, grnsh	....	....	Perf	....
107	5	3.05	5-6	Sol	Dark brown	....	....	Imperf	....
108	5	3.12	3	Gelat	Colorless	....	....	Fair	....
109	5	3.0	Inf	Ins	Leek to dark grn	....	....	Perf	Brittle

GROUP 8
Specific Gravity 3.32-3.00

INDEX OF REF.	NAME	COMPOSITION	REMARKS
1.613	MELIPHANITE	$2CaO \cdot 2BeO \cdot 3SiO_2 \cdot NaF$	B.B., like leucophanite but does not phosphoresce.
1.654	**DATOLITE**	$2CaO \cdot B_2O_3 \cdot 2SiO_2 \cdot H_2O$	**In C.T., yields water.**
1.636	SCHIZOLITE	$Na_2O \cdot 4(Ca,Mn)O \cdot 6SiO_2 \cdot H_2O$	
1.654	**DIOPTASE**	$CuSiO_3 \cdot H_2O$	**In C.T., blackens and yields water.**
1.626	SVANBERGITE	$Na_2O \cdot CaO \cdot Al_2O_3 \cdot SO_3 \cdot P_2O_5$	In C.T., yields acid water.
1.635	GOYAZITE	$3CaO \cdot 5Al_2O_3 \cdot P_2O_5 \cdot 9H_2O$	In C.T., gives off water and turns white and opaque.
1.621	EUCOLITE	$6Na_2O \cdot 6(Ca,Fe)O \cdot 20(Si,Zr)O_2 \cdot NaCl$	In C.T., gives off water. B.B., yields a light green, opaque glass; colors flame yellow.
1.378	SELLAITE	MgF_2	Treated with conc H_2SO_4, it yields HF and etches the glass.
1.616	**TREMOLITE**	$2CaO \cdot 5MgO \cdot 8SiO_2 \cdot H_2O$	**One of the amphiboles.**
1.632	MELILITE	$Na_2O \cdot 11(Ca \cdot Mg)O \cdot 2(Al,Fe)_2O_3 \cdot 9SiO_2$	B.B., fuses to a grnsh or yellowish glass.
1.629	WHITLOCKITE	$Ca_3(PO_4)_2$	
1.635	**DAHLLITE**	$2Ca_3(PO_4)_2 \cdot CaCO_3 \cdot \frac{1}{2}H_2O$	**With HCl, gives off CO_2.**
....	TORENDRICKITE	$Na_2O \cdot 4MgO \cdot CaO \cdot FeO \cdot Fe_2O_3 \cdot 10SiO_2$	An amphibole intermediate between glaucophane and reibeckite.
1.654	HUREAULITE	$5MnO \cdot 2P_2O_5 \cdot 5H_2O$	Fuses to a pearl that changes color with flaming; green flame.
1.612	HERDERITE	$Ca(F,OH)_2 \cdot CaO \cdot 2BeO \cdot P_2O_5$	B.B., phosphoresces with an orange light.
1.655	WILKEITE	$20CaO \cdot 3P_2O_5 \cdot CO_2 \cdot 3SiO_2 \cdot 3SO_3$	Tests for SO_3, P_2O_5 and CO_2.
1.624	LEWISTONITE	$15CaO \cdot (Na,K)_2O \cdot 4P_2O_5 \cdot 8H_2O$	
1.633±	**FLUORAPATITE**	$9CaO \cdot 3P_2O_5 \cdot CaF_2$	**Moistened with H_2SO_4, it colors the flame green.**
1.66	TILASITE (FLUORADELITE)	$2CaO \cdot MgO \cdot As_2O_3 \cdot MgF_2$	
1.7±	HAINITE	SiO_2 of Na,Ca,Ti and Zr	
1.667	**CHLORAPATITE**	$9CaO \cdot 3P_2O_5 \cdot CaCl_2$	**Moistened with H_2SO_4, it colors the flame green.**
1.653	LOVCHORRITE	$Fe_2O_3 \cdot MgO \cdot CaO \cdot MnO \cdot SiO_2 \cdot TiO_2 \cdot ZnO_2$	
1.622	DEHRNITE	$7CaO \cdot (Na,K)_2O \cdot 2P_2O_5 \cdot H_2O$	May be a member of the apatite group.
1.776	ORIENTITE	$4CaO \cdot 2Mn_2O_3 \cdot 5SiO_2 \cdot 4H_2O$	
1.633	AKERMANITE	$MgO \cdot 2CaO \cdot SiO_2$	A form of melilite.
1.66	BRANDISITE	$12(Mg,Ca)O \cdot 6(Al,Fe)_2O_3 \cdot 5SiO_2 \cdot 4H_2O$	In C.T., yields water. See seybertite.

GROUP 8
Specific Gravity 3.32-3.00

	H	SP. GR.	F	HCL	COLOR	STREAK	LUSTER	CLEAV-AGE	FRACTURE
110	5	3.01	Inf	Sol	Colorless, gray, bluish, ylw	....	V to R	Good	Uneven, splintery
111	5	3.08	......	....	Colorless, ylw	....	....	....	....
112	5	3.14-3.11	4	Sol	Rose, pink, ylw	....	V, Sr, G	Good	Conch to uneven
113	4.5-5	3.24-3.18	4	Sol	Ylwsh, wht, brwnsh	Whtsh, brwnsh	V to R	Imperf	Uneven
114	**4.5-5**	**3.23-3.17**	**5-5.5**	**Sol**	**Wht, grn, blue, ylw, etc**	**White**	**V to R**	**Imperf**	**Conch to uneven**
115	4.5-5	3.21	......	....	Flesh-red, ylw, white	....	Non-metallic	....	....
116	**4-5.5**	**4.3-2.7**	**Inf**	**Sol**	**Brwn to nearly blk, ylw**	**Ylwsh brwn to rdsh**	**S, Sm, E**	....	**Conch to uneven**
117	4-5	3.09	Inf	Ins	Leek green	....	V, P	Perf	Brittle
118	4-5	3.07	4	Dcpd	Pink, rose-red	Pale rose	....	Perf	....
119	4-5	3.16	......	Sol	Wht, ylw, pale grn	....	....	....	....
120	4-5	3.1-3.0	Inf	Sol	Rdsh brwn, copper-red	Uncolored	P, Sm	Perf	Brittle
121	4.5	3.23	4	Sol	Colorless, yellow tint	....	P, G, R	Perf	....
122	4.5	3.04	......	....	....	....	....	....	....
123	4.5	3.11	4-4.5	Sol	Siskin green	Pale green	V	Good	....
124	4.5	3.01	......	Sol	Colorless, flesh colored	....	V to P	Basal	....
125	4.5	3.1	Easy	Sol in HNO$_3$	....	....	....	....	....
126	4.5	3.19	......	....	Yellowish brwn	....	....	Poor	....
127	4.5	3.32	......	Pt sol	White	....	....	Perf	....
128	4-4.5	3.19-3.06	3	Dcpd	Gray, grn, brwn	Paler	P	Perf	Uneven
129	**3.5-4.5**	**3.12-3.0**	**Inf**	**Sol**	**Grysh, wht, ylwsh, brwnsh**	....	**V, S**	**Perf**	**Flat conch**
130	**3.5-4.5**	**3.08-2.99**	**Diff**	**Pt sol**	**Gray, rdsh, pink, white, ylwsh**	....	**P, V**	**Perf**	**Brittle**
131	**4**	**3.25-3.01**	**1.5**	**Pt sol**	**Wht, ylw, grn, red, purple, blue**	**White**	**V**	**Perf**	**Conch**
132	4	3.03-2.93	2.5-3	Dcpd	Rdsh brwn	Pale ylw or grysh brwn	V, G, R	Dist	....
133	**4**	**3.3-3.2**	**3?**	**Ins**	**Blue, green**	**Blue, green**	**S**	**Pris**	....
134	4	3.0	......	....	White, bluish	....	....	Good	....
135	4	3.01	Inf	Sol	White	....	....	Dist	....
136	4	3.22	......	....	Black	....	Pitchy	....	....

GROUP 8
Specific Gravity 3.32-3.00

INDEX OF REF.	NAME	COMPOSITION	REMARKS
1.674	SPURRITE	$5CaO \cdot CO_2 \cdot 2SiO_2$	B.B., gives a strong calcium light.
1.63	PODOLITE	$10CaO \cdot 3P_2O_5 \cdot CO_2$	
1.66	EOSPHORITE	$2(Mn,Fe)O \cdot Al_2O_3 \cdot P_2O_5 \cdot 4H_2O$	In C.T., gives water. In forceps B.B., whitens and sprouts.
1.678	CHILDRENITE	$(Mn,Fe)(OH)_2 \cdot AlPO_4 \cdot H_2O$	In C.T., gives H_2O. On coal, turns black and becomes magnetic.
1.66±	**APATITE**	**$3Ca_3(PO_4)_2 \cdot Ca(F,Cl)_2$**	**Moistened with H_2SO_4, it colors the flame bluish green.**
....	HARTITE	$(Sr,Ca)O \cdot 2Al_2O_3 \cdot P_2O_5 \cdot SO_3 \cdot 5H_2O$	
2.06±	**LIMONITE**	**$HFeO_2 \cdot nH_2O$**	**Usually in stalactitic, botryoidal or mammilary form.**
1.66	XANTHOPHYL-LITE	$14(Ca,Mg)O \cdot 8Al_2O_3 \cdot 5SiO_2 \cdot H_2O$	A rare green mica.
1.65	FRIEDELITE	$H_7(Mn,Cl)Mn_4 \cdot 4SiO_2$	B.B., fuses to a black glass.
1.678	IRON REDDINGITE	$9(Fe,Ca,Mg,Mn)O \cdot 4P_2O_5 \cdot 3H_2O + F$	
1.657	SEYBERTITE	$10(Mg,Ca)O \cdot 5Al_2O_3 \cdot 4SiO_2 \cdot 3H_2O$	Occurs in foliated, micaceous masses.
....	HAMLINITE	PO_4 of Al and Ba with H_2O and F	In C.T., gives much water and HF which etches the glass.
....	QUERCYITE	$6CaO \cdot 2P_2O_5 \cdot 2CaO \cdot 2CO_3 \cdot CaF_2$	
1.84	CHALCOSIDERITE	$CuO \cdot 3Fe_2O_3 \cdot 2P_2O_5 \cdot 8H_2O$	
1.636	WOODHOUSEITE	$2CaO \cdot 3Al_2O_3 \cdot P_2O_5 \cdot 2SO_3 \cdot 6H_2O$	In C.T., gives water. Champion silimanite mine, White Mts., Calif.
1.625	FRANCOLITE	$10CaO \cdot 3P_2O_5 \cdot CaF_2 \cdot CO_2 \cdot H_2O$	A member of the apatite group.
1.676	AKROCHORDITE	$4MnO \cdot MgO \cdot As_2O_5 \cdot 6H_2O$	
1.62	TIKHVINITE	$2SrO \cdot 3Al_2O_3 \cdot P_2O_5 \cdot SO_3 \cdot 6H_2O$	In C.T., yields water.
1.675	PYROSMALITE	$9(Fe,Mn)O \cdot 8SiO_2 \cdot FeCl_2 \cdot 7H_2O$	In C.T., yields acid water.
1.7	**MAGNESITE**	**$MgCO_3$**	**With HCl, gives CO_2 but reacts much slower than Calcite.**
1.643	**MARGARITE**	**$CaO \cdot 2Al_2O_3 \cdot 2SiO_2 \cdot H_2O$**	**In CT., yields water.**
1.434	**FLUORITE**	**CaF_2**	**In CT., decrepitates and phosphoresces. Decomposed by H_2OS_4 with liberation of HF.**
1.649	MOSANDRITE	$CaO \cdot Ce_2O_3 \cdot TiO_2 \cdot SiO_2$, etc	Treated with HCl and heated, it yields chlorine.
1.69±	**CROCIDOLITE**	**$NaFe(SiO_3)_2 \cdot FeSiO_3$**	**B.B., fuses to a black magnetic mass. Fibrous like asbestos.**
1.675	LISKEARDITE	$(Al,Fe)AsO_4 \cdot 2(Al,Fe)(OH)_3 \cdot 5H_2O$	
1.695	TARNOWITZITE	$(Ca,Pb)O \cdot CO_2$	Aragonite containing lead.
....	BELDONGRITE	$6Mn_2O_5 \cdot Fe_2O_3 \cdot 8H_2O$	Looks like lead.

GROUP 8
Specific Gravity 3.32-3.00

	H	SP. GR.	F	HCL	COLOR	STREAK	LUSTER	CLEAV-AGE	FRACTURE	S/T
137	4	3.13	......	....	Pale ylw, grn, wht	....	V to R	Good	....	N
138	4	3.13	Easy	Sol	Pale yellow			Dist	....	C
139	4	3.2	2	....	Blue-grn to blue			Perf		C
140	4	3.29	3	Sol	Brwnsh grn	Ylwsh grn	V, R, G	Dist	....	N
141	3.5-4	3.1-2.95	Inf	Sol	Wht, gray, rdsh	....	V, P	Perf		
142	3.5-4	3.4-3.2	2.5	Sol	Shades of green	Siskin grn	S	Indist	....	C
143	3.5-4	3.3-3.1	2-2.5	Sol	Leek grn, brwn	White	V, Sa, Sr	Imperf	Uneven	
144	3.5-4	3.31⌉	Easy	Sol	Colorless			Perf		T
145	3-4	3.12	2-2.5	Sol	Bright green	Grnsh wht	V	Perf		
146	3-4	3.0	Fus	Pt sol	Wht, ylw	White				
147	3-4	3.08	......	Sol	Colorless to pale green	....		Perf		N
148	3-4	3.37-3.27	3	Sol	Yellowish	....	V		Even	
149	3.5	3.15-3.07	4-4.5	Sol	Wht, grn, ylw	White	P, Sa	Perf	Uneven	
150	3.5	3.13	......	....	Black	....	V	....	Conch	
151	3.5	3.3±	......	....	....					
152	3.5	3.07	Fus	....	Pitch black	Brwnsh blk			Conch	
153	3.5	3.09	......	....	Drk bluish grn					
154	3.5	3.4-3.3	Inf	Sol	Brown, red	Chocolate brown	V, G	Perf	Uneven	
155	3.5	3.09	Easy	Sol	Honey ylw to brwn	....				
156	3.5	3.3	Inf	Sol	Colorless	....		Perf	....	
157	3-3.5	3.14	6	Sol	Gray tinted red	White	V, P	Perf	Conch	
158	3-3.5	3.0	......	....	Colorless, brwnsh	....		Perf		
159	3-3.5	3.1	2.5-3	Sol	Pink, ylwsh, red, brwn	....	V, Sr	Dist	Uneven	
160	3-3.5	3.25-3.0	......	Sol	Yellow	Yellow	P	Perf	....	
161	2.5-3.5	3.26-3.15	4.5	Sol	Ochre ylw, brwn	Yellow	V, Sa	Dist	Uneven	
162	3	3.2-3.0	4.5-5	Gelat	Red, brwnsh, blk, green	Grayish green	A, V	Perf	Brittle	
163	3	3.0-2.5	Diff	Dcpd	Blk, brwnsh blk	Ylwsh brwn	G, V	....	Conch	
164	3	3.0-2.93	1.5	....	Wht, colorless	....	V	Indist	Uneven	
165	3	3.2	4.5	Sol	Yellow, brwn	....		Dist	....	
166	3	3.16	3	Sol	Colorless, wht	....	V	Perf	....	

GROUP 8
Specific Gravity 3.32-3.00

INDEX OF REF.	NAME	COMPOSITION	REMARKS
1.554	LECROIXITE	$2(Na,F,OH)\cdot 2(Mn,Ca)O\cdot Al_2O_3\cdot P_2O_5\cdot H_2O$	
1.663	SEAMANITE	$3MnO\cdot(B,P)_2O_5\cdot 3H_2O$	Crystals striated. Close to reddingite.
....	SAMPLEITE	$Na.Ca.Cu_5(PO_4)_4\cdot Cl\cdot 5H_2O$	B.B., a black glass and green flame.
1.666	JOHNSTRUPITE	$Na_2O\cdot(Ti,Zr)O_2\cdot 3CaO\cdot 5SiO_2\cdot Ce(F,OH)_3$	
1.72±	**ANKERITE**	$2CaCO_3\cdot MgCO_3\cdot FeCO_3$	**B.B., on coal becomes magnetic.**
1.84	DUFRENITE	$FePO_4\cdot Fe(OH)_3$	In C.T., gives water.
1.77±	**SCORODITE**	$FeAsO_4\cdot 2H_2O$	**In CT., yields neutral water and turns yellow. Colors flame blue.**
1.625	PARAHOPEITE	$3ZnO\cdot P_2O_5\cdot 4H_2O$	Crystals are deeply striated.
1.675	LUDLAMITE	$2Fe_3(PO_4)_2\cdot Fe(OH)_2\cdot 8H_2O$	B.B., colors the flame green and leaves a black residue.
1.65	SZAIBELYITE	$10MgO\cdot 4B_2O_3\cdot 3H_2O$	B.B., splits open, glows, fuses to a horn-like, brownish gray mass.
1.614	PHOSPHO-PHYLLITE	$3(Zn,Fe,Mn)O\cdot P_2O_5\cdot 4H_2O$	
1.565	PINNOITE	$MgO\cdot B_2O_3\cdot 3H_2O$	Fuses to a dense, white mass.
1.644	FAIRFIELDITE	$Ca_2Mn(PO_4)_2\cdot 2H_2O$	In C.T., gives H_2O; turns yellow then brown; becomes magnetic.
1.85	TRIEUITE	$2Co_2O_3\cdot CuO\cdot 6H_2O$	Differs from heterogenite in containing no CoO.
....	VERNADSKITE	$2CuSO_4\cdot Cu(OH)_2\cdot 4H_2O$	An alteration of dolerophanite at Vesuvius.
....	MINDIGITE	$9Co_2O_3\cdot 2CuO\cdot 16H_2O$	Looses water easily.
1.622	ARAKAWAITE	$4CuO\cdot 2ZnO\cdot P_2O_5\cdot 6\frac{1}{2}H_2O$	
1.733	HEMATOLITE	$(Al,Mn)AsO_4\cdot 4Mn(OH)_2$	B.B., becomes first black then brown.
1.624	SZOMOLNOKITE	$FeSO_4\cdot H_2O$	Possibly identical with ferropallidite.
1.838	LIME	CaO	
.62	CHURCHITE	$3CaO\cdot 5Ce_2O_3\cdot 6P_2O_5\cdot 24H_2O$	In C.T., yields acid water and becomes opaque.
.653	MESSELITE	$4CaO\cdot 2(Fe,Mg)O\cdot 2P_2O_5\cdot 5H_2O$	Occurs in indistinct, minute, tabular, crystals and stellar aggregations.
.656	REDDINGITE	$Mn_3(PO_4)_2\cdot 3H_2O$	In C.T., whitens and turns yellow then brown.
....	RAIMONDITE	$2Fe_2O_3\cdot 3SO_3\cdot 7H_2O$	In C.T., yields water
.817	**JAROSITE**	$K_2O\cdot 3Fe_2O_3\cdot 4SO_3\cdot 6H_2O$	
.638	**LEPIDOMELANE**	$(H,K)_2O.3FeO\cdot 2(Fe,Al)_2O_3\cdot 5SiO_2$	**A mica. The acid solution deposits scales of silica.**
.57±	HISINGERITE	Hydrated ferric silicate	Fuses to a black magnetic slag. In C.T., yields water.
.413	PACHNOLITE	$NaF,CaF_2,AlF_3\cdot H_2O$	Reacts for fluorine.
.832	NATROJAROSITE	$Na_2O\cdot 3Fe_2O_3\cdot 4SO_3\cdot 6H_2O$	
.662	CAHNITE	$4CaO\cdot B_2O_3\cdot As_2O_5\cdot 4H_2O$	In C.T., yields water and becomes opaque but does not fuse.

GROUP 8
Specific Gravity 3.32-3.00

	H	SP. GR.	F	HCL	COLOR	STREAK	LUSTER	CLEAV-AGE	FRACTURE	S T
167	3	3.27	......	....	Bluish white	....	....	None	....	N
168	**3**	**3.4-3.3**	**2.5-3**	**Dcpd**	**Bronze-yellow**	**Golden**	**Sm, P**	**Perf**	**Brittle**	
169	3	3.03	5	Sol	Grayish brown	....	V to P	Perf	Uneven	
170	3	3.4-3.1	......	....	Gray-black	....	Bronze	....	.	
171	3	3.17	Easy	Dcpd	Dark green	Green	P	Perf	Flexible	N
172	3	3.03	5	Sol	Grayish brown	....	V to P	Perf	Uneven	
173	3	3.17	......	....	Brown, black	....	....	Good		N
174	3	3.14	Easy	Sol	White	....	....	Perf		
175	3	3.3	......	Dcpd		....	....	Trace	....	
176	2.5-3	3.2-2.82	2-2.5	Pt sol	Brwn, ylw, gray, violet	....	P	Perf	Flexible	N
177	**2.5-3**	**3.1-2.7**	**6**	....	**Brown, blk, grn**	**Uncolored**	**P, V, Sm**	**Perf**	....	
178	**2.5-3**	**3.01-3.0**	**4**	**Sol**	**Apple-green**	**Grnsh wht**	....	**Perf**	**Uneven**	
179	2.5-3	3.1	3?	Sol	Carmine	Rdsh wht	S	Perf	....	
180	2-3	3.14	3	Sol	Drk grn, bluish	....	V	Perf	Conch	N
181	2-3	3.3	......	....	Lemon-yellow	....				
182	2.5	3.19-3.15	3	Gelat	Brwn, green	Paler	P	Perf	Subconch	
183	2.5	3.13	3.5	Sol	Emerald to bluish green	Light grn	V, P	Perf	Brittle	
184	2.5	3.09	4-6	....	Grayish wht	....	D, S, R	....	....	
185	**2.5**	**3.0-2.95**	**2**	**Ins**	**Wht, rdsh, brwnsh**	....	**V to G**	**Perf**	**Uneven**	
186	2.5	3.0-2.9	1.5-2	Sol	Grn, brwn, ylwsh	Same, paler	A to G	Imperf	Uneven	
187	2.5	3.27-3.03	Inf	Sol	Wht, bronze, blk	....	P	Perf	Flexible	
188	2.5	3.38	......	Sol	Ylwsh grn	Black	....	....	.	
189	2-2.5	3.19-3.05	3	Sol	Yellow	Yellowish	P, Sa	Good	Brittle	
190	2-2.5	3.2	3	Sol in HNO₂	Green	....	P	Perf	Uneven	
191	**2-2.5**	**3.0-2.76**	**5**	**Ins**	**Grn, brwn, ylw, colorless, etc**	**Uncolored**	**V, P, S**	**Good**	**Flexible**	
192	2-2.5	3.19	Inf	Sol	Green	Paler	V	....		
193	2-2.5	3.24-2.47	......	Sol	Pale to deep grn	....	P	Good	....	
194	2	3.11-2.96	Inf	Sol	Apple-green	....	P, S	Perf	....	
195	2	3.3	......	....	Sulfur-yellow	....	....	....		
196	2	3.0-2.93	1.5	....	Colorless, wht, rdsh, brwn	....	V to P	Perf	Uneven	

GROUP 8
Specific Gravity 3.32-3.00

INDEX OF REF.	NAME	COMPOSITION	REMARKS
1.648	LOSEYITE	$7(Mn,Zn,Mg)O \cdot 2CO_2 \cdot 5H_2O$	Small lath-like crystals; radiating bundles.
1.705	**ASTROPHYLLITE**	**Si,Ti,Al,Fe,Zn,Mn, Mg,Ca,Na,K**	**In C.T., swells up and fuses to a black magnetic enamel.**
1.532	BETA HOPEITE	$3ZnO \cdot P_2O_5 \cdot 4H_2O$	Fuses to a clear colorless globule; tinges flame green.
....	BOODTITE	$5Co_2O_3 \cdot CuO \cdot Fe_2O_3 \cdot 11H_2O$	Occurs in friable masses.
1.649	DAPHNITE	$3FeO \cdot Al_2O_3 \cdot 2SiO_2 \cdot 3H_2O$	B.B., becomes black; does not exfoliate; fuses to a steel-gray globule.
1.591	ALPHA HOPEITE	$3ZnO \cdot P_2O_5 \cdot 4H_2O$	Fuses to a colorless globule; tinges flame green.
1.68	ANNITE	$K_2O \cdot Al_2O_3 \cdot 6FeO \cdot 6SiO_2 \cdot 2H_2O$	Mica group. Near lepidomelane.
.602	SPENCERITE	$4ZnO \cdot P_2O_5 \cdot 4H_2O$	
.625	PROTO-LITHIONITE	$K_2O \cdot Li_2O \cdot 2Al_2O_3 \cdot 3FeO \cdot 6SiO_2 \cdot 2H_2O$	A member of the mica group.
.578	ZINNWALDITE	$K_2O \cdot Li_2O \cdot 2FeO \cdot F_2 \cdot 2Al_2O_3 \cdot 6SiO_2 \cdot H_2O$	In C.T., gives off water and reacts for fluorine.
.64±	**BIOTITE**	$(K,H)_2O \cdot 2(Mg,Fe)O \cdot (Al,Fe)_2O_3 \cdot 3SiO_2$	**One of the common micas. Dcpd by H_2SO_4.**
.658	**ANNABERGITE**	$3NiO \cdot As_2O_5 \cdot 8H_2O$	**B.B., on coal, gives As fumes and a metallic button.**
.683	KOETTIGITE	$ZnO \cdot As_2O_5 \cdot 8H_2O$	In CT., gives much water.
.694	SPANGOLITE	$AlClO \cdot 6CuO \cdot SO_3 \cdot 9H_2O$	On coal in R.F., gives a globule of copper.
....	SALEITE	$MgO \cdot UO_3 \cdot P_2O_5 \cdot 8H_2O$	Magnesium analogue of autunite.
.66±	THURINGITE	$8FeO \cdot 4(Al,Fe)_2O_3 \cdot 6SiO_2 \cdot 9H_2O$	Fuses to a black magnetic globule.
.649	HERRENGRUND-ITE	$3CuO \cdot 2SO_3 \cdot 6H_2O$	On coal, looses its green color and becomes black.
....	FORBESITE	$(Co,Ni)_2H_2(AsO_4)_2 \cdot 8H_2O$	In C.T., yields water and becomes darker.
.339	**CRYOLITE**	**$3NaF \cdot AlF_3$**	**Treated with H_2SO_4 and heated, it yields HF which etches glass.**
.68±	PHARMACO-SIDERITE	$3FeAsO_4 \cdot Fe(OH)_3 \cdot 6H_2O$	In C.T., yields neutral water and turns yellow.
.723	PYROCHROITE	$Mn(OH)_2$	In C.T., becomes verdigris green, then dirty green, then brownish black.
.72	SHARPITE	$6UO_3 \cdot 5CO_2 \cdot 8H_2O$	Effervesces in HCl.
.575	AUTUNITE	$CaO \cdot 2UO_3 \cdot P_2O_5 \cdot 8H_2O$	In C.T., yields water.
.643	ZEUNERITE	$CuO \cdot 2UO_3 \cdot As_2O_5 \cdot 8H_2O$	On coal, yields As fumes and with soda a globule of metallic Cu.
.59±	**MUSCOVITE**	**$K_2O \cdot 3Al_2O_3 \cdot 6SiO_2 \cdot 2H_2O$**	**One of the common micas.**
.595	JOHANNITE	Hydrated sulfate of uranium and copper	In C.T., gives off H_2O and SO_2 and becomes brown and then black.
.625	NEPOUITE	$3(Ni,Mg)O \cdot 2SiO_2 \cdot 3H_2O$	B.B., in C.T., yields water and blackens.
.654	CABRERITE	$(Ni,Mg)_3(AsO_4)_2 \cdot 8H_2O$	In C.T., yields water and becomes grayish yellow.
....	FERGANITE	$U_3(VO_4)_2 \cdot 6H_2O$	
.414	THOMSENOLITE	$NaF \cdot CaF_2 \cdot AlF_3 \cdot H_2O$	Fuses to a clear glass. Decomposed by H_2SO_4.

GROUP 8
Specific Gravity 3.32-3.00

	H	SP. GR.	F	HCL	COLOR	STREAK	LUSTER	CLEAV-AGE	FRACTURE
197	2	3.03	......	....	Brown	....	....	Good	....
198	2	3.25	......	....	White	....	V	....	
199	1-2	3.01	......	Gelat	Grn to dark leek grn	....	V to G		
200	1.5	3.15	Inf	Sol	White, rose	....		Perf	....
201	1-1.5	3.1-3.02	2-2.5	Sol in HNO$_3$	Pale grn, blue	Lighter	P, V	Perf	Flexible
202	1	3.14	Diff	Dcpd	Green	Green	....	Perf	....
203	Soft	3.0-2.8	Diff	Gelat	Green	....	....	Micro	....
204	Soft	3.3	2.5	Sol	Lemon-yellow	....	P	Perf	
205	Soft	3.14?	......	....	Like Pyrrhotite			Perf	
206	?	3.16	3	Sol	Colorless				
207	?	3.3	Easy	Sol	Greenish blue	....		Perf	
208	?	3.01	3	Dcpd	White	....	....	....	
209	?	3.23	......	....	Violet, black			....	
210	?	3.29	......	....	Yellow	....		Perf	
211	?	3.1	......	....	Yellow	....		Good	
212	?	3.0	......	....	Greenish black			Perf	
213	?	3.2-3 14	Easy	Sol	Flesh-pink	....	....	....	
214	?	3.07	......	....	Lavender to rose	....	....	....	
215	?	3.28	Inf	Ins	Colorless, ylw	....	....	Perf	
216	?	3.3-3.0	......	....	Ylwsh wht	....	....	....	
217	?	3.29-3.27	......	....	Dark brown	....			
218	?	3.25	......	....	Deep brown	....		Good	....
219	?	3.15-2.85	......	....	Green				
220	?	3.25	1	Sol	Colorless	....	....	....	
221	?	3.02	......	....	Rose-red	....	....	....	
222	?	3.22	......	....	Lilac				
223	?	3.26	......	....	Green	....	....	....	
224	?	3.22	......	....	Rose-red	....	....	Good	....
225	?	3.1	......	Sol	Colorless	....	....	None	....
226	?	3.05	......	....	Flesh-red	....	....	....	
227	?	3.1	......					....	

SCORODITE   MANGANAPATITE   SCOLECITE   LEPIDOMELANE   AMBLYGONITE
QUARTZ

TREMOLITE   SPURRITE   APATITE   APATITE   XANTHOPHYLLITE
in VESUVIANITE

MAGNESITE   MARGARITE   FLUORITE   CROCIDOLITE   ANKERITE

JAROSITE   BIOTITE   ANNABERGITE   MUSCOVITE   CRYOLITE

AUTUNITE   APHROSIDERITE   ANDESINE   BERYL   TOURMALINE
TORBERNITE

POLLUCITE   PREHNITE   ANORTHITE   TURQUOISE   WERNERITE
in matrix

PLATE 26

GROUP 8
Specific Gravity 3.32-3.00

INDEX OF REF.	NAME	COMPOSITION	REMARKS
7 1.728	LANDESITE	$20MnO\cdot3Fe_2O_3\cdot8P_2O_5$ $27H_2O$	
8	DUNDASITE	$PbO\cdot Al_2O_3\cdot2CO_2\cdot4H_2O$	
9 1.689	BRUNSVIGITE	$6SiO_2\cdot3Al_2O_3\cdot9MgO\cdot$ $8H_2O$	
0 1.595	SZMIKITE	$MnSO_4\cdot H_2O$	
1 1.726	TYROLITE	$5CuO\cdot As_2O_5\cdot9H_2O$	In C.T., decrepitates; yields much water. Soluble in NH_4OH.
2 1.66	STRIGOVITE	$2FeO\cdot(Fe,Al)_2O_3\cdot$ $2SiO_2\cdot2H_2O$	In C.T., gives much water.
3 1.612	APHROSIDERITE	$6(Fe,Mg)O\cdot$ $2(Al,Fe)_2O_3\cdot4SiO_2\cdot$ $5H_2O$	
1.627	TROEGERITE	$3UO_3\cdot As_2O_5\cdot12H_2O$	
....	VALLERIITE	$Cu_2Fe_4S_7$	Ignites and burns. A metallic mineral having the appearance of pyrrhotite.
1.707	GENEVITE	$CaO\cdot MgO\cdot FeO\cdot$ $(Fe,Al)_2O_3\cdot SiO_2$	Possibly the same as vesuvianite.
1.748	FRIERINITE	$6(Cu,Ca)O\cdot3Na_2O\cdot$ $2As_2O_5\ 6H_2O$	Fuses with intumescence.
1.642	JAUNITE	$10CaO\cdot4MgO\cdot Al_2O_3\cdot$ $11SiO_2\cdot4H_2O$	Fuses to a translucent bead.
....	NEOPURPURITE	$7(Fe,Mn)_2O_3\cdot5P_2O_5\cdot$ $4H_2O$	An alteration product of lithiophilite.
1.701	TINZENITE	$Al_2O_3\cdot Mn_2O_3\cdot2CaO\cdot$ $4SiO_2$	Has a columnar structure.
1.574	BASSETITE	$CaO\ 2UO_3\cdot P_2O_5\cdot8H_2O$	
....	EASTONITE	$H_4K_2Mg_5Al_4Si_{15}O_{24}$	A mica related to biotite.
1.656	PALAITE	$5MnO\cdot2P_2O_5\cdot4H_2O$	From alteration of lithiophilite and alters to hureaulite.
....	ELLESTADITE	$CaO,SO_3,SiO_2,P_2O_5,$ CO_2,Cl,F	A sulfate-apatite with P_2O_5 almost entirely replaced by SO_3 and SiO_2.
1.654	CLINOENSTATITE	$MgO\cdot SiO_2$	One of the pyroxenes.
....	FERRAZITE	$3(Ba,Pb)O\cdot2P_2O_5\cdot$ $8H_2O$	
....	FERRI- SICKLERITE	$12(Mn,Li_2)O\cdot5Fe_2O_3\cdot$ $9P_2O_5$	
1.755	SURSASSITE	$5MnO\cdot2Al_2O_3\cdot5SiO_2\cdot$ $3H_2O$	A manganese epidote.
....	META GREENALITE	$9FeO\cdot Fe_2O_3\cdot8SiO_2\cdot$ $8H_2O$	
1.572	NITROBARITE	$BaO\cdot N_2O_5$	Soluble in water.
1.572	MANGANO- LANGBEINITE	$2MnO\cdot K_2O\cdot3SO_3$	From Vesuvius.
1.667	BIDALOTITE	Fe,Al,Mg silicate	A pyroxene. Occurs in small grains and plates.
....	MANGAN- APATITE	$9(Ca,Mn)O\cdot3P_2O_5\cdot$ $Ca(OH,F)_2$	See apatite.
1.664	SERANDITE	$(Mn,Ca,K,Na)Si\cdot$ $(O,OH)_3$	
1.623	MERRILLITE	$Na_2O\cdot3CaO\cdot P_2O_5$	Found only in meteorites.
....	PSEUDOPALAITE	$6(Mn,Fe)O\cdot2P_2O_5\cdot$ $5H_2O$	Slightly different from palaite.
....	CHROMITITE	$FeCrO_3$	

GROUP 8
Specific Gravity 3.32-3.00

	H	SP. GR.	F	HCL	COLOR	STREAK	LUSTER	CLEAV-AGE	FRACTURE	SY TE
228	?	3.31	......	....	Black	....	......	....	....	M
229	?	3.06-3.01	......	....	....	....	......	Fair	....	O
230	?	3.12	......	....	Pale rdsh brwn	....	......	....	....	
231	?	3.1	......	....	Colorless	....	......	Poor	....	H
232	?	3.1±	....	....	Brwn, rdsh	Ylwsh brwn	D	....	....	..
233	?	3.263	Inf	Sol	White	....	......	....	....	M

296

MINERAL IDENTIFICATION TABLES

GROUP 8
Specific Gravity 3.32-3.00

INDEX OF REF.	NAME	COMPOSITION	REMARKS
....	BABABUDANITE	$2Na_2Fe_2Si_4O_{12}\cdot$ $5(Mg,Fe,H_2,Ca)SiO_2$	Occurs in acicular crystals. A soda amphibole related to riebeckite.
1.64	BOEHMITE	$AlO(OH)$	Dimorphous with diaspore.
1.632	MAGNOPHORITE	$Ca,Na,K,Mg,Fe,Ti,$ Mn,Si,Al,Ti,O,OH,F	
1.625	WADEITE	$K_2CaZrSi_4O_{12}$	
2.16	BLAKEITE	Fe,Te compound	
1.608	WEINSCHENKITE	$(Y,Er)_2O_3\cdot P_2O_5\cdot 4H_2O$	

GROUP 9
Specific Gravity 2.99-2.66

	H	SP. GR.	F	HCL	COLOR	STREAK	LUSTER	CLEAV-AGE	FRACTURE	S. T.
1	7.5-8	3.0-2.97	Inf	Ins	Colorless, rose, yellow, brown	....	V	Dist	Conch	F
2	7.5-8	2.8-2.63	5.5	Ins	White, red, yellow, pink, green, blue	White	V, R	Imperf	Conch to uneven	H
3	7-8	2.77	......	....	Colorless			Good	....	F
4	7-7.5	3.2-2.98	3-Inf	Ins	Yellow, brown, black, red, green	Uncolored	V to R	Poor	Uneven to subconch	F
5	7-7.5	3.02-2.97	3.5	Ins	Colorless, wine, ylw, whtsh brwn	White	V to G	Poor	Uneven to subconch	C
6	7-7.5	2.66-2.60	5-5.5	Pt sol	Shades of blue	....	V	Dist	Subconch	C
7	7	2.87	Inf	Ins	Colorless	....	V	Imperf	....	I
8	7	3.0-2.9	2	Sol	White, gray, yellow, green	White	V to A	Traces	Conch to uneven	C
9	7	2.75	Easy	Ins	Ylw to rdsh or brownish gray	....	V, P	Perf	Uneven	T
10	6-7	2.67-2.65	3.5	Ins	White, various tints	....	V to P	Perf	Conch to uneven	T
11	6.5	2.9	Diff	Dcpd	Colorless	....	V, D	Traces	Conch	I
12	6.5	2.8	Inf	Ins	Bright azure blue		V	....		F
13	6.5	2.70	2.5	Sol	Colorless to pink		....	Perf	....	C
14	6-6.5	2.95-2.80	2	Sol	White, green, gray	Uncolored	V	Dist	Uneven	C
15	6-6.5	2.80	Diff	Ins	Colorless, white, flesh red	....	V	Perf	Conch	M
16	6-6.5	2.76-2.74	5	Gelat	White, grayish, reddish	....	....	Perf	Conch to uneven	T
17	5-6.5	2.8-2.5	2-3	Pt sol	Colorless, white, red, blue, gray, etc	Uncolored	V	Good	Conch	T
18	6	2.83-2.6	Inf	Sol	Sky blue, bluish green, green	White to greenish	W	None	Small conch	T
19	6	2.80	3	Sol	Yellow, brownish, bluish, violet	Pale yellow	D, V	Perf	Conch	M
20	6	2.93-2.54	3	Gelat	Reddish, white, red	....	V	....	Conch	T
21	6	2.68	......	....	Colorless	....	....	Perf	....	T
22	6	2.66	Easy	Sol	White	....	....	Fair	Uneven to conch	C
23	6	2.73	5	Gelat	Colorless	....	....	Perf	....	T
24	6	2.92	......	....	Apple green	....				C
25	5.5-6	3.07-2.9	5-7	Gelat	Light green, white, brown	Grayish, white	R to V	Imperf	Uneven, splintery	T
26	5.5-6	2.84	3	Sol	Colorless, white, yellowish	....	P to V	Perf	Conch	T
27	5.5-6	2.74-2.70	3	Dcpd	Colorless, white	....	V	Perf	Conch	T
28	5-6	2.72-2.70	3	Pt sol	Colorless, gray, brown, grayish	Uncolored	P, V, Sr	Perf	....	T

GROUP 9
Specific Gravity 2.99-2.66

INDEX OF REF.	NAME	COMPOSITION	REMARKS
1.654	PHENACITE	$2BeO \cdot SiO_2$	B.B., with soda, gives a white enamel.
1.598	BERYL	$2BeO \cdot Al_2O_3 \cdot 6SiO_2$	B.B., clear varieties become milky and cloudy.
1.559	ARMENITE	$Ba,Ca_2Al_6Si_8O_{28} \cdot 2H_2O$	
1.64±	TOURMALINE	Borosilicate of K, Li,Mg,Fe and Al	With $KHSO_4$ and CaF_2, gives strong reaction for boron.
1.633	DANBURITE	$CaO \cdot B_2O_3 \cdot 2SiO_2$	In O.F., colors flame green. Phosphoresces.
1.562±	IOLITE (Cordierite)	$4(Mg,Fe)O \cdot 4Al_2O_3 \cdot 10SiO_2 \cdot H_2O$	Decomposed by fusion with alkali carbonates.
1.596	ZUNYITE	$Al_2O_3 \cdot SiO_2 \cdot Al(OH,F,Cl)_3$	In C.T., yields acid water.
1.667	BORACITE	$MgCl_2 \cdot 6MgO \cdot 8B_2O_3$	Fuses with intumescence to a white pearl, colors flame green
1.609	NARSARSUKITE	Titanosilicate of Na,Fe,F,etc	B.B., fuses to a yellow blebby mass.
1.543	OLIGOCLASE	$(Na_2,Ca)O \cdot Al_2O_3 \cdot 5SiO_2$	One of the feldspars.
1.518	POLLUCITE	$(Na,Cs)_2O \cdot Al_2O_0 \cdot 5SiO_2 \cdot H_2O$	In C.T., becomes opaque and yields H_2O at high temperatures.
1.626	BAZZITE	Silicate of Sc, etc	B.B., becomes dark and opaque.
1.583	XONOTLITE	$5CaO \cdot 5SiO_2 \cdot H_2O$	The HCl solution separates flaky silica.
1.625	PREHNITE	$2CaO \cdot Al_2O_3 \cdot 3SiO_2 \cdot H_2O$	Brittle. In C.T., yields water.
1.545	HYALOPHANE	$(K_2,Ba)O \cdot 2Al_2O_3 \cdot 8SiO_2$	Brittle. B.B., yields a blebby mass.
1.584	ANORTHITE	$CaO \cdot Al_2O_3 \cdot 2SiO_2$	Brittle. B.B., a colorless glass.
1.55±	SCAPOLITE	A tetragonal group of Ca,Na,Al,SiO_2	
1.62	TURQUOIS	$CuO \cdot 3Al_2O_3 \cdot 2P_2O_5 \cdot 9H_2O$	In C.T., decrepitates, yields water and turns brown or black.
1.592	CATAPLEIITE	$(Na_2,Ca)O \cdot ZrO_2 \cdot 3SiO_2 \cdot 2H_2O$	Brittle. In C.T., yields water.
1.62±	SARCOLITE	$3CaO \cdot Al_2O_3 \cdot 3SiO_2 \cdot$ and Na	B.B., gives a white enamel.
1.559	ANEMOUSITE	$Na_2O \cdot 2CaO \cdot 3Al_2O_3 \cdot 9SiO_2$	One of the feldspar group.
1.549	CHKALOVITE	$Na_2Be(SiO_3)_2$	B.B., a clear bead. Semitransparent. From Kola peninsula.
1.572	BYTOWNITE	$AbAn_4$	Feldspar group.
1.642	FERRIPREHNITE	$2CaO \cdot (Al,Fe)_2O_3 \cdot 3SiO_2 \cdot H_2O$	Like prehnite.
1.691	GEHLENITE	$3CaO \cdot Al_2O_3 \cdot 2SiO_2$	B.B., fuses slowly with borax to a glass colored by iron.
1.558	BERYLLONITE	$NaBe(PO_4)$	Brittle. Colors flame yellow with green streaks on lower edge
1.607	MEIONITE	$4CaO \cdot 3Al_2O_3 \cdot 6SiO_2$	Brittle. A scapolite.
1.563	LABORADORITE	$(Ca,Na)_2O \cdot Al_2O_3 \cdot 3SiO_2$	Often a beautiful play of colors on the cleavage plane.

GROUP 9
Specific Gravity 2.99-2.66

	H	SP. GR.	F	HCL	COLOR	STREAK	LUSTER	CLEAV-AGE	FRACTURE	
29	5-6	2.86-2.85	Diff	Sol in HNO₃	Pale rose red, colorless	....	V	Dist	Uneven	N
30	5-6	2.73-2.66	3	Pt sol	White, reddish, bluish, grnsh, etc	Uncolored	R, V, P	Good	Subconch	
31	5-6	3.4-2.6	2-4	Ins	Black, white, green	Uncolored	V to P	Perf	Subconch to uneven	
32	5-6	2.69-2.68	4-4.5	Pt sol	White, gray, red, greenish, yellow	....	Sv, P	Perf	....	
33	5.5	2.72	......	....	White	....	....	Good	Fibrous	M
34	5.5	2.94	Inf	Ins	Colorless	....	....	Poor	....	T
35	5.5	2.83	......	....	Colorless	....	....	....	Fibrous	M
36	5.5	2.98			White		A		....	A
37	5.5]	2.69	Diff	Gelat	White	....	S	....	Fibrous	C
38	5.5	2.89	......	....	White	....	....	....	Fibrous	M
39	5-5.5	3.07-2.98	4	Sol	Colorless, yellow, red, green	White	V	Imperf	Uneven to splintery	N
40	5-5.5	2.80-2.78	......	....	White, yellowish, brownish	....	....	....	....	
41	5-5.5	3.0-2.9	2	Gelat	White, gray, green, yellow, red	White	V	....	Conch to uneven	M
42	5-5.5	2.93	3.5	Ins	Straw to wax yellow	....	S	....	Brittle	M
43	5-5.5	3.01-2.91	2.5	Gelat	Pale pink, red, brown	Uncolored	V	Perf	Subconch, splintery	N
44	5-5.5	3.13-2.97	......	....	Light red to brown	....	V	Perf	Uneven	T
45	5±	2.75-2.5	Easy	Insol	Red, blue, green, colorless, etc	....	V	None	Conch	A
46	4-5.5	4.3-2.7	Inf	Sol	Brown to nearly black, yellow	Ylwsh brwn to rdsh	S, Sm, E	....	Conch to uneven	
47	5.	3.15-2.97	4-5	Ins	Colorless	....	V	Perf	Conch	T
48	5.	3.1-2.9	4	Ins	Colorless, white, gray	Uncolored	V to P	Perf	Subconch to uneven	
49	5.	3.1-2.9	3	Gelat	White, yellow, brown, reddish	....	V to R	Dist	Conch to uneven	T
50	5	3.01-2.99	Diff	Sol	Yellowish to greenish	....	V, Sr	Poor	Subconch	C
51	5.	2.94	6	Sol	Ash gray, brown	White	V, D	Dist	Uneven	C
52	5.	2.76-2.68	2	Pt sol	Whitish, grayish	....	S, Sv	Perf	Uneven	
53	5.	2.97	......	....	Brownish	....	....	....	....	
54	5.	2.70-2.55	Inf	Ins	Milk white to light blue	....	....	....	....	
55	5	2.92	2.5	....	Colorless, yellow	....	....	Perf	....	M
56	5.	2.95	......	....	Gray, colorless	....	....	Perf	....	M

300

GROUP 9
Specific Gravity 2.99-2.66

INDEX OF REF.	NAME	COMPOSITION	REMARKS
1.595	CUSPIDINE	$3CaO \cdot CaF_2 \cdot 2SiO_2$	Brittle. From Vesuvius.
1.567	**WERNERITE**	**Ca,Al silicate**	**Brittle. A scapolite.**
1.70	**AMPHIBOLE**	$R''O \cdot SiO_2 \cdot R_2'''O_3 \cdot$ $2SiO_2 \cdot (Na_2,K_2,H_2)O$	**B.B., varies with different members of the group.**
1.553	**ANDESINE**	$(Na_2,Ca)O \cdot Al_2O_3 \cdot$ $4SiO_2$	**One of the feldspars.**
1.585	BAVENITE	$BeO \cdot 4CaO \cdot Al_2O_3 \cdot$ $9SiO_2 \cdot H_2O$	A zeolite.
1.647	AMINOFFITE	$Ca_{24}Be_9Al_3Si_{24}O_{84}$ $(OH)_3 \cdot 12H_2O$	
1.598	MILLISITE	$2CaO \cdot Na_2O \cdot 6Al_2O_3 \cdot$ $4P_2O_5 \cdot 17H_2O$	
....	WELDITE	SiO_2 of Al and Na	
1.610	HILLEBRANDITE	$2CaO \cdot SiO_2 \cdot H_2O$	B.B., gives a colorless glass bead and calcium flame.
1.616	LEHIITE	$5CaO \cdot Na_2O \cdot 4P_2O_5 \cdot$ $4Al_2O_3 \cdot 12H_2O$	
1.570	WAGNERITE	$Mg_3(PO_4)_2 \cdot MgF_2$	B.B., a greenish-gray glass; with H_2SO_4, flame is bluish-green.
....	HARBORTITE	$6Al_2O_3 \cdot 4P_2O_5 \cdot 17H_2O$	
1.654	**DATOLITE**	$2CaO \cdot B_2O_3 \cdot 2SiO_2 \cdot$ H_2O	**In C.T., yields much water.**
1.628	CARPHOLITE	$MnO \cdot Al_2O_3 \cdot 2SiO_2 \cdot$ $2H_2O$	In C.T., gives acid water.
1.606	EUDIALYTE	$Na_2O \cdot Ce_2O_3 \cdot FeO \cdot$ $MnO \cdot Zr_2O_3 \cdot SiO_2$	Brittle. Reacts for zirconium.
1.636	SCHIZOLITE	$Na_2O \cdot 4(Ca,Mn)O \cdot$ $6SiO_2 \cdot H_2O$	
1.52±	**GLASS**	$Na_2O \cdot CaO \cdot 6SiO_2 +$ Fe,K,Ba,B,Pb,etc	**Not a mineral but often mistaken for one. Very common.**
2.06±	**LIMONITE**	$HFeO_2 \cdot nH_2O$	**Usually in stalactitic, botryoidal or mammillary form.**
1.378	SELLAITE	MgF_2	Treated with H_2SO_4, it yields HF and etches the glass.
1.616	**TREMOLITE**	$2CaO \cdot 5MgO \cdot 8SiO_2 \cdot$ H_2O	**One of the amphiboles.**
1.632	MELILITE	$Na_2O \cdot 11(Ca,Mg)O \cdot$ $2(Al,Fe)_2O_3 \cdot 9SiO_2$	Fuses to a greenish or yellowish glass.
1.612	HERDERITE	$CaO \cdot 2BeO \cdot P_2O_5 \cdot$ $Ca(F,OH)_2$	B.B., phosphoresces with an orange light.
1.674	SPODIOSITE	$Ca_3(PO_4)_2 \cdot CaF_2$	Brittle. Fuses to a white enamel.
1.604	**PECTOLITE**	$Na_2O \cdot 4CaO \cdot 6SiO_2 \cdot$ H_2O	**In C.T., gives H_2O. Often gives light when broken in the dark.**
1.605	GRODNOLITE	$8CaO \cdot 2P_2O_5 \cdot CO_2 \cdot$ $H_2O + \frac{1}{4}H_4Al_2Si_2O_9$	Probably identical with collophanite. Collophanite group.
1.580	COERULEO-LACTITE	$3Al_2O_3 \cdot 2P_2O_5 \cdot$ $10H_2O$	Fibrous crusts.
1.622	PSEUDO-WAVELLITE	$5CaO \cdot 6Al_2O_3 \cdot 4P_2O_5 \cdot$ $18H_2O$	
1.630	DELTAITE	$8CaO \cdot 5Al_2O_3 \cdot 4P_2O_5 \cdot$ $14H_2O$	

GROUP 9
Specific Gravity 2.99–2.66

	H	SP. GR.	F	HCL	COLOR	STREAK	LUSTER	CLEAV-AGE	FRACTURE	S T
57	5	2.70	Inf	Pt sol	Colorless, pale red	....	P	Perf	....	N
58	5	2.91	Diff	Gelat	Greenish-gray	....	G to V	Good	Brittle	N
59	5	2.96	5	....	White, greenish-gray	....	....	....	....	C
60	5	2.71	2	....	Colorless, clear	....	V	Perf	....	N
61	5	2.71	2	....	Clear, colorless	....	V	Good	....	T
62	5	2.79	3	Ins	Light apple green	....		Perf	....	N
63	5	2.87	3	Pt sol	Light grn, bluish green, colorless	White	V	Perf	....	T
64	5?	2.92	1	Sol	Light brown	....		Poor	Even	C
65	**4.5-5**	**2.9-2.8**	**4**	**Dcpd**	**White, gray, red, yellow, brown**	**White**	**V, P**	**Perf**	**Uneven**	
66	4.5-5	2.77	......	Gelat	Colorless	....	V	Perf	....	N
67	4-5	2.71	Diff	Ins	Dark gray	....		Fair	....	T
68	4.5	2.89	Inf	....	Colorless, white, grayish	....	V	Dist	Uneven	N
69	4.5	2.71-2.69	5	Gelat	White, gray, pink	....	V	Perf	Subconch to uneven	
70	4.5	2.85	......	....	Colorless	....		Perf	Fibrous	
71	4.5	2.73	Inf	Sol	Pink	....	V	Fair	Conch	
72	4.5	2.92	Inf	....	Brown	....		Perf	....	
73	4.5	2.9-2.7	Fus	Sol	White	....				
74	4.5	2.88	Easy	....	Colorless to pale red	....		Good	....	C
75	4.5	2.95	Easy	Ins	Colorless, white	....		Perf	....	
76	4-4.5	2.84	3	Gelat	Brown	....	V	Perf	....	
77	4	2.96	3	Ins	Green to pale yellow	....	V	Perf	Conch	
78	4	3.03-2.93	2.5-3	Dcpd	Reddish brown	Pale ylw or grayish brwn	V, G, R	Dist	....	
79	4	2.88	......	....	Yellow buff	....		Dist	....	
80	4	2.68-2.61	......	....	Black	....				
81	4	2.69	Fus	Sol	Colorless	....				
82	4	2.94	Easy	Ins	Wine red, white	....		Perf	....	
83	4	2.75	2	Sol	White	....	S		Fibrous	
84	**3.5-4.5**	**3.08-2.99**	**Diff**	**Pt sol**	**Gray, rdsh, pink, white, yellowish**	....	**P, V**	**Perf**	**Brittle**	
85	3.75	2.76	2.5-3	Sol	Pinkish red	....		Perf	....	
86	3.75	2.87	2.5-3	Sol	Pinkish red	Yellowish white	V	Poor	....	

302

GROUP 9
Specific Gravity 2.99-2.66

INDEX OF REF.	NAME	COMPOSITION	REMARKS
1.576	AUGELITE	$2Al_2O_3 \cdot P_2O_5 \cdot 3H_2O$	In C.T., yields water.
1.590	CUSTERITE	$3CaO \cdot CaF_2 \cdot 2SiO_2 \cdot H_2O$	In C.T., phosphoresces with a yellow light.
1.60	CEBOLLITE	$5(Ca,Mg)O \cdot Al_2O_3 \cdot 3SiO_2 \cdot 2H_2O$	In C.T., gives water. In fibrous aggregates.
1.636	HILGARDITE	$Ca_8(B_6O_{11})_3Cl_4 \cdot 4H_2O$	In C.T., gives acid water. B.B. on coal, a white globule.
1.636	PARAHILGARDITE	$2[Ca_8(B_6O_{11})_3Cl_4] \cdot 4H_2O$	Very close to hilgardite.
1.63±	MARIPOSITE	Chromiferous mica	A member of the mica group.
1.590	WARDITE (SOUMANSITE)	$2Na_2O \cdot CaO \cdot 6Al_2O_3 \cdot 4P_2O_5 \cdot 17H_2O$	B.B., swells up and colors flame intensely yellow.
1.660	ROWEITE	$H_2MnCa(BO_3)_2$	Brittle. Lath-like crystals. B.B., a black glass; green flame.
1.632	**WOLLASTONITE**	**$CaSiO_3$**	**Brittle. B.B., with soda, a blebby mass, with more swells and is infusible.**
1.606	SCAWTITE	$4CaO \cdot 3SiO_2 \cdot 2CO_2$	With HCl, it effervesces leaving a gelatinous residue.
1.501	DIDYMOLITE	$2CaO \cdot 3Al_2O_3 \cdot 9SiO_2$	B.B., gives a white slag.
1.503	PROSOPITE	$CaF_2 \cdot 2Al_2(OH,F)_3$	Brittle. In C.T., yields H_2O and SiF_4. Soluble in H_2SO_4.
1.549	EDINGTONITE	$BaO \cdot Al_2O_3 \cdot 3SiO_2 \cdot 3H_2O$	B.B., yields water and becomes opaque.
1.601	DENNISONITE	$6CaO \cdot Al_2O_3 \cdot 2P_2O_5 \cdot 5H_2O$	
1.590	BULFONTEINITE	$Ca_2SiO_2 \cdot (OH,F)_4$	In C.T., a little H_2O. B.B., the needles become white and enamel-like.
1.639	ROSCHERITE	$2FeO \cdot 3MnO \cdot 3CaO \cdot 2Al_2O_3 \cdot 4P_2O_5 \cdot 10H_2O$	
1.64	BAKERITE	$8CaO \cdot 5B_2O_3 \cdot 6SiO_2 \cdot 6H_2O$	Fuses to a white transparent bead coloring flame green.
....	VALLEITE	$(Fe,Mg,Mn,Ca,K_2)O \cdot SiO_2$	Fuses to a white opaque bead.
1.561	JEZEKITE	$CaO \cdot Al_2O_3 \cdot 2(Na,Li)F \cdot P_2O_5 \cdot 2(Na,Li)(OH)$	
1.603	GANOPHYLLITE	$7MnO \cdot Al_2O_3 \cdot 8SiO_2 \cdot 6H_2O$	Resembles mica. Reacts for Mn.
1.595	LEUCOPHANITE	$NaF \cdot CaO \cdot B_2O_3 \cdot 2SiO_2$	Brittle. In C.T., whitens and phosphoresces with a bluish light.
1.649	MOSANDRITE	$CaO \cdot (Ti,Si)O_2 \cdot Zr,Ce,Na,etc.$	Treated with HCl, and heated, it gives off chlorine.
1.66	SALMONSITE	$Fe_2O_3 \cdot 9MnO \cdot 4P_2O_5 \cdot 14H_2O$	
....	BONDSDORFFITE	$K_2(Mg,Fe)_2Al_8(SiO_2)_7 \cdot 7H_2O$	
1.488	VANTHOFFITE	$3Na_2O \cdot MgO \cdot 4SO_3$	Soluble in water.
1.562	MORINITE	$3Al_2O_3 \cdot 2Na_2O \cdot 4P_2O_5 \cdot 6CaF_2 \cdot 18H_2O$	In C.T., yields acid water that etches the glass.
1.576	JURUPAITE	$7CaO \cdot MgO \cdot 8SiO_2 \cdot 4H_2O$	Fibers are soft and silky without brittleness but across them the hardness is 4. From Crestmore quarries.
1.643	**MARGARITE**	**$CaO \cdot 2Al_2O_3 \cdot 2SiO_2 \cdot H_2O$**	**In C.T., yields water.**
1.725	PHOSPHO-SIDERITE	$4FePO_4 \cdot 7H_2O$	Gives off water and becomes opaque. Fuses to a black magnetic bead.
1.72±	STRENGITE	$FePO_4 \cdot 2H_2O$	B.B., a shiny black bead. Colors flame bluish-green.

GROUP 9
Specific Gravity 2.99-2.66

	H	SP. GR.	F	HCL	COLOR	STREAK	LUSTER	CLEAV-AGE	FRACTURE	SY TY
87	3.5-4	3.1-2.95	Inf	Sol	White, gray, reddish	....	V, P	Poor	....	R
88	3.5-4	2.99-2.93	Inf	Sol	Colorless, white, and colored	Uncolored	V, R	Dist	Subconch	O
89	3.5-4	2.99-2.84	1.5	....	White	....	V	Perf		T
90	3.5-4	2.9-2.8	Inf	Sol	White, colored and black	....	V, P	Perf	Subconch	R
91	3.5-4	2.75-2.58	Inf	....	White, grayish, reddish	White	V, P	Dist	Conch to uneven	R
92	3-4	2.8-2.64	4-6	Dcpd	Brown to black	Same	D	....	Conch	.
93	3-4	2.86-2.81	2	Sol	Colorless	....	G to V	....	Conch	I
94	3-4	2.83	......	....	Dark brown	Yellow	V to G	....	Subconch	.
95	3-4	2.76	6	....	Reddish brown	Pale red		Perf	....	M
96	3-4	2.79	1?	Sol	Green, brown, black	Grayish green	R	None	Conch	I
97	3-4	2.80	......	Ins	Grysh, bluish, wht, ylwsh grn	....	S, D	Pris-matic	....	.
98	2.5-4	2.9-2.8	2.5	Pt sol	Purple, rose red, ylwsh, grayish, wht	....	P	Perf	....	M
99	3.5	2.77	4.5	Dcpd	Black, greenish, yellowish, bronze	....	P, V	Perf	....	M
100	3.5	2.84	Easy	Sol in HNO₃	Reddish brown	....		Perf	....	C
101	3.5	2.75	3	....	Pale yellowish white	....	V	Dist	Uneven	T
102	3.5	2.96	......	....	Pale green	....		Good	....	N
103	3.5	2.70	3-4	Sol	Reddish brown	Same	W	None	Conch	C
104	3.5	2.75	......	....	White	....				
105	3.5	2.79	......	Sol	Carmine red	....		Perf	....	
106	3.5	2.89	......	....	White	....		Perf	....	
107	3.5	2.74	5-6	....	Colorless, green, yellowish	....	P	Perf	....	
108	3.5	2.83	......	Sol	Greenish white	....		Perf	....	
109	3.5	2.95	3	Sol	Light brown	....	S	Good	....	
110	3.5	2.73	Diff	Sol	Colorless	....		Perf	....	
111	3.5	2.95	......	Sol	Emerald green	....				
112	3.5	2.8	......	....	....	....				
113	3.5	2.78	3.5	Ins	Greenish yellow	Grayish white	V to P	None	....	
114	3-3.5	2.98-2.90	3	Sol	White, bluish, brick red	Grayish white	P	Perf	Uneven	
115	3-3.5	2.89	......	....	Leek green	....	P	Perf	Micaceous	
116	3-3.5	2.91-2.83	3.5	Dcpd	Pale yellow, brown	....	P	Perf	....	
117	3-3.5	2.66-2.63	1.5	Sol	White tinged with blue or green	....	V, R	Fair	....	

GROUP 9
Specific Gravity 2.99-2.66

INDEX OF REF.	NAME	COMPOSITION	REMARKS
1.72±	ANKERITE	$2CaCO_3 \cdot MgCO_3 \cdot FeCO_3$	On coal, becomes dark and magnetic.
1.680	ARAGONITE	$CaCO_3$	Brittle. B.B., whitens and falls to pieces. The powdered mineral boiled with cobalt nitrate solution turns violet.
1.349	CHIOLITE	$5NaF \cdot 3AlF_3$	In O.T., gives acid water and HF. Soluble in H_2SO_4.
1.681	DOLOMITE	$CaCO_3 \cdot MgCO_3$	Brittle. Acted on only slowly by HCl in the cold.
1.572	ALUNITE	$K_2O \cdot 3Al_2O_3 \cdot 4SO_3 \cdot 6H_2O$	Brittle. Soluble in H_2SO_4. In C.T., yields water.
1.50±	NEOTOCITE	$(Mn,Fe)O \cdot SiO_2 \cdot H_2O$	In C.T., yields much water.
1.533	LANGBEINITE	$K_2O \cdot MgO \cdot 3SO_3$	Dissolves slowly in water.
1.64	PICITE	$3Fe_2O_3 \cdot 2P_2O_5 \cdot 10H_2O$	
1.598	MANGANO-PHYLLITE	$K_2O \cdot 6(Mg,Mn)O \cdot (Al,Fe,Mn)_2O_3 \cdot 6SiO_2 \cdot 2H_2O$	A member of the mica group.
1.602	VOLTAITE	$15H_2O \cdot 2(Al,Fe)_2O_3 \cdot 5(Mg,Fe)O \cdot 10SiO_2$	Difficultly soluble in water.
1.57	SHILKINITE	$K_2O \cdot 4Al_2O_3 \cdot 8SiO_2 \cdot 4H_2O$	
1.555	LEPIDOLITE	$(K,Li)_2O \cdot Al_2O_3 \cdot 3SiO_2$ with F	In B.T., gives water and reacts for fluorine. A mica.
1.73±	STILPNOMELANE	SiO_2 of Fe,Mg,Al	In C.T., much water. Fuses to a black shining magnetic globule.
1.725	BERMANITE	Mn,Fe,Mg,P_2O_5	Occurs in minute tabular crystals. B.B., on coal, first swells and separates into scales then fuses into a globule.
1.614	MONETITE	$CaHPO_4$	Brittle. In C.T., gives water.
1.348	WEBERITE	Na_2MgAlF_7	Small grains in cryolite.
1.64±	BORICKITE	Hydrated Ca and Fe phosphate.	In C.T., yields water.
....	CALAFATITE	$Al_2(SO_4)_3 \cdot K_2SO_4 \cdot Al(OH)_3 \cdot H_2O$	
1.328	VILLIAUMITE	NaF	Soluble in water.
1.566	FLUOBORITE	$6MgO \cdot B_2O_3 \cdot 3(H_2O,F_2)$	Soluble in H_2SO_4.
1.575	LEUCHTEN-BERGITE	$12MgO \cdot 3Al_2O_3 \cdot 7SiO_2 \cdot 10H_2O$	Resembles talc. Soluble in H_2SO_4.
1.613	ANAPIÄTE	$2CaO \cdot FeO \cdot P_2O_5 \cdot 4H_2O$	
1.642	COLLINSITE	$2CaO \cdot (Mg,Fe)O \cdot P_2O_5 \cdot 2\frac{1}{2}H_2O$	
1.478	CREEDITE	$CaO \cdot 2Al(F,OH)_3 \cdot 2CaF_2 \cdot SO_3 \cdot 2H_2O$	
1.695	KEMPITE	$MnCl_2 \cdot 3MnO_2 \cdot 3H_2O$	Treated with HCl, it yields chlorine.
....	KRUGITE	$K_2SO_4 \cdot 4CaSO_4 \cdot MgSO_4 \cdot 2H_2O$	Partly soluble in cold water and partly in hot water.
1.594	ASTROLITE	$(Na,K)_2O \cdot (Al,Fe)_2O_3 \cdot FeO \cdot 5SiO_2 \cdot H_2O$	B.B., fuses to a gray enamel.
1.575	ANHYDRITE	$CaSO_4$	On coal with soda, it reduces to a sulfide.
....	VIRIDITE	$4FeO \cdot 2SiO_2 \cdot 3H_2O$	An iron chlorite.
1.64+	CARYOPILITE	$4MnO \cdot 3SiO_2 \cdot 3H_2O$	Reacts for manganese.
1.487	APHTHITALITE	$(Na,K)_2SO_4$	Soluble in water. Tastes bitter.

GROUP 9
Specific Gravity 2.99-2.66

	H	SP. GR.	F	HCL	COLOR	STREAK	LUSTER	CLEAV-AGE	FRACTURE	
118	3-3.5	2.69-2.57	Inf	Sol	Emerald green	Paler	V	....	Conch	
119	2.5-3.5	2.78	......	....	....	....	....	Micace-ous	....	
120	3	3.1-2.5	Diff	Dcpd	Black, brownish black	Yellowish brown	G, V	....	Conch	
121	3	2.95	......	....	Pale blue	....	....	None	....	
122	3	3.0-2.93	1.5	....	White, colorless	....	V	Indist	Uneven	
123	3	2.83	3	Sol	Straw yellow, buff	....	....	....	....	
124	3	2.72-2.71	Inf	Sol	White, blue, varied	Same, grayish	....	Perf	Conch	
125	3	2.8-2.7	......	....	White, yellowish, brownish	....	....	Perf	....	
126	3	2.76	Easy	Gelat	Colorless, white	....	P	Perf	....	
127	3	2.84	3	Ins	Copper red, purple	....	P, V	Perf	....	
128	3	2.92	......	Pt sol	White	....	....	....	....	
129	3	2.75	......	....	Violet	White	....	....	....	
130	3	2.94-2.92	3?	Pt sol	Green, brown	....	P	Perf	....	
131	2.5-4	2.9-2.8	2.5	Pt sol	Purple, rose-red, ylwsh, gray, wht	....	P	Perf	....	
132	2.5-3	3.2-2.82	2.5-3	....	Brown, yellow, violet, gray	....	P	Perf	Flexible	
133	2.5-3	3.1-2.7	6	....	Brown, black, green	Uncolored	P, V, Sm	Perf	....	
134	2.5-3	2.9-2.78	Diff	Ins	White, yellowish, green, grayish	....	P	Perf	....	
135	2.5-3	2.85-2.76	5	Sol	Grayish, brown	White	V, P	Perf	Uneven	
136	2.5-3	2.78	Easy	Sol	Gray, colorless	....	V	Dist	Uneven	
137	2.5-3	2.85-2.78	6	....	Brown, green, white	....	P	Perf	Elastic	
138	2.5-3	2.85-2.7	1.5	Sol	Colorless, yellow, gray, red	White	V	Perf	Conch	
139	2.5-3	2.78-2.77	1.5	Sol	Flesh red, yellow	Red	R, P	Good	....	
140	2.5-3	2.67-2.60	Inf	Sol	White, pink, yellowish	....	D, P	Perf	....	
141	2.5-3	2.86	Easy	Sol	Colorless, tinged blue	....	....	Perf	....	
142	2.5-3	2.82?	......	Sol	Purplish, blue, black to brown	Yellowish, same	....	....	Conch	
143	2-3	2.78-2.70	Inf	Sol	White	....	V	Traces	....	
144	2-3	2.84	Inf	....	Violet	Cherry red	M	Perf	Brittle	
145	2-3	2.69-2.68	1.5-2	Sol	White, brown	....	V	Dist	Uneven	

GROUP 9
Specific Gravity 2.99-2.66

INDEX OF REF.	NAME	COMPOSITION	REMARKS
1.59+	ZARATITE	$NiCO_3 \cdot 2Ni(OH)_2 \cdot 4H_2O$	In C.T., yields H_2O and CO_2 and leaves a grayish-black magnetic mass.
1.582	HYDROBIOTITE	$2K_2O \cdot 10MgO \cdot 3Al_2O_3 \cdot 12SiO_2 \cdot 6H_2O$	A member of the mica group.
1.57+	HISINGERITE	Hydrated ferric silicate	In C.T., yields H_2O. B.B., fuses to a black magnetic slag.
1.587	LEIGHTONITE	$CuO \cdot 2CaO \cdot K_2O \cdot 4SO_3 \cdot 2H_2O$	Slender laths and blades. From Chile.
1.413	PACHNOLITE	$NaF \cdot CaF_2 \cdot AlF_3 \cdot H_2O$	Reacts for fluorine.
1.660	MAGNESIO-SUSSEXITE	$2(Mg,Mn)O \cdot B_2O_3 \cdot H_2O$	
1.658	**CALCITE**	$CaCO_3$	**Clear crystals (Iceland spar) are strongly doubly refractive.**
1.669	PLUMBOCALCITE	$(Ca,Pb)O \cdot CO_2$	Calcite in which lead replaces a portion of the calcium.
1.565	ZEOPHYLLITE	$3CaO \cdot CaF_2 \cdot 3SiO_2 \cdot H_2O$	A zeolite.
1.594	ALURGITE	$6(H,K)_2O \cdot 2(Mg,Mn)O \cdot 3Al_2O_3 \cdot 12SiO_2$	Similar in cleavage to mica.
1.547	FLUOBORITE	$6MgO \cdot B_2O_3 \cdot 3(F_2,H_2O)$	
1.74	VILATEITE	$Mn_2O_3 \cdot P_2O_5 \cdot 4H_2O$?	
1.685	**ROSCOELITE**	$4H_2O \cdot 2K_2O \cdot 2(Mg,Fe)O \cdot 2Al_2O_3 \cdot 3V_2O_3 \cdot 10SiO_2$	**B.B., fuses to a black glass.**
1.555	**LEPIDOLITE**	$(Li,K)_2O \cdot Al_2O_3 \cdot 3SiO_2 \cdot$ with **F**	**In C.T., gives water and reacts for fluorine.**
1.578	ZINNWALDITE	$(K,Li)_2O \cdot 2FeO \cdot F_2 \cdot 2Al_2O_3 \cdot 6SiO_2 \cdot H_2O$	In C. T., gives water and reacts for fluorine.
1.64±	**BIOTITE**	$(H,K)_2O \cdot 2(Mg,Fe)O \cdot (Al,Fe)_2O_3 \cdot 3SiO_2$	**One of the common micas. Black mica. Decomposed by** H_2SO_4**.**
1.60	PARAGONITE	$Na_2O \cdot 3Al_2O_3 \cdot 3SiO_2 \cdot 2H_2O$	One of the micas.
1.585±	HOPEITE	$Zn_3(PO_4)_2 \cdot H_2O$	Brittle. In C.T., gives off water.
1.339	CRYO-LITHIONITE	$3NaF \cdot 3LiF \cdot 2AlF_3 \cdot 2K_2O \cdot 10(Mg,Fe)O$	In C.T., decrepitates violently, fuses to a colorless liquid.
1.598±	**PHLOGOPITE**	$3Al_2O_3 \cdot 12SiO_2 \cdot 3H_2O$	**In C.T., a little water. Dcpd by** H_2SO_4**. One of the micas.**
1.535	**GLAUBERITE**	$Na_2SO_4 \cdot CaSO_4$	**B.B., decrepitates, turns white, fuses to a white enamel.**
1.560	**POLYHALITE**	$K_2SO_4 \cdot 2CaSO_4 \cdot MgSO_4 \cdot 2H_2O$	**In C. T., gives water. Partially soluble in water.**
1.587	LANTHANITE	$La(CO_3)_2 \cdot 9H_2O$	In C.T., yields water.
....	TAENIOLITE	$(K,Li)_2O \cdot MgO \cdot 3SiO_2 \cdot 2H_2O$	B.B., a colorless blebby mass. Colors flame intensely red.
....	CORVUSITE	$V_2V_{12}D_{34} \cdot nH_2O$	
1.583	ALUMIAN	$Al_2O_3 \cdot 2SO_3$	B.B., yields a fine blue color with cobalt solution.
1.765	MURMANITE	$2Na_2O \cdot (Fe,Mg,Ca)O \cdot 4SiO_2 \cdot 4(Ti,Zr)O_2 \cdot 4H_2O$	Soluble in HSO_4.
1.477	**THENARDITE**	Na_2SO_4	**Brittle. Soluble in water**

GROUP 9
Specific Gravity 2.99-2.66

H	SP. GR.	F	HCL	COLOR	STREAK	LUSTER	CLEAV-AGE	FRACTURE
146 2-3	2.77	Inf	Dcpd	Pale bluish green	....	P	Porf	Flexible
147 2-3	2.8	Easy	....	Black, brownish	....	V, P	....	Conch
148 2.5	2.85	Inf	Dcpd	Reddish brown	....	Bronze	Perf	....
149 2.5	**3.0-2.95**	**2**	**Ins**	**White, reddish, brownish**	....	**V, G**	**Parting**	**Uneven**
150 2.5	2.81	......	....	Deep blue	....		Perf	Flexible
151 2.5	3.0-2.9	1.5-2	Sol	Yellow, green, brown	Green, brown, yellow, pale	A to G	Imperf	Uneven
152 2.5	**2.67±**	......	H₂SO₄	**White**	....		**Micro**	....
153 2.5	2.96	Inf	Dcpd	Pale indigo, green	Bluish white	P, V	Perf	Uneven
154 2.5	2.86	5	Ins	Green	....		Micro	
155 2.5	2.90	Diff	....	Green	....	P	Perf	Flexible
156 2.5	2.89	Diff	Sol	Olive to blackish green	Gray to green	....	Mic	....
157 2.5	2.68	Diff	....	White, pink, yellowish green	....	P	Perf	....
158 2.5	2.68	......	....	Green			Perf	....
159 2.5	2.72	......	....	Chestnut brown	....	....	Perf	Brittle
160 2.5	2.84	Inf	Sol	Yellowish green	White	V	Perf	Brittle
161 2.5	2.91	Easy	Sol	Ash gray, greenish blue	....	S	....	....
162 2-2.5	**3.0-2.76**	**5**	**Ins**	**Green, brown, yellow, colorless, etc.**	**Uncolored**	**V, S, P**	**Perf**	**Flexible and elastic**
163 2-2.5	2.93-2.79	Easy	Sol	Green, black	....	....	Perf	....
164 2-2.5	**2.78-2.65**	**5-5.5**	**Pt sol**	**Violet, green, red, yellowish**	**Greenish white, uncolored**	**P**	**Perf**	**Flexible**
165 2-2.5	**2.85-2.60**	**5-5.5**	**Pt sol**	**Green, red, violet, yellow, white**	....	**P, V**	**Perf**	**Flexible**
166 2-2.5	2.73-2.64	2.5	Sol	White, grayish, red tinge	White	V, P	Perf	Uneven
167 2-2.5	**2.70**	**4.5-5**	**Sol**	**White**	....	**D**	....	**Conch**
168 2-2.5	2.98-2.88	3-3.5	Sol in HNO₃	Blue to green	Same	V, R	Indist	Subconch to uneven
169 2-2.5	3.24-2.47	......	Sol	Pale, deep green		P	Perf	....
170 2	3.11-2.96	Inf	Sol	Apple green	....	P, S	Perf	....
171 2	2.69	......	....	White	....	....	Perf	....
172 2	3.0-2.93	1.5	....	Colorless, white, reddish, brown	....	V to P	Perf	Uneven
173 2	2.66-2.4	2-2.5	....	Deep emerald green	Paler	P, V, Sa	Perf	....

GROUP 9
Specific Gravity 2.99-2.66

INDEX OF REF.	NAME	COMPOSITION	REMARKS
1.597	AMESITE	$2(Mg,Fe)O \cdot Al_2O_3 \cdot SiO_2 \cdot 2H_2O$	A member of the chlorite group.
....	YUKONITE	Hydrous arsenate of Fe and Ca	Brittle. Decrepitates when immersed in water.
1.65+	IDDINGSITE	$MgO \cdot Fe_2O_3 \cdot 3SiO_2 \cdot 4H_2O$	Has a lamellar structure.
1.339	**CRYOLITE**	**$3NaF \cdot AlF_3$**	**Treated with H_2SO_4, it gives off HF etching the glass.**
1.692	BANDYLITE	$CuB_2O_4 \cdot CuCl_2 \cdot 4H_2O$	Occurs in thick tabular crystals. The water solution leaves a residue of copper borate.
1.68±	PHARMACO-SIDERITE	$3FeAsO_4 \cdot Fe(OH)_3 \cdot 6H_2O$	In C.T., yields neutral water and turns yellow.
1.581	**CHLORITE**	**$9MgO \cdot 3Al_2O_3 \cdot 5SiO_2 \cdot 8H_2O$**	**Pearly on cleavages. A member of the chlorite group.**
1.668	SYMPLESITE	$Fe_3(AsO_4)_2 \cdot 8H_2O$	In C.T., much water. Colors outer flame light blue.
1.594	FUCHSITE	Chromium mica	Mica group. Near muscovite.
1.607	CORUNDO-PHILITE	$H_{20}Mg_{11}Al_8Si_6O_{45}$	A member of the chlorite group. Decomposed by H_2SO_4.
1.619	DELESSITE	$4(Mg,Fe)O \cdot 2Al_2O_3 \cdot 4SiO_2 \cdot 5H_2O$	In C.T., yields water and becomes brown.
1.579	COOKEITE	$(Li,Na)_2O \cdot 3Al_2O_3 \cdot 4SiO_2 \cdot 6H_2O$	B.B., fuses and exfoliates.
1.580	SHERIDANITE	$9MgO \cdot 3Al_2O_3 \cdot 5SiO_2 \cdot 8H_2O$	A member of the chlorite group.
1.63	GUILDITE	$2(Fe,Al)_2O_3 \cdot 7SO_3 \cdot 3(Cu,Fe)O \cdot 17H_2O$	
1.650	KRAUSITE	$K_2O \cdot Fe_2O_3 \cdot 4SO_3 \cdot 2H_2O$	In C.T., decrepitates; gets yellow then brown; melts. B.B., yields a black scoria.
....	SILICOMAGNESIO-FLUORITE	$H_2Ca_4Mg_3Si_2O_7F_{10}$	In C.T., yields water. B.B., gives a clouded greenish glass.
1.59+	**MUSCOVITE**	**$K_2O \cdot 3Al_2O_3 \cdot 6SiO_2 \cdot 2H_2O$**	**One of the common micas.**
1.595	DIABANTITE	$12(Mg,Fe)O \cdot 2Al_2O_3 \cdot 9SiO_2 \cdot 9H_2O$	Fuses to a dark gray somewhat magnetic glass.
1.58±	**CLINOCHLORE**	**$5(Mg,Fe)O \cdot Al_2O_3 \cdot 3SiO_2 \cdot 4H_2O$**	**Decomposed by H_2SO_4.**
1.576	**PENNINITE**	**$5(Mg Fe)O \cdot Al_2O_3 \cdot 3SiO_2 \cdot 4H_2O$**	**In C.T., yields water. B.B., exfoliates.**
1.589	PHARMACOLITE	$CaHAsO_4 \cdot 2H_2O$	In C.T., yields water and becomes opaque.
1.59±	**COLLOPHANITE**	**$Ca_3(PO_4)_2 \cdot H_2O$**	**B.B., decrepitates violently.**
1.652	LIROCONITE	$18CuO \cdot 4Al_2O_3 \cdot 5As_2O_5 \cdot 55H_2O$	In C.T., yields much water and turns olive green.
1.625	NEPOUITE	$3(Ni,Mg)O \cdot 2SiO_2 \cdot 3H_2O$	In C.T., blackens and yields water.
1.654	CABRIERITE	$(Ni,Mg)_3(AsO_4)_2 \cdot 8H_2O$	In C.T., yields water and becomes grayish yellow.
1.553	VEATCHITE	$Ca_2B_6O_{11} \cdot 2H_2O$	Occurs in white cross fibers and viens in limestone and howlite at Lang, Calif.
1.414	THOMPSENOLITE	$NaF \cdot CaF_2 \cdot AlF_3 \cdot H_2O$	B.B., fuses to a clear glass. Decomposed by H_2SO_4.
1.625±	CHALCOPHYLLITE	$7CuO \cdot As_2O_5 \cdot 14H_2O$	Soluble in HNO_3 and NH_4OH.

GROUP 9
Specific Gravity 2.99-2.66

	H	SP. GR.	F	HCL	COLOR	STREAK	LUSTER	CLEAV-AGE	FRACTURE
174	2	2.66	......	....	Blue to steel gray	White, pale blue	....	....	
175	2	2.9	2	....	Pale green			Perf	
176	2	2.98-2.87	3	Sol	Reddish brown to hyacinth red	Yellow	V, P	Dist	....
177	2	2.77	1.5-2	Sol	White chalky	....	D		
178	2	2.67	Fus	Sol	Black	....		Perf	
179	1.5-2.5	2.95	2	Sol	Crimson to gray	Paler	P, A, V	Perf	Flexible
180	1.5-2.5	2.85	2.5	Sol	White	White	V, P	Perf	Flexible
181	1.5-2	2.68-2.58	1.5	Sol	Colorless, green, blue	Colorless to indigo	P, V	Perf	Flexible
182	1-2	2.96-2.78	5-5.5	....	Green	Green, uncolored	P	Perf	Flexible
183	1-2	2.83	......	....	Grayish, green	....	D	....	....
184	1-2	2.9-2.8	Diff	....	White, gray, green	....	P	Good	Flexible
185	1.5	2.92	4?	Sol	Colorless, white	....	V, P	Perf	
186	1-1.5	2.8-2.7	6	Ins	White, greenish	White	P	Perf	....
187	1-1.5	2.67	Inf	Ins	Greenish white	....	....	Perf	
188	1-1.5	2.89	......	....	White, yellow, gray, brown	....	P	Perf	Brittle
189	1	2.75	......	....	Sky-blue	....	....	....	Fibrous
190	Soft	3.0-2.8	Diff	Gelat	Green	....	....	Mic	....
191	Soft	2.98	3.5	Dcpd	Pale grayish yellow	....	P	Perf	....
192	Soft	2.84	......	Sol	Leek green	....	....	Good	....
193	Soft	2.66	1	Sol	Yellow brown	Yellow	V to G	....	
194	Soft	2.8-2.3	Inf	Dcpd	Apple green	....	D	....	....
195	?	2.9	Inf	Sol	White, yellowish	....	V		
196	?	2.68	......	....	Reddish brown				
197	?	2.67	......	Gelat	White, colorless			Dist	....
198	?	2.88	......	....	Amber brown	....	R	....	Fibrous
199	?	2.9	......	....	Black	....	....	....	Fibrous
200	?	2.8	......	Sol	Green, yellow, brown	....	....	....	....
201	?	3.15-2.85	......	....	Green				
202	?	2.94	......	....	Yellow	....	....	Good	....
203	?	2.76-2.69	......	....	White				
204	?	2.74	......	....	Dark gray to black	....	....	....	....

GROUP 9
Specific Gravity 2.99-2.66

INDEX OF REF.	NAME	COMPOSITION	REMARKS
....	PARAVIVIANITE	$(Fe,Mn,Mg)_3P_2O_8 \cdot 8H_2O$	A Mn, Mg vivianite.
..565	POLYLITHIONITE	$(Na,K)_3Li_5Al_2Si_8O_{22}F_2$	A member of the mica group.
..786	BERAUNITE	$3Fe_2O_3 \cdot 2P_2O_5 \cdot 8H_2O$	Fuses to a black bead.
.454	GEARKSUTITE	$CaF_2 \cdot Al(F,OH)_3 \cdot H_2O$	Fuses to a white enamel. In C.T., gives water.
.576	EKMANNITE	$5(Fe,Mn,Mg,Ca)O \cdot (Al,Fe)_2O_3 \cdot 8SiO_2 \cdot 7H_2O$	Fuses to a black magnetic slag.
.661	**ERYTHRITE**	$Co_3(AsO_4)_2 \cdot 8H_2O$	**HCl solution is rose-red. In C.T., yields H_2O and turns bluish.**
.602	HAIDINGERITE	$CaHAsO_4 \cdot H_2O$	Test for arsenic.
.603	**VIVIANITE**	$Fe_3(PO_4)_2 \cdot 8H_2O$	**On coal a grayish-black magnetic globule and bluish-green flame.**
.60±	**PROCHLORITE**	$2(Mg,Fe)O \cdot Al_2O_3 \cdot 2SiO_2 \cdot 2H_2O$	**Decomposed by H_2SO_4.**
....	PYCNOCHLORITE	$(Fe,Mn,Ca,Mg)O \cdot (Al,Fe)_2O_3 \cdot SiO_2$	
.588	**PYROPHYLLITE**	$Al_2O_3 \cdot 4SiO_2 \cdot H_2O$	**Decomposed on fusion with alkalies.**
.568	ISOCLASITE	$Ca_3(PO_4)_2 \cdot Ca(OH)_2 \cdot 4H_2O$	B.B., it glows.
.589	**TALC**	$3MgO \cdot 4SiO_2 \cdot H_2O$	**Has a greasy feel. Sectile.**
.587	RUMPFITE	$7MgO \cdot 8Al_2O_3 \cdot 10SiO_2 \cdot 14H_2O$	B.B., becomes brown.
.650	EPISTOLITE	$5Na_2O \cdot 2Cb_2O_5 \cdot 9(Si,Ti)O_2 \cdot 10H_2O$	
....	GLAUCO-KERINITE	$10(Zn,Cu)O \cdot 2Al_2O_3 \cdot SO_3 \cdot 7H_2O$	
..612	APHRO-SIDERITE	$6(Mg,Fe)O \cdot 2(Al,Fe)_2O_3 \cdot 4SiO_2 \cdot 5H_2O$	
..64±	BEMENTITE	$2MnSiO_3 \cdot H_2O$	Fuses to a black glass.
..680	SINCOSITE	$V_2O_4 \cdot CaO \cdot P_2O_5 \cdot 5H_2O$	The HCl solution is blue.
..65±	EGUEIITE	$6Fe_2O_3 \cdot CaO \cdot 5\frac{1}{2}P_2O_5 \cdot 23H_2O$	In C.T., blackens and gives off water.
..59	**GARNIERITE**	$(Ni,Mg)O \cdot SiO_2 \cdot nH_2O$	**A serpentine.**
..606	MARTINITE	$5CaO \cdot P_2O_5 \cdot 1\frac{1}{2}H_2O$	B.B., burns white and falls to pieces.
....	ERRITE	$7MnO \cdot 8SiO_2 \cdot 9H_2O$	Massive. May be a variety of parsettensite.
..545	**EUCRYPTITE**	$Li_2O \cdot Al_2O_3 \cdot 2SiO_2$	
..65	FERRI-SYMPLESSITE	$3Fe_2O_3 \cdot 2As_2O_5 \cdot 16H_2O$	
....	KURSKITE	$2Ca_3(PO_4)_2 \cdot CaF_2 \cdot CaCO_3$	
..65	GREENALITE	$FeO \cdot SiO_2 \cdot nH_2O$	Resembles glauconite but contains no potash.
....	META-GREENALITE	$9FeO \cdot Fe_2O_3 \cdot 8SiO_2 \cdot 8H_2O$	
..66	STEWARTITE	$3MnO \cdot P_2O_5 \cdot 4H_2O$	An alteration product of lithiophilite.
....	BASSANITE	$CaSO_4$	Found in rocks ejected from Vesuvius.
....	TARTARKAITE	$R_2O \cdot 11RO \cdot 13R_2O_3 \cdot 30SiO_2 \cdot 19H_2O$	

GROUP 9
Specific Gravity 2.99-2.66

	H	SP. GR.	F	HCL	COLOR	STREAK	LUSTER	CLEAV-AGE	FRACTURE
205	?	2.866	......	....	Blue, green	....	....	....	....
206	?	2.82	......	Gelat	White	....	....	None	....
207	?	2.74	3	Sol	Bright blue	....	P	....	....
208	?	2.89	Easy	Ins	White	....	P	Perf	....
209	?	2.96	......	....	White, brownish	....	....	....	....
210	?	2.62-2.56	......	....	Colorless	....	....	None	....
211	?	2.75	......	....	Gray	....	....	Good	....
212	?	2.725	......	Dcpd	White, colorless	....	....	....	....
213	?	2.98	......	....		....	....	....	....
214	?	2.8	......	....	Red, yellow, brown	....	....	....	....
215	?	2.70	......	Ins	Yellow	....	....	....	....
216	?	2.80	......	Sol	Blue	....	....	....	....
217	?	2.86	Fus	Dcpd	Blackish-green	....	....	....	....
218	?	2.93	......	....	White	....	....	....	....
219	?	2.90	......	....	Creamy white	....	....	....	Fibrous
220	?	2.7	......	....	Green or brown	....	....	....	....
221	?	2.84	......	....	Wax yellow	....	....	....	....
222	?	2.67	......	Sol	White	....	....	Good	Uneven to to conch
223	?	2.74	......	....	Yellow	....	....	Fair	....
224	?	2.91	Fus	....	Emerald-green	....	....	Perf	....
225	?	2.75	......	....	Colorless	....	....	....	....
226	?	2.73	......	....	....	....	....	....	Fibrous
227	?	2.88-2.77	......	....		....	....	....	Fibrous
228	....	2.87	......	....	Blue to black becomes grnsh ylw	....	....	....	....

312

GROUP 9
Specific Gravity 2.99-2.66

INDEX OF REF.	NAME	COMPOSITION	REMARKS
1.627	CUPRO-RIVAITE	$2(Ca,Na)(Cu,Al)(Si,Al)_4(O,OH)_{10}H_2O$	From Vesuvius.
1.635	TILLEYITE	$3CaO \cdot SiO_2 \cdot CO_2$	
1.617	CYANOTRICKITE	$4CuO \cdot Al_2O_3 \cdot SO_3 \cdot 8H_2O$	
1.6±	MANANDONITE	$2Li_2O \cdot 7Al_2O_3 \cdot 2B_2O_3 \cdot 6SiO_2 \cdot 12H_2O$	
1.509	NOCERITE	$2MgO \cdot MgF_2 \cdot CaF_2$	Found in volcanic bombs.
1.542	KALSILITE	$KAlSiO_4$	
1.339	HIERATITE	$2KF \cdot SiF_4$	Soluble in hot water. From volcanic fumeroles.
1.525	BRADLEYITE	$Na_3MgCO_3PO_4$	Slowly decomposed by cold water.
....	SCACCHITE	$MnCl_2$	Delequesent. From Vesuvius.
....	MOLYSITE	$FeCl_3$	Unstable. From Vesuvius.
....	RADIOTINE	$H_4Mg_3Si_2O_9$	In C.T., yields much water becoming brown. Like serpentine.
....	CERULEITE (COERULEITE)	$CuO \cdot 2Al_2O_3 \cdot As_2O_5 \cdot 8H_2O$	Loses water only at high temperatures.
....	MINGUÉTITE	$17SiO_2 \cdot 4Fe_2O_3 \cdot 8FeO \cdot K_2O \cdot 8H_2O$	In C.T., yields water. B.B., fuses to a black magnetic enamel. Chlorite group.
1.590	KOCHITE	$2Al_2O_3 \cdot 3SiO_2 \cdot 5H_2O$	Gives off water at high temperatures.
....	STRONTIUM-ARAGONITE	Aragonite containing $SrCO_3$	
1.57	LAWRENCITE	$FeCl_2$	Unstable. From Vesuvius.
....	XANTHOXENITE	$FePO_4$ with Mn,Ca, Fe,Mg,Al oxides	
1.494	ARCANITE	$K_2O \cdot SO_3$	Brittle. Soluble in water. Close to aphthitalite.
1.722	TARAPACAITE	$K_2O \cdot CrO_3$	Found with soda niter in Chili.
1.58	CRYOPHYLLITE	$3(Li,K)_2O \cdot 2FeO \cdot 4Al_2O_3 \cdot 2)SiO_2 \cdot 3H_2O \cdot 8(Li,K)F$	Near zinnwaldite. A member of the mica group.
1.312	MALLADRITE	$2NaF \cdot SiF_4$	From Vesuvius.
....	BARDOLITE	$K_2O \cdot 5MgO \cdot FeO \cdot Fe_2O_3 \cdot Al_2O_3 \cdot 12SiO_2 \cdot 21H_2O$	A chlorite-like mineral.
....	BEACONITE	$H_2(Mg,Fe)_3(SiO_4)_3$	A variety of talc resembling asbestos.
....	TUHUALITE	SiO_2 of Na,K,Al, Fe, etc.	An amphibole.

GROUP 10
Specific Gravity 2.65-2.33

	H	SP. GR.	F	HCL	COLOR	STREAK	LUSTER	CLEAV-AGE	FRACTURE
1	7.5-8	2.8-2.63	5.5	Ins	White, red, yellow, pink, green, blue	White	V, R	Imperf	Conch to uneven
2	7.5	2.35	Inf	Ins	Grayish white		V	Perf	Brittle
3	7-7.5	2.66-2.60	5-5.5	Pt sol	Shades of blue		V	Dist	Subconch
4	7	2.65	Inf	Ins	Colorless, various shades	White	V, G	Poor	Conch to uneven
5	7	2.6-2.5							
6	7	2.33-2.28	Inf	Ins	Colorless		V, P	Indist	Conch
7	7	2.59-2.52			White to brick red		S	Fair	
8	6.7	2.67-2.65	3.5	Ins	White, various tints		V to P	Perf	Conch to uneven
9	6-7	2.64							
10	6-7	2.6-2.59	Inf	Ins	Pale yellow to colorless		V, P	Perf	
11	6-7	2.64-2.6	Inf	Ins	White, gray, brown, red, blue, etc	White	V, W	None	Conch
12	6-7	2.50	Easy	Sol	Reddish violet		V, P	Perf	
13	6.5	2.55	Diff	Ins	Brown			Fair	
14	6-6.5	2.65-2.62	4	Ins	Colorless, white, reddish, greenish	Uncolored	V, P	Good	Uneven to conch
15	6-6.5	2.57-2.54	5	Ins	White, pale yellow, red, green		V, P	Perf	Uneven
16	6-6.5	2.46-2.39	5	Ins	Colorless, white, reddish, greenish	Uncolored	V, P	Perf	Subconch
17	6-6.5	2.62-2.50	5	Ins	White, colorless, pink, ylw, red, gray	Uncolored	V, P	Perf	Conch to uneven
18	5-6.5	2.8-2.5	2-3	Pt sol	Colorless, white, red, blue, gray, etc	Uncolored	V	Good	Conch
19	6	2.83-2.6	Inf	Sol	Sky blue, green, bluish-green	White to greenish	W	None	Small conch
20	6	2.6-2.49	3.5	Gelat	Colorless		S	Perf	Brittle
21	6	2.93-2.54	3	Gelat	Reddish, white, red		V		Conch
22	6	2.53-2.42	Diff	Gelat	Colorless		S, V	Perf	
23	6	2.57	Easy	Ins	Colorless			Prismatic	
24	6	2.60-2.57	Inf	Ins	White, pale yellow, red, green	Uncolored	V, P	Perf	Uneven
25	6	2.50	Fus	Gelat	Colorless			Perf	
26	5.5-6	2.65-2.55	3.5	Gelat	Colorless, green, gray, red, brown		V to G	Dist	Subconch
27	5.5-6	2.62	3	Pt sol	Colorless, white		V	Fair	
28	5.5-6	2.59-2.55	3	Ins	Pale green, colorless		V		Conch

GROUP 10
Specific Gravity 2.65-2.33

INDEX OF REF.	NAME	COMPOSITION	REMARKS
1.598	BERYL	$2BeO \cdot Al_2O_3 \cdot 6SiO_2$	B.B., clear varieties become milky and cloudy.
1.591	HAMBERGITE	$4BeO \cdot B_2O_3 \cdot H_2O$	Completely dissolved in HF.
1.562±	IOLITE (CORDIERITE)	$4(Mg,Fe)O \cdot 4Al_2O_3 \cdot 10SiO_2 \cdot H_2O$	Decomposed by fusion with alkali carbonates.
1.544	QUARTZ	SiO_2	A very common mineral.
....	QUARTZINE	SiO_2	Anhydrous silica having a fibrous structure. Fibrous chalcedony.
1.47	TRIDYMITE	SiO_2	Soluble in boiling Na_2CO_3; this differentiates it from quartz.
1.565	ELPIDITE	$Na_2O \cdot ZrO_2 \cdot 6SiO_2 \cdot 3H_2O$	
1.543	OLIGOCLASE	$(Na_2,Ca)O \cdot Al_2O_3 \cdot 5SiO_2$	One of the feldspars.
1.529	BERLINITE	$3(AlPO_4)$	
1.605	BERTRANDITE	$4BeO \cdot 2SiO_2 \cdot H_2O$	B.B., becomes opaque.
1.537	CHALCEDONY	SiO_2	Occurs in botryoidal masses, massive and lining rock cavities. A variety of quartz.
1.508	USSINGITE	$2Na_2O \cdot Al_2O_3 \cdot 6SiO_2 \cdot H_2O$	
1.686	TITANOELPIDITE	$Na_2O \cdot (Ti,Zr)O_2 \cdot 6SiO_2 \cdot 3H_2O$	
1.529	ALBITE	$Na_2O \cdot Al_2O_3 \cdot 6SiO_2$	A feldspar. B.B., a colorless or white glass. Yellow flame.
1.526	MICROCLINE	$K_2O \cdot Al_2O_3 \cdot 6SiO_2$	A member of the feldspar group.
1.510	PETALITE	$Li_2O \cdot Al_2O_3 \cdot 8SiO_2$	B.B., gently heated, emits a blue phosphorescent light.
1.524	ORTHOCLASE	$K_2O \cdot Al_2O_3 \cdot 6SiO_2$	A common constituent of rocks. A feldspar.
1.55±	SCAPOLITE	A tetragonal group of Ca,Na,Al,SiO_2	
1.62	TURQUOIS	$CuO \cdot 3Al_2O_3 \cdot 2P_2O_5 \cdot 9H_2O$	In C.T., decrepitates, yields water and turns black or brown.
1.532	KALIOPHILITE	$K_2O \cdot Al_2O_3 \cdot 2SiO_2$	In bundles of slender, acicular crystals and fine threads.
1.62±	SARCOLITE	$3CaO \cdot Al_2O_3 \cdot 3SiO_2 \cdot +Na$	B.B., a white enamel.
1.521	MICROSOMMITE	$3(K,Na)_2O \cdot SO_3 \cdot 4(Na,K)Cl \cdot 4CaO \cdot 6Al_2O_3 \cdot 12SiO_2$	
1.518	LEIFITE	$Na_2O \cdot Al_2O_3 \cdot 9SiO_2 \cdot 2NaF$	
1.525	ANORTHOCLASE	$(Na,K)_2O \cdot Al_2O_3 \cdot 6SiO_2 \cdot Ab_{65}Or_{35}$	One of the feldspar group.
1.522	NATRODAVYNE	Davyne with no K and much CO_2	
1.539	NEPHELITE	$3(K,Na)_2O \cdot 4Al_2O_3 \cdot 9SiO_2$	Brittle.
1.54±	MIZZONITE	Near marialite	A scapolite.
1.532	MILARITE	$K_2O \cdot 4CaO \cdot 2Al_2O_3 \cdot 24SiO_2 \cdot H_2O$	Brittle. Fuses to a white blebby mass.

GROUP 10
Specific Gravity 2.65-2.33

	H	SP. GR.	F	HCL	COLOR	STREAK	LUSTER	CLEAV-AGE	FRACTURE	S T
29	5.5-6	2.56	3-4	Pt sol	Colorless, white	....	V	Fair	....	M
30	5.5-6	2.5-2.4	4.5	Gelat	Blue, green, red, yellow	Bluish to colorless	V, G	Dist	Conch to uneven	I
31	5.5-6	2.5-2.45	Inf	Gelat	Colorless, gray, white	Uncolored	V	Imperf	Conch	I
32	5.5	2.4-2.25	4.5	Gelat	Blue, gray, black, brownish	....		Poor	....	I
33	5.5	2.56	......	....	Brown, gray, red					
34	5.5	2.4±	Fus	Gelat	White, colorless	....	V, P	Perf	....	E
35	5-6	2.5-2.40	2	Sol	Colorless, gray, red, ylw, blue-grn	Uncolored	Sv, P, G	Perf		H
36	4.5-6	2.48-2.3	2-3	Gelat	White, gray to black	....	V			E
37	5-5.5	2.45-2.38	3	Gelat	Azure to grnsh-blue	....	V	Poor	Uneven	I
38	5-5.5	2.4-2.16	2	Gelat	White	....	V, S	Perf	....	N
39	5-5.5	2.4-2.3	2	Gelat	Reddish, greenish, white, brown	Uncolored	V, P	Perf	Uneven to subconch	O
40	5±	2.75-2.5	Easy	Insol	Red, blue, green, colorless, etc	....	V	None	Conch	A
41	5	2.46	Inf	Sol	Green	....	V	Fair	....	O
42	5	2.70-2.55	Inf	Ins	Milk white to lt blue	....	....	....	....	.
43	5	2.45	3	Dcpd	White, yellow, gray	....	V, P	Perf	Uneven	M
44	5	2.4-2.2	2-2.5	Gelat	White, gray, yellowish	....	V, S	Perf	Brittle	N
45	5	2.52	Inf	Ins	Green, colorless	....	V	None	....	O
46	5	2.65	......	Pt sol	Green, colorless	....		None	....	.
47	5	2.36	Easy	Inf	Colorless	....		Fair	....	O
48	5	2.55	Easy	Ins	Blue	....			....	M
49	5	2.44	2	Gelat	Colorless	....		Perf	....	H
50	5	2.61	......	....	White needles	....				T
51	5	2.38	Easy	Ins	Brown to black	Brown	R	....	Uneven to conch	.
52	4.5-5	2.4-2.3	1.5	Dcpd	Colorless, white, tinted	....	P, V	Perf	Uneven	T
53	4-5	2.6±	Diff	....	Green	White	Sr, G, P, D	Fair	Conch, splintery	M
54	4.5	2.62-2.56	Inf	....	Colorless, white, yellowish	....	V	None	Uneven	I
55	4.5	2.57	Fus	Sol	Gray, red, green, yellow	Yellowish to bluish white	V, G	....	....	O

GROUP 10
Specific Gravity 2.65-2.33

INDEX OF REF.	NAME	COMPOSITION	REMARKS
1.54±	**MARIALITE**	$3Na_2O \cdot 3Al_2O_3 \cdot 8SiO_2 \cdot 2NaCl$	A scapolite.
1.496	**HAUENITE**	$3Na_2O \cdot Al_2O_3 \cdot 2SiO_2 \cdot CaSO_4$	On coal with soda gives the sulfide test.
1.508	**LEUCITE**	$K_2O \cdot Al_2O_3 \cdot 4SiO_2$	Brittle. B.B., with cobalt solution, gives a blue color.
1.495	**NOSELITE**	$5Na_2O \cdot 3Al_2O_3 \cdot 6SiO_2 \cdot 2SO_3$	On coal with soda, gives the sulfide test.
1.540	IGALIKITE	$NaKAl_4Si_4O_{15} \cdot 2H_2O$	Minute scales in pseudo-hexagonal arrangement.
1.518	DAVYNE	$4(Na,K)_2O \cdot CaO \cdot 2CO_2 \cdot 4Al_2O_3 \cdot 9SiO_2 \cdot 3H_2O?$	Fuses with intumescence, coloring the flame yellow.
1.524	**CANCRINITE**	$4Na_2O \cdot CaO \cdot 4Al_2O_3 \cdot 2CO_2 \cdot 9SiO_2 \cdot 3H_2O$	In C.T., gives water.
1.490	HYDRO-NEPHELITE	$2Na_2O \cdot 3Al_2O_3 \cdot 6SiO_2 \cdot 7H_2O$	
1.50±	**LAZURITE**	$3(Na_2O \cdot Al_2O_3 \cdot 2SiO_2) \cdot 2Na_2S$	B.B., on heating, glows with a beetle-green light.
1.519	**SCOLECITE**	$CaO \cdot Al_2O_3 \cdot 3SiO_2 \cdot 3H_2O$	B.B., sometimes curls up like a worm.
1.525±	**THOMSONITE**	$(Ca,Na_2)O \cdot Al_2O_3 \cdot 2SiO_2 \cdot 2\frac{1}{2}H_2O$	B.B., gives a white enamel. A zeolite.
1.52±	**GLASS**	$Na_2O \cdot CaO \cdot 6SiO_2 +$ Fe,K,Ba,B,Pb, etc	Not a mineral but often mistaken for one. Very common.
1.534	FISCHERITE	$AlPO_4 \cdot Al(OH)_3 \cdot 2\frac{1}{2}H_2O$	Soluble in H_2SO_4. B.B., becomes white and clouded.
1.580	COERULEO-LACTITE	$3Al_2O_3 \cdot 2P_2O_5 \cdot 10H_2O$	Occurs in fibrous crusts.
1.512	BREWSTERITE	$(Sr,Ba,Ca)O \cdot Al_2O_3 \cdot 6SiO_2 \cdot 5H_2O$	Brittle. Fuses to a white enamel.
1.505	**MESOLITE**	$Na_2O \cdot 2CaO \cdot 3Al_2O_3 \cdot 9SiO_2 \cdot 8H_2O$	B.B., becomes opaque and swells up to worm-like forms.
1.571	VARISCITE	$Al_2O_3 \cdot P_2O_5 \cdot 4H_2O$	Soluble in HCl after ignition.
1.517	PLANERITE	$3Al_2O_3 \cdot 2P_2O_5 \cdot 18 \pm H_2O$	B.B., decrepitates. Probably identical with coeruleolactite.
1.59	STERRETTITE	$Al_6(PO_4)_4(OH)_65H_2O$	In C.T., fuses, yields water, leaving a dark infusible residue.
....	RIVAITE	$(Ca,Na_2)Si_2O_5$	Prisms of wollastonite embedded in glass. B.B., a glass and yellow flame.
1.507	SULPHATIC CANCRINITE	$4Na_2O \cdot CaO \cdot 4Al_2O_3 \cdot CO_2 \cdot SO_3 \cdot 9SiO_2 \cdot 3H_2O$	
1.536	ASCHROFTINE	$Na_4K_4(Ca,Mg,Mn)_5 \cdot Al_{18}Si_{22}O_{80}35\frac{1}{2}H_2O$	
1.561	LOVOZERITE	Hydrous zircono-silicate of calcium	B.B., an opaque white bead.
1.536	**APOPHYLLITE**	$K_2O \cdot 8CaO \cdot 16SiO_2 \cdot 16H_2O$	In C.T., exfoliates, whitens and yields acid water.
1.502	**ANTIGORITE**	$3MgO \cdot 2SiO_2 \cdot 2H_2O$	In C.T., yields water. A serpentine.
1.427	RALSTONITE	$(Mg,Na_2)F_2 \cdot 3Al(F,OH)_3 \cdot 2H_2O$	Brittle. Decomposed by H_2SO_4 with evolution of HF.
1.660	BARRANDITE	$(Al,Fe)PO_4 \cdot 2H_2O$	B.B., splits open and becomes dark color.

GROUP 10
Specific Gravity 2.65-2.33

	H	SP. GR.	F	HCL	COLOR	STREAK	LUSTER	CLEAV-AGE	FRACTURE	
56	4.5	2.5-2.44	3.5	Dcpd	White, yellow, red, brown	White	V	Easy	Uneven to subconch	
57	4.5	2.33	Easy	Sol	Emerald-green	....	....	Perf	....	N
58	4-4.5	2.5-2.49	4.5-5	Sol	Colorless to brown, yellow	Yellowish	R	Perf	....	I
59	4-4.5	2.43-2.42	1.5	Sol	Colorless, white, yellowish	....	V to A	Perf	Uneven to subconch	
60	4-4.5	2.37-2.28	2.5-3	Dcpd	Colorless to white	....	V	None	Brittle	N
61	4	2.58	Inf	Sol	Pale brown	....	....	Perf	....	I
62	4	2.54	Inf	....	Gray to blue	....	G, V	Dist	....	C
63	4	2.68-2.61	....	....	Black	....	....	....	....	
64	4	2.6	Inf	....	White	....	....	Dist	....	
65	4	2.53	....	....	Pale green to colorless	....	....	....	....	
66	4	2.5	....	....	Dark brown	Brown	P	....	Conch	
67	4	2.54	Inf	Ins	Green	....	....	....	....	C
68	4	2.5	....	....	Ashy brown	....	....	....	....	F
69	4	2.45-2.38	Fus	Sol	Colorless	....	D	Dist	Brittle	C
70	4	2.63	Diff	Sol	Colorless	....	....	Perf	....	N
71	4	2.41	....	....	Green, yellow	....	R, P	Perf	....	N
72	4	2.5	....	Dcpd	Green, brown, ylw	....	....	Perf	....	N
73	4	2.53	....	....	Grnsh, colorless	....	....	Perf	....	N
74	3.5-4	2.39	....	....	Blue to gray	....	....	Good	....	N
75	3.5-4	2.75-2.58	Inf	....	White, grayish, reddish	White	V, P	Dist	Conch to uneven	
76	3.5-4	2.36-2.25	2.5-3	Gelat	White, yellow, red	Uncolored	V, P	Perf	Uneven	
77	3.5-4	2.38	1	Sol	Colorless, gray, yellow, brown	....	....	None	Conch	I
78	3.25-4	2.34-2.32	Inf	Sol	White, yellow, green	White	V, P	Fair	Uneven to subconch	
79	3-4	2.41	....	Dcpd	Green	Greenish white	R	....	....	
80	3-4	2.58	Inf	Pt sol	Yellow	White	V, P	Dist	Conch	
81	3-4	2.8-2.64	4-6	Dcpd	Brown to black	Same	D	....	....	
82	3-4	2.39	Diff	Dcpd	White	....	V, P	Mic	....	
83	3.5	2.49	1	Sol	Greenish, yellow	....	V	None	....	
84	3.5	2.57	....	....	White, buff, gray	....	Glassy	None	Conch	C
85	3.5	2.59-2.55	2	Ins	White	....	Sv	....	Even	N
86	3.5	2.61	Easy	Sol	Clear, colorless	....	....	None	Brittle	

GROUP 10
Specific Gravity 2.65-2.33

	INDEX OF REF.	NAME	COMPOSITION	REMARKS
6	1.505	**HARMOTOME**	$(K_2,Ba)O\cdot Al_2O_3\cdot 5SiO_2\cdot 5H_2O$	**B.B., whitens, then crumbles and fuses to a white translucent glass.**
7	1.656	NATROCHALCITE	$Na_2O\cdot 4CaO\cdot 3SO_3\cdot 3H_2O$	Slowly soluble in water.
8	1.830	CARPHOSIDERITE	$3Fe_2O_3\cdot 3SO_3\cdot 10H_2O$	Insoluble in water.
9	1.592	**COLEMANITE**	$2CaO\cdot 3B_2O_3\cdot 5H_2O$	**B.B., decrepitates, exfoliates, sinters, fuse imperfectly.**
0	1.50	WELLSITE	$BaO\cdot K_2O\cdot 2Al_2O_3\cdot 6SiO_2\cdot 8H_2O$	In C.T., yields water. A member of the zeolite group.
1	2.137	OLDHAMITE	CaS	Treated with HCl, it yields H_2S. Decomposed by boiling water.
2	1.576	SPHAERITE	$4AlPO_4\cdot 6Al(OH)_3\cdot 7H_2O$	B.B., colors the flame bluish-green.
3	....	BONDSDORFFITE	$K_2(Mg,Fe)_2Al_8(Si_2O_7)_5\cdot 7H_2O$	An alteration product of cordierite.
4	1.585±	NATROALUNITE	$Na_2O\cdot 3Al_2O_3\cdot 4SO_3\cdot 6H_2O$	Soluble in HCl and partly in water after ignition.
5	1.574	OVERITE	$2[Ca_3Al_6(PO_4)_820H_2O]$	Prismatic crystals in variscite nodules.
6	1.758	ASOVSKITE	$P_2O_5\cdot 3Fe_2O_3\cdot 6H_2O$	Occurs in shells, veins, and nodules.
7	1.588	METAVARISCITE	$Al_2O_3\cdot P_2O_5\cdot 4H_2O$	Becomes lavender on heating. Soluble in HCl after gently heating.
8	....	CODAZZITE	$(Ca,Mg,Fe,Ce)CO_3$	
9	1.540	SULPHOBORITE	$6MgO\cdot 2B_2O_3\cdot 2SO_3\cdot 9H_2O$	Soluble in water. Colors flame green.
0	1.62	AFWILLITE	$3CaO\cdot 2SiO_2\cdot 3H_2O$	
1	1.545	PHOLIDOLITE	Like calcedonite with Al	
2	1.550	**CHRYSOTILE**	$3MgO\cdot 2SiO_2\cdot 2H_2O$	**Serpentine asbestos. Fibers usually long and flexible.**
3	1.578	MONTGOMERITE	$Ca_4Al_5(PO_4)_6(OH)_5\cdot 11H_2O$	
4	....	KOLBECKITE	$H_2O\cdot SiO_2\cdot P_2O_5$ of Be	Short prismatic crystals.
5	1.572	**ALUNITE**	$K_2O\cdot 3Al_2O_3\cdot 4SO_3\cdot 6H_2O$	**Brittle. Soluble in H_2SO_4. In C.T., yields water.**
6	1.524	**LAUMONTITE**	$CaO\cdot Al_2O_3\cdot 4SiO_2\cdot 4H_2O$	**B.B., a white enamel.**
7	1.514	NORTHUPITE	$MgO\cdot Na_2O\cdot 2CO_2\cdot NaCl$	B.B., froths and fuses to an alkaline mass.
8	1.534	**WAVELLITE**	$4AlPO_4\cdot 2Al(OH)_3\cdot 9H_2O$	**Brittle. Soluble in KOH.**
9	....	**GENTHITE**	$2NiO\cdot 2MgO\cdot 3SiO_2\cdot 6H_2O$	**In C.T., blackens and gives off water.**
0	....	LOEWIGITE	$K_2O\cdot 3Al_2O_3\cdot 4SO_3\cdot 9H_2O$	Similar to alunite.
1	1.50±	NEOTOCITE	$(Mn,Fe)O\cdot SiO_2\cdot 2H_2O$	In C.T., yields much water.
2	1.549	GYROLITE	$4CaO\cdot 6SiO_2\cdot 5(Na,K,H)_2O$	In C.T., yields H_2O; intumesces and separates into thin scales.
3	1.454	SULPHOHALITE	$2Na_2SO_4\cdot 2NaCl\cdot NaF$	Slowly soluble in water.
4	1.488	BURKEITE	$2Na_2SO_4\cdot Na_2CO_3$	Brittle. Soluble in water.
5	1.598	HOWLITE	$4CaO\cdot 5B_2O_3\cdot 2SiO_2\cdot 5H_2O$	Tests for boron.
6	1.440	SCHAIRERITE	$Na_2SO_4\cdot Na(F,Cl)$	Soluble in water. Colors flame intensely yellow.

319

GROUP 10
Specific Gravity 2.65-2.33

	H	SP. GR.	F	HCL	COLOR	STREAK	LUSTER	CLEAVAGE	FRACTURE	SY TH
87	3.5	2.45	......	....	White	......	......	......	......	O
88	3.5	2.45	......	....	Blue	......	......	None	......	T
89	3.5	2.59-2.46	1	Sol	Colorless	......	......	None	......	I
90	3.5	2.6	......	Sol	......	......	......	Good	......	R
91	3.5	2.62	Inf	Sol	White	......	......	......	Uneven	.
92	3.5	2.65	......	....	Brown	Light brown	......	......	......	.
93	3.5	2.38	Diff	Gelat	Iron black	Dark smoky gray	G to P	Basal	......	.
94	3.5	2.58-2.50	Diff	Dcpd	......	......	......	Perf	......	R
95	3.5	2.65	......	....	Dark green to nearly black	Green	......	......	......	.
96	3-3.5	2.66-2.63	1.5	Sol	White tinged with blue or green	......	V, R	Fair	......	R
97	3-3.5	2.57-2.52	2-3	Sol	White, yellowish	......	V	Perf	......	M
98	3-3.5	2.56	1.5	Sol	White, yellowish	......	V, D	Dist	Uneven to subconch	H
99	3-3.5	2.69-2.57	Inf	Sol	Emerald-green	Paler	V	......	Conch	.
100	3-3.5	2.5-2.49	Inf	....	Greenish white, green	White	G, V	Indist	Uneven to subconch	O
101	3-3.5	2.63	Fus	Ins	Ash gray	......	P to D	Perf	......	.
102	3-3.5	2.35	2-2.5	Sol	Colorless, white	......	V	None	Conch	O
103	**2.5-4**	**2.65-2.5**	**5-6**	**Dcpd**	**Green, brownish, red**	**White**	**S, G, P, R, E**	**Fair**	**Conch to splintery**	**M**
104	**2.5-3.5**	**2.4-2.3**	**Inf**	....	**Grayish, reddish, white, green**	......	**P, V**	**Perf**	......	
105	3	2.4	4.5-5	Sol	White	......	V	Perf	......	O
106	3	2.63	1	Sol	......	......	V	Dist	Conch	O
107	3	2.60	.....	....	Greenish	......	......	......	Fibrous	.
108	3	3.1-2.5	Diff	Dcpd	Black, brownish black	Yellowish brown	G, V	......	Conch	.
109	3	2.34	......	....	Colorless	......	......	......	......	M
110	3	2.47	......	Sol	White to colorless	......	......	Perf	......	N
111	3	2.36	Inf	Gelat	Snow white	......	S	......	Fibrous	.
112	3	2.64	2	Dcpd	White	......	S	......	Fibrous	C
113	3	2.65	......	....	Colorless	......	......	Mic	......	C
114	3	2.4	......	Sol	Snow white	......	......	Perf	......	T
115	3	2.34	Easy	Sol	Colorless, rose, yellow, brown	......	S	Perf	Splintery	H

GROUP 10
Specific Gravity 2.65-2.33

INDEX OF REF.	NAME	COMPOSITION	REMARKS
37 1.534	MINYULITE	$2K(OH,F) \cdot 2Al_2O_3 \cdot 2P_2O_5 \cdot 7H_2O$	Radiating groups of white needles like wavellite.
38 1.555	VAUXITE	$FeO \cdot Al_2O_3 \cdot P_2O_5 \cdot 6H_2O$	
39 1.508	TYCHITE	$2MgO \cdot 3Na_2O \cdot 4CO_2 \cdot SO_2$	Slightly soluble in water.
40 1.552	ZIRKLERITE	$2Al_2O_3 \cdot 9(Fe,Mg,Ca)Cl_2 \cdot 3H_2O$	Decomposed by H_2O with separation of Al_2O_3 and $Fe(OH)_3$.
41	GAJITE	Hydrous $(Ca,Mg)CO_3$	In C.T., yields alkaline water.
42	OXY-KERTSCHENITE	$(Mn,Mg,Ca)O \cdot 4Al_2O_3 \cdot 3P_2O_5 \cdot 21H_2O$	
43	MORAVITE	$H_4Fe_2(Al,Fe)_4 Si_7O_{24}$	B.B., gives a black shining bead.
44 1.564	REYERITE	$Ca,Al,SiO_2 + H_2O$	In C.T., yields alkaline water. After heating gives an alkaline reaction.
45	KERTSCHENITE	Hydrated basic ferric phosphate	
46 1.487	APHTHITALITE	$(Na,K)_2SO_4$	Soluble in water. Tastes bitter.
47 1.533	KIESERITE	$MgSO_4 \cdot H_2O$	Soluble in water.
48 1.481	HANKSITE	$9Na_2SO_4 \cdot Na_2CO_3 \cdot KCl$	Brittle. Soluble in water.
49 1.59±	ZARATITE	$NiCO_3 \cdot 2Ni(OH)_2 \cdot 4H_2O$	In C.T., yields water and leaves a grayish black magnetic mass.
50	PEGANITE	$AlPO_4 \cdot Al(OH)_3 \cdot 1\frac{1}{2}H_2O$	In C.T., yields water and assumes a violet or rose red color
51	SPODIO-PHYLLITE	$(Na_2 \cdot K_2)_2(Mg,Fe)_3 (Fe,Al)_2(SiO_3)_8$	B.B., gives a nearly colorless bead.
52 1.510	PIRSSONITE	$CaO \cdot Na_2O \cdot 2CO_2 \cdot 2H_2O$	Gives an alkaline reaction after heating.
53	**SERPENTINE**	$3MgO \cdot 2SiO_2 \cdot 2H_2O$	**In C.T., yields water. There are many varieties.**
54 1.566	**GIBBSITE**	$Al(OH)_3$	**Soluble in H_2SO_4. In C.T., yields water and becomes opaque and white.**
55 1.542	DAWSONITE	$Na_2O \cdot Al_2O_3 \cdot 2CO_2 \cdot 2H_2O$	B.B., swells up and colors flame deep yellow.
56 1.555	SHORTITE	$Na_2O \cdot 2CaO \cdot 3CO_2$	Strongly pyroelectric. Dcpd by H_2O.
57	NEMAPHYLLITE	As serpentine	A variety of serpentine containing Na_2O.
58 1.57±	HISINGERITE	Hydrated ferric silicate	In C.T., yields water. Fuses to a black magnetic slag.
59 1.561	METAVAUXITE	$FeO \cdot Al_2O_3 \cdot P_2O_5 \cdot 4H_2O$	
60 1.545	MOOREITE	$8(Mg,Mn,Zn)O \cdot SO_3 \cdot 11H_2O$	White tabular crystals.
61 1.594	FOSHAGITE	$5CaO \cdot 3SiO_2 \cdot 3H_2O$	B.B., water is expelled and it becomes pale blue. May be identical with hillebrandite.
62 1.60	RIVERSIDEITE	$2CaO \cdot 2SiO_2 \cdot 3H_2O$	B.B., fuses to a white glass.
63 1.572	ENGLISHITE	$4CaO \cdot K_2O \cdot 4Al_2O_3 \cdot 4P_2O_5 \cdot 14H_2O$	
64 1.591	PRICEITE	$4CaO \cdot 5B_2O_3 \cdot 7H_2O$	Chalky. In crystalline and cryptocrystalline compact masses.
65 1.589	RINNEITE	$FeCl_4 \cdot 3KCl \cdot NaCl$	The taste is astringent like ink.

GROUP 10
Specific Gravity 2.65-2.33

	H	SP. GR.	F	HCL	COLOR	STREAK	LUSTER	CLEAV-AGE	FRACTURE	SYTE
116	2.5-3	2.67-2.6	Inf	Sol	White, pink, yellowish	....	D, P	Perf	....	O
117	2.5-3	2.5	......	....	White	....	P	Perf	....	..
118	2.5-3	2.62-2.46	......	....	Yellowish green	Green	....	Perf	....	H'
119	2.5-3	2.37	1.5	Sol	White, yellowish, rdsh	....	V	Dist	Conch	T
120	2.5-3	2.51	Diff	Pt sol	White					H
121	2-3	2.5-2.2	Easy	Sol	Brown, yellowish, white	Yellowish to white	V, G	....		..
122	2-3	2.61	......	....	Silvery white, grayish	....	....	Perf	....	M
123	2-3	2.53	......	Dcpd	White	....	....	....	....	..
124	2-3	2.45	......	Sol	Clear glassy, yellow	....	....	Good	....	Tr
125	2-3	2.4	......	....	White, ylw tint	....	....	....	....	..
126	2.5	2.53	5	Sol	Yellow	....	....	....	....	H
127	**2.5**	**2.6-2.1**	**1.5**	**Sol**	**Colorless, red, blue, purple**	....	**V**	**Perf**	**Conch**	**I**
128	2.5	2.6	1.5-2	....	White	....	V	Perf	Conch	M
129	2.5	2.63	Inf	Pt sol	White	....	P	Perf	Flexible	..
130	2.5	2.53-2.52	Easy	Dcpd	Yellow, green	Sulfur yellow	P	Perf	Brittle	M
131	**2.5**	**2.4-2.38**	**Inf**	**Sol**	**White, blue, green**	....	**P, V, W**	**Perf**	....	**R**
132	2.5	2.44	Fus	Sol	Colorless	....	....	Perf	....	M
133	2.5	2.51	......	....	Green-yellow	....	....	Perf	....	.
134	2.5	2.51	Easy	Dcpd	White	....	P	Mic	....	..
135	2.5	2.46	Easy	Sol	Red to yellow, orange	Yellow	V, Sa	Poor	Conch	M
136	2.5	2.55	......	....	Deep orange	....	....	Perf	....	O
137	2.5	2.63	......	....	Sky blue	....	....	Perf	....	O
138	2.5	2.4	......	....	Bluish-green	....	V	Perf	Conch	O
139	2-2.5	2.5-2.0	2-3?	Sol	Apple green	Paler to white	V	Perf		O
140	**2-2.5**	**2.78-2.65**	**5-5.5**	**Pt sol**	**Violet, green, red, yellowish**	**Uncolored, greenish wht**	**P**	**Perf**	**Flexible**	**M**
141	**2-2.5**	**2.85-2.6**	**5-5.5**	**Pt Sol**	**Grn, red, violet, yellowish, white**	....	**P, V**	**Perf**	**Flexible**	**M**
142	2-2.5	2.73-2.64	2.5	Sol	White, grayish, red tinge	White	V, P	Perf	Uneven	M
143	**2-2.5**	**2.63-2.6**	**Inf**	**Ins**	**White, various tints**	....	**P, D, E**	**Perf**	**Flexible**	**M**
144	2-2.5	2.48	......	....	Colorless, white	....	V	Perf	....	M
145	2-2.5	2.35-2.15	2	Sol	Yellow	Pale yellow	....	Perf	....	O
146	2-2.5	3.24-2.47	......	Sol	Pale, deep green	....	P	Perf	....	H
147	**1-4**	**2.5±**	......	1-...	**Turquoise blue**	....	**D**	....	**Conch**	..

	INDEX OF REF.	NAME	COMPOSITION	REMARKS
16	1.587	LANTHANITE	$La(CO_3)_2 \cdot 9H_2O$	In C.T., yields water.
17	1.542	FOSHALLASSITE	$3CaO \cdot 2SiO_2 \cdot 3H_2O$	Scaly, spheroidal aggregates. Related to foshagite and centrallasite.
18	1.59±	CONNARITE	$2NiO_2 \cdot 3SiO_2 \cdot 2H_2O$	
19	1.490	LOEWEITE	$2Na_2SO_4 \cdot 2MgSO_4 \cdot 5H_2O$	Soluble in water.
20	1.56	COLERAINITE	$4MgO \cdot Al_2O_3 \cdot 2SiO_2 \cdot 5H_2O$	
21	1.635±	PITTICITE	Hydrated ferric AsO_4 and SO_4	In C.T., yields water and SO_2.
2	1.537	NAUJAKASITE	$3(Na_2,Fe)O \cdot 2Al_2O_3 \cdot 8SiO_2 \cdot H_2O$	Minute mica-like plates.
3	....	RADIOPHYLLITE	$CaO \cdot SiO_2 \cdot H_2O$	
4	1.770	ROSSITE	$CaO \cdot V_2O_5 \cdot 4H_2O$	Soluble in water.
5	1.542	KOLSKITE	Hydrous SiO_2 of Mg	
6	1.591	METAVOLTINE	$5(K_2,Na_2,Fe)O \cdot 3Fe_2O_3 \cdot 12SO_3 \cdot 18H_2O$	Partly soluble in water.
7	**1.544**	**HALITE**	**NaCl**	**Soluble in water. Common salt.**
8	1.517	SYNGENITE	$K_2SO_4 \cdot CaSO_4 \cdot H_2O$	Partly soluble in water. In C.T., decrepitates violently, yielding water.
9	1.729	DONBASSITE	H_2O,Al,SiO_2	B.B., splits into separate folia and whitens.
0	1.575	CALCIOFERRITE	$Ca_3(PO_4)_2 \cdot 2FePO_4 \cdot Fe(OH)_3 \cdot 8H_2O$	B.B., gives a shining black magnetic globule.
1	**1.559**	**BRUCITE**	**$Mg(OH)_2$**	**In C.T., yields water; becomes opaque and friable.**
2	1.52	HAUTEFEUILLITE	$3(Mg,Ca)O \cdot P_2O_5 \cdot 8H_2O$	Fuses to a greenish white globule.
3	1.542	SCHROECKIN-GERITE	$3CaCO_3 \cdot Na_2SO_4 \cdot UO_3 \cdot 10H_2O$	Erroneously renamed dakeite. Soluble in cold water. Decomposed by hot water.
4	1.548	CENTRALLASITE	$4CaO \cdot 7SiO_2 \cdot 3H_2O$	
5	1.815	PASCOITE	$3V_2O_5 \cdot 2CaO \cdot 11H_2O$	In C.T., yields much water. Soluble in water.
6	1.674	BUTLERITE	$(Fe,Al)_2O_3 \cdot 2SO_3 \cdot 5H_2O$	
7	1.643	RANSOMITE	$CuO \cdot (Fe,Al)_2O_3 \cdot 4SO_3 \cdot 7H_2O$	
8	1.685	ANTOFAGASTITE	$CuCl_2 \cdot 2H_2O$	Brittle. Usually in curved and verniform shapes.
9	1.662	LINDACKERITE	$3NiO \cdot 6CuO \cdot SO_3 \cdot 2As_2O_3 \cdot 7H_2O$	Fuses to a black bead. The HCl solution yields a yellow precipitate with H_2S.
0	**1.58±**	**CLINOCHLORE**	**$5(Fe,Mg)O \cdot Al_2O_3 \cdot 3SiO_2 \cdot 4H_2O$**	**Decomposed by H_2SO_4.**
1	**1.576**	**PENNINITE**	**$5(Mg,Fe)O \cdot Al_2O_3 \cdot 3SiO_2 \cdot 4H_2O$**	**Decomposed by H_2SO_4. B.B., exfoliates.**
2	1.589	PHARMACOLITE	$CaHAsO_4 \cdot 2H_2O$	In C.T., yields water and becomes opaque.
3	**1.565**	**KAOLINITE**	**$Al_2O_3 \cdot 2SiO_2 \cdot 2H_2O$**	**In C.T., yields water.**
4	....	WAPPLERITE	$2CaHAsO_4 \cdot 7H_2O$	
5	1.525	SIDERONATRITE	$2Na_2O \cdot Fe_2O_3 \cdot 4SO_3 \cdot 7H_2O$	Decomposed by boiling water.
6	1.625	NEPOUITE	$3(Ni,Mg)O \cdot 2SiO_2 \cdot 3H_2O$	In C.T., blackens and yields water. Reacts for nickel.
7	1.54±	AIDYRLITE	$4NiO \cdot 4Al_2O_3 \cdot 6SiO_2 \cdot 15H_2O$	

GROUP 10
Specific Gravity 2.65-2.33

	H	SP. GR.	F	HCL	COLOR	STREAK	LUSTER	CLEAVAGE	FRACTURE	SYSTEM
148	1-3	2.34	Diff	Pt sol	Green	Lighter	G	....	....	..
149	2	2.66-2.4	2-2.5	....	Deep emerald green	Paler	R, V, Sa	Perf	....	R
150	2	2.57-2.51	......	Pt sol	Dark green	....	....	Good	Scaly	..
151	2	2.58-2.55	1.5	Sol	White, green	....	....	Perf	....	R
152	2	2.43	......	....	Yellowish, gray	....	....	....	....	A
153	**2**	**2.4-2.2**	**Easy**	**Pt sol**	**Green, gray**	....	**D**	**Perf**	....	**M**
154	2	2.43	......	....	Pale yellow	....	....	....	....	..
155	2	2.49-2.13	......	Sol	Yellow	....	D, R	Perf	Uneven	O
156	2	2.6	Inf	Ins	White	....	....	Perf	....	M
157	**1.5-2**	**2.68-2.58**	**1.5**	**Sol**	**Colorless, blue, green**	**Colorless to indigo**	**P, V**	....	**Flexible**	**M**
158	1-2	2.41	Fus	Sol	Colorless, white	....	....	Good	....	M
159	1.5	2.33	Inf	Sol	Colorless, yellowish	....	P	Perf	....	O
160	1.5	2.6	Inf	....	White, green, yellow, brown	....	....	Mic	....	..
161	1.5	2.58	1	Sol in HNO$_3$	Orange-yellow	....	A	None	Brittle	O
162	1	2.47	2-3?	Sol	White	....	P	Perf	Flexible	M
163	1	2.62	......	....	Silvery bluish green	....	....	....	Fibrous	..
164	Soft	2.45	Easy	Sol	White	....	....	Perf	....	M
165	Soft	2.41	......	....	White	....	Chalky	....	....	A
166	Soft	2.47	......	....	White	....	....	Perf	....	..
167	Soft	2.57	......	....	White, cream	....	Chalky	....	....	..
168	Soft	2.50	Inf	Gelat	Yellowish green	....	....	Mic	....	O
169	Soft	2.58	......	....	White	....	P	Dist	....	M
170	Soft	2.37	......	Sol	Black	Black	....	....	....	..
171	**Soft**	**2.8-2.3**	**Inf**	**Dcpd**	**Apple green**	....	**D**	....	....	**O?**
172	Soft	2.6	1	Sol	Brownish yellow	Yellow	V to G	....	....	..
173	Soft	2.37	Inf	Pt sol	White	....	....	Dist	....	R
174	Soft	2.58±	3	Sol	Olive to apple green	....	E	Micro	....	..
175	?	2.59	Fus	Dcpd	Copper red	....	....	....	....	H
176	?	2.5	......	....	Light brown	....	....	Perf	....	..
177	?	2.63	......	....	....	....	....	....	....	..
178	?	2.50	......	....	....	....	....	....	....	O
179	**?**	**2.55**	**Inf**	**Ins**	**White, yellow, brown, green**	....	....	....	....	..

GROUP 10
Specific Gravity 2.65-2.33

INDEX OF REF.	NAME	COMPOSITION	REMARKS
....	HOEFERITE	$Fe_2O_3 \cdot SiO_2 \cdot H_2O$	B.B., becomes reddish brown then grayish black. Fuses to a black slag.
1.625±	CHALCO-PHYLLITE	$7CuO \cdot As_2O_5 \cdot 14H_2O$	Soluble in HNO_3 and NH_4OH.
1.581	SKOLITE	H_2O, SiO_2 of Al,Fe,K, etc.	Loses water easily but reabsorbs it.
1.559	FERRONATRITE	$3Na_2SO_4 \cdot Fe_2(SO_4)_3 \cdot 6H_2O$	Soluble in water.
1.535	TORNIELLITE	$(OH)_8Al_4(Si_4O_{10}) 2H_2O$	Clay-like. Amorphous form of halloysite.
1.63±	**GLAUCONITE**	**Hydrated silicate of K and Fe.**	**B.B., gives a black magnetic glass.**
1.535	TORNIELLITE	Hydrous SiO_2 of Al	Feels soapy. Very porous. Sticks to the tongue.
1.561	HUMBOLDTINE	$2FeC_2O_4 \cdot 2H_2O$	In C.T., yields water, turns black and becomes magnetic.
1.563	DICKITE	$Al_2O_3 \cdot 2SiO_2 \cdot 2H_2O$	One of the kaoline group.
1.603	**VIVIANITE**	**$Fe_3(PO_4)_28H_2O$**	**On coal, a grayish-black magnetic globule; bluish flame.**
1.520	BOBIERITE	$3MgO \cdot P_2O_5 \cdot 8H_2O$	Insoluble in water.
1.518	FELSOEBANYITE	$2Al_2O_3 \cdot SO_3 \cdot 10H_2O$	In C.T., yields water at high temperatures.
1.516±	BEIDELLITE	$Al_2O_3 \cdot 3 \pm SiO_2$	
1.665	DIMORPHITE	As_4S_3	On heating, turns red, then brown; gives yellow fumes; ignites and burns without residue.
1.571	HOERNESITE	$Mg_3(AsO_4)_2 \cdot 8H_2O$	In C.T., much water. On coal, an arsenical odor.
....	ISHKYLDITE	$H_{20}Mg_{15}Si_{11}O_{47}$	A variety of chrysotile.
1.533	SEARLESITE	$Na_2O \cdot B_2O_3 \cdot 4SiO_2 \cdot 2H_2O$	Partly soluble in water.
....	HYDROMAGNO-CALCITE	$CaCO_3 \cdot Mg(OH)_2$	
1.549	TRUSCOTTITE	$4(Ca,Mg)O \cdot 7SiO_2 \cdot 3H_2O$	
....	KAUAIITE	$2Al_2O_3 \cdot 3(K,Na,H)_2O \cdot SO_3$	Powdery.
1.59±	NONTRONITE	$(Ca,Mg)O \cdot Fe_2O_3 \cdot 2SiO_2 \cdot 2 \pm H_2O$	
1.632	PICRO-PHARMACOLITE	$3(Ca,Mg)O \cdot As_2O_5 \cdot 6H_2O$	
....	CUPRO-ASBOLANE	$(Cu,Mg,H_2)O \cdot (Fe,Al,Co,Mn)_2O_3$	HCl solution yields chlorine. From Katanga, Ruashi, etc.
1.59	**GARNIERITE**	**$(Ni,Mg)O \cdot SiO_2 \cdot nH_2O$**	**A serpentine.**
1.65	EQUEIITE	$18Fe_2O_3 \cdot 3CaO \cdot 16P_2O_5 \cdot 69 \pm H_2O$	In C.T., blackens and gives water. On coal, fuses with intumescence to a black globule.
....	NEWTONITE	$Al_2O_3 \cdot 2SiO_2 \cdot 5H_2O$	Gives aluminum reactions with cobalt solution.
1.63	CELADONITE	$R_2O_3 \cdot 3(RO,R_2O_3) \cdot 8SiO_2 \cdot 5H_2O$	Occurs in minute scales. Feels greasy.
1.576	PARSETTENSITE	$3MnO \cdot 4SiO_2 \cdot 4H_2O$	Probably identical with errite.
1.59	MANGANBRUCITE	$(Mg,Mn)O \cdot H_2O$	See brucite.
....	ALPHA-CHLORITITE	$4Al_2O_3 \cdot 5SiO_2 \cdot 7H_2O$	
....	FERRUCCITE	$NaBF_4$	Minute crystals from Vesuvius.
....	**BAUXITE**	**$Al_2O_3 \cdot 2H_2O$**	**In round concretionary masses; massive, oölitic, earthy, clay-like. A mixture; not a mineral.**

GROUP 10
Specific Gravity 2.65-2.33

	H	SP. GR.	F	HCL	COLOR	STREAK	LUSTER	CLEAV-AGE	FRACTURE	SYSTEM
180	?	2.65-2.30	......	....	White	....	Chalky	....	....	...?
181	?	2.63	......	....	Black	....	....	....	....	H?
182	?	2.58	......	....	Yellow-orange	....	....	....	....	M
183	?	2.42	......	....	Green, blue	....	....	....	....	T
184	?	2.57	......	....	Colorless	....	....	....	....	Tr
185	?	2.50	......	....	Yellow to pale green	....	....	Perf	....	O
186	?	2.34	Inf	Sol	White	....	....	....	....	...?
187	?	2.51	Easy	Sol	Deep red	Brown to maroon	S	....	....	O?
188	?	2.55	1-2	Sol	Red	Bronze, maroon	S	....	....	O
189	?	2.62	......	....	Yellowish to reddish sublimate	....	....	....	....	O
190	?	2.50-2.40	......	....	Yellowish	....	V	....	....	A
191	?	2.52	......	....	Bluish-green	....	....	Perf	....	O

GENTHITE	GMELINITE	PHILLIPSITE (white xtls)	POLYHALITE	SUCCINITE
NONTRONITE	VIVIANITE (dark xtls)	PECTOLITE	MARIPOSITE QUARTZ	WOLLASTONITE
BAKERITE	ARAGONITE	DOLOMITE	DOLOMITE	ALUNITE
LEPIDOLITE	ANHYDRITE	ZINNWALDITE	CALCITE	PARAGONITE
PHLOGOPITE	GLAUBERITE	THENARDITE	CHLORITE	CLINOCHLORE SERPENTINE
PENNINITE	FUCHSITE	EUCRYPTITE	PYROPHYLLITE	OPAL

PLATE 27

CHLOROPAL   SODALITE   OLIGOCLASE   AMAZONITE   ORTHOCLASE

ADULARIA
(moonstone)   BAUXITE   LABRADORITE   LEUCITE   CANCRINITE
ALBITE

LAZURITE   CHRYSOCOLLA   CHALCANTHITE   VARISCITE   UTAHITE

VERMICULITE   ANTIGORITE   JEFFERISITE   ASBESTOS
(Serpentine)   LAUMONTITE
(pink)

WAVELLITE   PISANITE   HANKSITE   MORENOSITE   GRAPHITE

SERPENTINE   SULPHUR   HALITE   SODA NITER   STILBITE

PLATE 28

GROUP 10
Specific Gravity 2.65-2.33

INDEX OF REF.	NAME	COMPOSITION	REMARKS
....	LEUCO-PHOSPHITE	$K_2(Fe,Al)_7(OH)_{11} \cdot (PO_4)_4 6H_2O$	
....	ANGARALITE	$5(Al,Fe)_2O_3 \cdot 6SiO_2$	B.B., on heating, becomes dark bronze.
1.635	SARMIENTITE	$SO_3 \cdot As_2O_5 \cdot Fe_2O_3$, etc	
1.637	MITCHER-LICHITE	$2KCl \cdot CuCl_2 \cdot 2H_2O$	From crater of Vesuvius.
1.52	CARNEGIEITE	$Na_2O \cdot Al_2O_3 \cdot 2SiO_2$	A feldspar.
1.510	URANOSPATHITE	$CuO \cdot 2UO_3 \cdot P_2O_5 \cdot nH_2O$	Previously considered to be autunite.
1.53±	KEHOITE	$3(Zn,Ca)O \cdot 2Al_2O_3 \cdot P_2O_5$ and $27 \pm H_2O$	Chalky.
2.10	METAHEWETTITE	$CaO \cdot 3V_2O_5 \cdot 9H_2O$	Slightly soluble in water. B.B., loses water and changes color to yellow-brown.
2.18	HEWETTITE	$CaO \cdot 3V_2O_5 \cdot 9H_2O$	B.B., loses water and changes color to bronze.
4.324	AVOGADRITE	$KBF_4 + 10\%CsBF_4$	A sublimate of Vesuvius.
....	VUDYAVRITE	$Ce_2(TiO_3)_3 \cdot 5(Ca,H)SiO_3 \cdot H_2O$	An alteration product of lovchorrite.
1.642	SERPIERITE	$(Cu,Zn,Ca)O \cdot SO_3 \cdot H_2O$	

GROUP 11
Specific Gravity 2.32-2.00

	H	SP. GR.	F	HCL	COLOR	STREAK	LUSTER	CLEAV-AGE	FRACTURE
1	7	2.32-2.28	Inf	Ins	Colorless	....	V, P	Indist	Conch
2	7	2.20	Inf	Ins	Colorless	....	....		
3	6.5-7	2.04	....	....	Colorless, lt brown	....	V	....	....
4	6-7	2.3	Inf	Ins	White	....	D	None	....
5	5.5-6.5	2.3-1.9	Inf	Ins	White, red, green, brown, yellow, etc	White	V, R, P	....	Conch
6	5.5-6	2.3-2.14	3.5-4	Gelat	Gray, grnsh, blue, ylwsh, red	Uncolored	V, G	Fair	Conch to uneven
7	4.5-6	2.48-2.3	ˋ-3	Gelat	White, gray, black	....	V	....	
8	5.5	2.4-2.23	4.5	Gelat	Blue, grnsh, brnsh, black	....	....	Poor	....
9	5-5.5	2.4-2.16	2	Gelat	White	....	V, S	Perf	
10	5-5.5	2.4-2.3	2	Gelat	White, grnsh, rdsh, brown	Uncolored	V, P	Perf	Uneven to subconch
11	5-5.5	2.29-2.22	2.5	Gelat	Colorless, white, grayish, grnsh, etc	....	V	Traces	Subconch
12	5-5.5	2.25-2.2	2	Gelat	White, grayish, yellowish, red	....	V, P	Perf	Uneven
13	5	2.4-2.2	2-2.5	Gelat	White, gray, ylwsh	....	V, S	Perf	Brittle
14	5	2.11	3-4	Ins	Colorless, white	....	V	Perf	....
15	5	2.22	2	Gelat	White	....	....	Perf	....
16	4.5-5	2.28	2.5	Gelat	White shaded ylw and green	....	P	Traces	....
17	4.5-5	2.23	Fus	Gelat	White	....	D	Good	....
18	4.5-5	2.4-2.3	1.5	Dcpd	Colorless, white, tinted	....	P, V	Perf	Uneven
19	4.5-5	2.25	......	....	White	....	S	....	
20	4-5	2.13	1	Sol	Colorless, white	....	V	Perf	....
21	4-5?	2.0±	Diff	Dcpd	Pale yellow	....	....	....	Granular
22	4-5	2.16-2.08	3	Dcpd	White, flesh red	Uncolored	V	Dist	Uneven
23	4.5	2.26	3	Gelat	Colorless, white, bluish, grayish, rdsh	....	V	None	Subconch
24	4.5	2.17-2.04	2.5-3	Dcpd	Colorless, ylwsh, greenish, reddish	....	V	Easy	Uneven
25	4.5	2.13	1	Sol	White	....	....	Perf	....
26	4-4.5	2.25	3	Pt sol	Colorless, white, yellowish	....	V	Perf	Uneven
27	4-4.5	2.21	3	Gelat	White, reddish	Uncolored	V	Fair	Uneven

GROUP 11
Specific Gravity 2.32-2.00

INDEX OF REF.	NAME	COMPOSITION	REMARKS
.47	**TRIDYMITE**	SiO_2	Soluble in boiling Na_2CO_3, differentiating it from quartz.
.462	LECHATE-LIERITE	SiO_2	Naturally fused quartz from fulgerite.
....	MELANO-PHLOGITE	$Fe_2O_3 \cdot SO_3 \cdot C \cdot SiO_2 \cdot H_2O$	In minute cubes and spherical aggregates. B.B., turns black.
.486	**CRISTOBOLITE**	SiO_2	
.44±	**OPAL**	$SiO_2 \cdot n H_2O$	Soluble in KOH. Sometimes a rich play of colors.
.483	**SODALITE**	$3NaAlSiO_2 \cdot NaCl$	Brittle. In C.T., blue varieties become white and opaque
.490	HYDRO-NEPHELITE	$2Na_2O \cdot 3Al_2O_3 \cdot 6SiO_2 \cdot 7H_2O$	B.B., gives a white enamel.
.495	**NOSELITE**	$5Na_2O \cdot 3Al_2O_3 \cdot 6SiO_2 \cdot 2SO_3$	On coal with soda, gives the sulfide test.
.519	**SCOLECITE**	$CaO \cdot Al_2O_3 \cdot 3SiO_2 \cdot 3H_2O$	B.B., sometimes curls up like a worm.
.525±	**THOMSONITE**	$(Ca,Na_2)O \cdot Al_2O_3 \cdot 2SiO_2 \cdot 2\frac{1}{2}H_2O$	B.B., gives a white enamel. A zeolite.
.487	**ANALCITE**	$Na_2O \cdot Al_2O_3 \cdot 4SiO_2 \cdot 2H_2O$	Brittle. In C.T., yields water.
.482	**NATROLITE**	$Na_2O \cdot Al_2O_3 \cdot 3SiO_2 \cdot 2H_2O$	In C.T., whitens and becomes opaque.
.505	**MESOLITE**	$Na_2O \cdot 2CaO \cdot 3Al_2O_3 \cdot 9SiO_2 \cdot 8H_2O$	B.B., becomes opaque, swells up; worm-like forms.
.475	PTILOLITE	$(Ca,Na_2,K_2)O \cdot Al_2O_3 \cdot 10SiO_2 \cdot 9H_2O$	B.B., gives a clear glass. A zeolite.
510	PSEUDO-MESOLITE	$2CaO \cdot Na_2O \cdot 3Al_2O_3 \cdot 9SiO_2 \cdot 8H_2O$	Near mesolite.
.52±	OKENITE	$CaO \cdot 2SiO_2 \cdot 2H_2O$	In C.T., yields water.
.475	LAUBANITE	$2CaO \cdot Al_2O_3 \cdot 5SiO_2 \cdot 6H_2O$	Fuses to a blebby mass.
.536	ANTHOPYLLITE	$K_2O \cdot 8CaO \cdot 16SiO_2 \cdot 16H_2O$	In C.T., exfoliates, whitens, yields acid water.
.508	GONNARDITE	$Ca_2Na_4Al_8Si_{12}O_{40} \cdot 14H_2O$	A zeolite.
....	HEINTZITE	$K_2O \cdot 4MgO \cdot 9B_2O_3 \cdot 16H_2O$	B.B., colors the flame green.
.56	FARATSIHITE	$(Al,Fe)_2O_3 \cdot 2SiO_2 \cdot 2H_2O$	B.B., gives a grayish glass. Clings to the tongue.
.483±	**CHABAZITE**	$(Na_2 \cdot Ca)O \cdot Al_2O_3 \cdot 4SiO_2 \cdot 6H_2O$	Brittle. B.B., intumesces; fuses to a blebby mass.
.539	GISMONDITE	$CaO \cdot Al_2O_3 \cdot 4SiO_2 \cdot 4H_2O$	In C.T., yields water; becomes opaque.
.47±	**GMELINITE**	$(Na_2,Ca)O \cdot Al_2O_3 \cdot 4SiO_2 \cdot 6H_2O$	Brittle. B.B., gives a white enamel.
.526	KALIBORITE	$K_2O \cdot 4MgO \cdot 11B_2O_3 \cdot 18H_2O$	B.B., a colorless glass. Slightly soluble in water; gives an alkaline reaction.
.510	EPISTILBITE	$CaO \cdot Al_2O_3 \cdot 6SiO_2 \cdot 5H_2O$	Brittle. B.B., gives a vesicular enamel
.500	**PHILLIPSITE**	$(K_2,Ca)O_2 \cdot Al_2O_3 \cdot 4SiO_2 \cdot 4\frac{1}{2}H_2O$	Brittle. B.B., crumbles and fuses to a white enamel.

GROUP 11
Specific Gravity 2.32-2.00

	H	SP. GR.	F	HCL	COLOR	STREAK	LUSTER	CLEAV-AGE	FRACTURE
28	4-4.5	2.16-2.09	2-2.5	Gelat	White, grnsh, rdsh, yellowish	....	V	Indist	Subconch
29	4-4.5	2.165	Fus	Dcpd	White	....	....	Perf	....
30	3.5-4	2.12	......	....	Light flesh red	....	....	Perf	....
31	3.5-4	2.36-2.25	2.5-3	Gelat	White, yellow, red	Uncolored	V, P	Perf	Uneven
32	3.5-4	2.22-2.18	2-2.5	Dcpd	White, tinted red, gray, brown	White	P, V	Perf	Subconch to uneven
33	3.5-4	2.2-2.09	2-2.5	Dcpd	White, brownish, yellow, red	Uncolored	V, P	Perf	Uneven
34	3.25-4	2.34-2.32	Inf	Sol	White, yellow, green	White	V, P	Fair	Uneven to subconch
35	3-4	2.15-2.08	4-5	Pt sol	Yellow, pink, white	....	V, P	Perf	Uneven
36	3.5	2.3	3	Sol	Yellow	Yellow	V	Fair	....
37	3.5	2.09	......	....	White	....	....	Good	....
38	3.5	2.18-2.14	Inf	Sol	White	White	V, S, P, E	Perf	Brittle
39	3.5	2.28	3	....	Colorless	....	....	Perf	....
40	2-4	2.24-2.0	Inf	Dcpd	Green to blue	White	V, E	....	Conch
41	3-3.5	2.17-2.10	4.5-5	Sol	Chestnut brown	....	V	Perf	Uneven
42	3-3.5	2.1	......	Sol	White	....	V	Perf	....
43	3-3.5	2.076	......	Sol	White or pale buff	....	V, G, D	....	Subconch
44	3-3.5	2.05-1.95	......	....	Grnsh, white, green, yellowish	....	....	....	....
45	3-3.25	2.15	3-3.5	Ins	White	....	V. P	Perf	....
46	3+	2.05	Diff	Dcpd	Black	Yellow-brown	....	....	Brittle
47	3	2.17	Inf	Ins	Colorless, white	....	V	Indist	....
48	3	2.15	Inf	Sol	Colorless, lt green	....	V, P	Perf	....
49	3	2.14-2.08	4.5-5	Sol	Red, brownish	....	G	Dist	....
50	3	2.27	......	....	Emerald green	....	....	....	Fibrous
51	3	2.12	5	Sol	Chestnut brown	Orange yellow	V	Perf	....
52	3	2.03	Easy	Sol	Brown, yellow	Uncolored	R, V	....	Conch
53	3	2.30	......	....	Colorless	....	....	Perf	....
54	3	2.18	Inf	Sol	Bluish-brown	....	....	....	....
55	3	2.25	Easy	Sol	Colorless, white, yellow	....	V	Indist	Conch
56	3	2.1	Diff	Sol	White, yellow, brown	Uncolored	R, V	....	Conch

GROUP 11
Specific Gravity 2.32-2.00

INDEX OF REF.	NAME	COMPOSITION	REMARKS
1.496	LEVYNITE	$CaO \cdot Al_2O_3 \cdot 3SiO_2 \cdot 5H_2O$	Brittle. B.B., intumesces and fuses to a white blebby mass.
1.496	DACHIARDITE	$3(Ca,Na_2,K_2)O \cdot 2Al_2O_3 \cdot 18SiO_2 \cdot 14H_2O$	A zeolite. B.B., decrepitates, exfoliates, fuses to a white enamel.
1.492	STELLERITE	$CaO \cdot Al_2O_3 \cdot 7SiO_2 \cdot 7H_2O$	A member of the zeolite group.
1.524	LAUMONTITE	$CaO \cdot Al_2O_3 \cdot 4SiO_2 \cdot 4H_2O$	B.B., gives a white enamel.
1.485	HEULANDITE	$CaO \cdot Al_2O_3 \cdot 6SiO_2 \cdot 5H_2O$	Brittle. B.B., exfoliates and curves into fan-like or vermicular forms.
.498	STILBITE	$(Na_2,Ca)O \cdot Al_2O_3 \cdot 6SiO_2 \cdot 6H_2O$	Brittle. B.B., exfoliates and curves into fan-like or vermicular forms.
.534	WAVELLITE	$4AlPO_4 \cdot 2Al(OH)_3 \cdot 9H_2O$	Brittle. Soluble in KOH.
.475	MORDENITE	$(Ca,Na_2)O \cdot AlCO_3 \cdot 9SiO_2 \cdot 6H_2O$	Brittle. B.B., gives a white enamel. A zeolite.
.60±	KONINCKITE	$FePO_4 \cdot 3H_2O$	
.524	GINORITE	$2CaO \cdot 7B_2O_3 \cdot 8H_2O$	
.527	HYDRO-MAGNESITE	$3MgCO_3 \cdot Mg(OH)_2 \cdot 3H_2O$	In C.T., yields water and CO_2.
.543	GORDONITE	$MgO \cdot Al_2O_3 \cdot P_2O_5 \cdot 9H_2O$	
.40±	CHRYSOCOLLA	$CuSiO_3 \cdot 2H_2O$	In C.T., blackens and yields water. Colors the flame green.
.571	ROEMERITE	$FeSO_4 \cdot Fe_2(SO_4)_3 \cdot 12H_2O$	Brittle. Soluble in water. Tastes saline. Astringent.
.518	NEWBERYITE	$MgHPO_4 \cdot 3H_2O$	Soluble in HNO_3.
....	TEEPLEITE	$Na_2B_2O_4 \cdot 2NaCl \cdot 4H_2O$	Flat beveled plates, usually rounded into flat cushions. Borax Lake, Calif.
.584	SCHROETTERITE	$8Al_2O_3 \cdot 3SiO_2 \cdot 30H_2O$	A clay mineral.
.479	FERRIERITE	$2(Mg,Na_2,H_2)O \cdot Al_2O_3 \cdot 5SiO_2$	
....	STURTITE	$6(Mn,Ca,Mg)O \cdot Fe_2O_3 \cdot 8SiO_2 \cdot 23H_2O$	B.B., gives a magnetic mass.
.490	FLUELLITE	$AlF_3 \cdot H_2O$	
.553	HYDROCALUMITE	$4CaO \cdot Al_2O_3 \cdot 13 \pm H_2O$	
.529	QUETENITE	$MgO \cdot Fe_2O_3 \cdot 3SO_3 \cdot 13H_2O$	Decomposed by water with separation of iron sesquioxide.
....	MAUFITE	$(Mg,Ni,Fe)O \cdot 2Al_2O_3 \cdot 3SiO_2 \cdot 4H_2O$	
.643	CASTANITE	$Fe_2O_3 \cdot 2SO_3 \cdot 8H_2O$	B.B., changes color from orange to brown to black. Decomposed by H_2SO_4.
.61±	DIADOCHITE	$2Fe_2O_3 \cdot 2SO_3 \cdot P_2O_5 \cdot 12H_2O$	In C.T., yields water, swells up and becomes lustrous.
.558	PARAVAUXITE	$FeO \cdot Al_2O_3 \cdot P_2O_5 \cdot 5H_2O$	
....	MELITE	$2(Al,Fe)_2O_3 \cdot SiO_2 \cdot 8H_2O$	B.B., gives off water and the residue becomes brown.
.487	LEONITE	$K_2O \cdot MgO \cdot 2SO_3 \cdot 4H_2O$	Soluble in water.
.625	DESTINEZITE	$2Fe_2O_3 \cdot P_2O_5 \cdot 2SO_3 \cdot 13H_2O$	In C.T., yields much water.

GROUP 11
Specific Gravity 2.32-2.00

	H	SP. GR.	F	HCL	COLOR	STREAK	LUSTER	CLEAV-AGE	FRACTURE
57	3	2.22	Easy	Dcpd	White	....	V, D	....	....
58	2-4	2.24-2.0	Inf	Dcpd	Green to blue	White	V, E	....	Conch
59	2.5-3.5	2.4-2.3	Inf	....	Grysh, grnsh, rdsh white, white	....	P, V	Perf	....
60	2-3.5	2.2-2.0	5-6	Dcpd	White, yellow, green, red	....	G	....	Brittle
61	2.5-3	2.26	Inf	Sol	White, bluish	....	....	....	....
62	2.5-3	2.19-2.07	1.5-2	Sol	Colorless, white, red	....	V	Dist	....
63	2.5-3	2.2	Inf	Sol	White, violet	....	....	Cubic	....
64	2.5-3	2.14-2.11	1.5	Sol	White, gray	....	V	Perf	Uneven to subconch
65	2.5-3	2.18	......	Sol	Brown	....	....	....	....
66	2-3	2.5-2.2	Easy	Sol	Brown, yellow, white	Yellow to white	V, G	....	....
67	2-3	2.14	Inf	Sol	White, pink, ylwsh, bluish	White	P	Perf	....
68	2-3	2.2	3	Sol	Rose, pink	....	....	....	....
69	2-3	2.1	......	Sol	Pale blue	....	....	....	....
70	2-3	2.2	......	Sol	Pale blue	....	....	....	....
71	2-3	2.15	Easy	Sol	Black	....	....	....	....
72	2-3	2.2	3	Sol	Pale green, white	....	....	....	....
73	2-3	2.10	3	Sol	Pale pink	....	....	....	....
74	2-5	2.14-2.1	Inf	Sol	Golden, white, green	....	W, V, P	Perf	Flexible
75	2-3	2.151	Easy	Dcpd	Black	Brownish	R	None	Uneven
76	2.5	2.28-2.23	1.5	Sol	Colorless, bluish, green, yellow, rdsh	....	V	....	....
77	2.5	2.6-2.1	1.5	Sol	Colorless, red, blue, purple	....	V	Perf	Conch
78	2.5	2.1	2	Sol	White	....	....	Perf	....
79	2.5	2.3-2.12	3	Sol	Blue, greenish	Uncolored	V	Imperf	Conch, Brittle
80	2.5	2.11	4.5-5	Sol	Red orange	Lemon yellow	....	Perf	Brittle
81	2.5	2.12	4.5-5	Sol	Reddish violet	....	V	Perf	....
82	2.5	2.10	4.5-5	Sol	Yellow, reddish, violet	....	P	Perf	....
83	2.5	2.31	Easy	Sol	Yellow	....	V	None	Conch
84	2.5	2.14	......	....	White	....	....	Fair	....

GROUP 11
Specific Gravity 2.32-2.00

INDEX OF REF.	NAME	COMPOSITION	REMARKS
1.603	CRESTMORIETE	$4CaO \cdot 4SiO_2 \cdot 7H_2O$	B.B., gives a slightly vescular glass.
1.40±	**CHRYSOCOLLA**	$CuSiO_3 \cdot 2H_2O$	**In C.T., blackens and yields water. Colors the flame green.**
1.566	**GIBBSITE**	$AL(OH)_3$	**Soluble in H_2SO_4. In C.T., yields water and becomes white and opaque.**
....	DEWEYLITE	$4MgO \cdot 3SiO_2 \cdot 6H_2O$	In C.T., yields much water.
.534	ZINC-ALUMINITE	$6ZnO \cdot 3Al_2O_3 \cdot 2SO_3 \cdot 18H_2O$	In C.T., yields much water.
.505	**KAINITE**	$MgSO_4 \cdot KCl \cdot 3H_2O$	**Soluble in water.**
.52	HYDROPHILITE	$KCl \cdot CaCl_2$	Strongly hydroscopic. Tastes bitter.
.492	**TRONA**	$Na_2CO_3 \cdot NaHCO_3 \cdot 2H_2O$	**Soluble in water. In C.T., yields water and CO_2.**
.558	LOUDER-BACKITE	$2FeO \cdot 3(Fe,Al)_2O_3 \cdot 10SO_3 \cdot 35H_2O$	Soluble in water.
.635±	PITTICITE	Hydrated ferric AsO_4 and SO_4	In C.T, yields water and SO_2.
.540	BRUG-NATELLITE	$6MgO \cdot Fe_2O_3 \cdot CO_2 \cdot 12H_2O$	Micaceous, lamellar. B.B., turns golden and becomes magnetic.
.549	COBALT CHALCANTHITE	$CoO \cdot SO_3 \cdot 5H_2O$	Soluble in water.
.534	ZINC COPPER CHALCANTHITE	$ZnO \cdot CuO \cdot 2SO_3 \cdot 10H_2O$	Soluble in water.
.536	IRON COPPER CHALCANTHITE	$FeO \cdot CuO \cdot 2SO_3 \cdot 19H_2O$	Soluble in water.
.582	CHING-LUSUITE	$2(Na,K)_2O \cdot 5(Mn,Ca)O \cdot 3(Ti,Zr)O_2 \cdot 14SiO_2 \cdot 9H_2O$	Pale yellow in splinters. B.B., a dark glass.
.537	SIDEROTIL	$FeO \cdot SO_3 \cdot 5H_2O$	Soluble in water.
.508	MANGANESE CHALCANTHITE	$MnO \cdot SO_3 \cdot 5H_2O$	Soluble in water.
.565±	PYROAURITE	$6MgO \cdot Fe_2O_3 \cdot CO_2 \cdot 12H_2O$	B.B., turns brown and becomes magnetic.
.582	CHINLUSUITE	$2(Na,K)_2O \cdot 5(Mn,Ca)O \cdot 3(Ti,Zr)O_2 \cdot 14SiO_2 \cdot 9H_2O$	In C.T., swells, melts easily to a dark brown glass.
.486	BLOEDITE	$Na_2O \cdot MgO \cdot 2SO_3 \cdot 4H_2O$	Soluble in water. B.B., loses water rapidly.
.544	**HALITE**	$NaCl$	**Soluble in water. Common salt.**
.463	PICROMERITE	$K_2SO_4 \cdot MgSO_4 \cdot 6H_2O$	Soluble in water. In C.T., yields water.
.537	**CHALCANTHITE**	$CuSO_4 \cdot 5H_2O$	**Soluble in water. A drop of solution on bright iron coats it with copper.**
.605	AMARANTITE	$Fe_2O_3 \cdot 2SO_3 \cdot 7H_2O$	Decomposed by cold water.
.543±	QUENSTEDTITE	$Fe_2(SO_4)_3 \cdot 10H_2O$	Soluble in water.
.543	COPIAPITE	$2Fe_2O_3 \cdot 5SO_3 \cdot 18H_2O$	B.B. on coal, becomes magnetic.
.59	CHLORO-MANGANOKALITE	$4KCl \cdot MnCl_2$	Delequesent. From Vesuvius.
.525	KRAMERITE	$Na_2O \cdot 2CaO \cdot 5B_2O_3 \cdot 10H_2O$	Possibly identical with probertite.

GROUP 11
Specific Gravity 2.32-2.00

	H	SP. GR.	F	HCL	COLOR	STREAK	LUSTER	CLEAV-AGE	FRACTURE
85	2.5	2.29	5	Sol	Nile blue	....	....	Perf	....
86	2.5	2.23	Inf	Sol	Colorless	....	V, G, P	Good	Conch
87	2.5	2.2	Fus	Gelat	Cream, pink	....	P, G	....	Conch, splintery
88	2.5	2.20	1?	Sol	Colorless	....	....	Perf	....
89	2.5	2.29	......	Sol	Colorless, yellowish	....	Glassy	Perf	Uneven
90	2.5	2.1	Inf	Pt sol	Pale grnsh blue, indigo blue	....	....	Traces	....
91	2.5	2.14-2.08	Inf	Sol	Ylwsh to bwnsh wht	....	W, V, P	Perf	Flexible
92	**2-4**	**2.24-2.0**	**Inf**	**Dcpd**	**Green to blue**	**White**	**V, E**	....	**Conch**
93	2-3.5	2.2-2.0	5-6	Dcpd	White, yellow, green, red	....	G	....	Brittle
94	2-2.5	2.3-2.2	Inf	Gelat	Green, bluish	Bluish, green	D	....	Subconch
95	2-2.5	2.35-2.15	2	Sol	Yellow	Pale yellow	....	Perf	....
96	2-2.5	2.21	3	Sol	Colorless, yellowish	....	P, V	Perf	....
97	2-2.5	2.5-2.0	2-3?	Sol	Apple green	Paler to white	V	Perf	....
98	2-2.5	2.14-2.04	4.5-5	Sol	Red to yellow	Ochre yellow	V	Dist	....
99	2-2.5	2.10-2.09	4.5-5	Sol	White, yellow, violet, greenish	....	....	Imperf	....
100	2-2.5	2.1-1.9	Inf	Sol	Colorless, reddish, bluish, yellowish	....	V	Perf	Brittle
101	2-2.5	2.0	Inf	Sol	Apple green	White	V	Perf	....
102	**2-2.5**	**2.0**	**5-6**	**Gelat**	**White, tinged**	....	V	....	....
103	2-2.5	2.0	5-6	Gelat	White, tinged	....	....	....	Fibrous
104	**1.5-2.5**	**2.09-2.05**	**1**	**Ins**	**Yellow, grnsh, rdsh**	**White**	**R, G**	**Imperf**	**Conch to uneven**
105	**2**	**2.4-2.2**	**Easy**	**Pt sol**	**Green, gray**	....	**D**	....	....
106	2	2.04-1.89	4.5-5	Sol	Yellowish white	....	S	....	....
107	2	2.28	3	....	Chocolate brown	Dk orange-ylw	G	....	....
108	**2**	**2.14-2.09**	**1**	**Sol**	**White**	**White**	**V**	**Perf**	**Subconch to uneven**
109	2	2.09-2.03	Inf	Sol	White, brwnsh tint	White	P, W	Perf	Flexible
110	2	2.0-1.9	2	Sol	White with red spots	....	....	Perf	....
111	2	2.49-2.13	......	Sol	Yellow	....	D, R	Perf	Uneven
112	2	2.19	Inf	Gelat	White	....	S	....	....
113	2	2.02	Easy	Sol	Light blue, green	....	....	....	....

GROUP 11
Specific Gravity 2.32-2.00

INDEX OF REF.	NAME	COMPOSITION	REMARKS
1.525	CHALCOALUMITE	$CuO \cdot 2Al_2O_3 \cdot SO_3 \cdot 9H_2O$	
1.555	WHEWELLITE	$CaO \cdot C_2O_3 \cdot H_2O$	Brittle.
1.525	SPADAITE	$5MgO \cdot 6SiO_2 \cdot 4H_2O$	In C.T., gives water. B.B., gives a glassy enamel.
1.481	DARAPSKITE	$3Na_2O \cdot N_2O_5 \cdot 2SO_3 \cdot 2H_2O$	Soluble in water. In C.T., yields water.
....	UNGEMACHITE	$Na_4(K,Fe''')_2(OH) \cdot (SO_4)_3 \cdot 5H_2O$	Brittle.
1.55	MILOSCHITE	$(Al,Cr)_2O_3 \cdot 2SiO_2 \cdot 2H_2O$	In C.T., yields water.
1.573	SJOGRENITE	$Mg_6Fe_2(OH)_{16}CO_3 \cdot 4H_2O$	B.B., exfoliates; turns golden-brown then yellow-brown and becomes magnetic.
1.40±	**CHRYSOCOLLA**	**$CuSiO_3 \cdot 2H_2O$**	**In C.T., blackens and yields water. Colors the flame green.**
....	DEWEYLITE	$4MgO \cdot 3SiO_2 \cdot 6H_2O$	In C.T., yields much water.
1.585	VOL-CHONSKOITE	$(Cr,Fe,Al)_2O_3 \cdot 2SiO_2 \cdot 2H_2O$	B.B., blackens. In C.T., yields water.
1.525	SIDERO-NATRITE	$2Na_2O \cdot Fe_2O_3 \cdot 4SO_3 \cdot 7H_2O$	Decomposed by boiling water.
1.546	BRUSHITE	$CaHPO_4 \cdot 2H_2O$	In C.T., whitens and gives off water at red heat.
1.662	LINDACKERITE	$3NiO \cdot 6CuO \cdot SO_3 \cdot 2As_2O_5 \cdot 7H_2O$	B.B., gives a black bead. The HCl solution yields a yellow precipitate with H_2S.
1.529	BOTRYOGEN	$MgO \cdot FeO \cdot Fe_2O_3 \cdot 4SO_3 \cdot 18H_2O$	Slightly soluble in water. In C.T., yields water leaving a reddish yellow earth.
1.550	COQUIMBITE	$Fe_2(SO_4)_3 \cdot 9H_2O$	Soluble in water. Decomposed by boiling water.
.480	GOSLARITE	$ZnO \cdot SO_3 \cdot 7H_2O$	Soluble in water. In C.T., yields water.
.489	MORENOSITE	$NiSO_4 \cdot 7H_2O$	Soluble in H_2O. B.B. on coal, glows strongly and yields SO_2.
.52	**SEPIOLITE**	**$2MgO \cdot 3SiO_2 \cdot 2H_2O$**	**In C.T., yields water. Fibrous is alpha or para and the amorphous is beta sepiolite.**
.506	PARASEPIOLITE	$2MgO \cdot 3SiO_2 \cdot 2H_2O$	The fibrous sepiolite is *Alpha or Para*. *Beta* is amorphous variety.
.037	**SULPHUR**	**S**	**Burns readily with a blue flame giving SO_2.**
.63±	**GLAUCONITE**	**Hydrated silicate of K and Fe**	**B.B., gives a black magnetic mass.**
.488	HALOTRICHITE	$FeSO_4 \cdot Al_2(SO_4)_3 \cdot 24H_2O$	Soluble in water. Fuses first in its own water of crytallization.
....	ELBRUSSITE	Al,Fe,Mg,etc $SiO_2 \cdot H_2O$	
.504	**NITER**	**KNO_3**	**Brittle. Soluble in water. Colors flame violet.**
.512	HYDRO-TALCITE	$6MgO \cdot Al_2O_3 \cdot 15H_2O$	In C.T., yields water.
.534	HYDRO-BORACITE	$CaO \cdot MgO \cdot 3B_2O_3 \cdot 6H_2O$	In C.T., yields water. B.B., gives a clear glass.
.561	HUMBOLDTINE	$2FeC_2O_4 \cdot 3H_2O$	In C.T., yields water, turns black and becomes magnetic.
.48	ZEBE-DASSITE	$5MgO \cdot Al_2O_3 \cdot 6SiO_2 \cdot 4H_2O$	Fibrous.
.483	ZINC COPPER MELANTERITE	$CuO \cdot ZnO \cdot 2SO_3 \cdot 14H_2O$	Soluble in water.

GROUP 11
Specific Gravity 2.32-2.00

	H	SP. GR.	F	HCL	COLOR	STREAK	LUSTER	CLEAV-AGE	FRACTURE	
114	2	2.23	Inf	Sol	Colorless	....	P	Perf	Flexible	
115	2	2.03	......	....	White	....				
116	2	2.1-2.0	......	....	Wht, bluish, grysh, brwnsh wht	....	W, P	Perf	Flexible	
117	2	2.12	Easy	Sol	Colorless	....	V to S	Perf	....	
118	1.5-2	2.16	Inf	Sol	Rose, lilac, pink	Pale lilac to pink	W, G, P	Perf	Flexible	
119	1.5-2	2.32	2.5-3	Sol	**Wh, various shades**	**White**	**P, Sv**	**Perf**	**Conch**	
120	1.5-2	2.15-2.05	......	....	Lilac, rose-pink	Pale lilac	W, P	Perf	Flexible	
121	1.5-2	**2.29-2.24**	**1**	**Sol**	**White, red, brown, gray, yellow**		**V**	**Perf**	**Flexible**	
122	1.5	2.2	......	....	Brown	....	....	....	....	
123	1.5	**2.30**	**Fus**	**Dcpd**	**Yellowish, brwnsh**	....	**P**	**Perf**	**Flexible**	
124	1-2	**2.23-2.09**	**Inf**	**Ins**	**Black to gray**	....	**M, D, E**	**Perf**	....	
125	1-2	**2.2-2.0**	**Inf**	**Dcpd**	**Wh, gray, grnsh, ylwsh, bluish, rdsh**	....	**P, W, D**	....	**Conch**	
126	1-2	2.15-2.0	Inf	Dcpd	White	....	Glim-mering	....	....	
127	1-1.5	2.166	......	Dcpd	Ylwsh wht, ylwsh brwn	....				
128	1	2.03	Fus	Sol	Colorless	....	V			
129	Soft	2.30-2.24	Diff	....	Colorless, tinted ylw, green, blue	....	G			
130	Soft	2.31	4	Gelat	Dark green	....	....	Mic	....	
131	Soft	2.32	......	....	Red	....	....	....	Fibrous	
132	Soft	2.30-2.18	Inf	....	White, grayish, reddish	Greasy	G	....	....	
133	Soft	2.25±	Inf	Ins	White, gray, red, grn	....		Perf	....	
134	**Soft**	**2.8-2.3**	**Inf**	**Dcpd**	**Apple green**	....	**D**	....	....	
135	Low	2.07	......	....	Pale yellow, greenish cast	....				
136	?	2.31	Inf	Sol	Colorless, brown, amethyst	....	S	Good	....	
137	?	2.1	Inf	Ins	Yellow	....				
138	?	2.31	......	....	Sky-blue	....	....	....	....	
139	?	2.05	Fus	Sol	Colorless	....		Pris-matic Perf	Fibrous	
140	?	2.16	Easy	Gelat	Colorless, yellow	....		Perf	....	

GROUP 11
Specific Gravity 2.32-2.00

INDEX OF REF.	NAME	COMPOSITION	REMARKS
1.574	PORTLANDITE	$Ca(OH)_2$	Sectile, cleavage plates flexible. Slowly soluble in water.
1.534	ARTINITE	$2MgO \cdot CO_2 \cdot 4H_2O$	
1.524	MANASSEITE	$Mg_6Al_2(OH)_{16}CO_3 \cdot 4H_2O$	Greasy feel.
1.535	MEYER-HOFFERITE	$2CaO \cdot 3B_2O_3 \cdot 7H_2O$	B.B., gives an opaque enamel. Colors flame green.
1.542	STICHTITE	$6MgO \cdot Cr_2O_3 \cdot CO_2 \cdot 12H_2O$	Occurs in micaceous scales.
1.523	**GYPSUM**	$CaSO_4 \cdot 2H_2O$	**In C.T., yields water and becomes opaque.**
1.557	BARBERTONITE	$Mg_6Cr_2(OH)_{16}CO_3 \cdot 4H_2O$	Greasy feel.
1.587	**SODA NITER**	$NaNO_3$	**Soluble in water. Tastes cooling.**
....	FERRO-HALLOYSITE	$(Al,Fe)_2O_3 \cdot 2SiO_2 \cdot 3H_2O + Al_2O_3 \cdot Fe_2O_3$	
1.560	**JEFFERISITE**	$10(Mg,Fe)O \cdot 4(Al,Fe)_2O_3 \cdot 10SiO_2 \cdot 7H_2O$	**A vermiculite. B.B., opens out in worm-like forms. A hydrated mica.**
2.0±	**GRAPHITE**	C	**Burns at high temperatures. Thin laminea are flexible. In contact with metallic Zu in $CuSO_4$ solution, it is coated with copper.**
1.555	**HALLOYSITE**	$Al_2O_3 \cdot 2SiO_2 \cdot 2H_2O$	**In C.T., yields water.**
....	COLLYRITE	$2Al_2O_3 \cdot SiO_2 \cdot 9H_2O$	In C.T., yields water. Sticks to the tongue. Gelatanizes with HNO_3.
....	HANUSITE	$H_2Mg_2Si_8O_9 \cdot H_2O$	
.487	TAMARUGITE	$Na_2SO_4 \cdot Al_2(SO_4)_3 \cdot 12H_2O$	Fibrous.
.53+	SAPONITE	Hydrous silicate of Al and Mg	Decomposed by H_2SO_4. B.B., gives off water and blackens.
.565	GRIFFITHITE	$4(Mg,Fe,Ca)O \cdot (Al,Fe)_2O_3 \cdot 5SiO_2 \cdot 7H_2O$	A member of the chlorite group.
.520±	JANITE	$H_2O \cdot SiO_2$ of Fe,Al,Ca,Mg, etc	Related to chloropal or celadonite.
....	CIMOLITE	$2Al_2O_3 \cdot 9SiO_2 \cdot 6H_2O$	In C.T., yields water. Adheres to the tongue.
.516±	MONTMORILLON-ITE	$(Mg,Ca)O \cdot Al_2O_3 \cdot 5SiO_2 \cdot nH_2O$	Softens in water. A clay-like mineral.
.59	**GARNIERITE**	$(Ni,Mg)O \cdot SiO_2 \cdot nH_2O$	**A serpentine.**
....	ROSICKYITE	S	Natural gamma-sulfur modification. Minute crystals. Czeckoslovakia.
.581	KORNELITE	$Fe_2O_3 \cdot 3SO_3 \cdot 8H_2O$	B.B., turns brown and assumes worm-like shapes.
....	DEECKEITE	$(H,K,Na)_2O \cdot (Mg,Ca) \cdot (Al,Fe)_2(Si_2O_5)_5 \cdot 9H_2O$	B.B., becomes opaque. A pseudomorph after melilite.
.491	MERCALLITE	$KHSO_4$	A stalactite from the crater of Vesuvius.
.541	LUENEBERGITE	$Mg_3(PO_4)_2 \cdot B_2O_3 \cdot 8H_2O$	In flattened masses; fibrous to earthy structure.
.501	EPIDESMINE	$CaO \cdot Al_2O_3 \cdot 6SiO_2 \cdot 6H_2O$	In C.T., gives water.

GROUP 11
Specific Gravity 2.32-2.00

	H	SP. GR.	F	HCL	COLOR	STREAK	LUSTER	CLEAV-AGE	FRACTUE	
141	?	2.3	Diff	Sol	Wht, grnsh, bluish, grn, rdsh, ylwsh	....	G	Perf	....	
142	?	2.11	......	Sol	Colorless	....		Basal	Granular	
143	?	2.16	Easy	Sol	White	....		Good	....	
144	?	2.17-2.15	......	....	Light gray	....		....	....	
145	?	2.22	......	....	White	....		Perf	....	
146	?	2.26	Inf	Pt sol	Red, white, various colors	....		Perf	Fibrous	
147	?	2.20	......	....	Yellowish	....		....	....	
148	?	2.23	Inf	Sol	Chalky white, pale blue	....		Mic	....	
149	?	2.25	......	....	Yellowish green	....		....	Fibrous	
150	?	2.2	Inf	Sol	Yellow, brown	....		....	....	
151	?	2.23	1?	Sol	Clear blue	....		Perf	....	
152	?	2.25	......	....	Dark gray	....		....	....	
153	?	2.0	......	....	Gray	....		Perf	....	
154	?	2.3	......	....	Gray, grnsh tinge	....		....	....	
155	?	2.11	......	....	Pale violet	....		....	....	
156	?	2.0	Easy	Sol	White	....	P	....	Fibrous	
157	?	2.18	......	....	....	....	P	....	....	
158	?	2.15	......	....	....	....		....	....	
159	?	2.16	......	....	....	....		....	....	
160	?	2.0	......	....	....	....		....	....	
161	?	2.3	......	....	White, light yellow	....		....	....	

GROUP 11
Specific Gravity 2.32-2.00

INDEX OF REF.	NAME	COMPOSITION	REMARKS
1.57±	BOWLINGITE	Silicate of Fe,Mg,Al and H_2O	B.B., gives water and blackens. Close to saponite.
1.528	PATERNOITE	$MgB_8O_{13} \cdot 4H_2O$	Related to larderellite.
1.480	KALICINITE	$K_2O \cdot 2CO_2 \cdot H_2O$	Soluble in water.
....	HYDRO-GIOBERTITE	$2MgO \cdot CO_2 \cdot 3H_2O$	Probably a mixture.
1.500	NAHCOLITE	$Na_2O \cdot 2CO_2 \cdot H_2O$	
1.476	ARDUINITE	$CaO \cdot Na_2O \cdot 2Al_2O_3 \cdot 3SiO_2 \cdot 5H_2O$	In C.T., yields water. A zeolite.
....	KARACHAITE	$MgO \cdot SiO_2 \cdot H_2O$	An asbestiform variety of chrysotile.
.553	ALUMOHYDRO-CALCITE	$CaO \cdot Al_2O_3 \cdot 2CO_2 \cdot 5H_2O$	
....	LABITE	$H_2MgSi_3O_8 \cdot H_2O$	Occurs as fibers in serpentine.
.5±	ROSIÉRÉSITE	Hydrous phosphate of Al,Pb and Cu	B.B., blackens. In C.T., yields water.
.486	CYANOCHROITE	$K_2O \cdot CuO \cdot 2SO_3 \cdot 6H_2O$	Soluble in water. From Vesuvius. Isomorphous with picromerit.
....	LUCIANITE	A clay	Colloidal. In water swells to many times original volume.
.370	CRYPTOHALITE	$2NH_4F \cdot SiF_4$	Observed in a Vesuvius fumerole.
.641	ABKHAZITE	Variety of amphibole asbestos	
....	PARACOQUIMBITE	$Fe_2(SO_4)_3 \cdot 9H_2O$	Rhombohedral coquimbite.
.44	ERIONITE	$(Na,K)_2O \cdot 2Al_2O_3 \cdot CaO \cdot 12SiO_2 \cdot 12H_2O$	A zeolite. B.B., gives a clear colorless glass.
....	BATAVITE	$4MgO \cdot Al_2O_3 \cdot 4SiO_2 \cdot 4H_2O$	Occurs in pearly micaceous scales.
.470	CHLELÖEWEITE	$K_2Na_4Mg_2(SO_4)_5 \cdot 5H_2O$	May be identical with loëweite.
.488	DOUGLASITE	$2KCl \cdot FeCl_2 \cdot 2H_2O$	Formed by alkaline waters at Douglas Springs, Arizona.(?)
....	HYDRO-THOMSONITE	$(H_2,Na_2,Ca) \cdot Al_2Si_2O_8 \cdot 5H_2O$	A decomposition product of thomsonite or scolecite.
....	ARDEALITE	$CaHPO_4 \cdot CaSO_4 \cdot 4H_2O$	Fine crystaline powdery mineral.

GROUP 12
Specific Gravity 1.99 And Lower

	H	SP. GR.	F	HCL	COLOR	STREAK	LUSTER	CLEAV-AGE	FRACTURE
1	5.5-6.5	2.3-1.9	Inf	Ins	White, yellow, red, brown, green, etc	White	V, R, P	....	Conch
2	5	1.92	3	Dcpd	White, brown	....	V, A	Dist	Uneven
3	2.5-4.5	1.87-1.73	Inf	Pt sol	Orange, green, ylw	....	....	Perf	Conch to splintery
4	3.5-4	1.94	Inf	Sol	Colorless, white, tinged yellow or blue	White	V, R	....	Subconch
5	3.5-4	2.0-1.57	......	....	Jet-black	....	Brilliant	None	Conch
6	3-4	1.91	Easy	Sol	Colorless	....	Prismatic	Brittle
7	3.5	1.88	Inf	Dcpd	White	....	G, D	Traces	Subconch
8	3-3.5	2.05-1.95	......	....	Greenish-white, green, yellowish	....	....	....
9	3	1.89-1.85	Inf	Gelat	Colorless, green, blue, yellow	Uncolored	V, Sr	....	Conch
10	3	1.85	Fus	Sol	....	....	Indist	....
11	3	1.88	1	Sol	White	....	....	....
12	3	1.83	......	Sol	Yellowish gray	....	....	....
13	2.5-3.5	1.93	......	....	Colorless, white	....	V	Good	Conch
14	2.5-4.5	1.87-1.73	Inf	Pt sol	Orange, grn, ylw	....	....	Perf	Conch to splintery
15	2-3	1.95-1.93	1.5	Sol	White, yellowish white	Uncolored, gray	V	Perf	Conch
16	2-3	1.82	Diff	Dcpd	Yellow to bronze, red	Yellow	G	Perf	....
17	2-3	1.96	Inf	Sol	White, yellow, brown	....	D	....	....
18	2-3	1.9	Easy	Sol	Blue	....	V	Easy	....
19	2.5	1.98	1	Sol	Azure blue	....	V	Dist	Conch
20	2.5	1.98-1.94	......	Pt sol	Bluish grn changing to black	Nearly white	D	None	Conch
21	2.5	1.84	Inf	Sol	Colorless, white	....	V, G	Perf	Splintery
22	2.5	1.69-1.54	Inf	Sol	White	....	V, D	Dist	....
23	2.5	1.91	Easy	Sol	White to colorless	....	V, P	Perf	....
24	2.5	1.99-1.85	......	Sol	Brown, reddish	....	....	....	....
25	2.5	1.09	......	....	....	....	....	....	....
26	2.5	1.05	......	....	Pale ylw to reddish brown	....	....	....
27	2.5	1.93	Inf	Sol	Amber, yellow	....	....	Perf	....
28	2.5	1.725	......	Sol	Water-clear, yellow	....	......	None	Conch
29	2.5	1.76	......	Sol	Yellowish	....	....	Perf	....
30	2.5	1.05	......	....	Yellow, whitish	....	....	....	....
31	2.5	1.81	4.5-5	Sol	Orange-yellow	....	....	....	....

GROUP 12
Specific Gravity 1.99 And Lower

INDEX OF REF.	NAME	COMPOSITION	REMARKS
1.44±	**OPAL**	$SiO_2 \cdot nH_2O$	**Soluble in KOH. Sometimes a rich play of colors.**
1.480	FAUJASITE	$Na_2O \cdot CaO \cdot 2Al_2O_3 \cdot 10SiO_2 \cdot 20H_2O$	B.B., fuses with intumescence to a white blebby enamel.
....	CHLOROPAL	$Fe_2O_3 \cdot 3SiO_2 \cdot 5H_2O$	In C.T., yields water. B.B., turns black and becomes magnetic.
1.485	EVANSITE	$3Al_2O_3 \cdot P_2O_5 \cdot 18H_2O$	In C.T., gives neutral water; decrepitates, leaving a milk-white powder.
....	THUCHOLITE	C and rare elements	Brittle. A carbonaceous material from a pegmatite. Explodes when heated.
1.520	PROBERTITE	$Na_2CaB_6O_{11} \cdot 6H_2O$	B.B., whitens then fuses quietly to a clear glassy bead. Crushes into long splinters.
1.507	**THAUMASITE**	$CaSiO_3 \cdot CaCO_3 \cdot CaSO_4 \cdot 15H_2O$	**In C.T., decrepitates giving much water.**
1.584	SCHROETTERITE	$8Al_2O_3 \cdot 3SiO_2 \cdot 30H_2O$	A clay mineral. Resembles allophane. May be a mixture.
1.48±	ALLOPHANE	$Al_2SiO_5 \cdot 5H_2O$	Brittle. In C.T., gives much water.
1.51	KURNAKOVITE	$Mg_2B_6O_{11} \cdot 13H_2O$	B.B., a white enamel.
1.458	MENDOZITE	$Na_2SO_4 \cdot Al_2(SO_4)_3 \cdot 24H_2O$	In C.T., yields water.
....	IDRIZITE	$(Mg,Fe)(Al,Fe)_2 \cdot Si_3O_{13} \cdot 16H_2O$	Insoluble in water.
1.521	INDERBORITE	$CaMgB_6O_{22} \cdot 11H_2O$	
....	CHLOROPAL	$Fe_2O_3 \cdot 3SiO_2 \cdot 5H_2O$	In C.T., yields water. B.B., turns black and becomes magnetic.
1.516	**GAY-LUSSITE**	$CaCO_3 \cdot Na_2CO_3 \cdot 5H_2O$	**In C.T., decrepitates and becomes opaque.**
....	STILPNO-CHLORAN	$H_{24}(Al,Fe)_{10}(Ca,Mg) \cdot Si_9O_{46}$	In C.T., yields water and blackens. Feels greasy.
1.505	VASHEGYITE	$4Al_2O_3 \cdot 3P_2O_5 \cdot 30H_2O$	Sticks to the tongue.
1.479	PISANITE	$(Fe,Cu)O \cdot SO_3 \cdot 7H_2O$	Soluble in water. B.B., reacts for copper.
1.578	KROEHNKITE	$CuSO_4 \cdot Na_2SO_4 \cdot 2H_2O$	B.B., fuses to a green mass. Soluble in water giving an acid solution.
1.51	RACEWINITE	$2(Al,Fe)_2O_3 \cdot 5SiO_2 \cdot 9H_2O$	Adheres to the tongue. In H_2O slacks and falls to pieces.
1.501	NESQUEHONITE	$MgCO_3 \cdot 3H_2O$	
1.468	LANSFORDITE	$3MgCO_3 \cdot Mg(OH)_2 \cdot 21H_2O$	Alters to nesquehonite.
1.472	KERNITE	$Na_2O \cdot B_2O_3 \cdot 4H_2O$	Fuses to a glass. Breaks into long thin fibers and laths.
1.716±	DELVAUXITE	$2Fe_2O_3 \cdot P_2O_5 \cdot 9H_2O$	Amorphous concretions.
1.542	TELEGDITE	A fossil resin	Partly soluble in alcohol.
1.541Na	AJKAITE	A fossil resin.	On heating gives off H_2S.
1.560	TRUDELLITE	$4AlCl_3 \cdot 3Al_2O_3 \cdot 3SO_3 \cdot 36H_2O$	Deliquescent.
1.485	**PHOSPHOR-RÖSSLERITE**	$MgHPO_4 \cdot 7H_2O$	**Probably identical with wapplerite. Sol in H_2O. In C.T., whitens.**
1.476	KIROVITE	$(Fe,Mg)SO_4 \cdot 7H_2O$	Magnesium melanterite.
....	BACALITE	A fossil resin	
1.543±	IHLEITE	$Fe_2(SO_4)_3 \cdot 12H_2O$	Soluble in water.

GROUP 12
Specific Gravity 1.99 And Lower

	H	SP. GR.	F	HCL	COLOR	STREAK	LUSTER	CLEAV-AGE	FRACTURE
32	2-2.5	1.85	4.5-5	Sol	Pale yellow, white	....	S, P	....	....
33	2-2.5	2.1-1.9	Inf	Sol	Colorless, rdsh, yellowish, bluish	....	V	Perf	Brittle
34	2-2.5	1.07	Easy	Ins	Black	Rich brown	Brilliant	None	Conch
35	2-2.5	1.76	1	Sol	Yellowish gray, lemon yellow	....	V	Dist	....
36	2-2.5	1.75	Inf	Sol	Colorless	....	....	Perf	....
37	2-2.5	1.75	1	Sol	White	....	V	....	....
38	2-2.5	1.10-1.05	Melts	....	Yellowish, rdsh, brown, whitish	White	R	None	Conch
39	2-2.5	1.75	1	Sol	White	White	V, E	Perf	Conch
40	2-2.5	1.72-1.69	1-1.5	Sol	White, sometimes tinted	White	V, R	Perf	Conch
41	2-2.5	1.65-1.55	....	....	Yellow, rdsh, brwnsh	White	R, V	Indist	Conch
42	2-2.5	1.94	Fus	Sol	Blue	....	....	Imperf	Uneven
43	2	2.0-1.9	2	Sol	White with red spots	....	....	Perf	....
44	2	1.19	....	....	Brown				
45	2	1.97	1.5	Sol	White, blue, ylw, red, from inclusions	....	V	Perf	Uneven
46	2	1.89	Easy	Sol	Green to white	Uncolored	V	Perf	Conch
47	2	1.8-1.7	4.5	Sol	Yellowish	Yellow	....	....	....
48	2	1.7-1.65	3	Sol	Ylw to brown, white	....	V	Good	Conch to uneven
49	2	1.61	1	Sol	White stained yellowish brown	....	V	....	....
50	2	1.87	Fus	....	Colorless	....	V	Good	Irregular
51	2	1.87	....	....	White to yellow	....	....	....	....
52	2	1.67	1	Sol	Yellow	....	....	Good	....
53	2	1.76	1	Sol	Colorless	....	....	None	....
54	2	1.21?	Diff	Pt sol	White	....	....	None	....
55	2	2.04-1.89	4.5-5	Sol	Yellowish white	....	S	....	....
56	2	1.92	Easy	Sol	Flesh to rose red	....	V	....	....
57	2	1.72-1.68	1	Sol	Colorless	....	....	None	....
58	1.5-2	1.8-1.6	Inf	Sol	White tinged red or yellow	....	V, S	....	....
59	1.5-2	1.53	1	Sol	White, yellowish, grayish	....	V	Imperf	Conch
60	1.5-2	1.48	1.5	Sol	White	....	V	Perf	....
61	1-2	1.50	1	Sol	White	....	V	None	Conch

GROUP 12
Specific Gravity 1.99 And Lower

INDEX OF REF.	NAME	COMPOSITION	REMARKS
.533	FIBROFERRITE	$Fe_2O_3 \cdot 2SO_3 \cdot 10H_2O$	In C.T., yields H_2O and H_2SO_4. Decomposed by boiling water.
.480	GOSLARITE	$ZnO \cdot SO_3 \cdot 7H_2O$	Soluble in water. In C.T., yields water.
....	**GILSONITE**	**Hydrocarbon**	**Brittle. A natural asphalt from Utah. Burns with a brilliant flame like sealing wax.**
.523	MASCAGNITE	$(NH_4)_2SO_4$	In C.T., yields water and sublimes. With lime gives NH_3.
.488	ETTRINGITE	$6CaO \cdot Al_2O_3 \cdot 3SO_3 \cdot 33H_2O$	Slightly soluble in water. B.B., swells up.
.452	**KALINITE**	$K_2SO_4 \cdot Al_2(SO_4)_3 \cdot 24H_2O$	**Melts in its own water of crystallization.**
.535±	**SUCCINITE (AMBER)**	**Hydrocarbon**	**Fossil resin. Sometimes contains bugs and sticks.**
.455	EPSOMITE	$MgSO_4 \cdot 7H_2O$	Fuses at first then finally gives an infusible alkaline mass.
.470	**BORAX**	$Na_2B_4O_7 \cdot 10H_2O$	**B.B., puffs up before fusing.**
.539	MELLITE	$Al_2C_{12}O_{12} \cdot 18H_2O$	In C.T., yields water. Soluble in HNO_3.
.48	BOOTHITE	$CuO \cdot SO_3 \cdot 7H_2O$	Brittle.
.534	HYDROBORACITE	$CaO \cdot MgO \cdot 3B_2O_3 \cdot 6H_2O$	In C.T., yields water. B.B., gives a clear glass.
.542	KISCELLITE	Hydrocarbon	A sulfur-bearing resin. When heated H_2S is evolved and it burns with a smoky flame.
.490	**SYLVITE**	**KCl**	**Heated with H_2SO_4, it yields HCl. Colors flame violet.**
.478	MELANTERITE	$FeSO_4 \cdot 7H_2O$	On coal, becomes brown, red, black and magnetic. Soluble in water.
.820	CYPRUSITE	$7Fe_2O_3 \cdot Al_2O_3 \cdot 10SO_3 \cdot 14H_2O$	Slightly soluble in water.
.496	STRUVITE	$NH_4MgPO_4 \cdot 6H_2O$	In C.T., gives off water and ammonia.
.441	STERCORITE	$HNa(NH_4)PO_4 \cdot 4H_2O$	Fuses to a clear colorless glass that is soluble in water.
.505±	INYOITE	$2CaO \cdot 3B_2O_3 \cdot 13H_2O$	Colors the flame green. B.B., decrepitates and fuses with intumescence.
.500	BILINITE	$FeO \cdot Fe_2O_3 \cdot 4SO_3 \cdot 24H_2O$	A ferric iron halotrichite.
.526	TACHHYDRITE	$CaCl_2 \cdot 2MgCl_2 \cdot 12H_2O$	Deliquescent.
.456	ALUM	$K_2O \cdot Al_2O_3 \cdot 4SO_3 \cdot 24H_2O$	Natural potash alum. Soluble in water.
.403	TERMIERITE	$Al_2O_3 \cdot 6SiO_2 \cdot 18H_2O$	Clay-like.
.488	HALOTRICHITE	$FeSO_4 \cdot Al_2(SO_4)_3 \cdot 24H_2O$	Soluble in water. Fuses first in its own water of crystallization.
.483	BIEBERITE	$CoSO_4 \cdot 7H_2O$	In C.T., yields water and SO_2.
.470	BOUSSING-AULTITE	$(NH_4)_2SO_4 \cdot MgSO_4 \cdot 6H_2O$	Soluble in water.
.476	ALUNOGEN	$Al_2(SO_4)_3 \cdot 18H_2O$	In C.T., yields water and H_2SO_4.
.639	SAL AMMONIAC (SALMIAC)	NH_4Cl	In C.T., it sublimes.
.395	MIRABILITE	$Na_2SO_4 \cdot 10H_2O$	Soluble in water. In air loses its water and falls to a powder.
.459	TSCHERMIGITE	$(NH_4)_2SO_4 \cdot Al_2(SO_4)_3 \cdot 24H_2O$	In C.T., yields water. B.B., sublimes.

GROUP 12
Specific Gravity 1.99 And Lower

	H	SP. GR.	F	HCL	COLOR	STREAK	LUSTER	CLEAV-AGE	FRACTURE
62	1-2	1.1	Easy	Ins	Black, pitch-like	....	Brilliant	None	Conch
63	1-2	1.66	Inf	Sol	White	....	D, E	....	Earthy
64	1-2	1.65	Fus	Sol	Colorless, white	....	V, D	....	
65	1.5	1.78	Inf	Sol	White tinged green, rose or yellow	....	S	....	
66	1.5	1.45	Vol	Sol	Yellowish to white				
67	1.5	0.92	Vol	Sol	White, bluish	Colorless	V	....	Conch
68	1-1.5	1.6-1.5	1.5	Sol	White, grayish, ylw		V	Diff	
69	1-1.5	1.46-1.42	1	Sol	White, gray, yellow	....	V, E	Dist	Conch
70	1	1.85	Easy	Sol	White, yellowish, rose red		S	....	
71	1	1.65	1	Sol	White	....	S	....	
72	1	1.60	1-1.5	Sol	White, reddish		G	None	Conch
73	1	1.48	1	Sol	White, yellowish		P	Perf	Flexible
74	1	0.9	1-	Ins	White, reddish, gray, green		P, R		
75	1	0.96	Easy	Ins	White, yellowish, greenish	....	P, G	Perf	....
76	1	0.9	1-	Ins	White, yellow, brown, green	....			
77	Soft	1.50-1.46	Easy	Sol	Yellowish, white	....	S	Imperf	
78	Soft	1.97	Ins	Pt sol	Yellowish green	Yellowish	D		
79	Soft	1.06	1-	Ins	Colorless, white				
80	Soft	1.21	1-	....	Yellow to greenish		V, A	Perf	Conch
81	Soft	1.98	......	Sol	Red, brown			Perf	
82	Soft	1.09	1-	....	Colorless			Imperf	
83	Soft	1.89	Fus	Pt sol	Yellowish			Good	
84	?	1.81	Diff	Sol	White		S		
85	?	1.95-1.80	......	....	Pale yellow, white				
86	?	1.81	Vol	....	Colorless, cloudy			Poor	
87	?	1.80	......	....	White				
88	?	1.19	......	....	Bluish violet or grnsh		P		
89	?	1.59	......	Sol	Blue				
90	?	1.12-1.03	......	....	Yellow, black, green				
91	?	1.48	......	....	White				
92	?	1.76	Inf	Sol	White with green tone	....	P	Perf	Conch
93	?	1.88	......	....	Colorless, white			None	....
94	?	1.90	......	....	Yellowish green				....
95	?	1.43	......	....	Colorless			Perf	....
96	?	1.818	......	....					
97	?	1.868	......	....					
98	?	1.66	......	....	Lemon-yellow	....	V	....	Conch

GROUP 12
Specific Gravity 1.99 And Lower

INDEX OF REF.	NAME	COMPOSITION	REMARKS
....	ALBERTITE (LIBOLITE)	Hydrocarbon.	A mineral asphalt.
1.464	ALUMINITE	$Al_2O_3 \cdot SO_3 \cdot 9H_2O$	In C.T., gives much H_2O which at high temperatures is acid.
1.507	BISCHOFITE	$MgCl_2 \cdot 6H_2O$	Soluble in water.
1.482	APJOHNITE	$MnSO_4 \cdot Al_2(SO_4)_3 \cdot 24H_2O$	Soluble in water. Tastes like alum.
1.536	TESCHE-MACHERITE	$(NH_4)_2 \cdot CO_2 \cdot H_2CO_3$	In C.T., yields water and ammonia fumes.
1.309	**ICE (WATER)**	**H_2O**	**Melts at ordinary temperatures to neutral water.**
1.506	THERMONATRITE	$Na_2CO_3 \cdot H_2O$	Sectile. Tastes alkaline.
1.425	**NATRON**	**$Na_2CO_3 \cdot 10H_2O$**	**Brittle. Soluble in water.**
1.480	PICKERINGITE	$MgSO_4 \cdot Al_2(SO_4)_3 \cdot 22H_2O$	Soluble in water. Has an alum taste.
1.504	**ULEXITE**	**$Na_2O \cdot 2CaO \cdot 5B_2O_3 \cdot 16H_2O$**	**Not soluble in cold water but some in hot water.**
1.474	**CARNALLITE**	**$KMgCl_3 \cdot 6H_2O$**	**Strongly phosphorescent. Tastes bitter.**
1.456	**SASSOLITE**	**$B(OH)_3$**	**Soluble in water and alcohol.**
1.502	PARAFFIN	Hydrocarbon	Burns and melts easily.
1.523	HATCHETTITE	$C_{38}H_{78}$	Burns. Hydrocarbon. Soluble with difficulty in alcohol and ether.
1.515	**OZOCERITE (OZOKERITE)**	**Hydrocarbon**	**Melts and burns easily.**
1.547	OXAMMITE	$(NH_4)_2C_2O_4 \cdot 2H_2O$	Soluble in water.
....	MUELLERITE	$Fe_2Si_3O_9 \cdot 2H_2O$	B.B., slowly loses water and finally becomes brown.
1.555	BOMBICCITE	$C_7H_{10}O_{13}$	Soluble in alcohol and ether.
1.734	CURTISITE	$C_{24}H_{18}$	In C.T., melts to a clear liquid but discolors rapidly.
1.52	KOENENITE	$Al_2O_3 \cdot 3MgO \cdot 2MgCl_2 \cdot 8H_2O$	Thin folia flexible. Decomposed by boiling water.
1.512	FLAGSTAFFITE	$H_{20}C_{10}O_{22}H_2O$	Soluble in alcohol.
1.572	HANNAYITE	$Mg_3(PO_4)_2 \cdot 2H_2(NH_4)PO_4 \cdot 8H_2O$	In C.T., yields water and ammonia.
1.455	WATTEVILLITE	$CaSO_4 \cdot Na_2SO_4 \cdot 4H_2O$	Tastes first sweet then astringent. Soluble in water.
....	EARLANDITE	$Ca_3(C_6H_5O_7)_2 \cdot 4H_2O$	Fine grained nodules. From sediments of Weddell Sea. Antarctica.
1.526	LETOVICITE	$H(NH_4)_3(SO_4)_2$	Soluble in water.
....	INDERITE	$Mg_2B_6O_{11} \cdot 15H_2O$	Small nodules and aggregates of small needles.
1.725	KRATOCHVILITE	$C_{13}H_{10}$	Hydrocarbon. Pearly scales from burning coal heaps.
1.556	JULIENITE	Hydrated nitrate of cobalt.	Soluble in water.
....	ROMANITE	Hydrocarbon	Amber from Rumania.
....	LASSALITE	$2MgO \cdot 2Al_2O_3 \cdot 10SiO_2 \cdot 7H_2O$	Fibrous.
1.453	HEXAHYDRITE	$MgO \cdot SO_3 \cdot 6H_2O$	Fibrous, salty, bitter taste. B.B., exfoliates and yields water.
1.461	TINCALCONITE	$MgO \cdot 2B_2O_3 \cdot 5H_2O$	From dehydration of borax or hydration of kernite.
1.530	SLAVIKITE	$(Na,K)_2O \cdot 5Fe_2O_3 \cdot 13SiO_2 \cdot 66H_2O$	Product of oxidation of pyrite.
1.75	HOELITE	$C_{14}H_8O_2$	Produces by burning coal seams. Delicate needles.
1.471	JAROSITE	$(Fe,Mg)SO_4 \cdot 7H_2O$	
1.472	CUPROJAROSITE	Cu,Mg melanterite.	
1.513	CADWALADERITE	$AlOCl \cdot 5H_2O$	

GROUP 13
Specific Gravity Not Reported

	H	SP. GR.	F	HCL	COLOR	STREAK	LUSTER	CLEAV-AGE	FRACTURE
1	5.5-6.5								
2	6±				Brown			Perf	
3	5.5-6		4	Sol	Black	Dark chocolate brown	M		
4	5-6				Emerald-green			Good	
5	5+				Black				
6	5	?			Brown	Brown			
7	5				Green			Perf	
8	5		Fus	Sol	Yellow-green			Perf	
9	5		Inf	Pt sol	White or pale reddish			Fair	
10	5				Dark olive-green				
11	5±		Easy	Sol	Red				
12	4.5-5		Fus	Sol	Pistachio, olive, leek green	Ylwsh, ylw, gray, grnsh	V	Dist	
13	4				Whitish gray	Same		Good	Brittle
14	4			Sol	Lead gray	Red	Brilliant	Perf	Brittle
15	4				Black	Cherry red	M		
16	4±				Brown			Perf	
17	3.5		Easy	Sol	Brownish red	Yellowish brown		Good	
18	3.5				Gray		M	Good	
19	3-4	High			Reddish, steel gray	Black		Good	
20	3-3.5				Dark lead gray		M		Conch
21	3+				Pale lemon yellow				Conch
22	3		Easy	Sol	Yellow, reddish-ylw				Conch
23	3			Sol in HNO₃	Sulfur-yellow		A		
24	3				Yellowish-green to brown	Chrome yellow		Basal	Brittle
25	3				Brown, black			Perf	
26	3			Sol	Lemon-yellow		E	Perf	
27	3				Lead to steel gray	Black, chocolate tinge			Conch
28	2.5-3		Inf	Sol	Sisken-green	Same, paler	V, P	Dist	
29	2-3				Brownish black	Grayish brown	D, P		Flat conch
30	2-3				Light brown				
31	2.5		2.5-3	Dcpd	Brownish yellow		A	Perf	
32	2.5		2-2.5	Sol	Virdigris-green		S		
33	2.5				Turquoise-blue		D		Conch
34	2-2.5		Fus	Sol	Greenish yellow		V, D	Perf	

GROUP 13
Specific Gravity Not Reported

INDEX OF REF.	NAME	COMPOSITION	REMARKS
....	COULSONITE	$FeO \cdot (Fe,V)_2O_3$	Occurs in magnetite.
1.699	SCHEFFERITE	$(Mg,Mn)O \cdot CaO \cdot 2SiO_2$	A manganese pyroxene.
....	SKEMMATITE	$3MnO \cdot 2Fe_2O_3 \cdot 6H_2O$	In C.T., gives water and oxygen. B.B., a magnetic globule.
....	COSMOCHLORE	A chromium silicate.	Found as embedded splinters in the Toluca meteorite.
....	WEINBERGERITE	$NaAlSiO_4 \cdot 3FeSiO_3$	From a meteorite. Spherical aggregates and radiating fibers
....	MAGHEMITE	Fe_2O_3	
1.70	ARROJADITE	$6R_2O_3 \cdot 27RO \cdot 11P_2O_5$	
2.09±	EMMONSITE	Hydrated ferric teluride	In C.T., fuses to a deep red globule.
....	MUNKFORSSITE	$CaO \cdot SO_3 \cdot P_2O_5 \cdot Al_2O_3$	Does not give a blue color with cobalt solution.
....	TURANITE	$5CuO \cdot V_2O_5 \cdot 2H_2O$	Radial aggregates.
....	YUKSPORITE	$5(Na_2,K_2,Ca)O \cdot 6SiO_2 \cdot 5H_2O$	In fibers and scales. Near pectolite but more Na and K.
2.15	CUPROTUNGSTITE	$CuWO_4$	In C.T., blackens and gives water. On coal, fuses with intumescence.
....	ELFESTORPITE	Hydrated manganese arsenate?	
....	LAMPROSTIBIAN	$FeO \cdot MnO$	Red in thin layers. The HCl solution yields chlorine.
....	MELANOSTIBIAN	$6(Mn,Fe)O \cdot Sb_2O_3$	
1.718	FERRO-SCHALLERITE	$12(Mn,Fe)O \cdot 9SiO_2 \cdot As_2O_3 \cdot 7H_2O$	Schallerite rich in iron.
1.794	ARSENIOPLEITE	$9RO \cdot R_2O_3 \cdot 3As_2O_5 \cdot 3H_2O$	Blood red in splinters. B.B., a black slag and trace of Pb sublimate.
....	BENJAMINITE	$(Cu,Ag)_2S \cdot 2PbS \cdot 2Bi_2S_3$	
....	HAMMARITE	$Pb_2Cu_2Bi_4S_9$	Short needles.
....	GOLDFIELDITE	$Cu_{10}Sb_4Te_3S_{16}$	Brittle. Forms a mineral crust.
2.065	MOSEITE	Hg,NH_4,Cl,SO_3,H_2O	
....	CHONDRARSEN-ITE	$6MnO \cdot As_2O_5 \cdot 3H_2O$	May be sarkinite. In C.T., gives water. On coal, gives a black bead and arsenical fumes.
2.34Li	OCHROLITE	$4PbO \cdot Sb_2O_3 \cdot 2PbCl_2$	Soluble in caustic potash.
....	PLANOFERRITE	$Fe_2O_3 \cdot SO_3 \cdot 15H_2O$	
1.670	SIDEROPHYLLITE	$K_2O \cdot 5FeO \cdot 2Al_2O_3 \cdot 5SiO_2 \cdot 2H_2O$	Biotite mica with much iron.
1.621	ZIPPEITE	$2UO_3 \cdot SO_3 \cdot 4H_2O$	
....	MARRITE	Composition unknown.	Brittle.
1.503	URAROTHALLITE	$2CaO \cdot UO_3 \cdot 4CO_2 \cdot 10H_2O$	Gives bead tests for uranium.
....	RILANDITE	H_2O,SiO_2 of Cr,Al	
....	CALCIUM FERRI-PHOSPHATE	$2CaO \cdot 3Fe_2O_3 \cdot P_2O_5 \cdot 10H_2O+$	
2.27	RASPITE	$PbO \cdot WO_3$	
1.686	TRICHALCITE	$3CuO \cdot As_2O_5 \cdot 5H_2O$	When heated it decrepitates, yields much water, becomes dark brown.
1.54±	AIDYRLITE	$2NiO \cdot 2Al_2O_3 \cdot 3SiO_2 \cdot 7\frac{1}{2}H_2O$	
1.955	DURDENITE	$Fe_2O_3 \cdot 3TeO_2 \cdot 4H_2O$	B.B., gives a magnetic residue.

347

GROUP 13
Specific Gravity Not Reported

	H	SP. GR.	F	HCL	COLOR	STREAK	LUSTER	CLEAV-AGE	FRACTURE	SY TE
35	2-2.5		Diff		Colorless		V, P	Perf		
36	2-2.5		1		Colorless		V	Pris-matic Fair		O
37	2-2.5		Inf	Sol	Apple green		V	Fair		..
38	2-2.5		Easy		Blackish gray	Black	M	Perf	Brittle	.
39	2-2.5			Sol	Green	Apple green				
40	2		Fus		Dirty white, brownish yellow		S		Fibrous	M
41	2				Steel gray	Same	M			O
42	2		1.5		Yellowish white					O
43	2				Colorless, gray			Basal		O
44	2			Sol in HNO$_3$	Creamy white, mauve		M	Perf		M
45	2				Dark lead gray	Dark gray		Good		M
46	1.5-2				Scarlet-vermilion	Same	A	Good	Conch	R
47	1-2			Sol	Pinkish buff					
48	1				White		G	Perf	Brittle	M
49	Soft		1-	Sol	White to yellowish			Perf		M
50	Soft		1-	Sol	White to yellowish		Bright	Perf		M
51	Soft				Pale blue, white					C
52	Soft				Silver white				Granular	A
53	Soft		1		Colorless					E
54	Soft				Yellow, brownish, black	Yellow, brown	R, E			.
55	Soft		Easy	Sol	Dull yellow		P, D	Perf		.
56	Soft				White, gray		S	Perf		.
57	Soft				White, chalky					.
58	Soft			Sol	Rose-colored	Pale rose				.
59	Soft		Easy	Sol	Bluish-green			Perf		T
60	Soft			Sol	Lemon-yellow					C
61	Soft		Inf	Sol	Emerald-green		P			T
62	Soft				Blood red					.
63	Soft				Dark blood red					.
64					Pale ochre, yellow			Dist		F
65					White to brick red					.
66					Flesh-red					M
67				Sol	Steel blue		M, Sm			.
68			Easy		White					T
69			Diff	Ins	White					T

GROUP 13
Specific Gravity Not Reported

INDEX OF REF.	NAME	COMPOSITION	REMARKS
1.564	KOSSMATITE	$3MgO \cdot 7CaO \cdot 3Al_2O_3 \cdot 7SiO_2 \cdot 9H_2O$	Contains some F. A brittle mica.
1.452	LECONTITE	$(Na,NH_4,K)_2O \cdot SO_3 \cdot 2H_2O$	Soluble in water. Bitter taste. In C.T., gives NH_3.
....	LIEBIGITE	$CaCO_3 \cdot (UO_2)CO_3 \cdot 20H_2O$	Probably identical with urarothallite. In C.T., gives much water, and becomes yellowish-gray.
....	SELENTELLURIUM	Se,Te	On coal, fuses easily, colors flame blue with greenish tinge.
1.655	URANOCHALCITE	UO_4,CuO,CaO,SO_3, H_2O	
1.480	DIETRICHITE	$(Zn,Fe,Mn)O \cdot Al_2O_3 \cdot 4SO_3 \cdot 22H_2O$	Soluble in water.
....	HISTRIXITE	$Cu_5Fe_5Bi_4Sb_{14}S_{32}$	Radiating groups of prismatic crystals.
1.448	TAYLORITE	$K_2O \cdot (NH_4)_2O \cdot 6SO_2$	Tastes pungent and bitter. Unaltered in the air.
1.551	RHOMBOCLASE	$Fe_2O_3 \cdot 4SO_3 \cdot 9H_2O$	
....	PARPERITE	NiS_3	Resembles molybdenite. Effervesces.
....	FIZELYITE	$Pb_5Ag_2Sb_8S_{18}$	
2.6Li	TRECHMANNITE	$Ag_2S \cdot As_2S_3$	Brittle. Transparent to translucent.
1.638	HYDROTHORITE	$ThSiO_4 \cdot 4H_2O$	Radio active. Alteration product of mackintoshite.
1.578	FICHTELITE	$C_{18}H_{32}$	Soluble in ether. Solidifies at 36. Distills without decomposition.
1.52	LARDERELLITE	$(NH_4)_2O \cdot 5B_2O_3 \cdot 5H_2O$	Gives off NH_3 in C.T. Fuses to a colorless glass.
1.487	AMMONIOBORITE	$(NH_4)_2O \cdot 5B_2O_3 \cdot 5H_2O$	In C.T., gives NH_3. Fuses to a colorless globule.
1.625	BISBEEITE	$CuO \cdot SiO_2 \cdot H_2O$	Fibrous. Very thin laths. From hydration of shattuckite.
....	CHILENITE	Ag_6Bi	Antergrowth of native Ag and cuprite.
1.675	CHLORO-MAGNESITE	$MgCl_2$	Very deliquescent. From Vesuvius.
1.8±	GLOCKERITE	$2Fe_2O_3 \cdot SO_3 \cdot 6H_2O$	Insoluble in water. Sometimes in stalactitic forms.
1.85+	METAROSSITE	$CaO \cdot V_2O_5 \cdot 2H_2O$	Soluble in water. The HCl solution is mahogany red.
1.498	NITROCALCITE	$CaO \cdot N_2O_5 \cdot nH_2O$	Tastes sharp and bitter. On coal, fuses with a slight detonation.
1.470	PARALUMINITE	$2Al_2O_3 \cdot SO_3 \cdot 15H_2O$	Probably from alteration of aluminite.
....	REMINGTONITE	Hydrous cobalt carbonate	Cobalt reactions. May be a mixture.
1.90	TRIPPKEITE	$nCuO \cdot As_2O_3 \cdot$	In C.T., becomes emerald green, then brownish then green.
1.79	URACONITE	SO_3,UO_3,H_2O, etc.	
1.547	VOLGITE	Hydrous carbonate of U,Ca,Cu	In C.T., blackens and yields water; colors flame green.
....	ALAITE	$V_2O_5 \cdot H_2O$	In dark bluish-red moss-like masses. Rare.
....	ALAITE	$V_2O_5 \cdot H_2O$	From Turkestan. Occurs in moss-like masses.
1.80	AMMONIO-JAROSITE	$(NH_4)_2O \cdot 3Fe_2O_3 \cdot 4SO_3 \cdot H_2O$	Occurs in flattened grains. Member of the alunite group.
1.482	ASHTONITE	$(Ca,Na_2,K_2)O \cdot Al_2O_3 \cdot 9SiO_2 \cdot 5H_2O$	A zeolite. Occurs in radiating crystals.
1.657	BALDAUFITE	$3(Fe,Mn,Mg,Ca)O \cdot P_2O_5 \cdot 3H_2O$	Isomorphous with wenzelite.
....	BASILIITE	$11(Mn_2O_3 \cdot Fe_2O_3) \cdot Sb_2O_5 \cdot 21H_2O$	Non-magnetic. In C.T., yields H_2O; turns black then red-brown.
....	BECHILITE	$CaO \cdot 2B_2O_3 \cdot 4H_2O$	Found in crusts as a deposit from springs. In C.T., yields H_2O.
....	BELONESITE	$MgMoO_4$	From Vesuvius. Dissolves readily in S.Ph, less readily in borax.

349

GROUP 13
Specific Gravity Not Reported

	H	SP. GR.	F	HCL	COLOR	STREAK	LUSTER	CLEAV-AGE	FRACTURE
70				Sol	White			Good	
71				Sol	White				
72				Sol	Yellow		E		
73			1.5?		Black	Yellow			
74					Amber brown			Perf	
75					Colorless, white or yellow				
76					Bluish green			None	
77					Sulfur yellow				
78				Sol in HNO₃	Colorless		V, A		Subconch
79			Fus		Brown	Brownish yellow			
80					Yellow				
81					**White**			**Fair**	
82					Red				
83				Sol	Dull green				Fibrous
84			Dcpd		Yellow, brownish yellow				
85					Golden brown		Brilliant	None	Fibrous
86					Lemon yellow				
87				Sol	Green, brownish, yellowish, sky blue				
88					Violet black	Brown-violet		Mic	
89				Sol	Clear green				
90			Easy		Greenish, yellowish, pinkish white			Basal	
91			Easy	Sol	Greenish yellow		V, A	Perf	Brittle
92					Dark green				
93					Ruby red				
94					Yellow				
95				Gelat	White, gray			Good	
96					White		S		
97			2-2.5		White		S		
98			Inf	Sol	Colorless				Fibrous
99			Inf	Sol	Black	Brownish		Good	
100			Easy	Sol	Blue		V	Perf	
101			Easy	Sol	White		S		Fibrous
102					White				
103			Easy		Colorless				Fibrous

GROUP 13
Specific Gravity Not Reported

INDEX OF REF.	NAME	COMPOSITION	REMARKS
1.525	BIALITE	$CaO \cdot MgO \cdot P_2O_5 \cdot H_2O$	Magnesian variety of tavistockite.
1.494	BIANCHITE	$FeO \cdot 2ZnO \cdot 3SO_3 \cdot 18H_2O$	Soluble in cold water.
1.816	BORGSTROEMITE	$3Fe_2O_3 \cdot 4SO_3 \cdot 9H_2O$	From oxidation of pyrite or pyrrhotite.
2.36Li	BRACKEBUSCHITE	$3(Pb,Mn,Fe)O \cdot V_2O_5 \cdot H_2O?$	
1.580	CANBYITE	$Fe_2O_3 \cdot 2SiO_2 \cdot 4H_2O$	May be crystalline phase of the amophous hisingerite.
1.60±	CHLOR-ALLUMINITE	$AlCl_3 \cdot 6H_2O$	From Vesuvius.
1.54±	CORNUITE	$mCuO \cdot nSiO_2 \cdot H_2O$	Isotropic chrysocolla.
....	CUPRO-IODARGYRITE	$CuI \cdot AgI$	Close to miersite. Harder and less sectile than iodyrite. A decomposition product of stromeyerite.
....	DAVIESITE	Oxychloride of Pb	Yields metallic Pb with soda on coal.
	IODARGYRITE		
....	DOLEROPHANITE	$2CuO \cdot SO_3$	Partly soluble in water. B.B., a black scoriaceous residue.
1.89	DUMONTITE	$2PbO \cdot 3UO_3 \cdot P_2O_5 \cdot 5H_2O$	
1.590	**EGGONITE**	$Al_2O_3 \cdot P_2O_5 \cdot 4H_2O$	
1.75	ERYTHRO-SIDERITE	$2KCl \cdot FeCl_3 \cdot H_2O$	Very delequesent. Found in the cone of Vesuvius.
2.05	FERNANDINITE	$CaO \cdot V_2O_4 \cdot 5V_2O_5 \cdot 14H_2O$	Slightly soluble in water giving a green solution.
1.80	FERRO-TUNGSTITE	$Fe_2O_3 \cdot WO_3 \cdot 6H_2O$	In C.T., yields water. Product of oxidation of wolframite.
2.222	FERVANITE	$2Fe_2O_3 \cdot 2V_2O_5 \cdot 5H_2O$	Insoluble in water.
....	FLAJOLOTITE	$4FeSbO_4 \cdot 3H_2O$	Compact or earthy. In nodular masses.
1.733	HYDROCYANITE	$CuO \cdot SO_3$	Soluble in water. Effervesces readily. From Versuvius
1.900	IANTHINITE	$2UO_2 \cdot 7H_2O$	Acicular crystals. An alteration product of uraninite.
1.518	ILESITE	$(Mn,Zn,Fe)O \cdot SO_3 \cdot 4H_2O$	Bitter taste. Soluble in water.
....	IRVINGITE	A lithia mica.	Folia tough and elastic.
2.61Li	KOECHLINITE	$Bi_2O_3 \cdot MoO_3$	In C.T., fuses and forms a sublimate.
2.04	KOLOVRATITE	Nickel vanadate	In crusts.
....	KREMERSITE	$KCl \cdot NH_4Cl \cdot FeCl_2 \cdot H_2O$	Soluble in water. Unstable.
1.64	LAGONITE	$Fe_2O_3 \cdot 3B_2O_3 \cdot 3H_2O$	Occurs as an incrustation at the Tuscan lagoons.
1.715	LARNITE	$2CaO \cdot SiO_2$	Slowly attacked by H_2O giving an alkaline solution.
1.628	LAUSENITE	$Fe_2O_3 \cdot 3SO_3 \cdot 6H_2O$	Silky fibers.
1.807	LEUCOCHALCITE	$4CuO \cdot As_2O_3 \cdot 3H_2O$	Slender needle-like crystals. B.B., becomes a green then black glass.
....	MALLARDITE	$MnO \cdot SO_3 \cdot 7H_2O$	On exposure rapidly loses water. B.B., decomposes.
1.95	MANGANO-STIBIITE	$10MnO \cdot Sb_2O_5$	On coal, an Sb coating; with soda Mn reactions.
1.530	MINASRAGITE	$V_2O_4 \cdot 3SO_3 \cdot 16H_2O$	Soluble in cold water. In C.T., fuses and yields water.
1.480	MISENITE	$K_2O \cdot 2SO_3 \cdot H_2O$	Soluble in water. Tastes acid and bitter. Violet colored flame.
....	NITRO-GLAUBERITE	$6NaNO_3 \cdot 2Na_2SO_4 \cdot 3H_2O$	Fibrous crystalline structure.
1.506	NITRO-MAGNESITE	$MgO \cdot N_2O_5 \cdot nH_2O$	Soluble in water. Tastes bitter.

GROUP 13
Specific Gravity Not Reported

	H	SP. GR.	F	HCL	COLOR	STREAK	LUSTER	CLEAV-AGE	FRACTURE	SYTE
104	....	....	......	Sol	White, reddish	....	A	....	....	R
105	....	....	1	Sol in HNO₃	White	....	V, G	Dist	....	H
106	....	....	3?	Sol	Lemon-yellow	....	P	....	....	M
107	....	....	......	....	Green	....	.	....	....	..
108	....	....	Easy	Sol in HNO₃	Siskin to olive green	....	.	....	....	..
109	....	....	......	....	Red, brown	....	.	....	....	.
110	....	....	Easy	....	Lead gray, reddish tinge	Blackish lead gray	M	....	Uneven to conch	H
111	....	....	Inf	Pt sol	White	....	P	Perf	Fragile	O
112	....	....	......	Sol	White	....	D	....	....	..
113	....	....	......	....	Light blue	.	.	....	....	A
114	....	....	......	....	Black	....	.	Cubic	....	I
115	....	....	Diff	....	Orange-yellow	....	S	....	....	R
116	....	....	......	....	Brownish yellow	....	.	Good	Granular	O
117	....	....	......	....	Dark green	....	.	....	....	.
118	....	....	......	....	Grayish yellow	....	.	....	....	I
119	....	....	Inf	Sol	White	....	.	None	....	H
120	....	....	......	....	Flesh pink	....	.	....	....	M
121	....	....	......	....	Reddish	....	.	....	....	..
122	....	....	......	....	....	....	.	....	....	..
123	....	....	......	....	Pale greenish yellow	....	.	....	....	M
124	... ..	....	......	....	Pink to black	....	.	....	....	O
125	....	....	......	Sol	Greenish, yellowish brownish	....	.	Good	....	H
126	....	....	......	....	Ash gray	....	.	....	....	O
127	....	....	......	....	Sulfur yellow	....	.	....	....	.
128	....	....	......	....	Blue-gray	....	.	....	....	T
129	....	....	......	....	Blue-green	....	.	....	....	C
130	....	....	......	....	Light green	....	.	....	....	.
131	....	....	......	....	Black	....	.	....	....	C
132	....	....	......	....	Green	....	.	Perf	....	.
133	....	....	......	....	....	....	.	....	....	.
134	....	....	......	....	....	....	.	....	....	N
135	....	....	......	....	Yellow	....	.	....	....	.

GROUP 13
Specific Gravity Not Reported

INDEX OF REF.	NAME	COMPOSITION	REMARKS
....	OTAVITE	Basic cadmium carbonate	
2.13	PENFIELDITE	$PbO \cdot 2PbCl_2$	In C.T., decrepitates and yields sublimate of lead chloride.
1.720	PHOSPHURANY-LITE	$3UO_3 \cdot P_2O_5 \cdot 6H_2O$	In C.T., yields water and becomes brownish yellow on cooling.
....	PINTADOITE	$2CaO \cdot V_2O_5 \cdot 9H_2O$	An efflorescence.
....	PSITTACINITE	$4(Pb,Cu)O \cdot V_2O_5 \cdot 2H_2O$	Considered a variety of descloizite. B.B., a black shining mass. Reacts for Pb, Cu and V.
....	SELEN-SULPHUR	Se,S	Found in volcanoes.
....	STÜTZITE	Ag_4Te	O.T., gives tellurium dioxide. With soda a globule of silver.
1.530	TAVISTOCKITE	$3CaO \cdot Al_2O_3 \cdot P_2O_5 \cdot 2H_2O?$	Transparent. B.B., becomes opaque. Gives a blue color with cobalt solution.
1.57	TENGERITE	Y,Be,CO_3	Pulverulent. In thin coatings. Effervesces with acid.
1.565	TRAVERSOITE	$2(Cu,Ca)O \cdot Al_2O_3 \cdot 2SiO_2 \cdot 12H_2O$	A mixture of chrysocolla and gibbsite.
....	UHLIGITE	$CaO \cdot Al_2O_3 \cdot ZrO \cdot 2TiO_2$	Near zirkelite. Brown and transparent on thin edges.
....	UTAHITE	$3Fe_2O_3 \cdot 3SO_3 \cdot 4H_2O$	In C.T., gives acid water and turns red.
1.879	UVANITE	$2UO_3 \cdot 3V_2O_5 \cdot 15H_2O$	Insoluble in water. Soluble in $(NH_4)_2CO_3$.
2.04	UZBEKITE	$3CuO \cdot V_2O_5 \cdot 3H_2O$	Two varieties, alpha and beta, varying slightly in composition.
....	TANTALUM	Ta	Found in the gold washings of Ural and Altai mountains.
1.633	VOELCKERITE	$10CaO \cdot 3P_2O_5$	Apatite group.
1.655	WENTZELITE	$3(Mn,Fe,Mg)O \cdot P_2O_5 \cdot 5H_2O$	May be hureaulite.
....	ALMERAITE	$KCl \cdot NaCl \cdot MgCl_2 \cdot H_2O$	
....	AMARGOSITE	$MgO \cdot Al_2O_3 \cdot 5SiO_2 \cdot 7H_2O$	Trade name of bentonite clay. Same as montmorillonite.
....	AMARILLITE	$Na_2O \cdot Fe_2O_3 \cdot 4SO_3 \cdot 12H_2O$	
....	AMBATOARINITE	$5SrCO_3 \cdot 4(Ce,La,Di)_2(CO_3)_3 \cdot (Ce,La,Di)_2O_3$	Skeleton-like groups of crystals.
....	AMELETITE	$6Al_2O_3 \cdot 9Na_2O \cdot 12SiO_2 \cdot \frac{1}{2}NaCl$	Occurs in minute crystals and grains.
....	AMOSITE	$(Fe,Mg,Ca)O \cdot SiO_2 \cdot xH_2O$	Fibrous. An asbestos.
....	ARSENOSTIBITE	$3(Sb,As)_2O_3 \cdot 5(Sb,As)_2O_5 \cdot 25H_2O$	
....	ARSENSCHWEFEL	$As_2S_3 \cdot H_2O$	Granular crystaline aggregates.
....	ARZRUNITE	$PbSO_4 \cdot PbO \cdot 3(CuCl_2 \cdot H_2O)Cu(OH)_2$	Drusy incrustations.
....	ATTAPULGITE	$(OH)_2 \cdot H_2(Mg,Al_{4/3}) Si_3H_4O_{10}$	A fuller's earth.
....	BAECKSTROE-MITE	$Mn(OH)_2$	In prismatic crystals.
....	BATCHELORITE	$Al_2O_3 \cdot 2SiO_2 \cdot H_2O$	Has a foliated structure.
....	BENTONITE	A soapy clay	Swells up when mixed with water. Montmorillonite.
....	BLEIMALACHITE	$2CuCO_3 \cdot PbCO_3 \cdot Cu(OH)_2$	
....	BOSPHORITE	$3Fe_2O_3 \cdot 2P_2O_5 \cdot 17H_2O$	

GROUP 13
Specific Gravity Not Reported

	H	SP. GR.	F	HCL	COLOR	STREAK	LUSTER	CLEAV-AGE	FRACTURE	S T
136	....	....	....	....	Greenish yellow	....	....	....	....	C
137	....	....	....	....	Gray, white	....	....	....	....	I
138	....	....	....	....	White	.....	....	....	....	.
139	....	....	....	....	Colorless	.....	....	....	....	N
140	....	....	....	....	Emerald green	....	....	....	....	C
141	....	....	....	....	Greenish gray	....	....	....	....	.
142	....	....	Easy	Sol in HNO$_3$	Yellowish white	....	S	....	Fibrous	
143	....	....	....	....	Green	....	....	....	....	.
144	....	....	....	....	Black	....	....	....	....	.
145	....	....	....	....	Black	....	....	....	....	A
146	....	....	....	....	Reddish white	....	....	Good	....	F
147	....	....	....	....	Pale bluish green	....	....	....	....	F
148	....	....	....	....	Orange red	....	....	....	....	.
149	....	....	....	....		....	....	....	....	.
150	....	....	....	....	Violet	.....	....	....	....	.
151	....	....	....	....		....	....	....	....	.
152	....	....	....	....	Colorless, yellow	....	....	....	....	.
153	....	....	....	....	Yellowish green	....	....	....	Fibrous	A
154	....	....	....	....	Bluish green	....	....	....	....	.
155	....	....	....	....	Black	....	....	....	....	A
156	....	....	....	....		....	....	....	....	.
157	....	....	....	....		....	....	....	....	F
158	....	....	....	....	Purplish black	....	....	....	....	.
159	....	....	....	....	Black	....	....	....	....	.
160	....	....	....	....		....	....	....	....	.
161	....	....	....	....		....	V	....	....	.
162	....	....	....	....	White	....	....	....	....	.
163	....	....	....	Sol	Yellow	Yellow	....	....	....	
164	....	....	....	Dcpd	Canary yellow	....	W	....	....	.
165	....	....	....	....	Olive green	....	....	....	Fibrous	
166	....	....	....	....	Black to grayish black	....	....	....	....	.
167	....	....	....	....	Black	....	....	....	....	.
168	....	....	....	....	Pale blue	....	....	....	....	.
169	....	....	....	....	Dark brown, gray	....	....	....	....	.

GROUP 13
Specific Gravity Not Reported

INDEX OF REF.	NAME	COMPOSITION	REMARKS
....	CUPRO-SKLODOWSKITE	$CuO \cdot 2UO_3 \cdot 2SO_2 \cdot 6H_2O$	
....	DIENERITE	Ni_3As	
....	DOUGHTYITE	$Al_2(SO_4)_3 \cdot 5Al_2(OH)_6 \cdot 21H_2O$	From alkaline waters of Doughty Springs, Colo.
....	ENELECTRITE	Hydrocarbon?	Lath-like crystals occurring in amber.
....	EUCHLORINE	$4(K,Na)_2SO_4 \cdot 6CuSO_4 \cdot 3Cu(OH)_2$	In the lava from Vesuvius.
....	FERRI-PARALUMINITE	$2(A,Fe)_2O_3 \cdot SO_3 \cdot 15H_2O$	Occurs in crusts.
....	FRAIPONTITE	$8ZnO \cdot 2Al_2O_3 \cdot 5SiO_2 \cdot 11H_2O$	Fibrous crust like asbestos.
....	HYDROMELANO-THALLITE	$CuCl_2 \cdot CuO \cdot 2H_2O$	Scales from Vesuvius.
....	IOZITE	FeO	Minute grains in lava.
....	JEROMITE	$As(S,Se)_2$	Globular.
....	KUTNOHORITE	$(Ca,Mg,Fe,Mn)CO_3$	
....	LEUCOGLAUCITE	$Fe_2O_3 \cdot 4SO_3 \cdot 5H_2O$	
1.732	LOPEZITE	$K_2Cr_2O_7$	Occurs as minute crystals and balls.
....	MEYERSITE	$AlPO_4 \cdot 2H_2O$	Agate-like masses in lava.
....	MILLO-SEVICHITE	Normal Fe,Al sulfate	A volcanic incrustation.
....	MITHRIDATITE (MITRIDATITE)	$2CaO \cdot 2Fe_2O_3 \cdot 2P_2O_5 \cdot nH_2O$	Alteration product of vivianite.
....	MUNKRUDITE	P_2O_5 and SO_3 of Fe and Ca	Occurs foliated and crystalline.
....	OLIVEIRAITE	$3ZrO_2 \cdot 2TiO_2 \cdot 2H_2O$	Minas Geraes, Brazil. Associated with Euxenite.
....	PARA-URICHALCITE	Zn malachite?	Botryoidal or earthy.
....	PATRONITE	VS_4?	
....	PHOSPHOROUS	P	Reported in stone meteorite, Saline township, Kansas.
....	PLUMBO-MALACHITE	$2CuCO_3 \cdot Cu(OH)_2 \cdot PbCO_3$	
....	RAUVITE	$CaO \cdot 2UO_3 \cdot 6V_2O_5 \cdot 20H_2O$	
....	ROBELLAZITE	V,Nb,Ta,W,Al,Fe,Mn	Occurs as concretionary masses with carnotite in Colorado.
....	SCHERTELITE	$Mg(NH_4)_2H_2(PO_4)_2 \cdot 4H_2O$	Crystals in bat guano. Like hannayite.
....	SHANYAVSKITE	$Al_2O_3 \cdot 4H_2O$	Colloidal. From near Moscow, Russia.
....	SIMONELLITE	$C_{15}H_2$	A hydrocarbon incrustation on lignite.
....	SJÖGRUFVITE	$H_2O \cdot As_2O_5 \cdot Fe_2O_3 \cdot MnO,PbO,CaO$	Red in splinters. Crystalline.
....	STEIGERITE	$Al_2O_3 \cdot V_2O_5 \cdot 6\frac{1}{2}H_2O$	Powdery appearance. The acid solution is deep cherry-red.
2.01	TANGEITE	$2CaO \cdot 2CuO \cdot V_2O_5 \cdot H_2O$	
....	ULRICKITE	UO_2	
....	VANOXITE	$V_4V_2O_{13} \cdot 8H_2O$	
....	WISCHNEWITE	$3Na_2Al_2Si_2O_8 \cdot Na_2SO_4 \cdot 3H_2O$	
....	ZINK-MANGANERZ	Hydrous zinc manganate	

GROUP 13
Specific Gravity Not Reported

	H	SP. GR.	F	HCL	COLOR	STREAK	LUSTER	CLEAV-AGE	FRACTURE	
170	....	....	......	....	Greenish gray	....	....	....	Fibrous	
171	....	....	Fus	Sol	Sulfur-yellow	....	....	....	Brittle	
172	....	....	......	Sol	Black	Black	M	....	....	
173	....	....	......	....	Brown to violet	....	....	....	....	
174	....	....	......	....	....	....	....	....	....	
175	....	....	......	....	Yellow	....	....	....	....	
176	....	....	......	....	Silver-white	....	....	....	....	
177	....	....	......	....	Blk, blue, blue-blk	....	....	....	....	
178	....	....	......	Sol	Black	Black	M	....	....	
179	....	....	......	....	White	....	....	....	....	
180	....	....	......	....	Silver-white to pale steel-gray	....	Bright	Good	....	
181	....	....	......	....	White	....	....	....	....	

356

GROUP 13
Specific Gravity Not Reported

INDEX OF REF.	NAME	COMPOSITION	REMARKS
1.633	PICROAMOSITE	Like amphibole	Brittle. An orthorhombic amphibole.
....	KELBELSBERGITE	Basic SO_4 of Sb with Fe,Mg,Na,K,Bi,P_2O_5	Occurs as tufts and minute needles in stibnite.
....	KOLBECKINE	Sn_2S_3	Occurs as minute black scales resembling pyrolusite.
....	ALOISIITE	H_2O,SiO_2 of Ca,Fe'', Mg and Na.	A cement in tuff. From Uganda.
....	NORILSKITE	Alloy of Pt,Fe,Ni,Cu	
....	NICKEL OXIDE	Ni_3O_4	Magnetic. Yellow scales in the black sands of Fraser River, B. C.
....	IGELSTROMITE	$Mg_6Fe_2(OH)_{18}\cdot6H_2O$	On ignition, turns chocolate-brown and becomes magnetic.
....	ILSEMANNITE	$MoO_3\cdot Mo_3O_8\cdot nH_2O$	Earthy masses.
....	HERZENBERGITE	Zn_2S_3	In fine grains. Soluble in H_2SO_4 with evolution of H_2S.
....	VOLGERITE	Sb,O,H_2O,etc.	Massive or as a powder. Probably an alteration product of stibnite.
....	ALLOPALLADIUM	Pd,Hg,Pt,Ru,Co?	Opaque.
....	SELENOLITE	SeO_2	Reported as white needles on cerussite and molybdomenite.

GENERAL INDEX

MINERAL INDEX

Emplectite, 102–2
Empressite, 54–1
Enalite, 113–4
Enargite, 91–4, 115–5, 36-B, plate 23
Endeiolite, 107–7
Endlichite; vanadinite with vanadium partially replaced by arsenic
Enelectrite, 139–13
Englishite, 113–10
Enigmatite (acnigmatite)
Enstatite, 72–8, 17-D
Eosphorite,112–8
Ephesite, 42–8
Epiboulangerite; probably a mixture of boulangerite and galena
Epidesmine, 140–11
Epididymite, 75–7
Epidote, 20–7, 21–8, 113-A, plate 24
Epigenite, 78–4
Epistilbite, 26–11
Epistolite, 188–9
Epsomite, 39–12, 7-A
Epsom salts (epsomite)
Equeiite, 172–10
Erikite, 60–7
Erinite, 69–5
Erionite, 156–11
Ernita (grossularite)
Errite, 196–9
Erythrite, 179–9, 67-A
Erythrosiderite, 82–13
Eschwegeite, 33–3
Eschynite, 27–3
Esmeraldaite; shown to be a mixture
Ettringite, 36–12
Eucairite, 93–1
Euchlorine, 140–13
Euchroite, 123–7
Euclase, 8–8
Eucolite, 90–8
Eucryptite, 197–9, plate 27
Eudialite, 81–8, 43–9
Eulytite, 29–2
Eumanite; probably brookite
Euxenite, 20–3, 15–4, plate 21
Evansite, 4–12

Facillite (kaliopilite)
Fairfieldite, 149–8
Falkmanite, 87–2
Famatinite, 76–4, plate 22
Faratsihite, 21–11
Faroelite (thomsonite)
Faujasite, 2–12
Fava; rolled mineral pebbles from the diamond sands of Brazil
Fayalite, 19–5
Feldspar, common, see orthoclase
Feldspars; a series of monoclinic and triclinic silicates of aluminum with either potassium, sodium or calcium

Felsoebanyite, 159–10
Ferberite, 33–2
Ferganite, 195–8
Fergusonite, 19–3, plate 20
Fermorite, 89–7
Fernandinite, 83–13
Ferrazite, 216–8
Ferrierite, 45–11
Ferrimolybdite, 110–4, plate 21
Ferri-paraluminite, 141–13
Ferri-prehnite, 24–9
Ferri-sicklerite, 166–7, 217–8
Ferrisymplessite, 198–9
Ferroanthophyllite (actinolite)
Ferrocolumbite, 6–2
Ferrohalloysite, 122–11
Ferrohastingsite, 173–7
Ferronatrite, 151–10
Ferropallidite (szmolnokite)
Ferroschallerite, 16–13
Ferrotungstite, 84–13
Ferruccite, 178–10
Fersmannite, 74–7
Fervanite, 85–13
Fibroferrite, 32–12
Fibrolite (sillimanite)
Fichtelite, 48–13
Fiedlerite, 93–3
Fillowite, 102–7
Finnemanite, 84–1
Fire opal; opal with rainbow color reflections
Fischerite, 41–10
Fizelyite, 45–13
Flagstaffite, 82–12
Flajolotite, 86–13
Flinkite, 59–6
Flint; impure chalcedony with dull colors
Float stone; a porous stone that floats on water
Flokite (mordenite)
Florencite, 87–7
Fluellite, 47–11
Fluoborite, 106–9
Fluocerite, 23–2
Fluoradelite (tilasite)
Fluorapatite, 101–8, 56-A
Fluorite, 131–8, 1-C, plate 26
Fluorspar (fluorite)
Forbesite, 184–8
Formanite, 17–3
Forsterite, 22–7, 20–8, 138-A, plate 23
Foshagite, 111–10
Foshallassite, 117–10
Fouqueite (clinozoisite)
Fourmarierite, 41–2
Fraipontite, 142–13

371

Iceland spar; clear crystallized calcite
Iddingsite, 148–9
Idocrase (vesuvianite), 28–7, 111-A
Idrizite, 12–12
Igalikite, 33–10
Iglestromite, 176–13
Ihleite, 31–12
Ilesite, 89–13
Illite (bravaisite)
Ilmenite, 25–4, 88-A, plate 22
Ilsmannite, 177–13
Ilvaite, 35–5, 31–6, 115-A, plate 21
Impsomite; natural asphalt, similar to al-
      bertite
Inathite (ianthinite)
Inderborite, 13–12
Inderite, 87–12
Indicolite; blue tourmaline
Inesite, 46–8
Infusorial earth; siliceous shells of diatoms,
      etc.
Inyoite, 50–12
Iodembolite (iodobromite)
Iodobromite, 141–3
Iodyrite, 139–3
Iolite, 6–9, 3–10, 135-A
Ionite (anauxite)
Iozite, 144–13
Iridium, see iridosmine
Iridosmine, 3–1
Iron, 39–1
Iron akermanite, 74–8
Iron anthophyllite, 22–6
Iron-copper chalcanthite, 70–11
Iron meteorite, plate 19
Iron reddingite, 119–8
Iron rhodonite, 48–7
Irvingite, 90–13
Ishikawaite, 14–2
Ishkulite, 11–3
Ishkyldite, 163–10
Isoclasite, 185–9
Itacolumite,
Ivaarite, 25–6
Ixiolite, 10–1

Jacobsite, 17–4
Jade (nephrite and jadeite)
Jadeite, 17–7, 19-D, plate 24
Jamesonite, 108–3, 44-A, plate 22
Janite, 131–11
Jarlite, 83–6
Jarosite, 161–8, 96–12, 73-A, plate 26
Jasper; impure, opaque chalcedony of various
      colors
Jaunite, 208–8
Jefferisite, 123–11, plate 28

Jeffersonite, 105–7
Jeremejevite, 26–8
Jeromite, 145–13
Jezekite, 75–9
Joaquinite, 24–6
Johannite, 192–8
Johannsenite, 46–7
Johnstrupite, 140–8
Jordanite, 54–2
Joseite, 106–1
Josephinite, plate 19
Julienite, 89–12
Jurupaite, 83–9

Kaemmererite, plate 24
Kaersutite; titanian hornblende
Kainite, 62–11, 3-A
Kalgoorlite; mixture of coloradoite and petzite
Kaliborite, 25–11
Kalicinite, 143–11
Kalinite, 37–12, 4-A
Kaliophilite, 20–10
Kalkowskite, 107–5, 87–6
Kaliphite; mixture of iron and manganese
      oxides with zinc silicates
Kalsilite, 210–9
Kamerezite, 94–6
Kaolinite, 143–10, 35-D
Karachaite, 147–11
Kasoite, barium feldspar
Kasolite, 52–3
Kauaiite, 167–10
Kayserite, 55–7
Keeleyite (zinkenite)
Kehoeite, 186–10
Keilhauite, 26–7
Kempite, 111–9
Kentrolite, 20–2
Kermesite, 112–4
Kernite, 23–12, 18-A
Kertschenite, 95–10
Keweenawite; a mixture
Khlopinite, 143–3
Kidney ore; reniform masses of hematite
Kidney stone (nephrite)
Kielhauite, 17–6
Kieserite, 97–10
Kilbrickenite (geocronite)
Kipushite (arakawaite)
Kirovite, 29–12
Kirrolite (cirrolite)
Kiscellite, 44–12
Klaprothite, 81–2
Klebelsbergite, 171–13
Kleinite, 49–1
Klockmannite, 89–3
Knebelite, 18–5, 15–6